The Computer System Risk Management and Validation Life Cycle

The Computer System Risk Management and Validation Life Cycle

R. Timothy Stein

Paton Press LLC
Chico, California

Most Paton Press books are available at quantity discounts when purchased in bulk.
For more information, contact:

Paton Press LLC
P.O. Box 44
Chico, CA 95927-0044
Telephone: (530) 342-5480
Fax: (530) 342-5471
E-mail: *books@patonpress.com*
Web: *www.patonpress.com*

10 09 08 07 06   5 4 3 2 1

ISBN-13: 978-1-932828-09-2
ISBN-10: 1-932828-09-5

Library of Congress Cataloging-in-Publication Data
Stein, R. Timothy (Roger Timothy), 1942-
The computer system risk management and validation life cycle / R. Timothy Stein.
p. cm.
 ISBN 1-932828-09-5
 1. Business enterprises—Computer networks—Management. 2. Risk management. 3. Management information systems. 4. Computer networks—Management. 5. Computer software—Validation. 6. Industrial management—Computer networks—Management. I. Title.
HD30.37.S735 2006
004.068'1ædc22
2005034116

Staff
Publisher: Scott M. Paton
Editor: Taran March
Book design: David Hurst

To Vishakha, Jonathan, and Kevin for their love and support.

Contents

Medatech Case Study

Tables, Figures, and Exhibits

Acronyms

AAMI: Association for the Advancement of Medical Instrumentation

AD: active directory

ANSI: American National Standards Institute

ASQ: American Society for Quality

AQL: acceptable quality level

BIOS: basic input/output system

BOM: bill of material

BPA: Business Performance Associates

CDRH: Center for Devices and Radiological Health

CFR: Code of Federal Regulations

CNI: computer and network infrastructure

COTS: commercial-off-the-shelf system

CPU: central processing unit

EC: European Community

ECO: engineering change order

EDMS: electronic document management system

EIA: Electronics Industries Alliance

ERP: enterprise resource planning

FAT: factory acceptance test

FDA: Food and Drug Administration

FMEA: failure mode and effects analysis

GAMP: good automated manufacturing practices

GMP: good manufacturing practices

GxP: good x practice

HACCP: hazard analysis and critical control points

HPLC: high-pressure liquid chromatography

ID: identification

IEEE: Institute for Electrical and Electronics Engineers

IP: Internet protocol

IT: information technology

IQ: installation qualification

IVT: Institute of Validation Technology

JAD: joint application design

KLOC: thousand lines of code

LAN: local area network

MAC: mandatory access control

MES: manufacturing execution system

MRB: material review board

OQ: operational qualification

PC: personal computer

PDA: Parenteral Drug Association

PDM: product data management

PLC: programmable logical controller

PQ: performance qualification

QC: quality control

QSR: quality system regulation

RAID: redundant array of inexpensive discs

RiskVal: computer system risk management and validation life cycle

RFP: request for proposals

SEI: Software Engineering Institute

TCP: transmission control protocol

VPN: virtual private network

WAN: wide area network

Foreword

An organization can't be successful or competitive in today's business world without computer systems that provide the tools needed to sustain and scale business efficiency. Start-ups and smaller organizations might do without computer systems initially to preserve capital and lower financial risk. However, as a business grows, computer systems are needed to create efficiency and convergence in the growing organization. Organizations can also use computer systems to promote product quality and improve customer service without raising operational risks.

Unfortunately, computer systems aren't altogether reliable. As businesses become more dependent on computer systems, the potential effect of system failure rises proportionately. Computer system failures can disrupt critical supply chains, erode business efficiency, jeopardize product quality, and put high-valued data at risk. These kinds of failures could also result in the loss of corporate compliance to government regulations that are prevalent in the biomedical, patient-care, finance, defense, aerospace, and telecommunication industries. The risk associated with computer system failures can be largely mitigated using a life cycle management approach to software selection, implementation, testing, and maintenance.

Government health care watch groups are well aware of the risks posed by computer systems and require the validation of computer systems that support the manufacture of pharmaceuticals, biologics, medical diagnostic products, and medical devices. Government agencies such as the U.S. Food and Drug Administration (FDA), Environmental Protection Agency (EPA), and the European Agency for the Evaluation of Medicinal Products (EMEA), have provided regulatory guidance on what's required to properly implement and control the use of electronic records and electronic signatures.

What's needed is an efficient, practical approach to managing the business and regulatory compliance risks associated with computer system failure. The investment to ensure that the system won't fail should correlate to the costs incurred and the harm suffered from a failure. Instead of buying an insurance policy, processes are implemented to build quality into system implementation and prevent or detect defects that would otherwise lead to operational risk. Today, quality practices are surfacing in the rapidly changing world of computer technology. Technology offers automated tools to monitor and defend against harmful entities that could target the security, integrity, and performance of our networked systems and high-valued data. However, there still isn't enough quality built into the foundation of our computer systems.

This book presents an integrated process structured around quality principles to implement and maintain computer systems that promote product quality and increase business efficiency. The process focuses on ensuring that computer systems function as required and minimizes the risks associated with failure by employing a risk-based approach to system life-cycle management and computer system validation. The process is called "RiskVal."

Computer system validation is required in the biotech, pharmaceutical, medical diagnostic, and medical device industries, and is regulated by government agencies such as the FDA and EMEA. To validate a system, objective evidence needs to be collected demonstrating that the computer system functions reliably for its intended uses. Different government agencies and industry groups have published several guidance documents on what needs to be done to validate a computer system.

This book provides a practical, hands-on methodology to execute the best practices derived from these guidance documents. It also addresses the implementation of major systems that are used to support business processes enterprisewide. The methodology includes the definition of requirements, functional testing, user training, change control, and a maintenance program to keep a computer system effective and under control. This book also emphasizes the use of a systematic process for managing the risk associated with failure. Many FDA-regulated industries have begun to use the risk associated with computer system failure to determine the extent of testing that should be done to validate and maintain systems.

However, risk management is much more than testing and includes developing methods to reduce the frequency of failures and the effect of resulting harm. Impetus for this risk-based approach comes from regulators' encouragement, as is evident in the FDA's reexamination of its approach to the pharmaceutical good manufacturing practices (Pharmaceutical cGMPs for the 21st Century—A Risk-Based Approach, Final Draft, U.S. Food and Drug Administration, September 2004) and from the publication of the 2000 revision of ISO 14971, Medical devices—Application of risk management to medical devices. ISO 14971:2000 presents a thirteen-step process for risk management that includes identifying potential risks, determining if a mitigation is needed, the development and implementation of mitigation, and ongoing monitoring of system failures. The thirteen-step process is integrated into the RiskVal life cycle.

In this book, these three practices (i.e., system life-cycle management, computer system validation, and systematic risk management) are fully integrated to provide an efficient process as well as guidance on:

- Defining requirements for the system
- Selecting a system that meets your business needs and regulatory requirements
- Qualifying software vendors, including how to evaluate their development methodologies to determine if quality is being built into their software
- Quantifying the risks associated with the system
- Identifying, reducing, and managing the risks associated with computer system failures, including how to include validation testing as a risk mitigation
- Validating the computer system in a way that both meets regulatory requirements and limits the resources required based on the harm that could result from a system failure. Although regulatory guidance documents and industry publications advise organizations to align validation efforts to risk levels, little methodology is provided. This book employs the Institute for Electrical and Electronics Engineers approach to software verification and validation (V and V) to reflect the risk level in the rigor and intensity of the V and V activities.

This book also addresses the strategy of putting effective controls on the underlying information technology (IT) infrastructure as the foundation of the operating environment. Many computer system safeguards are derived from the IT infrastructure. The hardware, operating system software, and ancillary software that support and protect the system are included in the IT infrastructure. Examples of IT infrastructure services include the firewall; antivirus (or malware) software; and backup, restore, and disaster recovery services used to recover data and system functionality. Because these infrastructure services are critical pieces of the computer system risk management picture, risk mitigation includes verifying that these services are operating properly.

Computer system risk management and validation require the expertise of many different roles within an organization. For example, the system owner is the manager with organizational responsibility for the business processes that's being supported. The purpose of computer system validation is to establish that the supported process functions reliably to meet the user requirements. The system owner may also define what to test and how to test it. The IT function understands the system's technical requirements and must ensure that a technical configuration adequately supports a business operation. IT's role includes defining the technical requirements, qualifying the infrastructure, installing the system, testing the technical aspects of the system, and providing operation and maintenance support. An expert in computer system risk management and validation is needed. Such an individual is referred to as a "validation engineer" and might be employed in the IT or quality assurance function. This person's role is to ensure that the risk management and validation process is carried out according to official standard policies and procedures, regulatory requirements, and industry best practice. Finally, a member from QA is needed to provide oversight and ensure that any regulatory requirements are met. In addition, the QA expert can contribute by identifying any potential risks to product quality and quality systems in the event of a failure. Throughout this book, case studies follow a team that represents these roles and illustrate how this methodology is used to select, implement, test, and use a document control system.

This book articulates state-of-the-art thinking on how to manage the risks of computer systems and validate the system based on defined business requirements. It can serve as a hands-on guide for managing a computer system's life cycle. The scope of this book's applicability transcends many industries. Although it's steeped in an understanding of government regulations regarding the biomedical field, its content is applicable to other industries where computer systems pose a substantial risk to business continuity, efficiency, and the integrity of high-valued data.

—Michael Louie, Ph.D.
Director, Information Technology
Gilead Sciences Inc.

Preface

Every company needs computer systems that consistently perform as they're expected to, without a system crash, calculation error, or single bit of corrupted data. Yet most companies' computer systems are far from meeting these expectations. Problems are encountered: Software is defective, wasn't designed to work the way users want it to, or it doesn't function properly in the user's operating environment. If one of these problems causes a computer system failure, the result could be catastrophic.

In awareness of these issues and in a desire to protect public health, regulatory and standard bodies have required companies to demonstrate that their computer systems are able to consistently perform to requirements.[1, 2, 3] These regulations cover software that's part of a medical device or diagnostic product as well as business systems used in production, for quality functions, or in conjunction with the electronic form of required records and signatures.

From a business perspective, ensuring the reliability of computer systems is a question of controlling risks—of lost productivity, defective products, and the liabilities associated with defective products. In addition, for industries regulated by the Food and Drug Administration (FDA), demonstrating reliable performance is a requirement of law. From either perspective, it's only reasonable that the time and money spent on ensuring that a system is reliable should be commensurate with the risk posed by system failures.

A computer system life cycle is the answer for how to select and implement software that reliably meets your needs and minimizes risk. Life cycles for developing software have been published by trade organizations, such as the Institute for Electrical and Electronics Engineers (IEEE), for a number of years.[4] A special-interest group of the Parenteral Drug Association (PDA) adapted the life cycle approach to purchased business systems in Technical Report 18, "Validation of Computer-Related Systems," published in 1995.[5] The need for a life cycle approach has been re-emphasized in recent standards from trade associates (e.g., ANSI/AAMI SW68:2001), and guidance documents from the FDA.[6, 7]

Although the published life cycles describe what to do, they present a number of problems for those who wish to implement them, including:

- Language usage that's not commonly understood by end users, quality, and information technology (IT) professionals
- Lack of information and examples that explain how to perform the mandated activities
- Little direction on preparing the necessary documentation of the activities
- Little or no direction on adapting the life cycle to different types of systems—(e.g., commercial off-the-shelf [COTS], configured, and custom)—or to systems that pose different levels of risk.

As a result, the use of a life cycle approach for business systems has been mostly limited to large companies that have a staff of application implementation specialists. For this approach to be widely applied, life cycle documents must be translated into activities that can be performed by IT and quality assurance (QA) professionals.

This book adapts and translates the PDA life cycle into actionable activities and defined deliverables. Equally important, it provides guidance on how to apply the life cycle to three types of systems (COTS, configurable, and custom) and to systems whose failures present different levels of risk: high, moderate, and low. The risk level is used in this volume as one determinate in whether an activity is needed, and in the level of rigor with which it should be carried out and documented. Cost effectiveness in implementing systems comes from using the system type and risk level to determine what must be done. The techniques and guidance provided here will enable readers to achieve such savings.

The objective of this book is to present a life cycle that can be used routinely by members of the IT and QA functions who want to achieve any or all of four objectives:

- Ensure the system's quality
- Ensure compliance with regulations
- Manage risks associated with potential failures
- Validate a computer system

The computer system risk management and validation (RiskVal) life cycle includes requirements definition, selection (or development), implementation, test, use, and retirement of a computer system. It meets the recommendations in the FDA's guidance document on software validation, the EC Commission's computer system validation requirements for the manufacture of medicinal products, the validation requirements of the worldwide standard for quality systems (i.e., ISO 13485), and the international standard for risk management, ISO 14971.[8, 9, 10, 11, 12] This book is an extension of two other published works of mine on managing the risk and validation of computer systems.[13, 14]

To help make the RiskVal life cycle practical for common use, this book:

- Describes how to apply the life cycle to COTS, configurable, and custom systems
- Provides a case study for illustration
- Indicates when activities and deliverables are needed based on the risk level of the system
- Provides briefs for twenty-seven deliverables. These outline the content of the deliverable, specify adjustments that can be made based on the risk level of the system, and provide preparation tips.
- Provides separate briefs for five methods used for analyses of various types. A methods brief defines the process to be used and the deliverables to be created, and provides productivity tips for improved efficiency.
- Uses language that's either defined in the glossary or commonly used

It's my intent to provide a "go to" guide that explains how to perform computer system validations. Consequently, this volume goes into levels of detail that aren't found in standards, regulations, and guidance documents. Some of the processes described here represent industry practice, while others are a matter of my personal preference or insight on how to do something. Readers must keep in mind that the explanations of how to do things aren't in themselves requirements. It's difficult to describe how to do something without sounding prescriptive. Remember that alternative methods that meet the underlying objectives and basic principles are equally acceptable.

Using a life cycle approach for defining the requirements, selecting and developing, implementing, testing, and using a computer system is a sound business practice that will help ensure that a system will consistently function as required. The rigor of the life cycle should be commensurate with the risk posed by the system. It doesn't matter if a regulatory body requires that a system be validated; it's simply a good system implementation and risk management practice. This practical "how to" presentation of the RiskVal life cycle will enable organizations to implement more reliable and suitable computer systems in a cost-effective manner.

CONTENTS AND STRUCTURE OF THIS BOOK

This book uses the Parenteral Drug Association's process (published as Technical Report 18, "Validation of Computer-Related Systems") and the ISO 14971:2000 risk management process (Medical devices—Application of risk management to medical devices) as the basis for the RiskVal life cycle.[15] The PDA process is written for systems purchased in conjunction with quality and manufacturing systems as well as custom systems. Most of the large computer systems used by organizations are purchased rather than developed internally. The first note of each chapter discusses the difference between the RiskVal activities for a phase and the discussion for the comparable phase presented in Technical Report 18.

ISO 14971:2000 was approved as a European standard by the Comité Européen de Normilasation. ISO 14971:2000 "specifies a procedure by which a manufacturer can identify the hazards associated with medical devices and their accessories . . . estimate and evaluate the risks, control these risks and monitor the effectiveness of the control."[16] I've adapted this to managing the risks associated with computer system failure because the process is well known and accepted in the medical device industry. In addition, its objectives of estimating, evaluating, and controlling risks as well as monitoring the effectiveness of the control are exactly what I wanted to incorporate into the RiskVal life cycle.

Chapter 2 provides an overview of the RiskVal life cycle. A separate chapter is dedicated to each of the nine life cycle phases. The main discussion of each chapter concerns the activities to be performed for COTS systems. These discussions are illustrated with a case study for a document control system. The differences in the activities for configured business, existing systems, and custom systems are presented in a section at the end of each chapter. Organizations implementing mixed systems can view their system as two or more subsystems, and can follow a life cycle that integrates the activities appropriate to the subsystems. Chapter 12 explains what the minimum requirements are per regulations and standards. The business justifications for these minimum deliverables are also stated. In addition, references that identify what regulations, standards, and/or guidance documents require or recommend are provided for all the RiskVal deliverables. Sttatements are also provided about when each deliverable is applicable, based on the risk level of the system.

Briefs are presented in appendix A for selected deliverables identified in each chapter. Each brief outlines the content of a deliverable and provides productivity hints on how to prepare it. When special tools or methods are required to create a deliverable, a methods brief is often provided on the tool or process to guide readers in its use.

A glossary provides definitions of terms and the source of each definition.

Fictitious case studies concerning a medical device manufacturer are used throughout the book to illustrate the RiskVal life cycle. The studies are an amalgam of my experience in helping several companies implement electronic document control systems. The examples cited in the text of the chapters are all authentic situations of which I've first-hand information unless another source is cited.

Regulations and Standards Addressed

The life cycle phases presented here include activities and deliverables needed to meet FDA requirements for validation, EC Commission's directives for medicinal products given in EC Annex 11, ISO 9001:2000 and ISO 13485 requirements for validation, ISO 14971 for risk management, and those aspects of Part 11 requirements related to validation and life cycle activities.[17, 18, 19, 20, 21] Appendix B shows how each of the thirteen steps in risk management are fulfilled during the RiskVal life cycle.

Following industry guidelines and the FDA's requirement, the assumption is made in chapter 6 that all software is developed with a minimum of defined methods, and the likelihood of its failure is at an unacceptable rate. This assumption affects the risk level assigned to the functions performed by the software and when risk mitigation is needed. In appendix C, guidance is provided to those who would rather use a risk analysis based on the methodology employed to develop the software.

Appendix D lists the policy and procedures that have been discussed in the book and indicates which ones are required by standards and regulations.

Readers who are familiar with computer system validation and want to get a quick look at what I believe is the minimum that must be done to meet regulatory requirements, or who want to see what's included in the RiskVal life cycle, can skim chapter 2 and jump ahead to chapter 12.

DISCLAIMER

The material presented in this volume represents the author's knowledge and experience at the time the book was written. Readers must be aware that this is a snapshot in time. Common practice and regulatory body expectations change, and when applying the concepts presented in this book, readers must be cognizant of differences in interpreting what meets regulatory requirements, the development of new regulations and guidance documents, and revisions to existing ones. Implementing this life cycle doesn't automatically ensure that a regulatory body will, in its judgment, determine that the system has been adequately validated, or that the process used meets its requirements.

Readers are responsibile for ensuring that the risk management and validation activities performed are appropriate for the system in light of regulatory requirements and business needs. Neither the author nor the publisher are responsible for the adequacy or effectiveness of the methods that are used. Implementing this life cycle, or a part of it, doesn't automatically ensure the prevention of adverse consequences (e.g., loss of life, bodily harm, or injury, mission failure, loss of system safety or security, loss or damage to records, or financial or social loss).

Acknowledgments

I'm most grateful for the invaluable contributions of Michael Louie, Gilead Sciences. In addition to writing the foreword, Michael was the major technical reviewer. His insights have helped shape this book's contents and draw clarity to the written word. The discussion of the qualification of the infrastructure and how it's integrated with applications can be attributed to Michael's profound insight, experience, and leading-edge thinking. I've enjoyed working with him on this project and am indebted to his assistance. Thanks are also extended to David Tsao, Gilead Sciences, for sharing his expertise on how to qualify infrastructure hardware and software.

Jonathan Stein has been a tremendous help in preparing the manuscript for submission. Thank you for editing the entire work.

Thank you, Walter Moeller of Principle Partners, for reviewing much of the text as a system implementation expert, and for bringing the perspective of unregulated industries to this project. I also want to thank Steve Gitelis, Lumina Engineering, for reviewing the section on risk assessment, and Tim Ziemann, Genentech, for preparing an early draft of the method brief on use cases. I also wish to thank Tom Brewster, Brewster and Associates, for help in thinking through parts of the case study, and Kevin Stein for pulling together the glossary.

Special thanks are also sent to Scott Paton, Taran March, and their colleagues at Paton Press for improving and publishing this book. I feel privileged for having the opportunity to work with them, and fortunate to work on my first book with people who are as dedicated and professional as the Paton Press staff.

I want to thank three individuals who helped shaped my thinking on the validation life cycle and how to approach this volume: Richard Love, Connetics Corp.; Tim Ziemann, Genentech; and Greg Meyer, Compliance Media. I had the pleasure of working with these three individuals during a consulting assignment with Connetics Corp. a number of years ago. During that project, the notion of a life cycle was translated into procedures and methods that are constantly in view in this text. Thank you for allowing me the opportunity to turn concepts into documented procedures, and for your input. I also want to thank Richard Love for his comments on the manuscript.

Thanks are also extended to John F. Murray Jr. and Paul J. Motise of the Food and Drug Administration for answering questions on the Part 11 regulation and the FDA guidance document on software validation.

This work weaves together multiple threads of knowledge and experience. The list of people I've learned from is endless; however, I wish to thank those who've had the most effect, in addition to those mentioned above. I'll begin with Capers Jones, of Software Productivity Research, from whom I learned much about software engineering and the effect of development practices on software quality. I'd also like to thank him for permission to reprint some of his research. Thanks to Ron Raumer, of Raumer and Associates, for a tutorial on implementing applications as he guided me through my first implementation as a project manager. I've learned much about the regulatory requirements placed on the biomedical industries from Vishakha Stein, Underwriters Laboratories; Gary Seeger, Stellartech Research Corp.; and Jeanne Bonelle, independent consultant.

Expertise in document control was gained through the guidance of Nancy Truher, Genentech, and by working with Suesan W. Taylor, SWT Consulting. My grounding in the ISO 9001:2000 quality systems comes from Bob Brockman, retired, and Vishakha Stein, Underwriters Laboratories. Knowledge of risk management (ISO 14971) was gained from Barry Craner, Lipid Sciences, and Geetha Rao. In addition, I wish to thank countless others whom I haven't mentioned.

During the past twelve years, I've have been fortunate to consult with and train employees of more than eighty companies from eighteen industry segments in validating computer systems, implementing quality systems, and enhancing business performance. I've learned much from this hands-on experience and am grateful to all these organizations for allowing me the privilege to work with them.

Chapter 1

The Case for Computer System Risk Management and Validation

All software is defective, even that created by the best developers. The best they can do is to mini mize defects that are inadvertently built into software and use multiple testing and non-testing methods to remove them. Consider the following from a May 2002 news brief in *USA Today*:

> Operations aboard the International Space Station were back to normal a day after a three-hour shutdown of life support and scientific equipment. . . . Engineers said bad computer data led to the automatic shutdown: A cooling system in the Russian-built living quarters stopped working, and onboard computers started shutting off equipment as a precaution.[1]

Periodic announcements by software companies also remind us of how difficult it is to create flawless software. Take for example this excerpt from a September 2002 article in the *San Jose Mercury News*:

> Microsoft on Thursday disclosed more flaws in its Windows operating systems, the most serious of which could let an outside attacker take over a computer. . . . The software company advised that all users of Windows install a free patch to

fix flaws in its 'virtual machine' for translating applications written in the Java programming language. Microsoft termed the threat "critical."[2]

Software engineering research has shown that systematically using defect prevention and detection methods will drastically reduce the number of software defects that would be present if such methods weren't used (see note 1). This fact has profound implications for developing custom software and—perhaps more important for most companies—selecting off-the-shelf products. The best a company can do to ensure that purchased software is safe and effective is to employ a similar risk management life cycle for selecting, testing, implementing, and using a computer system.

This book explains why using an appropriate life cycle approach for computer system risk management is a sound business practice. Such an approach not only manages the risk associated with system failure but also helps ensure that the system will consistently function as required and be in compliance with regulations. The rigor used in applying the life cycle as well as the intensity of the activities should be commensurate with the risk posed by the system.[3] With this perspective, it doesn't matter if a regulatory body requires that the system be validated; following such a life cycle is "good system implementation practice." However, if validation is required, the real possibility of having to defend the validation process to an external auditor should be kept in mind throughout the life cycle.

This chapter will explore:

- Why computer systems are unreliable
- The business need to control risk
- Regulatory bodies' requirements for computer system validation
- What is computer system validation?
- The life cycle approach to computer system risk management and validation
- Risk as a mediating factor in applying the life cycle

WHY COMPUTER SYSTEMS ARE UNRELIABLE

There are five reasons why computer systems aren't reliable:

- Defects are unintentionally built into software.
- Manufacturer testing is limited.
- Software is released with known defects.
- Many defects reported after release aren't corrected.
- The software might not work properly in a given environment.

Defects Are Unintentionally Built Into Software

Unfortunately, perfect software is virtually impossible to find. In "Conflict and Litigation Between Software Clients and Developers," Capers Jones reports that in an analysis of nearly 1,500 software projects, zero defects was observed in only two small projects during the first year of use.[4] Inevitably, errors will be made when designing and coding software—and even when fixing it.

The number of inherent defects depends on the practices used during software development. To oversimplify a wide range of development practices, software can be categorized as either engineered or handcrafted. Engineered software is created through "the disciplined application of engineering, scientific, and mathematical principles, methods, and tools to the economical production of quality software."[5] Such a disciplined approach is called a "life cycle." An engineering life cycle includes major steps in the development processes called phases. Various defect prevention and removal methods are used in the phases. When an organization creates its engineering life cycle, it determines which of the many possible defect-detection, -removal, and -prevention methods to incorporate. Jones notes that life cycles established by state-of-the-art software companies typically use the most defect-detection and -prevention methods, such as:

- Requirements inspection. Requirements review and clarification with users before a system is developed (defect removal)
- Risk analysis
- Creating a structured design (defect prevention)
- Design reviews. An independent review of the system design for system structure, program logic, data flow, and functionality (defect removal)
- Structured coding and code inspections. Code review by developers who didn't write it (defect removal)
- Using error-free modules from code libraries (defect prevention)
- Testing (e.g., unit, new function, regression, performance, integration, system, field)[6]

Handcrafted software is created in a very different manner. In extreme cases, it's created by a developer writing code from a concept of what the program ought to do. Creating handcrafted software often doesn't include developing a detailed set of requirements, or a design, or any of the other software engineering techniques mentioned above.

The difference in the software's quality is dramatic. Handcrafted software can harbor up to thirty undiscovered defects per thousand lines of code (KLOC) at the time it's released by the developer. Such problems are known as latent defects. Engineered software typically has fewer than five latent defects per KLOC. Major systems usually consist of more than a million lines of code. If a software system that size is handcrafted, it could have 30,000 latent defects compared to 5,000 for well-engineered software.

Jones also did studies on when latent defects are discovered as users encounter problems. The illustration presented in figure 1.1 compares handcrafted and well-engineered software on the number of defects detected by users over time. After six years, a handcrafted system that has thirty latent defects per KLOC at release will continue to present defects at a rate of four per KLOC, or 4,000 a year for systems with a million lines of code. Thus, even with a handcrafted system that's been in use for several years, it's possible that a new failure will occur when it's used in a new way. By comparison, very few new defects will be discovered with the well-engineered system.[7, 8]

Because software defects aren't simply coding errors, the key to software quality is a sound engineering process. The example data from Jones provided in exhibit 1.1 show that requirements and design errors combined can exceed coding errors, and the percentage of errors introduced when bugs are fixed could also be substantial.[9]

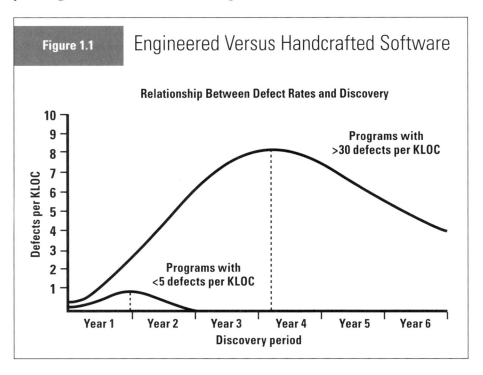

Figure 1.1 Engineered Versus Handcrafted Software

Relationship Between Defect Rates and Discovery

Exhibit 1.1 # Sources of Software Defects

Research performed by Software Productivity Research and reported by Capers Jones revealed the following types of defects found in software:

Type of Defect	Percent of Total
Requirement errors	20%
Design errors	30%
Coding errors	35%
Bad fixes	10%
Documentation errors	5%
Total	100%

Source: Capers Jones, "Software Quality in 2003: A Survey of the State of the Art." Software Productivity Research, February 20, 2003.

The superiority of engineered software is obvious: Fewer defects are created, and far more of them are detected before the software is sold. From a user's perspective, engineered software is more reliable, less disruptive to business, and has a lower maintenance cost. Unfortunately, only 30 percent of software built today is engineered.[10]

Manufacturer Testing Has Limited Success

It's impossible to test most systems completely. The tests that developers perform normally don't include every logical path or data combination that could be processed. In addition, developers are only able to test their systems in a limited range of the possible physical and logical environments in which the system might be used. Watts Humphrey estimates that only about 10 percent of the possible situations involved with using a system are tested. NASA clearly didn't test the circumstances of the International Space Station described in this chapter's introduction.[11]

A customized document control system built for an in vitro diagnostics company provides another example. The company used a different release of a UNIX operating system for running the application and encountered thirty-three "bugs." The application passed all tests in the developer's technical environment but failed thirty-three tests when run on the client's computers.[12]

Jones states that single forms of software testing are less than 30 percent efficient. That is, testing will find and remove less than one out of every three defects that are actually present. Using multiple types of testing as well as practices such as requirements review and formal design and code inspections will increase the percent of defects detected. The current average for the United States in finding software defects before selling the software is about 85 percent. Thus, if a large system has 30,000 defects, and the developer is 85-percent efficient in removing them, then 4,500 defects remain when the software is shipped to the first user. Jones reports that the best processes succeed in identifying 99 percent of the defects before the software is sold.[13]

Most Software Is Sold With Known Defects

In the world of commercial software, the business objective is regularly releasing software with new functionality. The first company with the latest and greatest features often wins a dominant position in the market. Within software companies, the pressure is unrelenting to make release dates. Ordinarily as the release date approaches, the list of discovered defects is reviewed. Decisions are made as to which defects to fix before the product is released for sale. Defects that aren't addressed might be fixed before the next release, or a decision might be made to never correct them. Although a majority of software developers can be trusted not to release software with defects that crash systems, an organization implementing the software system won't understand how the known defects will affect it unless it reviews the defects in advance.

Many Defects Discovered After Release Aren't Fixed

As noted previously, latent defects are discovered after the software is in use. However, each software company develops its own rules as to when it will fix defects that users report. A reputable software developer will repair problems that have significant effect on a user and issue a software modification (called a patch) that will prevent the problem from recurring. Defects that aren't considered grievous in nature normally are placed on a list. When the company plans the next release of the software, it will decide which defects it wants to repair. Because many defects are never repaired, the software's quality could show only limited improvement over time.

Software Might Not Work Properly in a Given Environment

Even software that works well in the developer's environment might not work well in yours. To illustrate the nature of the possible problems, one of the thirty-three bugs identified in the diagnostics company's system involved electronic approval security. The application was used for approving documents. In the developer's environment, actions by reviewers couldn't be changed. When the system was tested in the buyer's environment, however, a reviewer could change the acceptance or rejection of the previous reviewer.

THE BUSINESS CASE FOR COMPUTER SYSTEM RISK MANAGEMENT AND VALIDATION

Creating or finding software that's free of defects and will work perfectly to your expectations is extraordinarily difficult. We must assume that the software we build or purchase will be defective. The cost of a computer system failure could be trivial or astronomical depending upon the failure's effect.

Take a pharmaceutical company as an example. An incorrect analysis of clinical trial data could lead to rejecting a new and effective drug. Conversely, an "adverse events system" is used to analyze data concerning a drug's adverse consequences on patients once the product is placed on the market. If such a system failed to identify a major problem, patients could be harmed or killed. Or if such a system misreported events, a low-risk product might have to be withdrawn from the market. A malfunction in equipment that controls the level of active ingredients in a drug could result in an adulterated batch and, if undetected, serious difficulties for patients.

Of course, the risks associated with a computer system failure aren't limited to regulated industries. If an ATM or telecommunication network is down, the company could lose substantial business. If an automated production line is down, manufacturing will stop.

In addition to verifying a system's reliability before use, controlling the risk of system failure means controlling changes to the system once it's in use. As mentioned earlier, Jones reports that 10 percent of defects categorized in his studies were the result of bad fixes to other defects. Some software companies test only the program they changed to see if the problem has been resolved.[14] Such companies don't test to see if the change negatively affected other parts of the system.

A statistic published by the Food and Drug Administration (FDA) also shows the importance of controlling changes to software. In this case, the data concern software embedded in medical devices:

> The FDA's analysis of 3,140 medical device recalls conducted between 1992 and 1998 reveals that 242 of them (7.7%) are attributable to software failures. Of those software recalls, 192 (or 79%) were caused by software defects that were introduced when changes were made to the software after initial production and distribution. Software validation and other related good software engineering practices . . . are a principal means of avoiding such defects and resultant recalls.[15]

Given these potential problems, what can you do to be reasonably sure that your computer system will be safe and effective? The answer is to establish a life cycle for selecting or developing, testing, implementing, and using the system that will manage risk and help ensure that the system meets user requirements throughout its life. From a business perspective, computer-system reliability is a question of balancing risk management and loss prevention with economic considerations. The resources spent to prevent loss from computer system failures should be commensurate with the harm associated with potential failures. In other words, the time and effort spent to ensure that a system will perform reliably should be based on the consequences of failure.

The computer system risk management and validation (RiskVal) life cycle discussed in this book offers an effective way of identifying the risks of system failure and taking action commensurate with the risks to mitigate their occurrence. Risk management as described in chapter 3 includes risk analysis as an early step. Risk analysis is a systematic appraisal of potential system failures and the potential harm associated with them. Identifying potential failures has direct implications for user requirements, software design and testing, implementation, user training, system security and maintenance, and validation. Risk management includes taking appropriate steps to prevent the occurrence of failures or minimize their harm. For purchased systems, steps to mitigate risk might include system modifications, changes in what's done with the system, controls on using the system, using manual safeguards, and/or user training.

When the business consequences of system failure are considered, the requirements for a system implementation process extend beyond merely ensuring that user requirements are met. An organization must understand the risks associated with system failure and take appropriate steps to reduce them until the remaining risk is acceptable.

Using ISO 14971 As a Risk Management Model

The concepts and activities expressed in ISO 14971 have been applied throughout this book.[16] The FDA accepts ISO 14971 as a valid risk management process, and it's become the standard for risk management in the medical device industry. Each of the thirteen steps described in the standard have been incorporated into the RiskVal life cycle. Appendix B identifies the risk management activities that are performed during each of the RiskVal's nine phases. In addition, the RiskVal activities have been mapped to ISO 14971's thirteen steps so you can trace those steps more easily through the RiskVal life cycle.

REGULATORY BODIES' REQUIREMENTS FOR COMPUTER SYSTEM VALIDATION

Every organization needs computer systems that meet requirements and ensure data integrity and security. Many companies know that software is defective and that they might inadvertently purchase an application that doesn't serve their needs well. Regulatory bodies are aware of these issues. They have required that companies demonstrate that their systems are able to perform consistently to requirements, if those systems could affect product quality, or if they are used in quality systems. In this section we'll review regulatory requirements and the types of systems to which they apply.

From a regulatory perspective, software and computer systems that must be validated are divided into two broad categories based on use:

- *Device software.* A computer system that functions as a medical device (e.g., blood establishment software) or is used as a component of or accessory for a medical device. Examples of software that's a component of a medical device include programs that control the amount of energy delivered to surgical instruments and radiology machines, or that analyze spectroscopy results in performing medical tests.
- *Business systems.* Computer systems used in conjunction with production, quality assurance, or quality control. Examples include document control, quality management systems, ERP II, manufacturing execution systems, adverse events reporting, calibration, laboratory information systems, high-pressure liquid chromatography and other automated lab equipment, and Excel, Access, and SAS applications used to analyze or store test data and/or quality records.

The following regulations and standards require computer system validation. Relevant sections from the individual documents are quoted.

Quality System Regulation

The U.S. Food and Drug Administration's quality system regulation requires medical device manufacturers to validate computer systems used to automate any part of the device production process or quality system:

> When computers or automated data processing systems are used as part of production or the quality system, the manufacturer shall validate computer software for its intended use according to an established protocol. All software changes shall be validated before approval and issuance. These validation activities and results shall be documented.[17]

The FDA's guidance document, *General Principles of Software Validation,* elaborates on this requirement:

> Any software used to automate any part of the device production process or any part of the quality system must be validated for its intended used, as required by 21 CFR 820.70 (i). This requirement applies to any software used to automate device design, testing, component acceptance, manufacturing, labeling, packaging, distribution, complaint handling, or to automate any aspect of the quality system.[18]

Although the requirement is limited to functions covered by the regulations, the FDA advises in its guidance document that it might be important to validate other systems as well.[19] The FDA recommends that you consider validating other aspects of a system, or other systems, based on a justified and documented risk assessment. The assessment should determine the system's potential to affect:

- Your ability to comply with FDA regulations
- Product quality and safety
- The accuracy, reliability, integrity, availability, and authenticity of electronic signatures and records

Validating software that's a device or a component of one is required as part of the design control regulation of the Quality System Regulation, specifically 21 CFR, 820, Section 30 (g), Design Validation:

Each manufacturer shall establish and maintain procedures for validating the device design. Design validation shall be performed under defined operating conditions on initial production units, lots, or batches, or their equivalents. Design validation shall ensure that devices conform to defined user needs and intended uses and shall include testing of production units under actual or simulated use conditions. Design validation shall include software validation and risk analysis, where appropriate. The results of the design validation, including identification of the design, method(s), the date and the individual(s) performing the validation, shall be documented in the DHF [design history file].[20]

21 CFR Part 11

The FDA has issued a regulation concerning electronic records and electronic signatures that's identified as Part 11 of volume 21 of the *Code of Federal Regulations* and is commonly referred to as "Part 11." It applies to all industries regulated by the FDA and reiterates the need to validate software when other FDA regulations require it. (Note that requirements defined in FDA regulations are called "predicate rules.") Part 11 defines requirements beyond validation for computer systems used to generate electronic records and/or signatures.[21] In Part 11's scope section 11.1 (b), the FDA explains when the regulation applies:

This part applies to records in electronic form that are created, modified, maintained, archived, retrieved, or transmitted, under any records requirements set forth in agency regulations. This part also applies to electronic records submitted to the agency under requirements of the Federal Food, Drug, and Cosmetic Act and the Public Health Service Act, even if such records are not specifically identified in agency regulations.[22]

The FDA's guidance document for this regulation, *Guidance for Industry Part 11, Electronic Records; Electronic Signatures—Scope and Application*, states in Section III B 2 that Part 11 applies to:

- Records that are required to be maintained by predicate rules and that are maintained in electronic format in place of paper format
- Records that are required to be maintained by predicate rules, are maintained in electronic format in addition to paper format, and are relied on to perform regulated activities
- Records submitted to the FDA, under the predicate rules (even if such records aren't specifically identified in agency regulations), in electronic format

■ Electronic signatures intended to be the equivalent of handwritten signatures, initials, and other signings required by predicate rules[23]

(*Note:* chapter 3 includes a checklist to help you determine Part 11 applicability.)

European Community GMPs

The European Community good manufacturing practices (GMPs) also require validation of computer systems that pharmaceutical companies introduce "into systems of manufacturing, including storage, distribution, and quality control."[24] The directive states:

> The extent of validation necessary will depend on a number of factors including the use that the system is to be put, whether the validation is to be prospective or retrospective and whether or not novel elements are incorporated. Validation should be considered as part of the complete life cycle of a computer system. This cycle includes stages of planning, specification, programming, testing, commissioning, documentation, operation, monitoring and modifying.[25]

ISO 13485 and CAN/CSA-ISO 13485-98

ISO 13485:1996 is a harmonized international standard for applying ISO 9001:1994 to medical devices and is effective until 2006, at which time companies must complete their transition to the standard's revision, ISO 13485:2003.[26] Canada adopted ISO 13485:1996 without modification as its national standard for quality systems used in conjunction with developing and/or manufacturing medical devices. It was released as CAN/CSA 13485-98. All companies whose products are sold in Canada must be registered as meeting the requirements of CAN/CSA 13485-98. ISO 13485:1996 and its Canadian clone require the validation of all software used in process control:

> The supplier shall establish and maintain documented procedures for the validation of the application of computer software that's used for process control. The results of the validation shall be recorded.[27]

ISO 13485 was revised on July 30, 2003. Canada issued a notice in October 2003 indicating that all manufactures that needed to meet the requirements of CAN/CSA 13485–98 had until March 15, 2006 to comply with the requirements of ISO 13485:2003. ISO 13485:2003 clarifies the scope of what must be validated and specifies that validation should take place before the system is used:

The organization shall establish documented procedures for the validation of the application of computer software (and changes to such software and/or its application) for production and service provision that affect the ability of the product to conform to specified requirements. Such software applications shall be validated prior to initial use. The results of validation shall be recorded.[28]

Limits of Regulatory Validation Requirements

The regulations require validation only of system functions that are related to production or the quality system. In its software validation guidance document, the FDA states, ". . . a device manufacturer who chooses not to use all the vendor-supplied capabilities of the software only needs to validate those functions that will be used and for which the device manufacturer is dependent upon the software results as part of production or the quality system." The exception is that companies shouldn't run high-risk applications in the same operating environment with nonvalidated software. (See note 2.)

From a business perspective, the potential for business loss, customer dissatisfaction, employee inconvenience, and loss of the integrity of financial records as a result of a system failure must be added to the list of concerns.

WHAT IS COMPUTER SYSTEM VALIDATION?

In its software validation guidelines document, the FDA defines *software* validation as: "Confirmation by examination and provision of objective evidence that the software specifications conform to user needs and intended uses, and that the particular requirements implemented through the software can be consistently fulfilled."[29]

This definition can be extended to a computer system. The requirement to validate a computer system means that a predefined method must be used to gather evidence that the system will function reliably, that is, required system functionality operates correctly and completely. As we've seen, this is best achieved through a life cycle approach.

The Entire System Is Included

The entire computer system must function reliably to meet user requirements, not just the software that processes information or creates quality records. Thus, all hardware and software that's needed for the computer system to function properly must

Exhibit 1.2	Definitions

Application software is a set of macros, a computer program, or set of programs designed to fulfill specific needs of users. An application typically stores and/or processes data or information entered by input devices or users.

A **computer system** is a group of hardware components and associated software designed and assembled to perform a specific business function or group of functions. It includes the application software, any hardware and software dedicated to the operation of the application or the storage, access to, or transmission of data. When defining a computer system, care must be taken to draw a line between the computer system and the infrastructure. Ordinarily, if hardware and software are dedicated to an application (e.g., a server and the system software used on it), it's considered to be part of the same system as the application (e.g., the document control system). If hardware and software are used by more that one application (e.g., the hubs, switches, and concentrators in a network), they're considered part of the infrastructure. A computer system's components typically include, but aren't limited to:

- Application software
- Hardware dedicated to the system
- Operating systems and system software used by the dedicated hardware to run the application
- Network and communication devices that connect users to the system (if not included in the infrastructure)
- Dedicated data storage devices
- Dedicated peripherals such as data collection and output devices

The **infrastructure** includes what is referred to in this book as the infrastructure platform and infrastructure services. The infrastructure platform is the collection of hardware and software used to host business applications, to communicate within and outside of an organization, and to provide infrastructure services. The infrastructure services are functions performed by the infrastructure hardware and software to safeguard systems, preserve data integrity, and provide network communications. The infrastructure is discussed extensively in chapter 9.

The **system owner** is the manager (or his or her designee) of the department that's most affected by, or is the primary user of, the system.

| Exhibit 1.3 | Types of Systems |

- *Commercial off-the-shelf (COTS) system.* A system that uses only software products that are commercially available and haven't been specifically designed to meet an individual purchaser's specifications. The product is used as developed with minimal or no configuration; the system's software hasn't been modified through the customization of program code. If the system is customized, it's considered either a mixed or a custom system. COTS software doesn't include "freeware," "shareware," and other uncontrolled software that's available from the Internet and other sources.
- *Database package system.* A system that uses applications for storing, manipulating, and retrieving data that are created by using a database package. The user of the package typically creates an application by using tools provided in the package to create input screens, reports, and to define data processing. Examples of such database packages include Excel, Access, SAS, and data warehouse products.
- *Configured business system.* A system that uses applications which are tailored to the company's needs by configuring predefined modules and/or developing new application functionality by means of embedded tools. At least three types of configurations are possible: selecting preferences, creating functionality using embedded tools, and customizing input screens and reports.
- *Custom system.* A system that uses software that isn't available for COTS purchase but is designed and developed specifically to a company's specifications.
- *Mixed system.* A system that includes the combination of more than one of the previous types of systems.
- *Existing system.* Any of the above types of systems that are currently in use.

Note that parallel terms are used in reference to a system's application software. For example, software that's designed and developed specifically to a company's specifications is called "custom software."

---

be included in the validation. A list of what's usually part of a computer system is provided in exhibit 1.2. The system owner determines what a particular computer system includes, with input from information technology and validation experts. What to include or exclude when defining a system is discussed in chapter 3; chapters 6 and 9 explain how to handle validating an information technology infrastructure.

Validation Depends on System Type

Some of the activities performed as part of the RiskVal life cycle differ for different types of systems. Business systems can be identified based on what an owner must do to ready the system for use. Some can be used as purchased off the shelf, some must be configured, and others must be developed. Two types of configured systems exist: applications that are created using database packages and called, appropriately, "database package systems"; and "configured business systems." The requirements for demonstrating a COTS system's reliability are different from the requirements for a custom developed system, and so forth. This book explains how the RiskVal life cycle applies to all system types, including existing systems. (See exhibit 1.3, "Types of Systems.")

Mixed systems usually involve a combination of custom code and another system type. The system owner must determine how best to treat the system. If the custom code can be differentiated from the system's off-the-shelf portion by inputs, outputs, and transactions, then the life cycle activities performed for each of the two system parts can be based on an approach appropriate for each. However, both individual component testing and system integration must be included. If custom code functions can't be clearly differentiated from the off-the-shelf software, the entire system should be considered a custom system.

The different types of systems can be represented with document control automation examples:

- *Commercial off-the-shelf systems (COTS).* The company can purchase a document control system and use it as manufactured by the software company.
- *Database package systems.* Many companies create multiple Excel spreadsheets or Access databases as tools for managing a document control system. These tools might include logs of document numbers, logs of engineering change order numbers and their status, and lists of currently effective documents and their revision levels.
- *Configured business systems.* Some commercial document control packages include tools for constructing document approval routes. The system administrator can create the route by determining the routing sequence and recipients. The system will notify reviewers when they must review and approve an engineering change order and attached documents.
- *Custom systems.* A company can design and code its own document control package or contract with developers to do so.
- *Mixed systems.* In some document control packages, the approval routings are created not by using tools embedded in the program but through separate programs

that interface with the package as developed by its manufacturer. The programs created for the approval routes are considered custom code, although the rest of the program is an off-the-shelf system.

This book focuses on applying the RiskVal life cycle to commercial and configured business systems. However, at the end of each chapter, a short section discusses how the RiskVal life cycle can be applied to custom systems. Database package systems remain an enigma. Developing an application using Access or Visual Basic with another database package is basically the same as creating custom software. Spreadsheets can vary widely in complexity, length, and functionality. Some spreadsheets used for final product release in the medical diagnostics field can run into hundreds of pages and involve macros and complex statistical calculations. At the other extreme, some spreadsheets that are used to keep track of lists might be less than a single page. They certainly wouldn't require the rigor and intensity applied to custom development.

The proper treatment of spreadsheets isn't discussed in this book. An organization should first determine if the effort to develop a spreadsheet is complex enough to be considered custom software. If so, it should be treated accordingly. If not, consult chapter 12, review the list of minimally required validation deliverables, and create a short and easy way of meeting those requirements, perhaps by means of a form.

THE LIFE CYCLE APPROACH TO COMPUTER SYSTEM RISK MANAGEMENT AND VALIDATION

To summarize, the challenge that all organizations face is to obtain and use computer systems that perform reliably to their requirements—despite knowing that any software is likely to be defective, commercially available applications might not be designed to meet specific requirements, and the software might not work properly in the organization's environment. In addition, industries regulated by the FDA, the EC Commission, and similar bodies must demonstrate, through documented evidence, that applicable systems perform reliably to user requirements. These regulations apply to COTS, custom, database package, and configured business systems. The use of such a life cycle would help ensure software quality, complete the validation, and manage the risks associated with failure. In addition, it would help ensure that the system meets the requirements for the regulated activities that are automated by the system.

The best way to meet this challenge is to establish a documented life cycle for selecting/developing, implementing, testing, and using the computer system.

There are four major reasons for using a life cycle approach:

- A life cycle is a process that can be followed, with some modifications, for all types of systems.
- Engineered software is more reliable. Using a life cycle methodology for developing custom software will result in a more reliable, easier to maintain system.
- A life cycle approach is a proven method for implementing applications.
- Some regulations require a life cycle approach and many guidance documents urge it.

A Life Cycle Provides a Generic Process Applicable to All Systems

The life cycle provides a process of organized activities that can be modified for use with all types of software (commercial, database package, configurable, and custom). Organizations can modify the activities that are performed based on the type of system and the risk associated with it. Fundamentally, organizations will have one process that is followed for all systems rather than having to develop, train, and use several processes.

Engineered Software Is More Reliable

Using software engineering methods results in software with fewer design and coding defects than handcrafted software. In addition, because software engineering typically includes creating a design and using coding standards, problems are easier to diagnose and correct. Numerous software engineering life cycle standards have evolved for creating software (see, for example, IEEE/EIA 12207.0, and McConnell, 1996).[30, 31] These life cycles contain many of the same activities. The ANSI/AAMI standard SW68 and the FDA guidance document on software validation both discuss important aspects of a software development life cycle.[32, 33]

A Life Cycle Offers a Proven Method for Implementing Applications

Since the 1980s, information technology (IT) professionals specializing in implementing applications have used many of the activities described in this book. For example, in 1989 Tandem Computers, under the author's direction, created a life cycle methodology in conjunction with a consulting firm for affiliated companies that developed applications for Tandem's computers. The life cycle included designing and developing software as well as the process for collaborating with the customer in implementing the system.

Given the commonplace use of computer systems in companies of all sizes, these tools and methods can't be limited to application implementation specialists any longer. This book places these tools in the hands of IT and QA generalists as well as system owners.

Some Regulations Require a Life Cycle

As mentioned earlier, the EC regulation for pharmaceuticals states that validation should be integrated with the complete life cycle of a business system:

> Validation [of computerized systems introduced into systems of manufacture, distribution, and quality control] should be considered as part of the complete life cycle of a computer system. This cycle includes the stages of planning, specification, programming, testing, commissioning, documentation, operation, monitoring and modifying.[34]

The FDA guidance document on validating software that's part of a medical device or is used in producing a device or in a quality system, states that software should be developed using an established life cycle: "The final conclusion that the software is validated should be based on evidence collected from planned efforts conducted throughout the software life cycle."[35]

RISK AS A MEDIATING FACTOR IN APPLYING THE LIFE CYCLE

As mentioned previously, it's reasonable to apply resources for ensuring a system's appropriate functioning that are commensurate with the risks associated with system failures. The FDA recommends this approach in its guidance document on Part 11. "Persons must comply with all applicable predicate rule requirements for validation," it states, then continues with:

> We suggest that your decision to validate computerized systems, and the extent of the validation, take into account the impact the systems have on your ability to meet predicate rule requirements. You should also consider the impact

those systems might have on the accuracy, reliability, integrity, availability, and authenticity of required records and signatures. Even if there is no predicate rule requirement to validate a system, in some instances it may still be important to validate the system.

We recommend that you base your approach on a justified and documented risk assessment and a determination of the potential of the system to affect product quality and safety, and record integrity.[36]

Some of the life cycle activities described here (such as defining requirements) are strongly recommended for all systems in FDA guidance documents and industry standards. Other activities would normally be performed only with high-risk systems, such as a selection plan or a review of known defects before implementing the system.

Adapting the RiskVal life cycle to systems at different risk levels is a theme throughout this book. Risk-based guidelines are provided for:

- When an activity must be performed
- What approach or method to use to achieve the intended results
- The intensity applied to the task. Intensity includes greater scope of analysis for all normal and abnormal system operating conditions.[37]
- The rigor with which the activities are carried out. Rigor includes more formal techniques and recording procedures.[38]

The system's risk level is one of the major determinants of when a deliverable must be created. Each chapter on the life cycle phase ends with a table that identifies the deliverables created during that phase. The column headed "When Applicable" identifies when the deliverable is needed. In addition, the briefs provided on the deliverables include a section called "Risk-Based Adjustments," which discusses possible modifications to the deliverable based on the system's risk level.

Chapter 2

Overview of the Computer System Risk Management and Validation Life Cycle

The premise stated in chapter 1 is that effort to obtain an effective computer system should be focused on using a process called a life cycle that's designed to ensure the system's safety and efficacy. The life cycle includes defining requirements, selecting (or developing) the system, implementation, testing, controlled use, and retirement. If an appropriate life cycle is implemented, the risk of system failures can be managed, and the system will be validated. Deliverables from the life cycle serve as the validation record. The life cycle presented in this book is called the computer system risk management and validation life cycle and is referred to as the "RiskVal life cycle." This life cycle is an adaptation and translation of the Parenteral Drug Association (PDA) Technical Report 18 life cycle.[1] Although the RiskVal life cycle is appropriate for all types of systems, this book focuses on how the life cycle applies to commercial off-the-shelf (COTS) systems and configured business systems.

A diagram of the RiskVal life cycle is presented in figure 2.1. It includes the following phases:

- Conceptualize
- Define requirements
- Select vendors and systems
- Design solutions to issues
- Construct solutions to issues
- Prepare for use
- Qualify the system
- Use in a production environment
- Retire the system

This chapter summarizes the RiskVal life cycle. As each step of the life cycle is discussed, the activities and deliverables associated with COTS and configured business systems are discussed (see chapter 1 for definitions of the types of systems), then the differences for custom systems are summarized. The discussion of each life cycle phase will include:

- A description of the phase, including goals and activities
- The deliverables that are created for COTS and configured business systems. Note that all the deliverables created during the life cycle up to and including the validation final report in phase 8 are part of the validation record.

At the end of each phase, a table is given that includes:

- Deliverables for COTS and configured business systems. (Deliverables created only with custom systems aren't included.)
- A definition of each deliverable
- A statement as to when the deliverable is appropriate based on system type or risk level
- References to discussions of that activity in the regulations and/or the Food and Drug Administration's (FDA) guidance document on software validation, or my recommendation

A detailed discussion of each phase is presented in subsequent chapters.

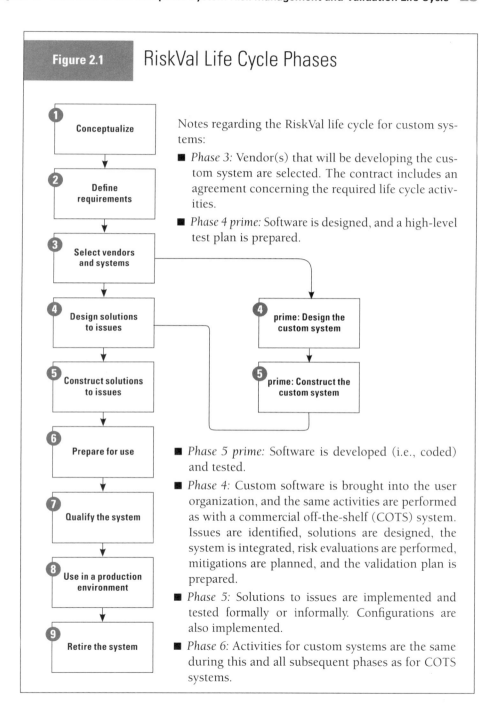

Figure 2.1   RiskVal Life Cycle Phases

Notes regarding the RiskVal life cycle for custom systems:

■ *Phase 3:* Vendor(s) that will be developing the custom system are selected. The contract includes an agreement concerning the required life cycle activities.

■ *Phase 4 prime:* Software is designed, and a high-level test plan is prepared.

■ *Phase 5 prime:* Software is developed (i.e., coded) and tested.

■ *Phase 4:* Custom software is brought into the user organization, and the same activities are performed as with a commercial off-the-shelf (COTS) system. Issues are identified, solutions are designed, the system is integrated, risk evaluations are performed, mitigations are planned, and the validation plan is prepared.

■ *Phase 5:* Solutions to issues are implemented and tested formally or informally. Configurations are also implemented.

■ *Phase 6:* Activities for custom systems are the same during this and all subsequent phases as for COTS systems.

MAJOR SOURCES OF INFORMATION FOR THE RISKVAL LIFE CYCLE

The RiskVal life cycle is built from many sources. As mentioned previously, the RiskVal life cycle is an adaptation and translation of the PDA Technical Report 18 life cycle.[2] The RiskVal life cycle includes all relevant FDA predicate rules from regulations for pharmaceutical (i.e., 21 CFR 211) and medical device (21 CFR 820) products.[3, 4] A predicate rule is a requirement in a regulation. For example, because a predicate rule in the pharmaceutical regulations requires that systems be backed up, the RiskVal life cycle includes backing up systems.

I've also included ISO 13485 requirements because many countries have incorporated the ISO 13485 into their medical device regulations. Companies from all parts of the world who want to sell their products into these companies must comply with ISO 13485.[5] For those who must comply with ISO 13485, the standard's requirements are equivalent to the FDA's predicate rules.

The FDA regulation on electronic records and electronic signatures also includes some specific requirements, which are included in the RiskVal life cycle.

The EC Commission Directive on medicinal products states specific requirements for computerized systems in EC Annex 11. All of these requirements have been included.

Although the FDA requires that systems be validated, it doesn't mandate how the validation be performed or what must be included in the validation. The manufacturer is responsible for determining what's needed to provide reasonable assurance that the system will function as intended throughout its normal operating ranges. The FDA does provide guidance on what it considers to be important in the validation process. The germane FDA guidance document is *General Principles of Software Validation; Final Guidance for Industry and FDA Staff*. This guidance document is referred to here as "CDRH" because it was published by the Center for Devices and Radiological Health.[6] The main body of the CDRH guidance applies to software developed for devices and the custom development of software used in production and quality systems. Section 6.3 discusses validation requirements for COTS systems used in manufacturing and quality systems.

The CDRH guidance is referenced throughout this chapter in conjunction with deliverables. These references indicate that the guidance advises device manufacturers to perform activities that correspond to the deliverable identified in the RiskVal life cycle. Often the guidance document recommends activities but doesn't use the same terms for deliverables that are used in this book. For example, the guidance document states that the validation documentation must include "test cases and results," whereas this book references installation qualifications (IQs), operational qualifications (OQs), and performance qualification (PQ) protocols and reports.

Before implementing the life cycle described here, you should read the guidance document to understand more completely the activities that it recommends. For deliverables not mentioned in the guidance document in reference to COTS systems, I've indicated my judgment as to the importance of the deliverable (e.g., highly recommended).

The risk management activities that are incorporated into the RiskVal life cycle are taken from ISO 14971 and the FDA guidance document on the use of COTS software in a medical device.[7, 8]

Table 2.1	Abbreviations for Documents Referenced in Tables
Abbreviation	**Document**
21 CFR 820	21 CFR 820, Medical Devices; Current Good Manufacturing Practices (cGMP) Final Rule; Quality System Regulation, *Federal Register 52602*. October 7, 1996, 2004 revision.
21 CFR 211	21 CFR 211, Current Good Manufacturing Practice for Finished Pharmaceuticals. Food and Drug Administration, 1963. *Federal Register 6385*. June 20, 1963, 2003 revision.
EC Annex 11	European Community Commission Directive, *The Rules Governing Medicinal Products in the European Union*, Vol. 4, Item 3, Good Manufacturing Practices, Annex 11, Computerised Systems, October 8, 2003.
Part 11	21 CFR Part 11, Electronic Records—Electronic Signatures. Food and Drug Administration. *Federal Register*, Vol. 62, No. 54, March 20, 1997. Page 13,429.
CDRH	*General Principles of Software Validation; Final Guidance for Industry and FDA Staff*, Center for Devices and Radiological Health, Center for Biologics Evaluation and Research, Food and Drug Administration. January 11, 2002.
ISO 14971	ISO 14971:2000, Medical devices—Application of risk management to medical devices. International Organization for Standardization, 2000.
ISO 13485	ISO 13485, Medical devices—Quality management systems—Systems requirements for regulatory purposes. International Organization for Standardization, 2003.
ISO 9001	ISO 9001:2000, Quality management systems—Requirements. International Organization for Standardization, 2000.
Gamp 4	GAMP Forum. Gamp 4, GAMP Guide for Validation of Automated Systems, Vol. 4, December 2001.

The Good Automated Manufacturing Practices Institute—a group of professionals from the pharmaceutical industry in the United Kingdom—has published a guidance document on computer system validation, the *Guide for Validation of Automated Systems*. Volume four is the latest revision of the guidance, which is known as Gamp 4.[9] This document wasn't used in developing the RiskVal life cycle, but it has many elements in common with it. Exhibit 12.1 in chapter 12 identifies which of the RiskVal deliverables are also discussed by the Gamp 4 guidance.

The abbreviations listed in table 2.1 are used to reference regulations, standards, and guidance documents in tables throughout this book.

If a brief has been written for a deliverable, the number of the brief is listed in parenthesis after the name of the deliverable. For example, the information technology (IT) policy is called D1.3. The number before the decimal (e.g., 1) refers to the phase, and the number after the decimal (e.g., 3) is a sequential number assigned to the briefs for each phase.

PHASE 1: CONCEPTUALIZE

Prior to initiating the conceptualize phase, an organization must document the policies and procedures it will use for risk management and validating computer systems. The policies and procedures are documented once, and the RiskVal activities are carried out in a compliant manner. Recommended documentation includes the IT policy, the risk management policy and procedure, the validation policy, and computer system life cycle and validation procedures. Specific IT procedures can be developed during phase 6—prepare for use.

The purpose of the conceptualization phase is to obtain management approval for beginning a computer system project.

The conceptualize phase begins informally when an individual begins thinking about how to solve a problem with a computerized business system. Through the activities of this phase, the system owner answers the question, "What do I need to automate?" As needs are explored, a concept of how to meet the need evolves. An initial risk assessment is conducted to identify the potential dangers associated with such automation.

The concept of the system and critical information concerning it are documented in a computer system project proposal. Both the IT and validation departments participate in preparing the proposal to assist the originator in understanding the high-level technical requirements and likely validation requirements.

Table 2.2	Policies and Procedures Created During Phase 1, if Needed		
Phase 1 deliverables	**Definition and explanation**	**When applicable**	**Deliverable references**
Validation policy (see deliverable 1.1)	A policy that defines what must be validated and when, and defines requirements for validation processes	All systems	21 CFR Part 11, 11.10 a
Computer system risk management and validation life cycle procedure (see deliverable 1.2)	A procedure that defines the process for the selection, procurement, validation, use, management, and retirement of a computer system	All systems	Part 11, 11.10 a
Information technology (IT) policy (see deliverable 1.3)	Policy governing the procurement, implementation, use, security, control, support, and administration of computer systems to ensure their efficiency, reliability, and security. A policy statement that holds individuals accountable for actions signed with electronic signatures.	All systems	Part 11, 11.10 j
Requirements for computer system validation plans, protocols, and reports (see deliverable 1.4)	A procedure that defines the content requirements for the computer system validation plan, protocols, and reports	All systems	Part 11, 11.10 a
Risk management policy	A policy that defines when a formal process needs to be used to manage risks and the requirements for such a process	All systems	ISO 14971
Risk management procedure	A procedure that defines the process for the assessment and management of risk	All systems	ISO 14971

Table 2.3	Summary of Phase 1 Deliverables Created for Each Computer System		
Phase 1 deliverables	**Definition and explanation**	**When applicable**	**Deliverable references**
Computer system project proposal (see deliverable 1.5)	A document that contains vital information about the system and its potential uses. The initial risk analysis is included. Management approval provides the authority to proceed with the project.	All systems	CDRH, 6.1 recommends an initial risk analysis
Computer system project plan	A project plan for the selection, procurement, implementation, and validation of a computer system	All except simple low- and moderate-risk systems	Highly recommended when applicable

After management approves the project proposal, a formal project is begun. Project plans are created for projects that are large, complex, or of moderate to high risk. Table 2.2 lists policies and procedures than are created during phase 1, if needed.

The two deliverables that are created in phase 1 for a specific computer system are shown in table 2.3.

PHASE 2: DEFINE REQUIREMENTS

During the second phase, the requirements are defined for the system. These will be used as the basis for selecting and testing the system.

A successful business application is one that reliably does what its users need it to do. Consequently, a system can't be properly designed (if it's a custom system), selected, or tested without an adequate definition of the requirements. Because the requirements will serve as a basis for choosing between different systems, they're usually written at a level that's independent of specific hardware and software.[10]

Three types of requirements are defined: user requirements, technical requirements, and requirements for software providers.

User requirements include:

- Operations the system must perform and, if appropriate, how the functions must be executed
- Interfaces the system must have with other systems
- How the system must perform (e.g., response time)
- Relevant regulations with which the system must comply

Technical requirements are defined for the hardware and system software. The hardware and system software might need to fit with the company's existing equipment and system software, and needs to meet the security, performance, and environmental requirements of the users.

A third set of requirements, vendor organizational requirements, is developed for evaluating vendors that will be relied upon for long-term product support. You want to select a vendor that has the expertise needed to understand the regulations placed on your industry; has a long-term, strategic commitment to the product or service; and is financially stable.

The processes used to define the requirements and the requirements documentation are reviewed in a phase review to ensure that the requirements are appropriate and fully specified. Table 2.4 lists phase 2 deliverables.

Table 2.4	Phase 2 Deliverables		
Phase 2 deliverables	**Definition and explanation**	**When applicable**	**Deliverable references**
User requirements (see deliverable 2.1)	Formal documentation of user requirements for the system	All systems	CDRH, 6.2
Technical requirements (see deliverable 2.2)	Formal documentation of technical requirements for the system	All systems except applications built with database packages	CDRH, 6.2
Vendor organizational requirements (see deliverable 2.3)	Formal documentation of requirements for determining if a vendor has the long-term potential to meet system needs	When a long-term solution from the same vendor is required	Recommended as needed
Phase 2 review minutes	High-level review of the processes used to prepare the requirements, and the requirements documents, with the oversight body (e.g., the steering committee)	Large or complex low-risk systems. All moderate- to high-risk systems	Highly recommended for moderate- to high-risk systems

PHASE 3: SELECT VENDORS AND SYSTEMS

The purpose of the third phase is to purchase from qualified vendors, hardware and software that will meet the system's user and technical requirements.

For large, complex, and/or high-risk systems, a selection team typically will be created. The team usually includes the process owner and a representative from the IT, validation, and quality assurance (QA) functions, and possibly representatives of user groups. The selection team will plan the evaluation of alternative hardware and software products. Recommended activities for selecting applications include researching systems and vendors, vendor demonstrations, and visits to other users of the system for on-site demonstrations of how they use the application. For high-risk systems, a review of known defects in the software is strongly recommended.

Hardware evaluation and selection involves identifying hardware that's compatible with the company's existing architecture and that meets the security, performance, and environmental requirements identified in the technical requirements document.

During the selection process, vendors are qualified using documented methods and criteria appropriate to how their product will be used and the risks associated with possible failures. The methods used to qualify application developers can range from accepting them based on a third-party registration—(e.g., ISO 9001)—to a vendor audit.[11] During a qualification audit, the auditor determines if a documented life cycle was used in developing the application to be purchased and evaluates the software development methods that were used.

If the selection process involves selecting a firm for custom software development or system integration, the vendor audit is a review of the process the vendor would use for the contracted work. Even groups within your company that develop software must be qualified to ensure that they're capable and that they use development methods appropriate to the risk of the system.[12]

Part of the purchasing process involves contracting for needed support from vendors. Support could include defect support and repair, and system maintenance and calibration. When an outside organization is used to provide a computer service, there should be a formal agreement including a clear statement of the responsibilities of that organization.[13]

Ordinarily, management approval is required prior to purchasing the hardware and software needed for COTS systems, or prior to contracting with developers or integrators to build or configure a system. For larger systems, concurrence on the selection is often required from the IT, purchasing, QA, and legal departments. It's recommended that management review the selection process and reports prior to signing off on the system, especially if it's large, complex, and/or of moderate or high risk.

The evaluation of database packages for creating applications also depends on the intended use and risk associated with potential failure. Although companies tend to assume that systems such as Excel, Access, and SAS are reliable under all circumstances, the manufacturers of these systems have defined security, capacity, and other limitations that must be reviewed against the intended uses of the system. Table 2.5 lists phase 3 deliverables.

PHASE 4: DESIGN SOLUTIONS TO ISSUES

There are five major activities during the "design solutions to issues" phase for COTS systems:

■ Bringing purchased systems into the company
■ Integrating the system with other systems
■ Addressing outstanding issues once the system has been selected regarding user requirements, mitigating risks, and achieving compliance

Table 2.5	Phase 3 Deliverables		
Phase 3 deliverables	**Definition and explanation**	**When applicable**	**Deliverable references**
Technical assessment of alternatives (see deliverable 3.1)	Data comparing alternatives in their ability to meet technical requirements. What constitutes adequate documentation depends on the risk level of the system and might range from a simple memo to extensive documentation of the evaluation of the alternatives.	All systems except for applications developed using database packages	Highly recommended
User assessment of alternative applications (see deliverable 3.2)	Data comparing alternatives in their ability to meet user and vendor organizational requirements, and documentation explaining why your top choices are preferred. What constitutes adequate documentation depends on the risk level of the system and might range from a simple memo to extensive documentation of the evaluation of the alternatives.	All systems except for applications developed using database packages	Highly recommended
Vendor audit report (see deliverable 3.3)	The audit report summarizes the findings of an audit and records any nonconformities discovered during the audit.	A report is prepared for all audits that are conducted	CDRH 6.3
Vendor qualification report (see deliverable 3.4)	Documentation of the process used to qualify the vendor, the information found, the decision reached, and any corrective actions. The extent of the qualification process and documentation depends on the risk level of the system. The documentation includes audit reports and reports on the review of known defects, if appropriate.	All systems except applications built with database packages	21 CFR 820, Section 50 a; ISO 13485, Section 7.4.1; CDRH 6.3; EC Annex 11, No. 5 requires evaluation of the vendor's quality system but doesn't require a report
System selection report (see deliverable 3.5)	This report summarizes the selection process and documents the reasons for making the selection. The report is submitted with the request for management approval to proceed with the purchases.	All moderate- and high-risk systems except applications built with existing database packages	Recommended
Hardware and software purchase agreements and/or documentation; quality agreements for contracted services	Includes specifications sheets for product purchased as well as all contracts and support agreements	As appropriate	21 CFR 820, Section 50 b; ISO 13485, Section 7.4.2; EC Annex 11, No. 18

- Preparing the validation plan, including defining criteria for when the system is acceptable for use
- Designing needed configurations

For custom systems, a computerized system specification is created, the structure of the software is designed, and a high-level test plan is created.[14]

The hardware and software are received into the company. Asset identification tags are placed on the hardware, and the software is secured. The system is set up as a test environment so that it can be used for the activities of this and the next two phases.

System interfaces and/or integrations with other systems are established and informally tested. (Note that if custom software is required to create the interface, those programs must be developed in a manner similar to custom systems.)

A COTS system often isn't an ideal match to user requirements and, as discussed in chapter 1, you must assume that it contains defects. To address requirements that aren't met and risks associated with system failure, the project team must determine which requirements the system isn't capable of meeting and conduct a detailed risk analysis of the system. Mitigations, which are planned to address deficiencies, can include changing user requirements, placing limitations on system use, making software changes, and developing manual processes to supplement system weaknesses. The effort required to develop and implement risk mitigations and to make accommodations for systems that don't meet requirements highlights the importance of defining requirements in advance, and selecting a system that meets your requirements and has built-in mitigations.

A validation plan is prepared for most systems to outline the approach that will be taken with the validation and the activities that will be included. The plan describes the system, the implementation strategy, the validation strategy, validation activities, a high-level validation test plan, responsibilities, and the criteria for accepting the system. The validation plan also identifies the life cycle deliverables that will constitute the validation record. Simple and/or low-risk systems might not require a validation plan. In such cases, the information can be included in a validation protocol.

After the validation plan is approved, the project plan is revised as appropriate to include the planned activities. Following that, the configuration of the application is designed.

For custom systems, the developer designs the system and prepares a high-level test plan. This has been depicted as phase 4 prime in figure 2.1. In phase 5 prime, the custom system is coded and tested by the developer and then released to the organization.

Table 2.6	Phase 4 Deliverables		
Phase 4 deliverables	**Definition and explanation**	**When applicable**	**Deliverable references**
Integration documentation or procedure	Information about how the system has been integrated with other systems so that the integration can be verified as part of the installation qualification (IQ), tested in the operational qualification (OQ), and repeated if the system must be rebuilt	All systems that are integrated with other systems	Highly recommended
Risk assessment and evaluation report (see deliverable 4.1)	Detailed risk assessment, based on the severity and probability of harm from failures and/or hazards of the actual system purchased or, in the case of custom systems, built	All moderate- and high-risk systems, unless a detailed risk assessment has already been completed	CDRH, 6.1; ISO 14971, Sections 4.4 and 5
Mitigation plan	A plan for mitigating risks that must be reduced, and addressing any requirements or regulations that aren't met by the system (e.g., 21 CFR Part 11). A separate mitigation plan is created only if needed to implement and evaluate the mitigations.	If needed	ISO 14971, Section 6
Validation plan (see deliverable 4.2)	Documentation of the validation approach and activities, including the deliverables from the life cycle that will become part of the validation report. The plan also defines responsibilities and sets criteria for accepting the system.	All systems except simple- and/or low-risk systems	Highly recommended
Documentation of system configurations	Hardware and software settings needed for the system to function properly, and functionality that must be created using system tools to meet requirements. A separate report can be prepared, the configurations can be documented in a procedure or the system specification, or the instructions can be included in installation instructions.	Systems that require configuration	Mandatory when necessary to meet requirements
Revised project plan	Describes the tasks to be performed, the person responsible, and the timeline	As needed	Highly recommended

Once the developer delivers the custom system, the project team performs the phase 4 activities described for COTS systems, such as integration, risk analysis, mitigation planning, and preparing the validation plan. Table 2.6 lists phase 4 deliverables.

PHASE 5: CONSTRUCT SOLUTIONS TO ISSUES

In phase 5 the objective for COTS and configured business systems is to implement the solutions developed during the previous phase (i.e., to execute the mitigation plan, formally or informally test the effectiveness of the mitigations, and to further reduce, if necessary, the residual risks associated with potential failures/hazards).[15] A mitigation report is prepared if formal testing is conducted. Phases 4 and 5 will overlap or mesh together if solutions are implemented and tested formally or informally when they're developed.

If the risk associated with a potential high-risk failure can't be further reduced, a risk-benefit analysis is performed to determine if the potential benefits from the use of the system outweigh the risks associated with failure.

With configured systems, the configurations designed in phase 4 are also set or built. The configurations are documented, as is the process of building configurations so that they can be re-created when needed. In the case of existing systems, the existing configuration settings are documented. These can be recorded in a separate document or incorporated into the IQ, which is written in phase 7.

At the end of phase 5, the system should be set; all of the needed mitigations should be in place. During phase 6, the final preparations for installation and use are made. During phase 7, the system is installed in a validation environment and tested.

Table 2.7	Phase 5 Deliverables		
Phase 5 deliverables	**Definition and explanation**	**When applicable**	**Deliverable references**
Mitigation report (see deliverable 5.1)	A report that describes the actions taken to mitigate risk and system weakness in meeting requirements and regulations. In addition, the report documents investigations and studies performed to determine the effectiveness of the remedial actions.	If formal testing of a mitigation is performed	ISO 14971, Section 6.3
Revised risk assessment and evaluation report	A revision of the risk assessment and evaluation report that was created in phase 4 (see deliverable 4.1)	If mitigations have been implemented	ISO 14971, Section 6.3
Update to documentation of configurations	Revision, update to, or creating documentation of system configurations (see chapter 6). A separate report may be prepared, or configurations can be included in the system specification, installation instructions, or the installation qualification (IQ).	Systems that require configuration.	Highly recommended

Although phase 5 could involve little or no activity for COTS and configured business systems, the activity for custom systems is far more extensive. During phase 5 prime, code is written and tested following a defined process for software development. After development is completed, the development team reviews its test results and the status of known defects, and determines if the system is ready for release to the customer. Once the software vendor releases the custom software, it's brought into the organization. The activities of phase 4—design solutions to issues—and phase 5—construct solutions to issues—as described for COTS systems, are then performed on the custom software. Table 2.7 lists phase 5 deliverables.

PHASE 6: PREPARE FOR USE

During phase 6 the project team learns about the system and gets ready to use it. The system owner and his or her staff learn the system so that they can prepare user procedures, training materials, and, during the next phase, validation tests. The IT

Table 2.8	Procedures Created During Phase 6, if Needed

Phase 6 deliverables	Definition and explanation	When applicable	Deliverable references
Information technology procedures: ■ Backup, archive, and restore (see 21 CFR 211, Section 68 b; and EC Annex 11, No. 14, for backup requirements) ■ Network adds, changes and deletes ■ Disaster recovery and contingency plans ■ Logical and physical security ■ System support (including recording and resolving errors as required by EC Annex 11, No. 17) ■ System maintenance ■ Printer setup and driver verification ■ Desktop and laptop setup ■ Other system-specific procedures (e.g., client installation)	Procedures needed to maintain a system in a validated state. Most of the procedures listed here are generic, (i.e., they can be used for many applications and/or systems). If a system requires a unique process, a separate procedure is written for it. For example, a generic backup-and-restore procedure will cover most of the items on a network; however, if a system requires a unique process for backup and restore, an additional procedure is written for that system.	All systems as appropriate	21 CFR Part 11, 11.10 d, i, j, k; 21 CFR 211, Section 68 b; EC Annex 11, No. 14
Change control procedure (see deliverable 6.2) and change request form (see deliverable 6.3)	A procedure that defines the process used to make controlled changes to a validated system, and the form used to request and approve the change	All validated systems	21 CFR 820, Section 820.70 i; ISO 13485, 7.5.2.1; EC Annex 11, No. 11; Part 11, 11.10 k (2)

Table 2.9	Summary of Phase 6 Deliverables Created for Each Computer System		
Phase 6 deliverables	**Definition and explanation**	**When applicable**	**Deliverable references**
System specification (see deliverable 6.1)	A specification for the system that includes a system description and lists all hardware and software components, their hierarchical relationships, and requirements for each component. A diagram showing the hardware components of a system and their connectivity may be included.	Recommended for low-risk systems that are complex or will change relatively often, and moderate- to high-risk systems	EC Annex 11, No. 4 (system description)
User procedures	User procedures define how the system is to be used by end users	Low-risk systems if predicate rules or quality system standards require procedures for automated functions; all moderate- to high-risk systems	Required if covered by a predicate rule; highly recommended with other systems
Application administration procedures	Administrative procedures define how the system is to be managed by application administrators	Low-risk systems with administrative functions if predicate rules require user procedures for automated functions. All moderate- to high-risk systems with administrative functions.	21 CFR 820, Section 25 b; 21 CFR Part 11, 11.10 d, i, j, k, 1, 11.300; EC Annex 11, No. 8
Contingency procedure	Alternative arrangements for systems which need to be operated in the event of a breakdown	All systems that can't have downtime	EC Annex 11, Nos. 15 and 16
Training materials	Manuals and other materials needed to train users and administrators. Such materials can be purchased or developed by the company.	All except systems where training isn't needed	Highly recommended

department prepares the procedures it needs to support users and maintain the system in a validated state. The IT staff who will support the users learn how to operate and support the system.[16]

The structure of the system is captured in a system specification that identifies the components of the system and the requirements for each component as specified in the technical requirements created in phase 2.

Generic IT procedures are written if they don't already exist, including procedures for system security, support (including issue recording and resolution), backup and restore, data archival, disaster recovery, maintenance, calibration (if applicable), change control, and printer setup and driver verification (optional, if data and/or records will be printed), and desktop and laptop setup (optional). If the generic procedures are insufficient for a specific system, then system-specific procedures are developed, such as a specific backup and restore procedure, and a specific maintenance and configuration procedure. Such procedures are critical to keeping the systems under change control and maintaining a validated state (i.e., one in which the system will continue to meet user requirements).

Those who are responsible for developing user procedures and training materials learn the system and prepare the procedures.

At the same time, the tests to be included in the validation testing can be drafted and checked. Preparing test protocols will be discussed as part of the next phase, but these can be developed while the activities of this phase are carried out.

During this phase, the system is informally tested as phase activities are performed; any defects that are discovered are tracked and addressed.

By the end of phase 6, the project team and other designated individuals should be finished exploring how the system works and debugging it.[17]

Configured business and custom systems are treated the same as COTS systems. Table 2.8 lists the procedures created during phase 6.

Table 2.8 presents the deliverables that are created in phase 6 for all systems as needed. Table 2.9 summarizes the phase 6 deliverables created for each computer system.

PHASE 7: QUALIFY THE SYSTEM

During this phase, the system is tested in a test environment before it's installed in the production environment during phase 8. The testing, called "qualification," demonstrates that the item (e.g., piece of equipment or computer system) has been properly installed and is capable of meeting a relevant set of requirements. (See note 1 for the difference between qualification and validation.) If a system uses the same network and/or servers as other applications, the qualification is usually split into application qualifications and infrastructure qualifications.

Qualification of a system or application begins by creating a validation instance of the system. The system includes application software; other software used only in conjunction with the application; infrastructure resources dedicated to the application, such as data space; and hardware dedicated to the application that isn't considered part

Table 2.10	Phase 7 Deliverables		
Phase 7 deliverables	**Definition and explanation**	**When applicable**	**Deliverable references**
Calibration records	Records of the calibrations and maintenance performed prior to the installation qualification (IQ)	When equipment requires calibration	21 CFR 211, Section 68 a; 21 CFR 820, Section 72; ISO 13485, Section 7.6
Maintenance records	Records of the maintenance performed prior to the IQ	When equipment requires maintenance	21 CFR 211, Section 67; 21 CFR 820, Section 70 g 1; ISO 13485, Section 6.3
IQ protocol	A protocol that defines the steps to verify the proper installation of hardware and software and that it meets technical requirements	All systems	21 CFR 820, Section 70 i; CDRH 6.2; EC Annex 11, No. 7; ISO 13485, Section 7.5.2.1
IQ report (test environment)	A report that summarizes the results from the IQ protocol and states a conclusion regarding the system's ability to meet the IQ protocol acceptance criteria	All systems	21 CFR 820, Section 70 i; CDRH 6.2; EC Annex 11, No.7; ISO 13485, Section 7.5.2.1
Operational qualification (OQ) protocol	A protocol developed to verify that the system operates, in a test environment, in accordance with requirements throughout all anticipated operational ranges	All systems	21 CFR 820, Section 70 i; CDRH 6.2; EC Annex 11, No. 7; ISO 13485, Section 7.5.2.1
Traceability matrix (user requirements to protocols)	A map of all user requirements to test steps in the protocols. The matrix documents that the requirements are being tested.	All systems except those with simple protocols	Highly recommended
Operational qualification (OQ) report	A report summarizing the OQ results, including variances. It states a conclusion regarding the system's ability to meet the OQ protocol acceptance criteria.	All systems	21 CFR 820, Section 70 i; CDRH 6.2; EC Annex 11, No. 7; ISO 13485, Section 7.5.2.1
Change control records	Records of the approval and testing of changes prior to their implementation in the production environment	All systems	21 CFR 820, Section 70 i; ISO 13485, 7.5.2.1; EC Annex 11, No. 11; 21 CFR Part 11, 11.10 k (2); CDRH 6.1
User training records	Records of the training provided to individuals to execute the validation protocols	All systems	21 CFR 211, Section 25; 21 CFR 820, Section 25 b; Part 11, 11.10 i; EC Annex 11, No. 1; ISO 13485, Section 6.2.2 e

of the infrastructure. Such dedicated hardware might include input, output, and communication devices. The application is installed following a documented procedure, and infrastructure devices used by the system are configured to provide the application with the resources it needs. Proper installation of the system is verified, as is the ability of the hardware and software to meet the technical requirements, by executing an approved IQ protocol. The IQ verifies that the hardware and software have the capability and capacity to support the application. Prior to beginning the IQ, the person executing it confirms that all measurement equipment (e.g., test instruments) is calibrated and maintenance is up to date for all instrumentation and equipment.

A report is prepared on the execution of the IQ protocol; it includes a summary of the results, including any problems encountered (i.e., discrepancies between actual and expected results), resolution of the problems, and a conclusion regarding the readiness of the system for operational qualification (OQ) testing—that is, if the system meets the IQ protocol-acceptance criteria. The executed IQ protocol is attached to, or referenced in, the report.

The OQ is performed following an approved protocol. This should include tests for user requirements and supportive operations as well as an evaluation of the users' ability to understand and correctly interface with the system. A traceability matrix is prepared that maps where in the OQ each user requirement and supportive operation is tested. As the protocol(s) is executed, discrepancies between expected and actual results are written up as variances. The resolution of each variance is documented and approved. Changes to the system to resolve problems are made following an approved change control procedure (see phase 6) or the variance report.

An OQ report is written that includes, or references, data collected while executing the OQ protocol, a discussion of the variances and their resolution, and a conclusion regarding the ability of the system to reliably meet requirements.

Validation packages provided by software vendors can be invaluable in speeding the validation process, although caution must be applied. To use these tests for the validation of your system, you must first verify that the tests adequately cover your requirements. The adequacy of the vendor's tests can be evaluated by creating a matrix that traces your user requirements and supportive operations to the OQ tests. You might need to develop and execute supplemental tests.

With configured business systems, configurations are created before the IQ and verified as part of the IQ process. Functionality created through the configurations is tested during the OQ and as part of the PQ during the next phase, if appropriate.

The infrastructure is delineated into two categories: providing automated services and providing the underlying hardware and software platform that hosts both infrastructure services and applications. Services provided by the infrastructure may play a critical role in safeguarding systems, preserving data integrity, and providing network communications. The infrastructure platform can include network equipment, shared servers and system software, database equipment and software, input and output devices, and devices specifically designed to provide a service, such as a firewall.[18]

Risk analysis is used to determine if an infrastructure service needs to be qualified and the extent of qualification required. The risk should be assessed based on the potential impact of a service on product quality and the criticality of the service for compliance, data integrity and security, business efficiency, and business continuity. An infrastructure service is qualified through an IQ for the hardware and software that provides the service and an OQ that demonstrates that the service functions as required.

Custom systems are treated in the same manner as COTS systems; that is, the proper installation of system components that meet technical requirements is verified and the system is tested in a validation environment.

None of the regulations, the ISO 13485 standard, or the FDA CRDH guidance document specify a type of protocol that's required, that is, an IQ, OQ, or PQ. The QSR does require an approved protocol.[19] In its list of five documents that manufacturers ought to have from its validation efforts, the FDA lists the "validation protocol used," and the "test cases and results."[20] The European Commission requires that the system be thoroughly tested and confirmed as capable of achieving desired results.[21] ISO 13485 states that documented procedures should be established for the validation of computer systems and that the results of the validation shall be recorded.[22] With the RiskVal life cycle, the mandate to use established protocols is met with the IQ, OQ, and PQ, as appropriate based on the risk level of the system. Table 2.10 lists phase 7 deliverables.

PHASE 8: USE IN A PRODUCTION ENVIRONMENT

Phase 8 spans the entire operational life of the system, from when it's officially installed in the production environment to when the system is retired.[23]

The purposes of this "use in a production environment" phase include:

- Verifying that the system functions appropriately in the production environment
- Using the system in compliance with approved user and application administration procedures

Table 2.11	Phase 8 Deliverables

Phase 8 deliverables	Definition	When applicable	Deliverable references
Installation qualification (IQ) report (production environment)	A report on the system installation in the production environment	When the system is installed to create a production environment	Highly recommended
User training records	Records of the training provided to end users, administrators, and those who execute validation protocols	All systems	21 CFR 211, Section 25; 21 CFR 820, Section 25 b; 21 CFR Part 11, Section 11.10 i; EC Annex 11, No. 1; ISO 13485, Section 6.2.2 e
Performance qualification (PQ) protocol	A test protocol developed to obtain documented evidence that the system performs effectively and reliably under normal production conditions	Moderate- and high-risk systems for which any production condition is different from that of the OQ test environment	21 CFR 820, Section 70 i; CDRH 6, 6.2, 6.3; EC Annex 11, No. 7; ISO 13485, Section 7.5.2.1
PQ report	A report that includes the data collected during the execution of the PQ protocol and a conclusion regarding the system's success in meeting the protocol acceptance criteria	All instances in which a PQ protocol is executed	21 CFR 820, Section 70 i; CDRH 6, 6.2, 6.3; EC Annex 11, No. 7; ISO 13485, Section 7.5.2.1
Risk management report	A report that summarizes the risk management process, including actions to implement and verify risk control measures, and an assessment of residual risk	Moderate- and high-risk systems	ISO 14971, Section 8
Validation final report	A report that summarizes the life cycle activities, identifies the deliverables from the life cycle that are part of the validation record, summarizes the results of the formal testing (IQ, OQ, PQ), addresses all variances, and states a conclusion as to the system's suitability	All systems. For low-risk and simple systems, the validation final report can be combined with a protocol report	21 CFR 820, Section 70 i; CDRH 6.2; ISO 13485, Section 7.5.2.1; EC Annex 11, No. 7
System backups	Backups made to be able to restore lost or corrupted programs, files and/or data	When backups are required or of sufficient business value. Moderate- and high-risk systems	21 CFR 211, Section 68 b; EC Annex 11, No. 14; 21 CFR 820, Section 180
Maintenance and calibration records	Records of the maintenance and calibration on the system during its life	When equipment requires calibration and/or maintenance	21 CFR 820, Sections 70 g 1 and 72; 21 CFR 211, Section 68 a; ISO 13485, Sections 6.3 and 7.6

(continues)

Table 2.11	Phase 8 Deliverables (continued)		
Phase 8 deliverables	**Definition**	**When applicable**	**Deliverable references**
Performance monitoring reports	Reports of activities performed to monitor system performance. Reports are prepared following documented procedures for system management.	When the system requires monitoring to ensure proper security, operation, and/or performance	Highly recommended
Issue reports	Records of problems and their resolution, and system enhancements	All systems	EC Annex 11, No. 17
Change control records	Records of the approval and testing of changes prior to their implementation in the production environment	All systems	21 CFR 820, Section 70 i; 21 CFR 11, Section 11.10 k 2; ISO 13485, 7.5.2.1; EC Annex 11, No. 11; 21 CFR 211, Section 68 b; CDRH 6.1
Periodic system review report	A report of a periodic review of system reliability and performance conducted to determine that the risk mitigations put in place are effective	Moderate- and high-risk systems	21 CFR 211, Section 68 b
Audit reports	Reports of the results of audits performed on system use, management, and maintenance	All systems	21 CFR 820, Section 22; EC Annex 11, No. 13; ISO 13485, Section 8.2.2

■ Supporting and managing the system following approved IT procedures to ensure it remains in a validated state.

Once the system is qualified in the test environment, it's installed in a production environment and verified using the IQ protocol. Further testing during the PQ is conducted under actual operating conditions to verify that the system performs its intended functions while operating in its normal production environment. The approach taken with the PQ depends on the risk associated with the system. Options include:

■ Testing functions by comparing results obtained with the electronic system with results obtained from a parallel manual system or electronic system
■ Executing designed tests of program logic and system functionality
■ Verifying end-result data but not testing processing steps
■ Monitoring the system by reviewing system data, logs, and problem reports
■ Combining any of the options

A PQ report is written and approved. A validation final report is also written that, when approved, completes the validation aspects of the life cycle.

Throughout the system's production use, it's carefully managed to ensure continued, reliable performance. During this phase:

- Trained users and administrators operate the system according to approved procedures.
- Security measures block the system from unauthorized use and safeguard data from unauthorized changes.
- System performance is maintained through calibration and maintenance.
- Problems are tracked and difficulties resolved using controlled methods.
- Changes are evaluated, approved, implemented, and tested in a test environment, and then introduced into the production environment. The system is monitored after the change to ensure that any unexpected negative effect is detected.
- The system and the control processes are audited. The system's operating experience is evaluated by reviewing problem reports and change control records. Audits are conducted on the procedures that control system use and maintain the system in a validated state.

When changes are extensive or system performance has degraded, a complete re-validation may be performed. Table 2.11 lists phase 8 deliverables

The statement made after table 2.10 also applies here, that is, a specific type of protocol, such as a PQ is not specified by the regulations or standards. With the RiskVal life cycle, the mandate to use established protocols is met with an IQ, OQ, and PQ, as appropriate, based on the risk level of the system.

PHASE 9: RETIRE THE SYSTEM

When the system is no longer needed, or when its obsolesced by more advanced technology, it's retired. Planning for the system's retirement normally is done simultaneously with implementing a new system. The new system is selected, implemented, tested, installed, and used following the RiskVal or similar life cycle.

Data preservation is often the most critical problem of system migration. There are several ways to address it:

- The new system can access data from the old system.
- The old system can be preserved to access the old data and the new system used exclusively for new data.

Table 2.12	Phase 9 Deliverables		
Phase 9 deliverables	**Definition**	**When applicable**	**Deliverable references**
System retirement and record migration report	Documentation that provides a traceable history of what systems were used throughout the records-retention period and how the records were migrated	All systems	21 CFR 820, Section 180 b; ISO 13485, Section 4.2.4

- Legacy data can be loaded into the new system.
- Records can be archived to non-electronic media such as microfilm, microfiche, and paper, or to a standard electronic file format such as PDF, XML, or SGML.

Table 2.12 lists the phase 9 deliverables.

MOST IMPORTANT ACTIVITIES AND DELIVERABLES

What are the minimum requirements for validation deliverables? From a regulatory perspective, the answer is whatever your industry's regulatory bodies require. From a business perspective, the minimum is what's needed to protect your company from risks associated with potential failure of the system.

The following tables provide lists of all procedures (table 2.13), deliverables (table 2.14), and records created during production use (table 2.15) that are required by at least one regulation, or are seen as necessary in the FDA guidance document on software validation. The regulations included are: FDA predicate rules for pharmaceutical products (21 CFR 211) and medical devices (21 CFR 820), Part 11 (21 CFR 211), and the EC Commission's directive on medicinal products. The tables indicate when the items are included in the list given by the FDA in its software validation guidance as documentation that the company should prepare.[24]

Table 2.13 provides a list of the policies and procedures mentioned in a regulation. These documents should be developed in advance to define a life cycle for the risk management and validation of all computer systems. Also provided is the deliverable number if a related brief appears in appendix 1.

Table 2.14 includes all the activities and deliverables that are required as part of the

Table 2.13	Software Validation Policies and Procedures Required by Regulations	

RiskVal policy or procedure and deliverable number	Requirement	Requirement reference
Validation procedure (see deliverable 1.2 and 1.4)	Procedures and control shall include validation of systems to ensure accuracy, reliability, consistent and intended performance, and the ability to discern invalid or altered records.	21 CFR 820 Section 70 i; 21 CFR Part 11, Section 11.10 a
Information technology (IT) policy (see deliverable 1.3)	The establishment of, and adherence to, written policies that hold individuals accountable and responsible for actions initiated under their electronic signatures to deter record and signature falsification.	Part 11, Section 11.10 j
Backup, archive, and restore	Data should be protected by backing up at regular intervals (see EC Annex 11).	cGMP 211.68(b); EC Annex 11, No. 14
Network adds, changes, and deletes	There shall be a defined procedure for the issue, cancellation, and alteration of authorization to enter and amend data, including the changing of personnel passwords.	EC Annex 11, No. 8
Disaster recovery and contingency plans	The procedures to be followed if the system fails or breaks down shall be defined and validated.	EC Annex 11, 16
Logical and physical security	Procedures and controls shall include limiting system access to authorized individuals, and adequate controls over the distribution of, access to, and use of documentation for system operation and maintenance (see Part 11).	Part 11, Section 11.10 c and d; EC Annex 11, No. 13
System support	A procedure should be established to record and analyze errors and to enable corrective action.	EC Annex 11, No. 17
Change control (see deliverable 6.2 and 6.3)	Alterations to a system or computer program should be made only in accordance with a defined procedure, which should include provision for validating, checking, approving, and implementing change (see Annex 11). Change control on system documentation (see Part 11).	21 CFR 820 Section 70 i; ISO 13485, 7.5.2.1; EC Annex 11, No. 11; Part 11, Section 11.10 k (2)

validation. The business reasons for the deliverable are also included. If a brief on the deliverable is provided in appendix 1, the deliverable's number is provided after the deliverable's name.

Table 2.15 lists the records that must be created during the ongoing use of a computer system after validation is complete. The business reason for the record is also given.

The question of what constitutes the minimum validation activities is discussed further in chapter 12. In addition, exhibit 12.1 compares the RiskVal deliverables with the recommendations of Gamp 4.[25]

Table 2.14	Minimum RiskVal Validation Activities and Deliverables Based on Regulatory Requirements and Business Reasons		
RiskVal activity	**Deliverable**	**Business reason**	**Regulations, standards, and guidance documents that indicated importance**
Writing user requirements	User requirements (see deliverable 2.1)	User requirements are the logical foundation for demonstrating that a system is capable of meeting requirements.	General Principles, 2002, Section 6.2
Qualifying vendors	Vendor qualification report (see deliverable 3.3 and 3.4)	Software quality must be built into software. Validation testing can't find all the defects. Vendors must be qualified based on their development practices.	EC Annex 11, No. 5
Executing hardware- and software-purchase contracts, including quality plans and support agreements	Hardware and software purchase agreements (including service agreements)	Purchase agreements are binding contracts and warranty agreements. Services and quality requirements for services must be defined. Support terms are important to ensure that the system remains in a validated state	EC Annex, No. 11, 18
Define and/or describe the system	System specification and/or system hardware configuration diagram (see deliverable 6.1)	The specification states technical requirements and ensures that the system has the hardware and software needed to function effectively. It provides a master list for the installation qualification and for replicating the system.	EC Annex 11, No. 4
Defining system acceptance criteria	The acceptance criteria can be given in the validation plan (see deliverable 4.2), or in a validation protocol (see deliverable 7.1, 7.3, and 8.1)	Acceptance criteria need to be defined in advance to set a standard for when the system is acceptable.	General Principles, 2002, Section 6.2
Define the appropriate use of the system	Instructions on system use can be provided in a separate user procedure, or in a procedure for the automated process.	Instructions for using the system within your automated process are needed to ensure user effectiveness.	EC Annex 11, No. 8
Define what to do to maintain the process when the system fails or breaks down	Contingency procedures. If a manual system is used as the contingency process, it can be included in the user procedure.	Employees need to know what to do in case the system is unavailable, even if that means waiting until the system is brought back up. If the system will be down for an extended period of time, a plan will avoid stopping the business.	EC Annex 11, No. 16

RiskVal activity	Deliverable	Business reason	Regulations, standards, and guidance documents that indicated importance
Calibrate measurement devices	Calibration records	Calibration is needed to ensure that measurements are accurate	21 CFR 211, Section 68 a; 21 CFR 820, Section 72
Perform maintenance	Maintenance records (performance of maintenance during the OQ can be used to qualify the maintenance process)	Unscheduled and scheduled preventive maintenance are necessary to ensure that the system will continue to function effectively.	21 CFR 211, Section 67; 21 CFR 820, Section 70 g (1)
Train users. If appropriate use is not obvious from the procedures, user training also is needed.	Training records	Early users who will perform the validation testing have to be trained to prevent operator errors during the execution of the protocols.	21 CFR 820, Section 25 b; 21 CFR 211, Section, 211.25; 21 CFR Part 11, Section 11.10 i; EC Annex 11, No. 1
Preparing and executing validation protocols and reports	Ordinarily installation- and operational-qualification protocols are prepared, but they can be combined, and at times a performance qualification (PQ) protocol isn't needed (see deliverable 7.1, 7.3, and 8.1).	The tests to be executed must be defined and written in advance with expected results. The executed protocols provide a permanent record of the tests performed and a comparison of the actual and expected results.	21 CFR 820, Section 70 i; General Principles, 2002, Section 6.2
Writing a validation final report	The final report can be a separate report or combined with the report for the last protocol to be written for the system, usually the PQ (see deliverable 8.3).	An approved final report closes the validation and releases the system for production.	EC Annex 11, No. 7 21 CFR 820, Section 70 i; General Principles, 2002, Section 6.2

Table 2.15	Records That Must Be Created During Ongoing Use	
Required record	**Business value of record**	**Requirement references**
User training records	To ensure that users are able to correctly use the system. To be able to verify that a user is competent before assigning user privileges.	21 CFR 820, Section 25 b; 21 CFR 211.25; 21 CFR Part 11, Section 11.10 i; EC Annex 11, No. 1
System backups	To be able to restore missing or corrupted files; preservation of intellectual property and work performed	cGMP 211.68 b; 21 CFR 820, Section 180; EC Annex 11, No. 14
Calibration records	To ensure the accuracy of measurements	21 CFR 211, Section 68 a; 21 CFR 820, Section 72
Maintenance records	To track that the regularly scheduled maintenance has been performed to prevent system failures; and to provide a history of unscheduled maintenance for troubleshooting	21 CFR 211, Section 67; 21 CFR 820, Section 70 g (1)
Issue tracking and resolution records	To ensure that issues get resolved, and to have a record of the occurrence of issues for troubleshooting	EC Annex 11, No. 17
Change control records	To ensure that only benign changes are made to the system. To be able to use the change history when reconstructing the system and troubleshooting problems.	EC Annex 11, No. 11; 21 CFR 11, Section 11.10 k (2)
Audit reports	To verify that the system is being used properly, including all measures implemented to manage risk	21 CFR 820, Section 22; General Principles, 2002, Section 6.2; EC Annex 11, No. 13

Chapter 3

Phase 1: Conceptualize

The conceptualize phase begins informally when an individual begins thinking about how to solve a problem with a computerized business system. Through the activities of this phase, the system owner answers the question, "What do I want to do?" As needs are explored, a concept of how to address the problem will evolve. An initial risk assessment identifies potential dangers associated with such automation.

The concept of the system and critical information concerning it are documented in a computer system project proposal. Both the information technology (IT) and validation departments participate in preparing the proposal to assist the originator in understanding the high-level technical requirements and potential validation requirements.

After management approves the project proposal, a formal project is begun. Project plans are created for projects that are large, complex, or of moderate to high risk.

Prior to initial approval of a project, the organization should establish the policies and procedures needed as a foundation for controlling the risks associated with, and validating, a computer system.

CLARIFY THE NEEDS FOR A SYSTEM BY DEFINING INTENDED USES

The computer system life cycle unofficially starts when an employee begins to think that a computerized business system is the solution to a business need (see note 1). This need must be clarified and defined to the point where the system owner can:

- Articulate the intended uses of the system.
- Explore some initial ideas of the type of system that might best meet the need.
- Explain to management why it is worth investing in a system.

For simple, straightforward problems, a single need might be identified. For more complex situations, several related needs and/or problems might have to be simultaneously addressed. The system owner can clarify the needs through discussions with colleagues who share responsibility for solving the problem or with individuals who are experiencing the problem. For example, if a document control manager recognizes a need to shorten the time it takes to approve engineering change orders, he or she can clarify the needs or problems to solve through discussions with his or her staff and those who use the existing process. The manager can talk with those who initiate engineering change requests, who review and approve engineering change orders, and who use the controlled documents. Discussions with other professionals or consultants might also help clarify the needs to be met by the computer system.

The process owner must sift through the possible problems and identify which of them the system will address. The needs are translated into statements of intended uses for the system as an initial definition of what it will do. During this exploratory stage, the system owner and other team members will develop requirements the system will need to meet. Keep track of these requirements. During phase 1 the focus is on high-level statements of intended use. In phase 2 written statements of both user and technical requirements will be created.

The case study introduced in the callout titled "Medatech 3.1" concerns a document control system needed by the document control manager of a small, rapidly growing medical device company. Medatech 3.1 provides background on the case study and the intended use statement for the document control system.

Medatech 3.1	Intended Uses of a Document Control System

Medatech, a medical device manufacturer, has grown from ten to sixty employees during the last few years. Its second product has been submitted for Food and Drug Administration (FDA) approval. A couple of years ago, Doc, who manages the company's document control department, personally processed a dozen change requests a month. His staff has grown to include a document control specialist and an administrator. The team currently handles the approval of twenty change requests monthly, and as Medatech prepares for the commercial production of its second product, document control will need to process forty to fifty change orders a month.

Medatech's document control function currently uses a paper-based system that includes a part-number log, change-request number log, manual routing of change requests for approval, and making fifteen hard copies of each newly released document for distribution to binder sets throughout the company. Doc has developed a database application for keeping information about the documents, such as title, number, revision level, originator, and effective date. This database is used to print out a master list, one copy of which is inserted in front of each binder of the controlled copies to serve as an index. All FDA-regulated activities are performed from controlled copies of the documents.

Doc realizes that the workload of his department will continue to grow as the company develops and manufactures more products. He believes that increasing staff is an approach that will solve his near-term needs but questions if it's a viable long-term strategy.

Doc wrote the following statement of his intended uses for an electronic document control system:

- The document control system will provide information about the documents stored in the system, including procedures, drawings, test protocols, assembly instructions, bills of materials, and quality assurance forms.
- Employees on-site will view documents online for use in performing FDA-regulated activities.
- Employees will use the system to search for the documents they need.
- Initial approval of documents and changes will occur electronically within the system. The ability to change documents will be controlled by the system.
- The system will keep an audit trail of all changes to documents, data, and approval information.

CREATE A VISION STATEMENT

A brief, clear high-impact statement of how the system will benefit the organization will help in gaining management approval. The more expensive the system and the more time and resources needed to implement it, the stronger the business justification for such a system must be. The value of a system is summarized in a vision statement.

A vision statement for a simple system will be a direct statement of its business purpose. If Doc, Medatech's document control manager, were to use a spreadsheet to create a master list of effective documents, the vision statement for the master list would say something like: "The master-list spreadsheet provides users of controlled documents with a method to identify the currently effective revision of a document."

The best vision statement for a large or high-risk system is one in which the value of the system is so obvious that the need for it can't be questioned. For this reason, the Medatech team chose to emphasize the effect of the document control system on manufacturing time rather than on cost savings for document control (see Medatech 3.2). The team's vision statement is: "Medatech is implementing an electronic document management system to speed manufacturing turnaround time through direct online access to drawings, assembly instructions, and test procedures from the manufacturing floor."

ANSWER THE MAKE-OR-BUY QUESTION

The conceptualize phase begins informally when individuals begin thinking about how to solve a problem with a computerized business system. As alternative approaches and solutions are explored, a concept of how the company wants to meet the need will evolve.

In most situations, a range of options is available. For example, in the document control area, solutions can range from a set of spreadsheets to a commercial-off-the-shelf (COTS) system, to a custom system. The least expensive solution is a set of spreadsheets used for keeping lists of effective documents, the assignment of part numbers, the assignment of engineering change request orders, and the status of the change orders. Documents can be placed on a server for access by means of the company intranet. There are several types of COTS systems that have document control capabilities; two types of systems that are built primarily for document control are electronic document management systems (EDMS) and product data management (PDM) systems. EDMS

Medatech 3.2	Vision Statement

Doc must convince management to commit resources to his document control project. Some of the options he's considering will require a lot of time from the information technology and quality assurance staffs and users. In addition, purchasing, validating, and implementing a package could cost a hundred thousand dollars. Doc will be most successful in selling his project if he can justify the system by addressing an obvious company need. He's in a weaker position if he tries to justify the system based on benefits limited to his department.

Doc is aware that document control is a service department. He must provide services in a manner that supports the business model of his primary users. When Medatech's second product is approved, the company will double in size and manufacturing will triple. Medatech's objective is a five-day turnaround from order to shipment with just-in-time manufacturing. Doc and Paula, the production manager, believe that using online drawings and assembly instructions is necessary to meet Medatech's production goal. It would take document control three days to manually prepare a packet of the documentation required to produce the product and record data from the manufacturing process. The typical time needed to fill the order would then be seven to eight days.

Doc will have to answer the question of why he's implementing the system over and over again during the nine-month process of selecting, validating, and implementing. He could assert that the system is necessary so that his department can keep up with the anticipated increased volume of change requests. However, because the cost and resource demands of his project are high, his best answer is a short, clear vision statement that shows how he'll solve an indisputable company need.

Doc and Paula crafted the following vision statement:

"Medatech is implementing an electronic document management system to speed manufacturing turnaround time through direct online access to drawings, assembly instructions, and test procedures from the manufacturing floor."

Although the vision statement identifies only the production staff as system users, all employees will have access to it for viewing documents (e.g., procedures, drawings, and bills of materials), and all reviewers will use the system to record and sign their approval or rejection of engineering change orders.

systems are designed to manage electronic files of controlled documents. Most EDMS systems include the electronic routing and approval of engineering change orders and associated documents. In addition to the functionality of EDMS systems, a PDM system can manage part information and the interrelationships between parts (e.g., bills of materials).

When individuals are experienced in using computer systems to address the need, potential solutions can be immediately clear. For example, if an employee has had experience using a system at another company, that experience might be sufficient to provide clear information on how the same or similar system could be used at the new company. In other cases, research might be required to understand the types of systems that are available and what they can and can't do. Some of the sources of information commonly used include:

- Internet searches
- Discussions with colleagues
- Conversations with sales representatives
- Demos of systems
- Trade shows

The first question the team must address is if the organization should purchase or develop a system. Table 3.1 describes for each type of system the pros and cons for selecting that approach. Many companies try to avoid the development of custom systems or the customization of a purchased system, which results in a mixed system. Custom software is costly to develop, maintain, and enhance over time. In addition, the time frame for development can be lengthy. However, if a system must be designed to meet unique needs or provide the company with a competitive advantage through a one-of-a-kind system, a custom system is needed.

DESCRIBE THE SYSTEM

Once a direction becomes clear, the system owner and IT can put together a preliminary description of the system they think they want. The description will include the type of system (COTS, configurable, or custom), type of hardware required, and the type of system software needed to support the system. This basic description of the system will be refined and expanded in phase 2 when the system requirements are documented, and in phase 3 when options are evaluated against the requirements, and a system is selected.

When describing the system, the system owner, with input from the IT and validation departments, must define what is and isn't included in the system. For example, most systems use the network to connect users to each other, to input and/or output devices, or to the application software or database. In defining the system, the system

Type of system	Reasons for selecting	Disadvantages
Commercial off-the-shelf (COTS) system	■ System is ready to install. ■ System is more feature- and function-rich than those created using a database package. ■ Vendor will enhance and evolve system over time. ■ Vendor will provide defect support.	■ System must be used as it's built. It might not meet your requirements, so you might have to modify how you do business. ■ Purchaser has little control over enhancements.
Configured business system	■ System is more flexible than COTS systems. Purchaser can adapt system to how it does business.	■ Configuration options might not support how you want to do business. ■ System might not meet your requirements, so you might have to modify how you do business. ■ Purchaser has little control over enhancements.
Database package system	■ A simple application can be developed quickly and at a lower cost than purchasing a system. ■ System is more efficient than manual operations.	■ Database package applications offer limited functionality unless they're professionally developed. ■ Database packages are usually isolated, which creates data-entry redundancies and the possibility of error.
Custom system	■ Unique features or functions enable an organization to do things its competitors are unable to do. ■ COTS systems are unavailable or unsuitable to the organization's needs. ■ System is too complex to build with a database package, or the package isn't robust enough to handle the demands that will be placed on the system (e.g., the number of concurrent users).	■ Organization must pay for development, maintenance, and enhancement costs. ■ Life cycle for custom systems takes longer than for other systems.
Mixed system	■ A COTS or configured business system meets many of the company's needs, but some customization is required to create critical functionality and/or integrate the system to other systems.	■ Organization is responsible for building and maintaining the custom code.

Table 3.1 Comparison of System Types

owner often must address the question of whether the network should be considered part of the system or a separate one to which this system is connected. If the network is dedicated to the application, then it's clearly part of the system. If the network is used by many systems, it's usually easier to consider it as a separate system. Items excluded from the system but used by it, such as the network or a data storage device, might need to be validated as a separate system or as a part of another system.

Medatech 3.3	Buy Decision

Doc explored several options for handling the increased workload. Should he piece together a number of tools built from database packages, such as using one Excel spreadsheet for part-number assignment and another for tracking assigned change-request numbers? One of the information technology (IT) specialists dabbles in Access and has offered to put together a database with a user-friendly interface for quick access to all the information. Or should Doc purchase a high-powered application that will do it all? Doc even wondered if he should have a system built from scratch so that it could do great things like downloading bills of materials to an enterprise resource planning system, or feed the latest batch record forms into a manufacturing execution system.

Because Medatech is a small company that doesn't have the resources to develop a custom system, Tec, the head of IT, has advised Doc to investigate commercial off-the-shelf (COTS) and/or configurable systems. Doc consulted with some of the key future users of the system, a few document control managers from other companies, and researched different options. He determined that a number of COTS applications were available that appeared to meet his needs. He decided as a preliminary measure to obtain a COTS system.

Medatech 3.4	High-Level System Description

Doc's preliminary description of the proposed system is:
- A commercial off-the-shelf document control application run from a dedicated server controlled by the information technology (IT) function.
- Documents and related data will be stored on the dedicated server or on a dedicated database server connected to the network.
- One dedicated printer in document control will be used to print official hard copies.

Although the system will use the network, from a validation perspective it isn't considered part of the system. The network will be qualified as part of the infrastructure. In addition, the workstations employees use to view or approve documents aren't considered part of the system but will be configured following an IT procedure. The validation testing of the document control system will be performed from a workstation that conforms to Medatech's standard configuration.

The same approach can be used to determine if input and output devices are part of the system. For example, dedicated printers are usually considered part of the system, and printers used for multiple applications could be considered part of the network. Sensors that feed data into a manufacturing control system are part of the manufacturing control system.

Personal computers (PCs) and workstations are also part of a system if they're used only for that system. The PCs that employees use for working with many systems are normally controlled by IT policy and aren't considered part of any specific system.

FORM A PROJECT TEAM

For a given computer system, the company should determine who needs to be involved to support the life cycle activities and to what degree. Personnel must be assigned who are required to ensure the appropriate selection and procurement of a system or development of a system, and its effective installation, testing, and implementation. For simple applications, such as a spreadsheet used to record the status of controlled documents, a user might be able to create the system and validate it with some support from validation. Implementing a major application will require the collaborative effort of a team that includes the system owner, IT, and validation, while quality assurance (QA) plays an oversight role. The roles and responsibilities of the system owner, IT, validation, and QA are described in exhibit 3.1.

DEVELOP THE COMPUTER SYSTEM RISK MANAGEMENT AND VALIDATION INFRASTRUCTURE

Before an organization begins to seriously pursue the selection of a system and its implementation, it must establish the policies and procedures needed to ensure the quality of a business application from conception through retirement.[1] That foundation will define how systems will be purchased, installed, validated, and maintained in the company. The following are the basic documents of such an infrastructure.

Exhibit 3.1	Functional Roles and Responsibilities in the RiskVal Life Cycle

The roles and responsibilities assigned to organizational functions in a system implementation process such as the computer system risk management and validation (RiskVal) life cycle can vary from organization to organization, but the following roles and responsibilities are common.

System Owner

The system owner ordinarily is the manager, or his or her designee, of the department or function that's most affected by, or is the primary user of, the system. Ownership is clear for systems that are primarily used by one department, such as document control and calibration systems. Systems used by multiple organizations, such as MRP II systems or statistical packages, are owned by one of the user groups or information technology (IT).

The system owner is responsible for the effectiveness of the business process, and any automation of that process. If the system owner uses automation in meeting his or her functional responsibilities, then he or she bears the responsibility for protecting the organization from any harm associated with the system's failure. It seems logical, then, that the system owner should be charged with the overall responsibility for the system's validation and risk management. The major responsibilities of the system owner in the RiskVal life cycle are:

- Determining that a system is needed
- Defining user requirements
- Ensuring that vendors and their products are adequately evaluated against user requirements and vendor organizational requirements during the selection process
- Obtaining management approval to procure or build the system
- Assessing risks associated with using the system and reducing those risks to an acceptable level
- Determining whether to modify the user requirements to resolve discrepancies between how the system functions and the requirements
- Preparing user procedures for the system
- Preparing and executing tests related to user requirements. Or, reviewing the tests developed by others for adequacy and evaluating the test results to determine if the system is suitable
- Training users

Information Technology

The IT organization is responsible for providing the hardware and system software required to operate the systems needed by the organization. That hardware and system software, referred to as "infrastructure," includes the network, servers used to operate the applications, and database hardware and software. The IT function procures, installs, manages, and supports the infrastructure. It's also responsible for protecting the organization against the risks of failure and improper use of the infrastructure. In addition to ensuring that an adequate infrastructure is established to support a specific application, the IT function provides technical expertise for selecting, implementing, and operating the application.

During the RiskVal life cycle, IT has the following major responsibilities:

- Preparing procedures needed by IT for managing the infrastructure and supporting the applications
- Defining technical requirements for the system
- Ensuring that commercial off-the-shelf systems are adequately evaluated against the technical requirements during the selection process
- Ensuring that the infrastructure is adequate to meet the intended uses and user requirements for the system
- Assessing risks associated with infrastructure failures and reducing those risks to an acceptable level
- Auditing the development practices of software vendors
- Determining and implementing solutions to any discrepancies between the system and the technical requirements for the infrastructure
- Installing the application and all components of the infrastructure used by the application
- Configuring infrastructure hardware and software as well as technical aspects of applications as needed
- Training IT staff
- Supporting the use of the application, including user access privileges (if appropriate), maintaining the application's availability and responsiveness, and resolving technical difficulties with the infrastructure and application
- Using the change-control process to repair software defects and enhance the system

Quality Assurance

QA is responsible for the establishment and effectiveness of the company's quality system. The quality system includes the following major aspects:[1]

- An established system for the production of quality products and services: defining the needed processes and ensuring adequate resources for the effectiveness of the processes
- Management taking responsibility for managing the processes to ensure their continual effectiveness and improvement
- Manufacturing quality products and providing quality services, including effective product design and development, qualifying vendors, developing and operating production processes, controlling materials, product, and the provision of services

(continues)

Exhibit 3.1

Functional Roles and Responsibilities in the RiskVal Life Cycle (continued)

- Determining whether the product meets specifications (e.g., product testing), the disposition of defective product, and taking action to determine and correct the causes of problems as well as prevent their reoccurrence

Of course, QA is the system owner of the applications it uses to carry out its function. In addition, QA is responsible for ensuring that automated processes that might affect the product's ability to meet specifications are capable of functioning as intended. In this capacity, QA plays an oversight role during the RiskVal life cycle.

In regulated companies, QA is also responsible for ensuring that the organization is compliant with product and quality system regulations, including regulations for computer system validation and for electronic records and signatures.[2]

Given these responsibilities, QA plays the following roles in the RiskVal life cycle:

- Defining validation policies and procedures
- Defining risk management policies and procedures
- Clarifying which regulatory requirements the system must meet (e.g., predicate rules and Part 11). Supporting the process owner in determining if the system meets regulatory requirements. Working with the project team to resolve issues of noncompliance.
- Providing direction in determining if the regulations require the system to be validated
- Qualifying vendors
- Evaluating the compliance risks associated with system failure
- Ensuring that an adequate system implementation process, such as the RiskVal life cycle, is used for systems that can affect the ability of a product to meet specifications
- Providing oversight during the implementation process to ensure that risk management and validation policies and procedures are followed, and that critical deliverables from the RiskVal life cycle meet the company's requirements for those deliverables

Validation and Risk Management Expert

Organizations need individuals who are trained in risk management and validation to advise system owners and IT staff in carrying out risk management and validation activities. Such expertise is often found in the quality assurance function in regulated organizations because validation is required as discussed in chapter 1. In the Medatech case studies, Val, a member of the QA function, is the risk management and validation expert. In many organizations, the validation and risk management expert resides in the IT function, especially if that department has a staff dedicated to implementing and supporting applications.

The role played by the risk management and validation expert vary from one organization to the next; however, here are some of the common activities performed by this expert:

- Providing direction on executing the RiskVal process, including what to do, how to do it, and how to document what was done
- Advising the project team on what RiskVal activities must be performed based on the system risk level
- Providing direction on how to adapt the rigor and intensity of the RiskVal activities to the system risk level
- Preparing or assisting the individual who is preparing the validation plan
- Assisting in writing the validation testing and recording the results. In some instances the RiskVal expert is asked to prepare the test protocols, especially those related to verifying that the system will meet user requirements.

1. ISO 9001:2000, Quality management systems—Requirements. International Organization for Standardization, 2000,

2. 21 CFR Part 11, Electronic Records—Electronic Signatures. Food and Drug Administration. *Federal Register,* Vol. 62, No. 54, March 20, 1997.

Validation Policy

The validation policy defines when systems must be validated, the requirements for the validation process, requirements for maintaining a system in a validated state, and the required validation records (see deliverable 1.1 in appendix A).[2] Nonregulated industries needn't formulate a separate validation policy. Ensuring that systems can reliably meet requirements can be included in an IT policy.

Computer System Risk Management and Validation Life Cycle Procedure

The company's computer system risk management and validation life cycle procedure defines the enterprise's computer system acquisition, implementation, validation, use, and retirement process. This procedure is referred to in this book as the "RiskVal procedure." It describes the set of activities the company will perform to validate and manage the risks associated with its computer systems (see deliverable 1.2). In the RiskVal procedure, each phase of the life cycle is described, including the responsibilities of different functional areas, the activities to be performed, and the deliverables to

---

| Medatech 3.5 | Project Team |

Medatech's project team included Doc, the system owner; Tec, the IT manager; and Val, a validation specialist from the company's validation function within quality assurance.

---

be produced for systems at various risk levels. The procedure is followed throughout the system's life cycle. The RiskVal life cycle deliverables form the validation record. Any life cycle approach, such as the one described here, can be used as a basis for the company's procedure.[3] The Association for the Advancement of Medical Instrumentation's (AAMI) SW68, Medical Device Software—Software Life Cycle Processes, and the Food and Drug Administration's (FDA) guidance document on software validation identify common elements of computer system life cycles and commonly used tools.[4, 5]

The RiskVal life cycle is applied to each computer system project following the guidelines defined in the procedure. At the end of this phase, the specific activities that will be performed are incorporated in the project plan, if one is developed, and in the validation plan that's written (if necessary) during phase 4. For simple systems that need neither a project nor a validation plan, the activities are listed in the first test protocol that's executed.

IT Policy

The IT policy defines the company's requirements for acquiring, managing, and using computer systems and the company's IT infrastructure (see deliverable 1.3).[6] The policy defines requirements for selecting and acquiring hardware and software, and developing systems. It also defines what measures must be taken to ensure that systems and data are secure, appropriately used and maintained, and comply with external regulations and standards such as 21 CFR Part 11.[7] User responsibilities are defined concerning the use of computer systems for company business, the use of e-mail and the Internet, installing and using personal software, and the correct use of passwords. The policy also defines requirements for the appropriate management of a network and systems, such as change control, system maintenance, IT support, system security, virus protection, backup and restore, and disaster recovery. Finally, the policy includes requirements regarding the types of systems that can be selected and used. Topics of this nature include Part 11 requirements for electronic records and signatures, and requirements related to standardizing hardware and system software.

Documentation of procedures used by IT in managing systems is prepared during phase 6, prepare for use.

Risk Management Policy

The risk management policy defines when the formal management of risk is necessary and the requirements for the risk management process, including assessing and managing risk, and monitoring the occurrence of failures after the item is placed in use.[8]

Risk Management Procedure

The risk management procedure defines a formal process for risk management, including risk analysis, evaluation and control, residual risk evaluation, and postproduction monitoring. Additional procedures can be prepared for the risk-assessment methods mentioned in the following section and discussed in detail in chapter 6.[9]

Requirements for Computer System Validation Plans, Protocols, and Reports

The computer system life cycle procedure defines all the activities required for ensuring quality, including all validation activities. An additional procedure provides more detailed requirements for those activities traditionally defined as validation, including the validation plan; installation, operational, and performance qualifications; qualification reports; and the validation final report (see deliverable 1.4).[10]

PERFORM AN INITIAL RISK ASSESSMENT

Uses for the Initial Risk Assessment

There are three reasons for conducting an initial risk analysis during the conceptualize phase. The first and most important is to alert the project team and the managers who will approve the computer system proposal of any risks associated with a system failure. Such knowledge is valuable. If a system failure poses high risk to patients, a high risk of noncompliance, or the potential for significant business loss, management will more critically examine both the need for the system and the selection of a specific system. The user requirements defined during phase 2 should include requirements for the proper functioning of the system in areas of moderate to high risk. For example, if the EDMS system doesn't protect controlled documents from unauthorized changes, Medatech will lose control over its products' safety. Consequently, the company's user requirements must include statements about controlling the ability to change documents.

Second, determining the risk level also serves as the index that guides the application of the RiskVal life cycle to a given system. The risk level is used to determine both whether a specific deliverable is needed and the rigor and intensity with which related activities are conducted.

The discussion of life cycle activities in each of the following chapters ends with a table identifying the deliverables created during that phase. In the "when applicable" column, the needed deliverable is identified; the system's risk level is one of the major determinants.

The risk level also provides guidance in regard to the intensity and rigor with which various life cycle activities should be pursued. "Intensity" applies to scope of analysis across all normal and abnormal operating conditions, while "rigor" relates to the formality of the methods used and the documentation of results.[11]

Selecting the system provides a good illustration. Examples of high-risk systems include the EDMS system, systems for clinical trial analyses, and adverse-event reporting systems. The selection process for such systems should include a thorough evaluation of alternatives on critical functionality and a review of known software defects that might lead to system failure. However, the selection of a low-risk system might be based only on general familiarity with the system and recommendations from users at other companies.

The documentation of the selection process should also increase in thoroughness as risk increases. For example, documentation isn't needed for how a low-risk system was selected. Documentation for how a moderate-risk system was selected can be less detailed than how a high-risk system was selected. The briefs provided for the deliverables include a section called "risk-based adjustments" that explain modifications to the deliverable based on the system's risk level.

The third use of the initial risk assessment is to set the priority of existing systems for validation. This is of greatest value when the company is working to set priorities for a group of existing systems that haven't yet been validated. Once an initial risk assessment has been completed for the existing systems, a validation master plan can be created in which systems are assigned priorities for validation. The priorities are based on how often the systems are used, their importance, and their risk levels.

Determining the Initial Risk Level

The initial risk level is based solely on the harm that is likely to result if the system fails to perform, or performs incorrectly, its intended functions. The probability of failure is the second factor normally used in a risk analysis. However, as will be explained in chapter 6, the assumption is made for software that it will fail at an unacceptable level.

During phase 1, determining the initial risk level involves the following critical activities if the specific system to be used isn't known:

- Identifying any possible failings of the system in fulfilling its intended uses and any hazards associated with its use
- Identifying the harm that can result from each failure and hazard, and the severity of the harm. Harm can be determined along any dimension that's relevant to your situation. The three dimensions most commonly used are:
  - ☐ The safety of the patient and, if appropriate, its operator. If the product is a medical device, the safety of both the patient and operator must be evaluated.
  - ☐ Noncompliance with regulations. For example, can a system failure corrupt electronic records?
  - ☐ The ease and cost of doing business. For example, what's the effect of a down system on the company's ability to perform work or manufacture a product?

- Identify and record any risk mitigations that might detect a failure and/or prevent it from causing harm. Examples of mitigations include:
  - ☐ Events later in the process that verify or test the system output (e.g., product)
  - ☐ Methods to detect the failure and prevent the harm from occurring
  - ☐ The number of failures that must occur simultaneously or in sequence before the harm occurs, and their likelihood

- Based on severity of the potential harm and the presence of mitigations, determine the risk level of the system to be low, moderate, or high. Use a predefined table, such as Table 3.2, to map the most severe harm from all the potential failures or hazards to a risk level, and then adjust the level as appropriate based on the mitigations.
- Recording the initial risk level in the computer system project proposal.

These examples don't take into account the frequency of the failure. High frequency of a specific failure might raise the risk level of the system to a higher risk classification.

Table 3.2	Definitions and Examples of System Risk Levels	
Risk level	**Definition**	**Severity of failures for the risk level**
Low	A system for which the highest risk associated with a potential failure is assessed through a formal process and considered broadly acceptable	■ No effect on product safety or efficacy, although customers might notice some change in product performance that's inconvenient or annoying. ■ No effect on quality records ■ Momentary inconvenience to employees
	Example: Spreadsheet for tracking the assignment of change-request numbers	
Moderate	A system for which the highest risk associated with a potential failure is assessed through a formal process and considered as low as reasonably practical	■ Potential injury or nonserious injury might result ■ Product is operable but operability and/or effectiveness is degraded. ■ Performance degradation or equipment failure that is inconvenient ■ Loss of records/data/programs that can be recovered by information technology
	Example: Failure of a system that controls the level of active ingredient of a product for which an overdose would result in a nonserious injury to a patient	
High	A system for which the highest risk associated with a potential failure is assessed through a formal process and considered unacceptable	■ Serious injury or death of the patient or operator ■ Product is inoperable or ineffective. ■ Loss of access to quality records for an intolerable period of time ■ Intolerable downtime, or loss of productivity or equipment leading to substantial cost ■ Inappropriate access to confidential information
	Examples: ■ Adverse-event tracking system: A failure could result in not identifying dangerous side effects of drugs. ■ SAS program to analyze clinical trials data: Incorrect analysis could result in discarding a product that was effective.	

If the life cycle is being applied to an existing system, a detailed risk analysis can be performed during this phase instead of the initial risk assessment. In such analyses, the severity of the harm, the probability of its occurrence, and the ability to detect an error before the harm occurs are used to set the risk level (see phase 4). The detailed analysis gives a more accurate evaluation of the risks posed by the actual system. The three methods used for a detailed risk assessment are failure mode and effect analysis, fault tree analysis, and the hazard analysis and critical control point method. See phase 4 for guidelines on when to use each method and a methods brief for each.

Medatech 3.6	Initial Risk Analysis

Doc, Tec, and Val conducted a risk analysis for commercial off-the-shelf document control systems and applied the intended uses listed in Medatech 3.1. The team decided that the system was a high-risk because at least some of the possible consequences of system failure were intolerable. Specifically, they determined that the potential failure of gravest effect would be if specifications, drawings, bills of materials, and assembly procedures could be changed outside of the official change-control process. If that happened, Medatech would lose control over the design of its products, the manufacturing process, and its quality control methods. Such lack of control could possibly lead to intolerable quality problems and to extreme nonconformances with the Quality System Regulation.

As a consequence of their analysis, the team will be careful to include the requirements for control of changes to documents in their user requirements, will provide extensive testing of these controls in both the operational qualification and performance qualification, and will treat the system as a high-risk system throughout its life cycle.

In addition, the team also examined the potential harm from the system failing to meet other intended uses, such as the ability to find the correct revision of a document through the search capability, the ability to view the correct document online during manufacturing and testing, obtaining correct data concerning the documents and drawings, and creating an audit trail of changes to documents, data, and approval information. From the analyses, the team identified additional user requirements and system functionality that needed to be tested.

DETERMINE IF 21 CFR PART 11 APPLIES

The FDA published 21 CFR Part 11, a regulation concerning electronic records and electronic signatures that's commonly known as Part 11. Determining if Part 11 applies to your computer system is critical. If Part 11 does apply, the system and processes associated with its use must meet the requirements set forth in the regulation. In Part 11's scope section, the FDA explains when the regulation applies: "This part applies to records in electronic form that are created, modified, maintained, archived, retrieved, or transmitted under any records requirements set forth in agency regulations. This part also applies to electronic records submitted to the agency under requirements of the Federal Food, Drug, and Cosmetic Act (the Act) and the Public Health Service Act (the PHS Act), even if such records are not specifically identified in agency regulations."[12]

To determine if Part 11 applies, identify the data that the system collects, creates, processes, stores, or reports, and check the relevant regulations to determine if any of those data are required by a FDA regulation. When determining if Part 11 applies, be careful to differentiate between records that are specifically required by the FDA and information that isn't required but is a part of your quality system.

For example, the FDA's Quality System Regulation, which applies to medical devices, states the following requirement for document approval: "Each manufacturer shall designate an individual(s) to review for adequacy and approve prior to issuance all documents established to meet the requirements of this part. The approval, including the date and signature of the individual(s) approving the document, shall be documented."[13] An electronic document control system that includes electronic approval of such documents must meet the Part 11 requirements for electronic signatures. On the other hand, a spreadsheet that's used to record what numbers have been assigned to controlled documents isn't a required quality record and wouldn't have to meet the Part 11 requirements.

A checklist for determining if Part 11 applies is provided in exhibit 3.2, Checklist for Part 11 Applicability. It includes examples of the types of records that are required by various FDA regulations. Although the checklist covers a broad range of records, it's not intended to be comprehensive. To verify whether a type of record is required by a regulation, consult the relevant regulations.

Medatech 3.7   Part II Applicability

The project team used exhibit 3.2, Checklist for 21 CFR Part 11 Applicability, to determine that Part 11 applied to the new document control system. They checked item nine because the document control system would use electronic signatures for approving engineering change orders and associated documents. Part 11 applies to, among other things, records created and used in electronic form that are required by predicate rule. The Quality System Regulation requires that records be kept of the approval of, as well as changes to, documents (21 CFR 820 40).

Validation is required because of a medical-device predicate rule requirement to validate computer systems used in the quality system (21 CFR 820 70 i). Because of the predicate rule requirement mentioned previously to maintain records of document approvals, the Part 11 requirement to validate systems that create, store, or retrieve electronic records also applies (21 CFR Part 11.10 a).

Exhibit 3.2	Checklist for 21 CFR Part 11 Applicability

21 CFR Part 11 applies to any computer system that creates, modifies, maintains, archives, retrieves, or transmits any of the following types of records:

- Records required to be maintained by Food and Drug Administration (FDA) regulations (i.e., predicate rules) and that are maintained in electronic format in place of paper format
- Records required to be maintained by predicate rules, are maintained in electronic format in addition to paper format, and are relied on to perform regulated activities
- Records submitted to the FDA under the predicate rules (even if such records aren't specifically identified in agency regulations) in electronic format
- Electronic signatures intended to be the equivalent of handwritten signatures, initials, and other signings required by predicate rules

Part 11 covers all types of data and reports required by the FDA. The records requirements vary by the type of product. To determine if a type of data or report is required for your company, consult the relevant regulation.

Here's a limited list of examples of the types of data and/or reports that are involved. Check whether the system creates, manipulates, changes, manages, or stores each of the types of electronic records.

A yes on any item means that Part 11 applies.

☐ Yes ☐ No   1. Reports that might be shared with the FDA as part of a regulatory filing

☐ Yes ☐ No   2. Design control data, reports, and/or records

☐ Yes ☐ No   3. Clinical data and records, including those required by the FDA regarding the conduct of a study, handling of a product, and participant consent, as well as data on the treatment provided, its efficacy, and the safety of the product

☐ Yes ☐ No   4. Process development data reports and/or records

☐ Yes ☐ No   5. Validation data and reports, including utilities, facilities, processes, analytical methods, equipment, computer systems, sterilization, and packaging

☐ Yes ☐ No   6. Production environment monitoring and use, including equipment cleaning and use, environmental monitoring, facilities and utilities maintenance, pest control, and storeroom control of good manufacturing practices (GMP) materials

☐ Yes ☐ No   7. Material and/or product data for GMP raw materials, in-process materials, and finished product, including receiv-

(continues)

Exhibit 3.2		## Checklist for 21 CFR Part 11 Applicability (continued)

ing and incoming inspection records, material control and manufacturing records, batch records, traceability data, product release records, storage data, and shipping and distribution data

☐ Yes ☐ No 8. Analytical methods and/or test data for product used in clinical trials or commercial use—including all inspection and testing for conformance to specifications, and chromatograms or other electronic machine output

☐ Yes ☐ No 9. Quality system data and records (e.g., document approval records, disposition of nonconforming materials, deviation and variance reports, investigation reports, corrective and preventive actions, management review records, training records, calibration and preventive maintenance, vendor qualification records, vendor and internal audit reports, contract review records, and purchasing records)

☐ Yes ☐ No 10. Material and product label production and control

☐ Yes ☐. No 11. Stability and/or shelf life or expiration dating data and reports

☐ Yes ☐ No 12. Product service reports

☐ Yes ☐ No 13. Advertising materials, labeling, package inserts, and product information communicated to physicians

☐ Yes ☐ No 14. Complaints, post-market surveillance data, adverse events reports

☐ Yes ☐ No 15. Other: _____

Reference: Guidance for Industry Part 11, Electronic Records; Electronic Signatures—Scope and Application. U.S. Department of Health and Human Services, Food and Drug Administration, August 2003.

PREPARE A COMPUTER SYSTEM PROJECT PROPOSAL

A computer system project proposal is a form used by companies to summarize the information needed to evaluate possible computer system projects and document management's approval of the project. In addition, QA can use the proposal to inventory all computer systems and determine whether they need to be validated. Both the IT and validation departments participate in preparing the proposal to assist the origi-

Table 3.3	Computer System Project Proposal

Information	Use or value
Users: Organizations and/or functions that will use the system; the approximate number of users and their locations	■ Provides a basis for estimating the number of needed licenses. ■ Provides information on the number of concurrent users that might be using the system (some systems become unstable once the maximum number of concurrent users is reached). ■ Provides insight into distributed processing, distributed database, and network requirements. ■ Notifies information technology (IT) of potential user support needs
System description: Information on the type of application, supporting hardware, and software. The system's initial description will be incomplete until a specific system is selected or designed.	■ Provides a basis for an initial cost estimate. ■ Alerts IT to special hardware and system software needs, possible compatibility problems with existing software and equipment, and potential support issues
Intended uses: ■ Vision statement ■ Data to be input or captured, stored, and/or retrieved ■ Business functions to be performed with the system, including data manipulation and calculations ■ Type of environment in which the system will be used	Helps to determine: ■ The system's value ■ If 21 CFR Part 11 applies ■ If validation is required
Part 11 applicability: ■ Quality records created, maintained, and retrieved ■ Electronic signatures created with the system ■ A statement of whether Part 11 applies	If Part 11 applies, the system must meet those requirements.
Risk level: The system's risk level	The risk level affects: ■ The rigor required during the validation ■ The effort that might be needed to manage the risk ■ The proposal's viability
Planned implementation: ■ Specify what types or groups of users will use which parts of the system and when they will begin to use them ■ Identify, at a high level, the training needed by users, administrators, and IT staff	■ Provides information on the extent, complexity, and time frame of the implementation ■ Training requirements provide additional information on the cost and complexity of the implementation.
Required validation: ■ A statement of whether validation is required ■ If validation is required, describe, at a high level, the scope of the validation and provide preliminary ideas on how to conduct the validation (i.e., how the system will be tested to verify that it can consistently function as required).	■ The scope of the validation provides valuable information on project costs and time requirements. ■ The system will need to be validated if the FDA regulations require it, or if the company decides the system must be validated. If validation isn't required, the life cycle is still recommended to ensure the quality of the application, but testing might not be as tightly controlled.

Medatech 3.8	Computer System Project Proposal

Doc prepared a computer system project proposal with help from Tec and Val. The proposal was a good summary of the work they had completed. It included the intended uses of the system (Medatech 3.1) and their vision statement (Medatech 3.2), the anticipated users (Medatech 3.2), a high-level description of the system (Medatech 3.4), the system's risk level (Medatech 3.6), the applicability of Part 11 (Medatech 3.7), and the validation requirement (Medatech 3.7).

In addition, Doc added the following statement on the planned implementation: "The system will be implemented in two phases. First, all employees will use the system to search for and access controlled documents. About six months later, after the users have gained a comfort level with the system, the approval of engineering change orders will be done online."

Doc and Val crafted the following statement on the required validation: "The validation will include all system functionality. The validation will include an installation qualification (IQ), operational qualification (OQ), and performance qualification (PQ). (These terms are explained in later chapters.) More stringent testing will be performed on functions that have high-risk consequences if they fail. The OQ testing will challenge all functionality, including engineering change order (ECO) approval, prior to the installation of the system in an environment for use. The process for loading the legacy data will also be tested during the OQ. The PQ testing will be split. Access to the documents and related functionality will be tested during the first phase of implementation. The PQ tests of the ECO approval process will occur at the beginning of the second phase."

nator in understanding the high-level technical requirements and potential validation requirements.

The information of greatest importance for a computer system project proposal and the reasons why are identified in table 3.3.[14] (See deliverable 1.5 for additional information.)

OBTAIN MANAGEMENT APPROVAL

The system owner or project team completes the computer system project proposal and submits it to senior management for review and approval. Management approval can take many forms. In some companies, project steering committees are formed for large projects; in others, a panel headed by IT reviews requests; and in still other

Medatech 3.9	Project Steering Committee

Doc understood that the cooperation and support of production, quality assurance, and information technology (IT) were essential for the success of his project. He spoke with his manager, the vice president of quality assurance and regulatory affairs, and requested that a management steering committee be formed.

At a senior staff meeting, Medatech's executive committee named the following individuals to the electronic document management system steering committee: the vice president of quality assurance and regulatory affairs, the vice president of manufacturing, and the director of IT. In addition, the project team (Doc, Tec, and Val) will be on the steering committee.

The electronic document management system steering committee reviewed and approved the project proposal. The head of the steering committee presented it to the executive committee. Authorization was given to the project team to define requirements and select a system. After the team has selected a system, they'll have to review their decision with the steering committee and obtain the executive committee's approval to purchase it.

companies, requests are reviewed through the management chain of command. In the latter case, the manager who has budgetary authorization to approve expenditures at the level the project costs approves the project. Senior managers' signatures commit resources to the project and authorize the project to move to the second phase, define requirements. Once the proposal is approved, the user organizations, IT, and QA can allocate the resources needed for selecting, implementing, and validating the system.

At the end of the third phase, select vendors and systems, management approves the purchase of the system. Managers will also review, if appropriate, the progress of the project at the end of each subsequent phase, or at least at critical points, such as before implementation. At these checkpoints, management has the opportunity to influence the project's direction and formally approve progressing to the next phase. Formal design reviews are one form of management review and will be described in the next chapter.

DEVELOP A PROJECT PLAN

A project plan should be developed for all systems, except for situations in which it doesn't add value. These would include simple applications or implementations.

A project plan includes:

- Identification of tasks to be performed and who's responsible for performing them
- Sequencing of dependent events
- Information that supports and encourages the allocation of resources
- Determination of the critical path for managing the project to a timely completion

A project plan is particularly important when:

- The efforts of a number of people or functional areas must be coordinated.

Medatech 3.10	High-Level Electronic Document Management System (EDMS) Plan

The project team created a project plan. In it was estimated the time that will be required for each of the RiskVal phases and the resources that will be needed. As the team transitions from one phase to the next, it will plan the next phase to a higher level of detail. The plan given in the table below doesn't include the required activities and deliverables for each phase.

RiskVal phase	Weeks required	Resources needed	Tasks performed by those outside the project team
2. Define requirements	2 to 3	Project team, users	Users to be interviewed
3. Select vendors and systems	6 to 8	Project team, legal, purchasing	Contract support
4. Design solutions to issues	2 to 3	Project team	Additional help not anticipated
5. Construct solutions to issues	1 to 2	Project team	Additional help not anticipated
6. Prepare for use	6 to 8	Project team, information technology, document control staff, training	Information technology (IT) staff to write user installation qualification (IQ) and prep IT procedures. Document control staff to write user procedures and assist Val in writing or reviewing operational qualification (OQ) protocols. Training help in preparing training materials, if not available from vendor.
7. Qualify the system	3 to 5	Project team, document control staff, IT	IT to run IQ and load legacy data and/or docs. Document control to execute OQ protocols.
8. Use in a production environment	6 to 8	Project team, IT, document control staff, training, production	IT to install in production environment. Training to train users. Documant control to execute PQ protocols.

Note: Plan created during phase 1. Phase 8 activities to be performed beyond the validation final report for the first part of the implementation (i.e., EDMS use for viewing documents) aren't included in this plan.

- The time to procure a system, resolve issues, and validate and implement it is expected to be lengthy.
- The risks associated with the system require careful planning and closer management of the RiskVal life cycle activities to ensure they're performed in the proper sequence and completed.
- A large number of activities must be performed.

Systems for which a project plan might not be required are simple applications, such as some spreadsheet applications, or those bundled with lab instrumentation, such as a statistical analysis package that's installed on a dedicated PC for use with an instrument to analyze the purity of pharmaceuticals. In both cases, an approved procedure can be used as a guide. In the case of simple spreadsheets, for example, a procedure for the risk management and validation of spreadsheets can be used to identify the steps to be performed. All of the RiskVal information that must be collected could be captured on a form—for example, a spreadsheet that's used to schedule and record the results of calibrations. In the example of lab equipment that includes analysis software, the RiskVal life cycle procedure can be used as a guide. Implementing major COTS packages such as calibration systems, which are much more than a spreadsheet, will usually require some level of planning to ensure that the life cycle activities are performed in the proper sequence and resources are coordinated.

The team determines which activities must be performed during the life cycle and creates an initial plan. Your plan should follow the RiskVal life cycle. It should identify the activities in the life cycle and the conditions under which they must be performed. Resource planning is the primary reason for developing a plan early in the life cycle. A plan will help the team members determine the amount of effort that will be required of them for the life cycle and identify additional resources that will need to be involved. For example, it could easily take a third- to half-time commitment of Doc, Val, and Tec for nine months to select, validate, and roll out a COTS EDMS package. Custom systems should have a project plan to ensure that an engineering rather than ad hoc approach is followed. In addition, custom systems take longer because of the added activities related to development.

The plan created during phase 1 is at a moderate level of detail. The required activities and deliverables can be identified from your RiskVal procedure. When one phase is completed, a more detailed plan can be created for the next phase.

Plans ordinarily are created using a project planning software tool. Tasks to be performed are identified and the interdependencies of the tasks shown. Tasks are assigned to project team members. When the required time for each task and due dates are added, a workload for each member is calculated.

DIFFERENCES IN TYPES OF SYSTEMS

As mentioned in chapter 1, the main discussion of the RiskVal life cycle is for COTS and configured business systems. At the end of each of the chapters, the application of the RiskVal life cycle to other types of systems is discussed.

The conceptualize phase activities described in this chapter apply to all types of new

Table 3.4	Policies and Procedures Created During Phase 1, if Needed		
Phase 1 deliverables	**Definition and explanation**	**When applicable**	**Deliverable references**
Validation policy (see deliverable 1.1)	A policy that defines what must be validated and when; defines requirements for validation processes	All systems	21 CFR Part 11, 11.10 a
Computer system risk management and validation life cycle (RiskVal) procedure (see deliverable 1.2)	A procedure that defines the process for selecting, procuring, validating, using, managing, and retiring a computer system	All systems	Part 11, 11.10 a
Information technology policy (see deliverable 1.3)	Policy governing the procuring, implementing, using, security, control, support, and administration of computer systems to ensure their efficiency, reliability, and security. A policy statement that holds individuals accountable for actions signed with electronic signatures.	All systems	Part 11, 11.10 j
Requirements for computer system validation plans, protocols, and reports (see deliverable 1.4)	A procedure that defines the content requirements for the computer system validation plan, protocols, and reports	All systems	Part 11, 11.10 a
Risk management policy	A policy that defines when a formal process must be used to manage risks and the requirements for such a process	All systems	ISO 14971
Risk management procedure	A procedure that defines the process for assessing and managing risk	All systems	ISO 14971

Table 3.5	Summary of Phase 1 Deliverables Created for Each Computer System		
Phase 1 deliverables	**Definition and explanation**	**When applicable**	**Deliverable references**
Computer system project proposal (see deliverable 1.5).	A document that contains vital information about the system and its potentials uses. The initial risk analysis is included. Management approval provides the authority to proceed with the project.	All systems	CDRH 6.1 recommends an initial risk analysis
Computer system project plan	A project plan for selecting, procuring, implementing, and validating a computer system	All except simple, low-, and moderate-risk systems	Highly recommended when applicable

systems, COTS, database package systems, configurable business systems, and custom systems. However, the process for existing systems requires some discussion.

With existing systems, the system owner and others in the organization obviously are aware of the needs the system is meeting, and it already has at least implicit management approval. When many existing systems aren't validated, the company must prepare a validation master plan that outlines the priorities and time frame for validating its systems. The priorities are set using the information about each system: description, statement of intended uses, applicability of Part 11, and the system's risk level. Capture this information by using a form.[15]

SUMMARY OF PHASE 1 DELIVERABLES

Table 3.4 summarizes the policies and procedures created during phase 1 if they don't already exist; these documents will be used for all computer systems.

The two deliverables that are created in phase 1 for the specific computer system are shown in table 3.5.

Chapter 4

Phase 2: Define Requirements

D uring the second phase, the system requirements are defined. These will be used as the basis for selecting and testing the system.

A successful business application is one that reliably does what its users need it to do. Consequently, a system can't be properly designed (if it's a custom system), selected, or tested without an adequate definition of the requirements. Because the requirements will serve as a basis for choosing between different systems, they're usually written at a level that's independent of specific hardware and software (see note 1).

Three types of requirements are defined: users requirements, technical requirements, and requirements for software providers.

User requirements include:

- The operations the system must perform and, if appropriate, how the functions must be executed
- The interfaces the system must have with others
- How the system must perform (e.g., response time)
- The relevant regulations with which it must comply

Technical requirements are defined for the hardware and system software. These might need to fit with the company's existing equipment and system software, and must meet the security, performance, and environmental requirements of the users.

A third set of requirements, vendor organizational requirements, is developed for evaluating vendors that will be relied upon for long-term product support. You want to select a vendor that has the expertise to understand the regulations placed on your industry; has a long-term, strategic commitment to the product or service; and is financially stable.

The requirements for moderate- and high-risk systems are reviewed in a phase review to ensure that they're appropriate and fully specified.

IMPORTANCE OF DOCUMENTED REQUIREMENTS

Critical for Success

Documented requirements are the foundation of a computer system life cycle. They're imperative for meeting user needs and regulatory requirements, ensuring a system's quality, managing the risks of system failure, and validating a system's effectiveness (see note 2). When documented and agreed-upon requirements are missing, and a project team proceeds anyway in selecting vendors and systems, the project is usually doomed to be over budget, late, and disappointing. Hidden disagreements between users on what the system must do will surface as disagreements over which system is the most suited for the organization. Key aspects of the system might be overlooked altogether when potential systems are evaluated. Without documented requirements, the risk associated with failing to meet requirements can't be accurately ascertained and managed, and any validation effort is without foundation or logic. When it's time to go live with the system, lingering disagreements over what the system must do will manifest in divergent evaluations of the system's performance and in differences in user enthusiasm and support.

One example that illustrates some of these difficulties involved customizing and configuring a document control system for a high-tech manufacturer. As purchased from the vendor, the system was a set of elaborate configuration tools and an object-oriented database. With added custom modules and by using the configuration tools, the system could be tailored to any wish. A software developer was contracted to write the necessary custom modules and do the configuration.

After several months of discussions to pin down the requirements and system design, the company and developer were unable to reach an agreement on a user requirement statement. The developer thought that the requirements were constantly changing, and the company thought that the vendor was unable to understand what it wanted. Finally, in frustration, the vendor cut off discussions on the design and requirements, and declared that it understood the company's wants. The developers went into seclusion after assuring the project team that it would be delighted with the results.

Several months later, the developers demonstrated the system they'd created. The results were predictable. As the system was unveiled, the project team was outraged. The system didn't work as the team had envisioned. The list of "design defects" became so long that the project manager ended the session halfway through the scheduled review. The project was put on hold for several months, and after requests for refunds and threatened lawsuits, both companies agreed to start over with an entirely new set of developers and project managers. More than a million dollars had been lost by each organization.

The difficulties the high-tech manufacturer had with the project resulted from not defining requirements, although the consequences of such a mistake aren't always as dramatic and expensive. Other examples of how purchased systems become "shelfware" are described in chapter 1. The probability of a disastrous outcome depends on a number of factors, including the diversity of the user groups and their visions of how the system should function, the differences in available software offerings, system complexity, and the cost of the system and losses associated with reversing decisions.

The process of recording and signing off on requirements forces the project team to resolve different opinions on what the system should do. It aligns expectations. Once agreement is achieved, the team can work harmoniously to obtain a system that will fulfill its vision. The team will come back to the documented requirements again and again as the guide for decision-making and the paramount criteria for evaluating the system and its success.

Important for Accuracy and Completeness

Care must be taken to develop complete and accurate initial requirements. You'll select your system or build it based on the requirements you define. If they're incomplete or in error, you might discover the deficiency after the system is purchased or built. Then you'll realize that the system doesn't function as you wish it would. You'll have a number of damage-control options, but each is time-consuming and incurs costs: modify the system, change how you do business, change how you use the system, purchase a new system, or terminate the project and revert to manual systems.

Keep Requirements Current Throughout the Life Cycle

The team might have to revise the requirements at several points in the life cycle to maintain resonance between the requirements and the system:

- Requirements will be used in phase 3 for selecting the system. However, if the best system the team can purchase doesn't fully match the requirements, it will have to be modified or the requirements revised to match the system. Revising requirements enables the team to accept the reality of the choice it made and provides an accurate basis for risk assessment and validation.

- When the detailed risk assessment is performed, risk mitigations can be designed and implemented. Or the risk evaluation might indicate that using the system for a particular function is too risky. A manual process might be used instead for that function. The requirements will have to be updated to reflect the risk mitigations and changes in the system's use.

- During or after validation testing, the team might decide not to use the system for certain functions that it performs poorly. Again, the requirements will be revised.

PRINCIPLES FOR DEFINING REQUIREMENTS

Before a discussion about the content of specific types of requirements, several principles regarding how requirements are defined should be considered. These principles apply to all types of requirements.

Use a Team to Define Requirements

Technical Report 18 points out that a team approach should be used for defining computer-related requirements. The report recommends that the team include users and all other disciplines involved in the design, implementation, validation, operation, and maintenance of the system. It further points out that through an iterative process requiring cooperation and close communication, preliminary requirements are refined, and the importance of each is determined.[1]

Uniquely Identify Each Requirement

Assign each requirement (e.g., user, technical, and vendor organizational requirements) a unique number. These will be used in traceability matrices to track each requirement to steps in a test (i.e., validation) protocol. Requirements for safety-related, safety-critical, and risk control measures should be traceable to the risk analysis performed during phase 4.[2] With custom systems, the requirements will also be traced to design elements, programs, and tests.

Use a numbering scheme that's easy to work with and reference in other documents. One such format is a sequential numbering of requirements such as 1.1.1, which shows the organization of, and relationships between, requirements.

Define Requirements Only to the Level of Detail Needed

Requirements should be defined to the most detailed level that covers what you want the system to do and how you want the system to do it. If you reach a level of detail where it doesn't matter to you which of several possible ways the system does something, write the requirement in general enough terms to allow any of the specific methods.

The amount of detail contained in user requirements varies greatly. Document control systems have user requirements that range from a one to forty-five pages. The length will depend on the system's complexity, the intended uses, and business and compliance restrictions. For example, a general statement such as, "change requests are routed for approval" is sufficient only if the organization is open to routing documents in all possible manners. Different systems have different approaches in determining to whom to route the change request. The following requirement statements for routing change requests for approval illustrate different ways in which routing can be done:

- The same four reviewers receive every change request.
- The department creating the change request, such as document control, creates a list of reviewers for that change request.
- The system selects the reviewers to receive the change request depending upon what types of items are attached to the change request for approval. (The database includes a list of qualified reviewers from each department for each type of document.)
- Reviewers can add additional reviewers dynamically in case they want to send the request to another person to get his or her opinion.

You might have to write your requirements to yet a lower level of detail than these statements. For example, if you want the change requests to go to the same four reviewers every time, does it matter who these people are? Will it work if the application designates that the reviewers are from production, quality assurance, marketing, and administration? Perhaps in your organization you want the four to be from manufacturing, development, quality, and regulatory. You must write your user requirements so that either your four functional areas are named or so you can determine the names of the functional areas. Your requirements might include the following three statements:

- The system must be able to route the change requests to the same four reviewers each time.
- The system will have a default designation of four reviewers.
- The system administrator will have the ability to change the four reviewers.

The requirements for custom systems are usually more detailed than requirements for commercial off-the-shelf (COTS) systems, especially if a custom system is being built because COTS systems aren't capable of meeting requirements. In such cases, developers can't rely on their knowledge of common functionality in such systems. Your requirements document must provide guidance to the developers on what you want the system to do and how you want it to work.

Identify the Criticality of Each Requirement

How important is a requirement to you? Most users believe that many of the features or functions that they want in a system are critical. However, a requirement should be considered critical only if the system can't be used if the requirement isn't met; such requirements are known as "show stoppers." Other noncritical requirements should be identified because they signify additional considerations that are important or express your preference for how something is done. Keep in mind that you can, and may have to, live without them.

Take the requirements discussed in the previous section as an example. You might prefer the system to automatically send every change request to the same four reviewers. However, what's critical here is that the system route the change request to reviewers. If you had to identify the four reviewers for each change request, the system wouldn't be as efficient, but you could still use it. To distinguish between critical and noncritical aspects of a requirement, you might want to break it into components and indicate the criticality of each; see table 4.1 for examples.[3]

The following definitions can be used for levels of criticality of the requirements:

- *Critical.* Absolutely required for an intended use the first day of production. The system can't be used for an intended use if this function isn't present or doesn't work

Table 4.1	Examples of User Requirements With Criticality Levels	
Requirement No.	**Requirement**	**Level of criticality**
1	The system must be able to route change requests to the same four reviewers each time.	Critical
2	The system administrator will have the ability to change the four reviewers. (*Note:* This is important because the system must keep up with any organizational changes. However, this requirement assumes that the system will meet the above critical requirement and automatically route the change request to the four designated reviewers.)	Important
3	The system will have a default designation of four reviewers. (*Note:* This is rated as "nice to have" because the system could still be used if document control had to select the four reviewers for every change request. However, the system would be less efficient than if it had a default setting for the four.)	Nice to have

properly; such a defect must be fixed before the system can be used for the intended use. The system isn't worth purchasing and installing for the intended use if such a feature or function is missing, malfunctions, or can never be achieved.

■ *Important.* Without this feature or function, the system is useable but loses significant value and effectiveness.

■ *Nice to have.* The absence or loss of this feature or function will have little effect on the system's effectiveness and value.

Include Requirements for Risk Mitigation

If your system is moderate or high risk, identify the aspects of the system whose failure is associated with those risk levels. At this point in the RiskVal life cycle, the analysis is based on the severity of harm that might result from failure. (During phase 4—design solutions to issues—a detailed risk assessment will be performed that takes into account the probability of system failure.) Review each of the critical and important requirements and ask the team what's the worst consequence if the system fails to meet this requirement. Assign a risk level to the item using table 3.2, Definitions and Examples of Risk Levels, presented in chapter 3, or the severity scale presented in exhibit 6.2 in chapter 6. For moderate- or high-risk items, determine if a system function or condition is needed to mitigate the risk, and include the mitigations in the requirements. Examples of mitigations include:

- A data or calculation check to detect or prevent the error
- System identification of a failure and an alarm that alerts an operator in time to intervene and prevent the harm from occurring
- Hardware, software, and/or data redundancy to eliminate loss of processing and/or data

A mitigation is valuable as a safeguard. For a system to cause harm, two failures must occur at the same time: the system and the mitigation. Validation testing is a way to reduce the risk estimate because a successful test provides assurance that the system will work as intended. During phase 8, you'll include the results of the validation testing in your likelihood-of-failure estimate. Successful validation test results probably will allow you to lower your estimate of the likelihood of failure and reduce the risk level to a limited degree.

However, a mitigation probably will have a much more powerful affect on the risk level because of the low probability that both the system and the mitigation will fail at the same time. Mitigations should be used in association with moderate- and high-risk aspects of the system, if practical. Examples of mitigations and their usefulness will be provided in chapter 6 when the detailed risk assessment is presented.

Review Requirements

The accuracy of the requirements can be improved not only by developing them as a team but also by having the team conduct a formal review of them. The review should:

- Verify that the process used to define the requirements was adequate.
- Determine whether the requirements are complete, accurate, testable, and at the appropriate level of detail.

A review of the process used to define the requirements will include questions such as:

- Are the methods used adequate for defining requirements for the full range of intended uses and users?
- Have the appropriate people been involved in defining the requirements, such as a representative sample of all user groups, experts with the type of system to be implemented, and experts in regulatory compliance who can articulate requirements for complying with regulations?

To review the content of the requirements, invite users or experts who weren't involved in writing the requirements to participate. During the review, go through at least every critical and important requirement and determine if it really is a requirement; if it's clear, complete and accurate; if its criticality is properly classified; if it's too general or specific; and if it's testable. As the review is being conducted, make sure that the requirements are consistent as a group. Keep records of the changes to be made along with any notes that might help understand the requirement in the future. The formality with which the changes to the requirements are documented should be commensurate with the importance of the requirements and the system's risk level.

DEFINE AND DOCUMENT USER REQUIREMENTS

During the conceptualize phase, the system is envisioned as the solution to a problem or a means to achieving a goal. To ensure that the system can fulfill that vision, the system owner must define user requirements.

Areas Included in User Requirements

Table 4.2 lists types of user requirements that can be included. See deliverable 2.1 in appendix A for information on the content and format of user requirements documentation.

User requirements must include regulatory requirements in addition to requirements based on what you want the system to do. When developing requirements related to regulations, review the following:

- Regulations that govern manufacturing and quality practices in a regulated industry, such as those for pharmaceuticals and medical devices
- Regulations that govern the use of computer systems in a regulated industry. For example, the European Community Commission Directive, *The Rules Governing Medicinal Products in the European Union,* Vol. 4, Good Manufacturing Practices, Annex 11—Computerised Systems, contains a number of functional requirements (see items 6, 8, 9, 10, 12, 13). One is the requirement that: "The system should include, where appropriate, built-in checks of the correct entry and processing of data."[4]
- Regulations that govern electronic signatures and electronic records. See, for example, sections of Part 11.[5]

Table 4.2	Areas to Include in User Requirements	
Type of requirement	**Explanation**	**Examples or things to include**
System functionality	■ The actions that the system performs on data and/or information ■ Built-in checks for correct processing of data ■ Error handling	■ Input data conversion. ■ Calculations performed on absorption data to determine the purity of a compound ■ Record user transactions and electronic signatures. ■ Document, store, retrieve, protect, control, and/or assemble information and generate reports or records. ■ Sort, calculate, and manipulate data. ■ Issue error messages when the system fails or an operator makes an error.
Information input and output, and integrations	■ Inputs from operators ■ Authorization to input data ■ Information or commands from devices, instruments, or other systems ■ Data input verification or checks for correct entry ■ Information or commands output to devices, instruments, or other systems ■ System outputs, including clear, printed copies of electronically stored data ■ Alarm management	■ Manual input of information concerning a controlled document ■ Obtain temperature information from a programmable logical controller (PLC). ■ Obtain real-time data on vessel pressure. ■ Sweep human resource database daily for changes in personnel status. ■ Tell a PLC to start pump to draw a vacuum. ■ Import weights obtained from a scale into a materials requirements planning system for inventory management. ■ Copy files from servers and PCs for backups. ■ Send text messages on alarms to cell phones and pagers.
Performance	■ Uptime of the application ■ Application response time ■ System bandwidth or capacity ■ Accessibility to users ■ Fault-tolerance (i.e., built-in ability to keep functioning despite a component failure) ■ System security ■ System recovery ■ Ease of use	■ Times during a day when the network can be down for maintenance ■ Length of unscheduled downtime that can be tolerated ■ Number of acceptable seconds for detecting a condition and issuing an alarm ■ Number of acceptable minutes for downloading a document at a remote site ■ Number of concurrent users that the system must accommodate ■ Full mirroring of database read and write transactions to ensure complete, accurate, and up-to-the-second data capture ■ Protection against any changes to data ■ Ability to completely restore the application and all data following a natural disaster ■ Users with a high school education and training on the system will be able to perform all user functions. ■ Maintenance information can be accessed and entered from the roof using a hand-held wireless device. ■ Context-sensitive help ■ Names of data fields can be easily changed to reflect company terminology. ■ Report output can be sent to the screen, a printer, or disk for saving.

Type of requirement	Explanation	Examples or things to include
Safety requirements	■ Risk-control measures for potential hardware or software failures ■ Methods of operation or maintenance related to safety ■ Safeguards needed based on the environment in which the system will be operated ■ Safety-related features and functions, such as sensors, alarms, interlocks, logical processing steps, command sequences, system startup or shutdown	■ Use of redundant hardware to mitigate the effect of a failed unit, such as array V disc drives ■ Automatic shutdown of a production line when a parameter related to the quality of the product exceeds an allowed value ■ Shutdown of the computer system in a failsafe mode during a power outage
Security	■ Control of access to the system and functions ■ Methods of deterring unauthorized entry to the system, or performance of unauthorized actions	■ Screening potential users of the system at logon ■ Notifying a designated individual when an unauthorized entry is attempted ■ Performing authorization checks before permitting an action or the entry of an electronic signature
Physical requirements	Aspects of the physical situation that affect the hardware or require functions or actions by the software	■ Use of equipment in a clean environment ■ Size restrictions for a central processing unit ■ Environmental conditions that the system must be able to withstand (e.g., humidity, temperature, vibration, electrical interference, and dirt)
Human factors	Considerations for ensuring that the software can be used appropriately by the intended user	■ User interface considerations based on characteristics of the user, e.g., font size; a verbal or auditory signal from the computer that provides feedback on what the user selected; displays that present data on diagrams, such as temperatures on an oven diagram ■ Ease of navigating through the data input screens so that a telephone operator can keep pace with responses from a customer ■ Designing an interface screen for a handheld device to minimize spelling out responses
Managing legacy data	Access to existing data either by transferring data to the new system or setting up access to the old data via the new system	■ Transfer of all approved documents and information about them to the new system ■ Transfer of all part and inventory information ■ Accessing the current customer, contact, and order database from the new system
Regulatory requirements or standards	Requirement on what the system must do, or how it must do it, to comply with applicable regulations and standards, including 21 CFR Part 11 and the European Community directive on medicinal products Annex 11	■ Audit trail on creating, modifying, or deleting a record ■ Authorization of a user who's issuing a command or performing an action ■ Requiring that some actions be complete before others can be performed ■ Printed bar codes are compliant with the DMM C850 bar-coding standard for parcels.

Ways to Identify User Requirements

Different methods are available for defining user requirements. Most often these are used in combination. Each of the following will be discussed in detail:

- Understanding available systems
- User interviews
- Business process flowchart
- Use cases
- Talking to colleagues at other companies

Understanding Available Systems

Knowledge of existing systems can be used in several ways to assist in developing user requirements.

- Knowing that different systems do different things, or do the same thing but in different ways, will prompt questions about how your organization wants something to be done.
- You can model the user requirements based on how the different systems do different things.
- If you know you want to implement a specific system because you've used it in the past with another company, you can use the materials available on the product to write the requirements.

The example used in the previous section for changing required reviewers is based on knowing that different systems select reviewers for approval routes in different ways. If you know that some systems allow a reviewer to dynamically add additional reviewers to the routing, then you can determine how important that feature is to your system owner and users.

There are a number of ways you familiarize yourself with existing systems, including:

- Reading articles or Web information about that type of system
- Talking with colleagues who are using such systems
- Attending meetings of professional organizations where vendors of such systems participate in the trade shows. Often they will make presentations or demonstrate their software to groups of attendees.
- Having a vendor or two give a demonstration. If you invite members of the organization to the demonstration, be careful to tell them that the purpose is to gain knowledge of the type of system so that requirements can be written. If the users

get excited, they might want to purchase the system they've just seen. However, before a purchase can be made, user requirements must be defined, two or more systems ought to be evaluated against the requirements, and then the system that best matches the requirements should be selected.

■ Attending user meetings

After a preliminary review of a few systems, you might think that none of them meets all of your needs, but a couple do different things that you want. Use the aspects of the systems you think are what you need as the basis for defining the requirements for those features or functions.

If you know a system well enough that you're certain it will meet your needs, write your user requirements based on that system. For example, a quality engineer used a calibration package at his previous company. Based on a thorough understanding of that system, he's certain that it will work in his new company. In addition, if he selects any other system, he'd have to spend at least some time learning how to use it. The engineer created the user requirements by reading through the user's manual and writing requirements based on the system's functions he plans to use. Although he's already selected a system, the user requirements must be defined because they're the basis for creating tests to confirm that the system functions as required in the new company's hardware and software environment.

User Interviews

In addition to knowing how existing systems function, you must know how your organization wants to use the system. There are at least four ways of gaining insight into user needs and desires: user interviews, subject-matter expert interviews, process flow diagrams, and use cases. Here's a description of each.

User interviews give you an opportunity to educate users on what a system can do and get them excited about it. It's a subtle way of selling your vision and gauging the response from others while you assess the intensity of their needs and the strength of their support. The interview can be structured into the following four parts:

■ A brief presentation that includes your phase 1 vision as well as a general demonstration of the common features and functions of the type of system, if needed.

■ A user survey, with numerical ratings, of satisfaction with current practices. When a current practice is given a low rating, probe to understand why the person is dissatisfied. What's the problem? Why is it occurring? This type of discussion will help you understand the issues that must be addressed and will increase support for the system when the person interviewed realizes that it will resolve his or her issue. If the issue lies outside the realm of the system, then you should determine the importance of addressing the issue relative to the need for the system.

- User ratings on the importance of specific features that such a system might provide
- User ratings on the importance of the benefits that might be derived from the system

After the interviews are conducted, the ratings are averaged and a report is prepared. The results of the interviews will give you an understanding of what users think should be improved. You'll understand the relative importance of specific software features, and the benefits that users recognize as the greatest value. Information on reasons why users are unhappy with aspects of the current process will help you determine if a new system will fix what they see as the problems. Perhaps you'll need to take some corrective actions in addition to implementing a system. Or, the new system might need to take a back seat until more critical needs are addressed. The user requirements, and especially the importance ratings, can be based at least in part on the information obtained from the interviews. These results can also provide objective data you can use to sell management on the value of the system when you ask them to sign a purchase order (phase 3—Select vendors and systems).

Of course, if there are subject matter experts in your company who won't be users, they too can be interviewed. Such experts might be individuals who have switched functional areas or who have had experience with such systems in the past. For example, in many pharmaceutical companies, scientists who have experience in developing compounds switch fields and work in the information technology (IT) function. They might have expertise with lab instrumentation and can speak to users' needs even though they won't be using the new instrumentation themselves.

Discussions With Colleagues at Other Companies

By understanding why process owners from other companies selected their systems and the benefits they are reaping from them, you can gain insight into the functionality that might have a high payoff for you. Discuss what their visions were for their systems and what functionality is central to fulfilling those visions. Learn about the problems they're experiencing with their systems to understand how yours should work. Find out what enhancements they would most like to see in the next release and why. Ask process owners what users like most about the system. Find out what has solved their problems or met their needs. Describe your vision and ask them what are the most important features or functions the system must have to bring the performance you want.

Process Flow Diagrams

Your vision is to automate a manual process or improve the current automation. One approach for determining what the new system should do is to review the current way things are done. If you create a flowchart of the current process, you'll identify current inputs, process activities, and outputs from which you can extract requirements for the new process.[6]

However, be careful to avoid the potential pitfalls of using flow diagrams to define requirements for a new system. First, don't replicate an ineffective manual process in an automated form. Understand where your current process fails to be efficient and/or to create a quality product. If you build the problems of your current process into the new process, you'll lose a lot of the potential gain from automation. When you document the process, you must not only document the steps but also record the problems associated with each step. The information gathered from user interviews, as discussed previously, will help you identify such problems. When defining the requirements for the new systems, include solutions to the current problems or ways to perform the activities that avoid the problems.

For example, the document control function of a medical diagnostic company was looking at document control systems because it wanted to speed the approval of change orders. However, during interviews, the users clearly identified that the policy of requiring four vice presidents to sign every document was a major problem. The change requests were routed for signature in a sequential manner (i.e., one after the other) instead of in parallel (i.e., everyone reviews the change request at the same time). Delays between reviewers were lengthy, and document control lost track of who had the change request as it was passed from one reviewer to another. Although a document might have been outside the expertise of a reviewer, he or she was still required to review and sign the change request. One reviewer, making a good faith effort to do his best under such circumstances, would request changes that were neither correct nor necessary. It took time for the document originator to convince the executive to change or withdraw such requests.

An automated document control system can correct only some of these problems. Reviews can be done in parallel, and document control can query the system to find out who has taken action so far and who hasn't. However, if the requirement that all four vice presidents must sign every change request were continued, only modest gains in reducing the approval time would be feasible.

The second pitfall to be avoided when creating user requirements from a process flow diagram is requiring the automated system to do everything the way it's done in the manual process. If the requirements for the new system constrain it unnecessarily to current practices, two consequences are likely. First, the process won't be improved beyond its current capability. Second, it will be difficult for you to find an automated system that perfectly matches your current practice. Your team might conclude that a COTS package must be customized, or a custom package should be built. Although the make-or-buy question is legitimate (see phase 1—Conceptualize), failing to allow flexibility in user requirements will often lead a company to the more expensive, less reliable, and a more-difficult-to-validate choice of a custom system.

Use Cases

Preparing a use case is a technique to get system users to articulate what they want the system to do and to think about what they might unconsciously assume it will do.[7] A use case is developed in a meeting using the method described in method 2.1 in appendix A. Participants include a user(s), the system owner, and others who are generally familiar with business applications and who can help extract requirements from the use case. A facilitator guides the meeting, if appropriate. A user talks about performing an action with the system in a selected scenario. Then the group lists what the system must do to perform the task as the user has envisioned it; requirements are generated from the list.

For example, a production manager might describe how she sees herself retrieving a specification for a controller's power cord from the document control system while sitting at her desk. She would describe herself as performing the following actions: logging onto the network and then the document control system. She would open a search window and type in the name of the controller. The search would result in a list of all documents related to the controller, including its bill of materials (BOM). After opening the BOM, she envisions clicking on the listing for the power cord, and its specification opens.

The participants would then extract requirements for the system based on her description. One obvious requirement is the need to enter a user name and password to log onto the system. It's also clear that the system must be capable of searching for documents, but the group might discuss what search capability is really required. A simple search mechanism is to search a list of key words associated with the documents. A search could be conducted for a specific value of an attribute—for example, all parts with the part type of "power cord." Or, the search might identify all the documents whose titles include a specific word or group of words. A full text search of all documents for specific words also is possible. To the extent it matters to the users, the method of conducting a search should be specified. Be careful not to make something a critical requirement when, in fact, it isn't. You might write a requirement that the system has a search capability that will help the user locate a document. This requirement might be classified as important. A second requirement might be written that the system has full text search capability so that it can identify every document in the system that contains a certain word. This requirement might be labeled as "nice to have."

Participants would also identify requirements associated with the system's readiness to perform the described task. Documents and associated data would have to be in the system (e.g., the document's title).

Requirements associated with the state of the system after the task is performed would also be identified; in this case, the document is unchanged after being viewed.

The first use case ordinarily is the most common: the production manager is at her desk, where her computer has a direct connection to the network. However, the participants should change the scenario to other situations in which a similar task had to be performed. There would be new requirements if a PC also needs to be used in a clean room. And there would be still additional requirements if a maintenance person had to have access to facilities diagrams from a walkway above the manufacturing floor.

Table 4.3	Reasons for Technical Requirements
Reason	**Why it's important**
Meet user needs.	What are the implications of what the users want to do with the hardware, system software, and communication software? If they want wireless access to the document control system using handheld devices, what are the implied requirements for hardware, software, and devices?
Compatibility with existing hardware and software	Compatibility could limit costs because the new applications might use existing equipment.
Ensure the ability to provide support.	Information technology departments often have policies that they will support some types of systems but not others. In addition to containing costs, this ensures that they have the expertise to support the system.

By repeating the use case meetings with different types of users in different scenarios, a list of user requirements is developed. Performing enough use case analyses to cover the full range of user types and what they'll do with the system might be time-consuming. One option is to develop use cases only for two reasons:

- To clarify how the system must be used by certain types of users to perform certain tasks
- To gain support of users through their involvement in defining requirements

---

Medatech 4.1	Define User Requirements

Doc and the project team decided that the best definition of requirements would result from both familiarity with the types of systems as well as a clear vision of how an electronic document management system (EDMS) would be used at Medatech. To learn more about an EDMS, Doc invited two vendors to give preliminary demonstrations at Medatech. In addition, he talked further with the users he'd contacted during the planning phase.

Doc interviewed the heads of several departments and some key individual contributors who would have to use the system. The departments he included were: production, engineering, quality assurance, quality control, and regulatory. Based on his knowledge, he created a structured interview guide that included questions about the current situation and how various new features would help users. Doc's findings were, in part, the following:

- The current lack of immediate access to controlled documents and records breaks the workflow in engineering and production. An individual might have to wait several hours to get a copy of what's needed.
- Access to documents and records stored in the document control department is limited to normal working hours. However, users often need documents and records at additional times.
- Users are highly supportive of using documents online and being able to print forms from the computer.
- The number of reviewers doesn't vary based on the severity of the change. Vice presidents must sign off on trivial formatting or grammatical changes.
- Reviewers sit on documents if they don't agree with the changes. (One reviewer had two stacks of "dead" documents on his desk.) Document control stops tracking documents once they're sent out for approval; the originator doesn't know where they are.

Based on the results of the interviews and what they'd learned from the demonstrations and other sources, Doc and the project team drafted a set of user requirements.

Table 4.4	Types of Technical Requirements

Item	Type of requirements
Client workstation	Operating system. Compatibility requirements (e.g., the new system must operate effectively with certain applications open on the workstation). Minimum hardware configuration, including CPU speed, RAM, hard-drive memory, and Ethernet card. Other software applications that must be on the workstations for use by or with the new system, such as MS Word or Excel.
Server	Manufacturer of the server. Type of server operating system. Server architecture to accommodate use in multiple locations (i.e., distributed processing and database versus centralized processing and database). Server hardware requirements based on the nature and volume of users and transactions.
Database	Hardware for the database (e.g., integrated with the server or separate data-storage device). Level of fault-tolerance. Type of database (e.g., flat files, relational, object-oriented). Database software manufacturer.
System integration	Requirements to import and/or export data (such as application program interface or type of file export). Other systems with which the new system must interface, including e-mail, report-generating applications, applications from which the system receives data, applications to which the system exports information, and tools such as viewers and browsers.
Communication	Communication protocols that the application uses such as transmission control protocol. Communication and network hardware required to provide the response time needed for remote use of the system.
Security	Level of security required: dedicated network, normal network security, and high security. Required security measures: network logon, restriction by workstation IP address, encryption during communication to off-site locations or use on the Internet, firewall protection needed to block intruders from getting to the application.
Network accessibility and availability	How much planned and unplanned downtime can be tolerated? What hours on what days can the system be taken down for maintenance?
Internet access	Do users or the system require access to the Internet?
Backup, archive, and recovery	Requirements for backup, data archiving, disaster recovery, and offsite storage.
Information technology service and support	What type of service is needed at what hours for user support and problem solving? What monitoring is needed of the network and application? What software tools are required for such monitoring?

Medatech 4.2	Prepare Technical Requirements

Tec led the effort to develop the technical requirements. He reviewed a draft of the user requirements for technology implications with Doc. In addition, Tec wanted to move to Web-based applications as much as possible because he felt that the user interfaces of such systems were generally easier to use, and that the technology was more current. Tec defined the technical requirements needed to select the system; these involved hardware and system software with which the applications must be compatible. Details of the hardware, such as the amount of server memory, would be finalized after the system was selected. Once the application is selected, the technical requirements will be revised to take into account any additional hardware and software requirements imposed by the application.

DEFINE TECHNICAL REQUIREMENTS

Three reasons drive the need for technical requirements, as described in table 4.3.

Document Technical Requirements

Table 4.4 provides a list of items for which technical requirements typically are determined. Some organizations take a list such as this and create a checklist so that requirements are easily defined by checking alternatives and filling in information on the form. See deliverable 2.2 in appendix A for additional information on the content and format of technical requirements.

DEVELOP VENDOR ORGANIZATIONAL REQUIREMENTS

In addition to user and technical requirements, vendor organizational requirements are also specified (see deliverable 2.3 in appendix A). Your software providers will become long-term business associates. You'll have a relationship with these vendors at least as long as you use their products. When deciding whether to purchase a software product from a provider or contract with a company for customization services, you should evaluate the vendor based on its industry knowledge, strategic

Medatech 4.3	Define Vendor Organizational Requirements

Because Medatech must adhere to Food and Drug Administration (FDA) and other regulatory requirements, Doc and the project team decided that whoever provided the new electronic document management system should have knowledge of document control practices in regulated industries. In addition, the team wanted a company that was both financially stable and dedicated to selling and supporting the system for at least five years. Medatech didn't want to be responsible for system enhancements, troubleshooting, and bug repair.

As a method of evaluating vendors on these important organizational variables, the team agreed to rate each vendor on the following characteristics:

- Financial stability
- Strategic importance of the product to the vendor
- Experience with and knowledge of FDA industries, especially medical devices
- Ability to provide help-desk support during Medatech's normal working hours
- Ability to provide installation support
- Ability to provide on-site training for users
- Availability of system administrator training

commitment to the product and/or service, and its long-term financial viability. Before you sign a contract:

- Determine if the vendor has sufficient knowledge of your type of business to develop and support a system that will meet requirements specific to your industry
- Determine if the vendor is able to provide the services and support you'll need
- Be reasonably sure that the vendor will stay in business and continue to support and enhance the product you buy from it.

If a hardware vendor's long-term viability is critical, organizational requirements will also be set for them. See the discussion following.

During phase 2, the vendor organization requirements are set, and during phase 3—Select vendors and systems—you'll evaluate the vendors against these requirements. Your formal assessment of the vendors during phase 3 will be limited to your top choices based on how well their products meet your user and technical requirements. You might eliminate a vendor from consideration at any time if you realize that it's unable to meet your critical organizational requirements. During phase 3 you'll also qualify vendors on their ability to produce and support a quality product; this type of vendor qualification will be discussed in chapter 5.

Recommended Organizational Requirements for Software Vendors

Seven requirements are recommended for evaluating a software vendor's organization. After a reasonable amount of effort is spent gathering data related to the requirements, the vendor can be rated on a one-to-five point scale on each requirement. The seven requirements and the type of information that can be used to rate the vendor on each dimension are presented in table 4.5. Although it's often assumed that large companies will maintain their product lines indefinitely and stay in business forever, keep in mind that they can change product direction and discontinue a product, or meet with financial difficulty.

Organizational Requirements for Hardware Vendors

Generally the long-term viability of hardware vendors isn't as important as it is for software vendors. Most hardware products can be replaced with products from competitors, and ordinarily a third party can be found to provide needed maintenance and support. However, in the unusual situations where the ongoing viability of a hardware vendor and its products is critical, similar organizational requirements should be set.

PHASE REVIEWS

Purpose and Content of Phase Reviews

At the end of each phase of the life cycle, a phase review is conducted, if needed, to ensure that the deliverables of that phase have been appropriately completed and the project is still viable. The reviews provide a forum for communicating progress to management and gaining its approval to proceed, as well as its support in resolving issues. During a phase review, the team and any oversight groups or individuals, such as a steering committee, meet and review the project's status. The review includes a formal determination of whether the deliverables required for that phase have been satisfactorily completed. The overall project status is evaluated, and issues and barriers to project success are resolved. As appropriate, approval for the beginning of the next phase is granted. Although work on items for the next phase can be done in parallel to completing actions of the current phase, the phase review can be used to keep aggressive teams from jumping ahead to complete the next phase activities before prerequisite activities from the current phase are finished.

Table 4.5	Vendor Organizational Requirements
Requirement	**Information about vendor's ability to meet requirement**
Financial stability	Privately owned companies won't release information on profitability. However, several indications of the company's financial health are available, including personnel growth, growth in the customer base, size of the installed base (an indication of revenue from service and support contracts), and the size of the staff providing paid services such as training and customization. You might also evaluate the vendors on a few indicators that could signal future financial difficulties, such as the amount of funding the company has received; its ability to raise additional funding; abnormally high cost structures in the business, such as a high number of developers working on product support versus the number who are working on the next release; and imbalances in the company's structure, such as the size and location of the sales force in comparison to the support and development staff. Is the vendor willing to put its source code in an escrow account you can access if it goes out of business?
Company commitment to this application	Will the company continue to offer the product in the future? How important is the product to the company's business success? Is the product mainstream business or an alternate line? What place does the product have in the company's long-term business objectives? What signs of commitment has management made to the product's success, such as the size of staff compared to that assigned to other products, or plans for enhancing the product? What is senior management's commitment to the business? Is it planning on selling the business? Or has the product been acquired by buying out a competitor? If the system is on an old platform the company doesn't plan to continue, are there plans to rewrite the application on a modern platform?
Fit to your industry	How many customers in your industry are already using the software? Does the company understand the regulatory challenges? Does the vendor have a users' group? Does the users' group have a focus group from your industry?
Industry expertise	Does the company have any sales or support staff who are knowledgeable about the way business is done in your industry? Do they know your industry requirements?
Software problem support	What type of problem-solving and defect support do you need and when? This will depend on the type of support your information technology department wants to provide. Will you need hotline and help desk support so that problems are called in directly? What hours of the day and what days of the week will you need such support? Will someone in your company help the users? How do you want to handle the resolution of defects? Do you want to forward them to the developer for support, or would you rather search databases for known defects and fixes? Do you feel you will need to talk with a support person about your problem or is communicating via e-mail sufficient?
Support services	Services you might consider necessary could include installation and system configuration; user, administrator, and developer training; and integration and customization services. Do you want a technical support person to be close enough to easily visit your site(s) to provide support services without extensive travel costs?
Quality	Although it can be difficult to obtain information on specific software development practices for preliminary screening of vendors, some indicators of the extent to which a software engineering approach is used might be available—for example, an independent assessment of a development process against the Software Engineering Institute capability maturity model. (See note 3.) Once the selection is narrowed to one or a few vendors, audits of the vendors can provide information on development practices related to quality.

The review could include the following topics:

- The quality and/or content of the deliverables from the phase
- Costs versus budget to date
- Project schedule and timeline
- Resource requirements
- Outstanding issues that could threaten the project's success
- Follow-up on action items from the last review
- Next steps

The outcomes of the phase review can include actions such as:

- Approval to proceed to the next phase
- Changes to the scope of the project
- Changes to the resources allocated
- Changes to the project plan
- Decisions on how to resolve issues and actions to take

Prepare minutes of the phase reviews to document that they were held and to record decisions and action items.

Phase reviews are performed based on the system's complexity and risk; in general, they aren't necessary for simple, low-risk, or low-cost systems. The project plan, if created, should identify when phase reviews will be done. For two phases, other management reviews could take the place of a phase review: approving the computer system project proposal during phase 1 and approving negotiations with the application vendor and signing contracts at the end of phase 3.

Medatech 4.4   ## Phase Review

After the three requirements documents were approved, Doc and the project team held a phase review with the electronic document management system steering committee. Doc chaired the session. Because this was the committee's first meeting, Doc reviewed the purpose for having a steering committee. He also reviewed the work that had been completed since the computer system project proposal had been approved, namely, completing the requirements documents. Doc reviewed the high-level project plan, and because they were behind schedule, he proposed modifications to the timeline. The committee agreed with the timeline changes and discussed Doc's ideas about how the project team would select a system.

Phase 2 Review

The review for phase 2—Define requirements—focuses on determining if the requirements have been appropriately and fully specified. A phase review is an examination by the oversight group of the deliverables of the phase to determine if they've been completed and approved, and if an appropriate process was used to create the documents. The detailed in-depth reviews of the requirements are conducted, as described above, before the phase review.

Circulate copies of the approved requirements documents and the results of the requirements reviews to the oversight group and project team for review in advance. During the phase review, review the methods used to develop the user, technical, and vendor organizational requirements with the oversight group. Additional topics as outlined in the previous section are covered, as appropriate, including the activities anticipated for the next phase.

DIFFERENCES IN TYPES OF SYSTEMS

Existing Systems

For existing systems the definition of user requirements is easy: Simply record how the system is being used. If you're planning on expanding the use of the system in the future, add requirements for changes you want to validate with the system. Remember that you have the option of validating existing systems as they're currently used and adding new uses under change control.

Because you already have the system that you'll be using, the detailed risk assessment and evaluation presented for phase 4 can be performed during the "define requirements" phase. The need for mitigations can then be determined based on the likelihood of failure as well as the severity of consequences, rather than on just of the severity of harm as discussed above.

Custom Systems

The definition of requirements and the control of changes to requirements are at least as important for custom systems as they are for purchased systems. In *Conflict and Litigation Between Software Clients and Developers*, Capers Jones lists uncertain and ambiguous requirements as one of the five problems he observed with large systems that failed. He points out that if the initial user requirements are gathered and analyzed in a hasty or careless fashion, the project will seem to be on or ahead of schedule. But later changes to the requirements will be difficult to absorb, and the project will start to fall behind. The development vendor might blame the client for the requirement changes, but as Jones points out, the problem is a result of the methods used to gather and analyze the initial requirements.[8]

For custom systems, it's advisable to be more explicit about inputs, outputs, and the details of what the system must do. The Food and Drug Administration guidance on software validation uses the term "software requirements" for such requirements and provides more information on what they should include.[9]

After user and software requirements are defined, the next step is to determine what the computer must do to fulfill them. A functional specification is written to describe the detailed functions of the system.[10]

In addition to carefully defining requirements with the methods discussed above, and conducting internal reviews to ensure the completeness and accuracy of the requirements, review the requirements with the system developers to determine if the requirements are sufficiently clear and detailed for custom development. Go through the requirements and allow the developers to ask questions and seek clarification. Provide whatever explanations are necessary to ensure that the developers understand how you want the system to operate.

Minutes from reviews ought to be recorded and revisions made to the requirements documentation as appropriate.

SUMMARY OF PHASE 2 DELIVERABLES

Table 4.6 summarizes the deliverables from phase 2 and identifies when each deliverable is applicable.

Table 4.6	Phase 2 Deliverables		
Phase 2 deliverables	**Definition and explanation**	**When applicable**	**Deliverable references**
User requirements (see deliverable 2.1)	Formal documentation of user requirements for the system	All systems	CDRH, 6.2
Technical requirements (see deliverable 2.2)	Formal documentation of technical requirements for the system	All systems except applications built with database packages	CDRH, 6.2
Vendor organizational requirements (see deliverable 2.3)	Formal documentation of requirements for determining if a vendor has the long-term potential to meet system support needs	When a long-term solution from the same vendor is required	Recommended as needed
Phase review minutes	High-level review of the processes used to prepare the requirements, and the requirements documents, with the oversight body (e.g., the steering committee)	Large or complex low-risk systems. All moderate- to high-risk systems	Highly recommended for moderate- to high-risk systems

Chapter 5

Phase 3: Select Vendors and Systems

The purpose of the third phase is to purchase, from qualified vendors, hardware and software that can meet the system's user and technical requirements.[1] During this phase you answer the question, "What system do I want?"

For large, complex, and/or high-risk systems, a selection team typically will be created. The team usually includes the process owner and a representative from the information technology (IT), validation, quality assurance (QA) functions, and possibly representatives of other user groups. The team will plan the evaluation of alternative hardware and software products. Recommended activities for selecting applications include researching systems and vendors, vendor demonstrations, and visits to other system users for on-site demonstrations of how they use the application, and an evaluation of the alternatives against the requirements. For high-risk systems, a review of known defects in the software is strongly recommended.

Hardware evaluation and selection involves identifying hardware that meets the technical requirements, including requirements related to security, performance, and environmental conditions identified in the technical requirements document.

During the selection process, vendors are qualified using documented methods and criteria appropriate to how their product will be used and the risks associated with possible failures. The methods used to qualify application developers can range from accepting them based on a third-party registration, such as ISO 9001, to a vendor audit.[2] During a qualification audit, the auditor determines what software development methods were used to develop the application to be purchased and if a documented (life cycle) was used. If the selection process involves selecting a firm for custom software development or system integration, the vendor audit is a review of the process the vendor would use for the contracted work. Even groups within your company that develop software must be qualified to ensure that they're capable and that they use methods of development appropriate to the risk of the system.[3]

Part of the purchasing process is contracting for needed support from vendors. Support might include defect support and repair, and system maintenance and calibration.

Ordinarily management approval is required prior to purchasing hardware and software needed for commercial off-the-shelf (COTS) systems, or prior to contracting with developers or integrators to build or configure a system. For larger systems, concurrence on the selection is often required from the IT, purchasing, QA, and legal departments. It's recommended that management review the selection process and reports prior to signing off on the system, especially if it's large, complex, and/or moderate to high risk.

The evaluation of database packages for creating applications also depends on the intended use and risk associated with potential failure. Although companies tend to assume that systems such Excel, Access, and SAS are reliable under all circumstances, the manufacturers of these systems have defined security, capacity, and other limitations that must be reviewed against the intended uses of the system.

This chapter is written primarily from the perspective of COTS software. Readers should refer to two Institute for Electrical and Electronics Engineers (IEEE) standards for additional information on selecting systems and vendors. The IEEE 12207.0 standard, Software Life Cycle Processes, includes a section on acquiring software.[4] The institute has also written a standard on software acquisition, IEEE 1062.[5] In it readers will find information about purchasing COTS software that's customized for the buyer, and purchasing customized software that will complement the information in this chapter.

GUIDELINES FOR SELECTING SYSTEMS

Expend an Appropriate Amount of Effort on Selecting the System

Although it might seem obvious that selecting a system that's right for your organization is critical, its importance can't be over emphasized. Organizations often don't spend enough time selecting a system. Here are some examples of how you can lose time and money by purchasing the wrong system:

- Acting on a Web description and supplemental literature, the quality manager of a supplier of genetic research materials purchased what he thought was an inexpensive document control system. After working with the system for two weeks, he discovered that what he purchased was only one of several modules he needed for a complete system and that the software he purchased required a database that couldn't be supported by IT. The system was discarded.

- A pharmaceutical company invested two years and $2.5 million working with software that offered a toolbox approach to document control. The system provided database management, security, and basic vaulting functionality. Tools were provided for developing software that controlled approval routings for change requests and defining attribute data for parts and documents. More than two hundred custom programs were written to develop the desired functionality and achieve 21 CFR Part 11 compliance. However, problems arose after the code was complete. First, document control staff thought the system was difficult to use. Second, the IT function didn't want the responsibility of supporting a system with so much custom code. Third, the validation staff didn't think the custom code had sufficient documentation to pass a Food and Drug Administration (FDA) audit. The project was aborted, and one year later the company purchased and implemented a COTS system.

For a system to be accepted by your organization, the diverse concerns of many stakeholders must be met. The search for a system, or the custom development of an application, must yield a system that:

- Fulfills the vision defined in phase 1 for the system
- Provides at least the most critical features and functions users need
- Is sufficiently easy to use so that users will accept it
- Ensures the integrity of data, records, and electronic signatures and, therefore, if your company is FDA-regulated, meets Part 11 requirements

- Fits with the company's hardware and software architecture requirements
- Fits with the company's ability and desire to develop, implement, and support a system
- Is designed and created in a way that the software is supportable and maintainable
- If the system is COTS, it must be provided by a vendor with sufficient financial stability and commitment to the product to provide ongoing system enhancements and support.
- Doesn't pose a safety or financial risk beyond a reasonable level

The effort organizations expend determining whether a system will meet the concerns listed previously ranges from directly placing an order to weeks of on-site testing of systems against highly specific requirements. For example, the calibration manager in one company was very familiar with a calibration management system he'd used in another company. He knew the system would meet the needs of his current company, and thus a selection process wasn't necessary. Another company put three vendors of manufacturing execution systems through rigorous tests. Each vendor was invited to spend a week at the company and asked to load its software onto one of the servers. During the demonstration, the system owner asked each vendor to demonstrate how its system would meet each of the user requirements, using the company's data. A selection committee evaluated the ability of each system to meet each of the requirements.

Despite their awareness of the high-level concerns listed previously, when many companies select a new type of system, one with which they have little familiarity, they simply watch a demonstration by one or two software vendors. Such companies usually don't tell the vendor what to include in the demonstration. Demonstrations from different vendors focus on the strengths of their systems and gloss over or ignore the weaknesses. All too often, those in attendance don't record their evaluations. Several weeks later, a decision is made on how well those who viewed the demonstrations like the systems, rather on how well the system meets defined requirements. By the time the decision is made, people's recollections of the systems are foggy, and they're not even completely clear about which system did what. This is an inadequate and dangerous approach.

This chapter provides guidelines for creating a selection process that's appropriate to the risk level of the system. The selection committee must gather enough information during the process to understand how well each application meets the high-level concerns discussed earlier. Although a system might excite the committee during a one-hour demonstration, an examination of how each system functions at a more detailed level could reveal important limitations. For example, one commercially available electronic document management system (EDMS) is programmed so that the last reviewer's approval will override the rejection of all previous reviewers. This detail wasn't mentioned during the vendor's demonstration. Many companies prefer that if any reviewer has rejected the system, it goes back to the originator to resolve the issues.

The price for selecting a system that doesn't meet your requirements, including desired built-in controls of possible system failures, can be excessive. As will be seen in the next two chapters, the system you purchase will be analyzed for risks associated with potential failures, deficiencies in meeting regulations such as Part 11, and discrepancies between your requirements and the system's capabilities. You'll decide how to correct all the issues you discover during phase 4 and will implement the solutions during phase 5. The effort involved in resolving issues can be as simple as deciding to continue to use a manual process for a function you hoped to automate to customizing the application you purchased.

The point is that an appropriate amount of effort should be made to select a system that's a good match for your requirements. To make such a selection, you should know how well the system meets each of your critical and important requirements before you sign the contract.

The following are general guidelines for evaluating applications during the selection process. They'll help you determine how much effort is needed.

Evaluate the System Against Your Requirements

Without defining requirements up front, it's easy to believe that a system you just saw demonstrated has everything you'll need and works just the way you'd want it to work. If your company is typical of most, there will be several system users, and it might even be used for different things by different departments. The only way to meet everyone's needs is to work together to set requirements, as described in chapter 4, and then evaluate alternative systems against them. Include in your evaluation user, technical, and vendor requirements. Software development is a difficult business with a high mortality rate. Do your best to make sure that the company you select will be in business longer than you'll need the system.

Include Relevant Regulations in the Selection Criteria

Regulatory requirements are at least as important as other types of user requirements. Therefore, the system's ability to meet regulatory requirements must be assessed at the same time as other user requirements and not after the system has been purchased.

Use Numeric Ratings

Using numeric ratings provides a clear statement of the evaluators' judgments and allows different applications to be easily compared.

Get to Know the Details of Each System

The selection committee's evaluations of the alternatives must be at least as detailed as the user requirements. It's a good idea to be even more detailed in case what the system does, or how it operates, is more important than you realized when the requirements were formulated. Most systems of the same type have the same high-level functionality; it's the details of how things are done that differentiate systems and determine if it's compliant with your requirements and regulations. For example, a simple, less expensive EDMS has four departments programmed to be reviewers. Only those four functions will sign all change requests. This approach works well when a change review board approves all change requests, but it doesn't work at all for document control processes designed to have different functions approve different types of documents.

Don't Accept a Vendor's Answer at Face Value

Ask to see the system perform. Sales personnel are reluctant to tell you that something won't work the way you want or as well as you'd like. For example, a medical diagnostics company's requirements for a document control system included the ability to view documents created both on a Mac and a PC. During the demonstration only documents created with a PC were viewed. When the sales representative was asked if documents created on a Macintosh could also be viewed, he replied, "Yes, but it takes a little longer to open that type of document." The evaluators accepted the answer and didn't ask to see the system actually open such a document. After the system was purchased, the project team discovered that it took at least 30 minutes to open a Macintosh document. As a result, one-third of the company had to switch from using Macintoshes to using PCs.

Place Significant Weight on Users' Experience

Talk to companies that have successfully implemented the system and, if possible, with some that have failed. After using a system for several months, the system owner at a user company will know the application's strengths and weaknesses.

THE SELECTION PLAN

Form a Selection Committee

Because systems are used by a number of individuals and, at times, diverse departments, it's recommended that organizations use a selection committee, instead of the process owner, to pick a system. Of course, the committee will include the core team—system owner, validation, and IT. Add to the team representatives from different user groups, especially people who will be using the system in different ways.

When Is a Selection Plan Needed?

Before the committee can plan the selection process, the committee needs to determine what information is needed to evaluate vendors and applications against the requirements. Once the information needs are known, the committee can determine what methods will be the most effective for obtaining that information, and then devise a selection plan. A selection plan is important for all new systems except those that are low risk or are database package applications built with existing software such as Excel, Access, or SAS. An exception can be made if employees are familiar with available systems from previous experience. A selection plan will help the team obtain all of the information needed in an efficient manner. Selecting a major system and subsequent negotiations with the vendor can easily take three to four months, even with a tight plan. The selection plan can either be incorporated into the project plan or developed separately.

A selection plan isn't needed if a system has been identified through past experience.

What Activities Are Included in a Typical Selection Process?

The activities typically performed during the selection process are outlined in table 5.1. The table gives recommendations as to when the activities should be included. Each of the activities will be discussed in this chapter.

Find and Screen Vendors and Their Applications

The objective of the initial screening phase is to identify companies and their products that merit further investigation. Many alternatives are available for most types of

Table 5.1	Application Software Selection Activities

Selection activity	Activity description or value	Use for
■ Find and screen software vendors and their applications.	Provides a list of viable vendors for that type of application	All commercial-off-the-shelf (COTS) and configurable systems
■ Become familiar with the vendors and their applications.	Vendors are invited to give demos or provide demo CDs. The selection committee can see how the system actually performs (or fails to perform) to the user requirements.	All COTS and configurable systems
■ Visit a couple of each vendor's customers.	Through on-site visits to companies that are already using the system, the selection committee can obtain knowledge from the users' experiences (e.g., how the system is being used, what problems have been encountered, and the quality of service provided by the vendor).	Moderate- and high-risk systems
■ Qualify the application vendors.	The selection committee determines if the vendors are financially sound, if software engineering practices used to develop the software are likely to produce quality software, and if needed support is available.	All systems; the nature of qualification depends on risk.
■ Decide on an application.	Based on a systematic assessment of alternatives, the selection committee decides which application it wishes to purchase.	All systems
■ Review known defects.	The selection team can avoid purchasing a system that's known to fail while performing functions that have been identified as high risk.	High-risk systems
■ Get management approval to negotiate a contract.	The selection committee presents its choice, along with cost estimates, to management and gets approval to negotiate a contract.	All systems
■ Negotiate a contract with the application vendor.	The project team and the legal and purchasing departments negotiate the terms of the contract with the selected application vendor.	All systems
■ Purchase needed hardware and system software.	The equipment and system software is purchased from qualified vendors.	As necessary
■ Select integrators and custom software developers.	Integrators might be needed if extensive configuration or integration with other systems is required. Customization could require the services of a custom software developer.	As necessary

Medatech 5.1   Medatech's Selection Committee

Doc understands it's important that the selected system meet the needs of the departments he serves as well as his own. To help ensure their agreement with the choice of a system and to ensure that they understand the reason for the choice, Doc has asked Paula, the production manager, and Inga, the engineering manager, to join the electronic document management system (EDMS) project team in selecting an EDMS system.

The selection committee prepared a plan that included all the activities listed in table 5.1.

Medatech 5.2   Getting to the Short List

After talking to colleagues and searching on the Web, the selection committee identified fifteen possible systems. Doc also contacted a number of people he knew from attending sessions of a documentation discussion group, an informal regional professional organization. Using Doc's information, the committee narrowed the list to three. Here are some of the reasons companies were eliminated:

■ One company's system seemed very promising, but its revenue for the past year was only $1 million, and it was projecting the same level for this year.

■ Another company, in addition to showing no growth, was losing a number of clients to a competitor.

■ A company that was well-known in the field didn't have any of the required 21 CFR Part 11 functionality, including electronic signatures.

■ The nearest support engineer for another company was several thousand miles away.

■ One company had just been bought, and the new owners considered the application to be an interim offering until a more fully featured system could be built.

systems. During the initial screening step, enough applications should be identified so that, after some are eliminated during subsequent steps, two or three viable applications will remain for the final decision. If selection committee members aren't familiar with the systems, three or four systems should be identified as candidates at the end of this initial screening step.

Criteria must be developed before the screening begins so that vendors or applications that are clearly not a fit for your company can be easily eliminated. The initial

Table 5.2	Criteria for Screening Possible Software Providers

Criterion	Questions to ask
Critical functionality	■ Can the application perform the major functions you want? ■ Is the product sufficiently new and exciting to risk going with a product with limited use, or with a company that's struggling financially?
Continuity of knowledge of the system	■ Did the company that now owns the system develop it or was it procured from another company? ■ How has information about the system and its development been preserved and communicated to new developers and the maintenance staff? ■ How are specifications maintained?
Ability to meet industry regulations	■ Does the system meet regulations specific to your industry? For example, is it 21 CFR Part 11-compliant? ■ Are there any indications that your industry is of strategic interest to the vendor?
Assumptions about product use	Applications are developed with different assumptions about how they will be used. Some are developed for use as is, others allow some flexibility through configurations, and others provide the core functionality and tools for building user interfaces and additional functionality. Do the product assumptions match what you're willing to do to get the system to meet your requirements?
Software maturity	■ How many companies have installed the system? ■ For how many years has it been available for purchase?
System architecture	■ Is the software built using a contemporary development language and architecture? Or is the system due for a major rewrite that might lead to instability? ■ Is the architecture compatible with your company's strategy? For example, a client-server system might not be acceptable to a company that's striving to conduct business using the Internet
Financial stability	■ Is the company financially stable? Although privately held companies won't release financial data, indirect indicators can tip you off to the financial health of the company. ■ What's the size of the company's current installed base? (The installed base generates maintenance revenue.) ■ Are sales growing year to year? ■ Is the company hiring employees or downsizing to cut costs? ■ If the company is a small startup, how long will its current funding last at its current burn rate? ■ Do industry watch groups hold the company and/or product in high regard? ■ What market share does the product have? Is it facing stiff competition that might overwhelm it?
Ease of implementation	What types of companies are successful in implementing this system: companies of all sizes or large companies with a lot of information technology resources?

Criterion	Questions to ask
Support capabilities	■ Where's the company's headquarters located? ■ Does it have a local office to provide on-site support if you need it? This is particularly important if your system will require a lot of configuration or customizations. ■ What dial-in or online support is available? ■ When is the support staff available? ■ What's the company's reputation for providing support? ■ How are defects and requests for enhancements maintained?
Cost	What's the approximate cost of the system?

screening criteria should include the most important user, technical, and vendor requirements that can be easily evaluated from product literature, Web sites, or phone calls to sales representatives. Table 5.2 provides examples of types of criteria that can be used. During the screening process, get information related to these questions that's easy to obtain. If the vendor makes the short list of potential vendors, you'll continue to gather information on these items during the selection process until sufficient information is obtained to determine whether each criterion is met.

Information on available software can be obtained from the following sources:

■ The Internet

■ Peers in your industry who have conducted searches and selected systems

■ Trade shows for your industry

■ Conferences or trade shows for that type of software

■ Industry watchdog reports, such as those published by the Gartner Group

■ Trade journal articles

■ Advertisements in trade journals

■ Resource compendiums in trade journals

■ System integrators

■ Consultants

■ Software vendors

Identify potential vendors and gather information about them based on the criteria given in table 5.2. If a vendor fails to meet one of the criteria, note which criteria it has failed and eliminate the vendor from further consideration. Conclude the search when a short list of about three to four acceptable candidates has been created.

EVALUATE HOW WELL VENDORS AND THEIR APPLICATIONS MEET REQUIREMENTS

Select a Method for Evaluating the Systems

Once the initial screening is complete, the selection committee must gain a more in-depth view of the applications and companies. The best way to become familiar with the application is to see it in action. Most vendors of expensive systems will have sales representatives who will demonstrate their product at your facility. Others will demonstrate the system over the Internet while they talk with you on the phone. Still others will send a demo CD that will show you how the system works.

Another approach is to issue a request for proposals (RFP). These typically have several sections. An introductory section provides information on your company, your needs, and your selection criteria. The second section identifies the information you'd like to have about the vendor so you can determine how well it meets your vendor requirements. The third section provides a detailed list of technical and user requirements. The vendor should indicate if its system meets each of the requirements. The fourth section asks for a description of relevant services the vendor provides, such as training, validation, and support. The fifth section requests a price and includes instructions on how to breakdown the price.

Responses to RFP are used to compare vendors and their solutions; rating scales can be used to aid in the comparison. Although RFPs were once the method of choice for selecting systems, many vendors now refuse to complete them because of the time required to respond. They'd prefer to demonstrate what their systems can do. Considering the principles laid out at the beginning of the chapter, demonstrations provide a vivid and more accurate description of system capabilities than the written word and should be used instead of a traditional RFP.

The extent to which you need in-depth knowledge of the system depends in part on the risk level of the system. Consequently, the effort you spend learning about the systems should be in line with the risks a system failure poses. You must clearly understand at least how the various systems perform the functions you've identified as moderate or high risk. Because of their power as a communication device, demonstrations are recommended for moderate- and high-risk systems. However, you must be careful not to be misled by a demonstration that doesn't tell you the whole story or doesn't tell it accurately.

Maximize the Value of Vendor Demonstrations

Demonstrations will be the first and most lasting impression of the system for many selection committee members. If the demonstration isn't effective, the system will be poorly regarded, even if it's a good match for your needs. To obtain the maximum value from demonstrations, you must be able to compare how well several applications meet your requirements. For this reason, you have to be in control of the demonstrations. Software vendors prepare demonstrations that highlight the features and functions of the system and that will give them a competitive advantage. The things their systems don't do well will either be hidden or glossed over.

To ensure that you get the information you need from a demo, plan the demonstration with the sales rep. Provide a copy of your user and technical requirements and an outline of how you want the demonstration organized. For instance, if you want the vendor to use your information or data during the demonstration, either provide the data in advance or have the data available beforehand for the demonstration team to upload into the system.

In more extreme cases, some companies ask vendors to stay on-site for several days to a week. Such companies ask the vendor to load the standard application onto the company server and then ask the demonstration team to make the system perform a number of tasks. This approach puts the purchaser more in control and allows for a systematic assessment. It also takes longer. The demonstration team might have to stop the demonstration to load or input data, and some functions might have to be repeated several times to perform different actions. A vendor probably will be unwilling to perform this type of demonstration unless you represent a large sale or an account it can showcase to your industry.

Some companies are concerned that the demonstration team will modify the standard application, use additional programs, or preprocess some of the data to get the system to perform according to your requirements during the demonstration. For example, to enhance transaction speed, the demonstration team might use a server that has more power or memory than is defined as the minimum or recommended configuration. Be sure to ask the team if what you're seeing is standard, out-of-the-box functionality and what hardware, software, and networking resources are used during the demonstration.

Schedule plenty of time for those attending the demonstration to ask questions. The time required depends on the depth with which the demonstrations will be conducted; however, demos of major applications will take at least three to four hours.

Invite the selection committee, members of the QA and IT functions, and any additional users that should review the systems to be evaluators during the demo. Brief the additional reviewers on the selection process, company requirements, and the plan for the demonstration.

Encourage evaluators to ask a lot of questions during the demonstration. Take a strong "show me" stance with the demonstration team. Don't be satisfied with statements that the system is capable of doing something or verbal descriptions of how the system does something. Ask to see the system perform the function.

Develop forms for those who will evaluate the system during the demonstration; organize the forms according to the structure of the demonstration. Include all user and technical requirements on the form. Have each evaluator rate how well the system meets each requirement. Encourage the evaluators to take notes and make ratings during the demo. If they view demonstrations of several systems during a few weeks without taking notes and then try to compare them, they'll be confused about which system did what, and some capabilities will have been forgotten.

The best way to accurately record what the system can do is to have the evaluators meet soon after each demonstration to review and agree on how well that system met the company's requirements. Substantial differences in ratings should be discussed. For example, if a five-point rating scale is used, a difference in the ratings given to a single requirement that's two points or higher ought to be discussed. If one evaluator gives an application a two on how well it meets a specific requirement, and another evaluator gives the same application a four, they have substantially different perceptions of how well the system meets that requirement. Individuals can change their ratings based on the discussion.

Compare the Systems on How Well They Meet User Requirements

When all the demonstrations are complete, the systems can be compared during a meeting of the evaluators. If each system has already been rated on the evaluation forms, a total or average score can be calculated for each system.

The scores can be weighted by the importance of the requirement. Multiply the rating by a value associated with the requirement's importance (e.g., each critical requirement is assigned a weight of five). Calculate a weighted score for each requirement and total or average the weighted scores assigned to each system.

Remember that although numbers are very useful, this isn't a numbers game. If the decision is based on numeric totals or averages, the differences on how the applications are rated on individual requirements become the deciding factors for the selection. For this reason, the ratings must match the evaluators' perceptions of the major strengths and weaknesses of the systems relative to each other. Consistency can be checked in two ways. First, evaluators must express their views on what each system's major strengths and weaknesses are. Check the ratings to verify that they're consistent with the perceptions. Second, review the major differences on the ratings to determine if the biggest differences match the perceived strengths and weaknesses of the systems relative to each other. Inconsistencies found with either approach should be discussed and ratings changed if necessary. The selection committee determines if there's a consensus as to which two systems would be the best for the company. These will be further examined during the rest of the selection process. The discussions that occur at this meeting must be documented, especially the discussion of the members' perceptions of the systems' strengths and weaknesses.

Evaluate the Alternatives on the Technical Requirements

Information should be gathered on the technical specifications of the application during the initial screening and demonstration. Obtain whatever additional information is needed from the vendor. Once the information is obtained, rate the application on how well it meets each technical requirement. The ratings can be weighted according to the importance of the requirements. Examine the ratings to ensure that they reflect the true differences between the applications. Total or average the ratings. Prepare a report on the technical assessment of the alternative systems (see deliverable 3.1 in appendix A).

Assess Vendors' Abilities to Meet Vendor Organizational Requirements

Collect information on the vendors' organizational requirements. As discussed in the previous chapter, information about a requirement, such as financial stability, might not be directly available. Indirect indicators might need to be assessed and data pieced together to make a judgment. Such indicators were presented in chapter 4 (see table 4.5). Once the companies have been researched, rate them on the organizational requirements. Usually enough information can be obtained to determine if the vendors are at least minimally able to meet the requirements and to determine the difference among them.

Ratings should be made similar to those discussed for user requirements. The ratings and a discussion of how well the vendors meet the vendor requirements are included in deliverable 3.2, User Assessment of Alternatives Report (see appendix A).

Medatech 5.3 | # Vendor Evaluations

The Medatech selection committee invited the three companies to give demonstrations of their systems. In preparation for these, the committee:
- Defined an outline for the demonstrations and asked the vendors to perform their demonstration in that sequence
- Provided the vendors with a list of user and technical requirements
- Prepared evaluation forms for the selection committee
- Scheduled a one-hour committee meeting to follow each three-hour demonstration

During the meeting following each of the demonstrations, members of the selection committee first individually completed their ratings of the system for each requirement. A five-point rating scale was used. The committee then reviewed the ratings assigned to each requirement and discussed any differences in ratings of two points or more. At the end of the meeting, each member described what he or she thought were the system's greatest strengths as well as any major shortcomings.

When this process was completed for all three of the systems, an additional meeting was held. The averages of each system's ratings were compared, and the overall strengths and weaknesses were discussed; the top two systems were selected. These two were similar, and both met the critical requirements. Some of the ways in which they differed included the systems' ability to:
- Refer a change request to a manager when a reviewer failed to make a decision within a specified time.

- Assign reviews to a proxy automatically when a reviewer notified the system that he or she would be absent for a period of time.
- Generate custom reports from within the package rather than by using a third-party report writer.
- Disable the login of a user after a set number of successive failed attempts to enter the password, and to notify the system administrator of the time, date, and source of the attempts.
- Integrate the document control system with other systems (e.g., enterprise resource planning systems). Though this currently is not a requirement, the team believed it may be in the future.

The third system was eliminated because drawings could be viewed only through PDF images rather than native mode formats.

After the demonstrations and a couple of follow-up phone calls with the vendors' system analysts, Tec completed deliverable 5.1, a technical assessment of alternatives report.

Information about some of the vendor organizational requirements, such as problem support and the availability of services, had been collected throughout the selection and evaluation process. Doc obtained additional information on other requirements through discussions with executives, including:
- Vice presidents of development concerning strategic product direction and staffing
- Vice presidents of sales and marketing concerning the installed base and growth in new accounts

Visit Customers of Each Vendor

Valuable insight can be obtained from a system's current users. Ask the vendor to provide names of its customers from your industry and that are located near your company. Speak with or visit two or three companies that use each system. For low-risk systems, a phone interview should be sufficient. For moderate or high-risk systems, a visit to their facility is highly recommended. Ask the system owner or a user to demonstrate how his or her company uses the system.

The objectives of these interviews include:

- Determining how easy or difficult the system was to install and get up and running. How long did it take? What was involved in transitioning from the old system to the new one? How difficult was it to access legacy data?
- Understanding, or seeing, how the system is currently used
- Obtaining information on how well the system performs against industry and company requirements
- Finding out what problems have been encountered since the system was installed. How supportive was the vendor in solving the problems? Are problems still unresolved that could affect you?
- Obtaining the system owner's or IT's perceptions of how effective the vendor is in fixing defects and responding to enhancement requests.
- Learning how users have reacted to the system. Is it easy to use?
- Asking what the company would like the system to do that it currently can't do.
- Inquiring whether the company, if it had to make the selection again, would make the same choice

For moderate- and high-risk systems, a formal questionnaire is recommended as a basis for interviewing a system owner either during a visit or by phone. The systems can be more easily compared if each company is asked the same open-ended questions—for example, "How have users reacted to the system?" Preparation for the customer's demonstration involves listing what functions you want to see the system perform (e.g., moderate- and high-risk functions). Such demonstrations usually are informal, but you can ask the demonstrator to show you how his or her company does something using the system.

The information gathered during the visit should be recorded so that it can be shared with members of the selection team who didn't make the visit and reviewed during the final assessment. Include relevant information in deliverable 3.2, User Assessment of Alternatives Report.

Medatech 5.4	Visiting Vendors' Customers

The selection committee visited two customers of each of their final two systems. Doc was surprised by the document control managers' willingness to host Medatech's visits. All of the customers were basically satisfied with the systems but recognized areas for improvement. The users of both software companies had organized a user group with the support and encouragement of the vendors. At the user group meetings, users presented papers on how they were using the applications. In addition, each group gathered input from members on recommendations for enhancements. One manager asked Doc for his support in raising the need for blocking the login of a user after a set number of successive failed login attempts.

Although the demonstrations and candid discussions with document control managers lead to new insights for the selection committee, one important difference surprised the committee members. Based on the documentation managers' demonstrations, the ease of use of the two systems was strikingly different. With one system, navigation to a needed screen was simpler and fewer screens had to be opened to perform the same operation. In addition, the display of information about the documents and change orders was also superior. These differences seemed to be reflected in the user responses to the two systems. Users warmed up more quickly to the easier-to-use system and had a generally positive reaction. Users of the more complex system found it superior to a paper-based system but weren't excited by it.

QUALIFY VENDORS

Chapter 1 points out that quality must be built into software. Vendors are qualified so you can gain a high level of confidence that their products and services are and will be of sufficient quality to provide the reliability and performance needed for that product and/or service. Vendors of all components of the system should be qualified.

Select Qualification Methods Based on System Risk

Follow your company's vendor qualification procedure when qualifying computer system vendors. If a procedure must be developed, use the guidelines provided in table 5.3, which gives requirements for qualifying different types of vendors whose products and services have various levels of associated risk.[6] A vendor can be qualified if it meets any one of the options marked with the value O (for option). For example, application vendors are qualified by evidence that there's an established life cycle for software development. For a low-risk system, any of the three types of evidence is sufficient: industry reputation, vendor survey or third-party certification, or on-site audit. The value of R (for required) means that it and all other criteria marked R for that type of vendor must be met. If, for example, a support services vendor is being qualified for a moderate or high-risk system, the vendor must meet both of the qualification criteria—an established procedure for providing support services and an on-site vendor audit that focuses on support. Ultimately, QA and IT must be satisfied that enough evidence has been obtained to determine that the vendor is capable of providing products and/or services at an appropriate quality level.

| Table 5.3 | Methods for Evaluating the Quality Systems of Computer System Vendors | | | |

Type of vendor	Qualification activity	System risk level		
		Low	Med.	High
Application software vendor	Established life cycle for software development, as known by:			
	■ Industry reputation	O		
	■ Vendor survey or third-party certification	O		
	■ On-site vendor audit	O	R	R
Support services	Established procedures for providing support services	O	R	R
	On-site vendor audit with focus on support services	O	R	R
Custom software development or integration services	Established life cycle for custom software development, as known by:			
	■ Industry reputation	O		
	■ Vendor survey or third-party certification	O		R
	■ On-site vendor audit	O	R	R
	A quality agreement with your company that specifies the development methodology to be followed in creating custom software. This agreement will be signed with the contract.	O	R	R
System software vendor	Established life cycle for software development, as known by:			
	■ Industry reputation	O		
	■ Third-party certification	O	O	R
	■ Vendor survey	O	O	R
Hardware manufacturer	Established quality system, as known by:			
	■ Industry reputation	O		
	■ Third-party certification	O	O	R
	■ Vendor survey	O	O	R

Qualify Application Vendors

Five dimensions can be evaluated in qualifying application vendors. Information on three of the dimensions has already been collected through the selection process: financial stability, industry experience, and the ability to provide support. If sufficient information hasn't been collected to determine if the vendor is acceptable on these dimensions, additional information should be obtained.

A fourth dimension is a review of direct evidence regarding the quality of the application.[7] The percent of defects that were discovered before release is compared to the percent that have been discovered after release. If most of the defects have been removed before release, the number of defects discovered after release should be relatively small and should taper off over time. The more severe the consequences of failure are, the more stringent the requirements for software quality should be.

The final dimension is the vendor's software development and quality system. The European Community Commission's directive on medicinal products emphasizes the importance of evaluating the vendor's quality system in requirement five in EC Annex 11:

"The software is a critical component of a computerised system. The user of such software should take all reasonable steps to ensure that it has been produced in accordance with a system of quality assurance."[8]

Note that the term "quality assurance" is used in Annex 11 and this book with the same meaning as it's used in ISO 9001, ISO 13485, and Quality System Regulation, and includes all practices and systems that ensure a quality product is designed, manufactured, installed, and supported. Because quality is built into software through engineering practices, the capability of the vendor to create quality software is assessed by reviewing the vendor's quality system, including the development process. The validation testing you perform in phases 7 and 8 verifies that a specific product can reliably meet your requirements in your environment. As discussed in chapter 1, it's not possible to test the use of a system in every potential logical circumstance. Although testing by the developer and yourself is critical, that alone isn't sufficient to provide a high level of certainty that the system will always function reliably.[9, 10] In a study published by Software Productivity Research, Capers Jones reports that formal testing by itself can detect 37 percent to 60 percent of the defects in software. When software development includes a formal quality assurance process, formal design inspections, and formal code inspections in addition to formal testing, 95 percent to 99.99 percent of the defects were detected.[11] In another source, Jones identifies the following combination of practices that leads to 99 percent defect removal:

- Personal checking of design or documents by the author
- Informal group design reviews
- Formal design inspections
- Modeling or prototyping during programming
- Personal checking of code by the author
- Formal code inspections
- Unit testing (single modules)
- Functional testing (related modules)
- Integrated testing (complete system)
- Field testing (live beta testing)[12]

Software engineering includes defect-prevention as well as defect-detection methods. Obviously, it's better to avoid creating defects in the first place. Jones concludes that the combination of defect prevention and detection approaches presented in exhibit 5.1 is the minimum needed to ensure good to excellent quality.[13] These practices should be included in an audit of software vendors.

The methods used to evaluate the vendor's quality system can vary with the system risk level. Alternatives for evaluating the vendor's quality system are given in table 5.3. The quality of low-risk applications can be assessed by using one of several methods: reviewing a questionnaire completed by the vendor; relying on a third-party registration, such as ISO 9001, as evidence of the existence of a formal quality assurance program; the vendor's reputation (i.e., information gathered from previous users or current users); or by performing an on-site audit of the vendor's quality system. For moderate-to high-risk systems, on-site audits are highly recommended.[14, 15] The FDA guidance document states:

> Where possible and depending upon the device risk involved, the device manufacturer should consider auditing the vendor's design and development methodologies used in the construction of the OTS software and should assess the development and validation documentation generated for the OTS software. . . . The audit should demonstrate that the vendor's procedures for and results of the verification and validation activities performed [for] the OTS software are appropriate and sufficient for the safety and effectiveness requirements of the medical device to be produced using that software.[16]

The IEEE standard for software verification and validation identifies verification and validation activities that the IEEE thinks should be performed based on the software integrity level that's appropriate for the software. The more critical the software and the higher the risk associated with failure, the higher the integrity of the software must be.[17] Based on your risk assessment, determine which of IEEE's four levels of software integrity is needed for your system. In general, IEEE's level four corresponds to what I refer to as high-risk systems. IEEE level three correspond to moderate-risk systems, and level one to low-risk systems. During your audit, determine if the vendor for the system in question has performed the verification and validation activities that

---

| **Exhibit 5.1** | Minimum Software Development Practices for Good to Excellent Quality |

In *Software Quality: Analysis and Guidelines for Success* (International Thomson Computer Press, 1997), Capers Jones concludes that the following sequence of defect prevention and removal activities is necessary to ensure good to excellent quality:

Defect Prevention Approaches
- Formal requirements analysis such as joint application design (JAD)
- Formal risk-analysis early in development
- Prototyping
- Structured or formal specifications methods
- Structured programming methods
- Certified reusable design and code components

Nontest Defect-Removal Methods
- Requirements inspections
- Design inspections
- Code inspections
- Test plan reviews
- Test-case inspections
- User documentation editing or reviews

Testing Defect-Removal Methods
- Unit test by individual programmers
- New function testing
- Regression testing
- Performance testing
- Integration testing
- System testing
- Field test (external beta test)

(Reprinted by permission)

IEEE considers necessary. Unfortunately, the IEEE standard on the development life cycle doesn't tie development activities to software integrity levels.

Method 3.1, Assessment of Vendor Software Development (see appendix A), lists aspects of the software development process to review through a questionnaire, or an audit, depending on the risks associated with the software.[18] A questionnaire or audit checklist can be developed using the list given in method 3.1 or other documents on the engineering life cycle referenced in the method.

Summarize the audit findings in a vendor audit report; see deliverable 3.3 in appendix A.

After the data gathering is complete, the audit team must determine if it thinks the quality system, including the development process, is capable of generating a quality product. Although some companies use a numerical score, such as 70 percent, as a cutoff for qualification, it's more effective to look at what practices are effectively implemented and what systems are missing or inadequate, and make a judgment about how well the software is being developed.

Vendors can be qualified, conditionally qualified, or disqualified. Conditional qualification will require the vendor to improve the quality system in some manner within a defined time frame. If it fails to do so, it will be disqualified, and the application won't be purchased.

Upon completing the qualification process for a vendor, a vendor qualification form such as the one described in deliverable 3.4 is prepared. The report summarizes the qualification process, the information obtained during the process, the conclusion reached, and the justification for the conclusion. All of the documentation obtained during the qualification process is attached.

Qualify Infrastructure Vendors

Vendors of hardware and system software must be qualified to ensure that the products and services they provide are of sufficient quality.[19] Table 5.3 provides guidelines for qualifying such vendors. Keep in mind that a vendor must be qualified for each type of equipment you'll purchase from it.

If the vendor's product is only hardware—(i.e., it doesn't include embedded software)—then the qualification process centers on the quality system related to the vendor's manufacturing processes. ISO 9001 provides a credible framework for such an assessment.[20] In addition, the quality of hardware components can be evaluated through retrospective analysis of the component's quality. The information on performance can come from your own experience or from the vendor's data. Key points to evaluate are durability, reliability, and accuracy while operating, preferably in conditions similar to your environment. These dimensions can be reflected in overall data on how often the hardware malfunctions.[21]

Medatech 5.5	Vendor Audits

Doc informed vendors A and B that Medatech had narrowed the field to the two companies. As one of the final steps in the selection process, Medatech needed to qualify the vendors. If their quality systems were found to be unacceptable, the vendor would be eliminated.

Quincy, a quality assurance specialist, headed Medatech's vendor qualification efforts. Because this was a high-risk system, Medatech's evaluation of the vendors' quality systems included an on-site visit and either verification of ISO 9001:2000 registration or the completion of Medatech's vendor survey. Vendor B wasn't ISO 9001:2000-registered, so Quincy sent it the survey.

In preparation for the on-site audit, Quincy asked each vendor to send him a copy of its software development procedures, quality manual, a list of procedures, and an organization chart. Audit schedules were planned in advance with the vendors' quality managers. An audit checklist was used while conducting the audit that covered the items identified in method 3.1, the assessment of vendor software development.

The audit was conducted by Quincy and Tec. Vendor A's quality system was sound in every regard. Vendor B performed a high number of defect-prevention and -removal activities but didn't document all of them. Quincy granted them a conditional pass. He explained to vendor B's quality manager that Medatech needed a commitment from senior management to address the following issues before Medatech could give further consideration to purchasing a system from the organization:

■ Records must be kept of employee training.
■ Input requirements for software development must be documented.
■ Records must be kept of design reviews and code reviews.
■ Traceability of each program back to the detailed design must be formally documented.
■ Management of off-site contract developers must include a periodic formal review.

Medatech received assurances from vendor B's head of development that he would address the issues. Quincy planned a follow-up audit with the organization to verify that the issues had been addressed.

A common practice in the industry is to purchase equipment from a manufacturer that's known to have reliable products. The equipment must meet the technical requirements and/or technical specification and is then qualified through the installation qualification process described in chapter 9. You must determine if such a practice is sufficient for your system or if extensive vendor qualification is appropriate.

If the equipment has embedded software (e.g., firmware), the quality systems for both hardware and software must be evaluated.

DECIDE ON AN APPLICATION

When making the final decision, first eliminate any vendors or applications that can't meet every critical requirement. As mentioned in chapter 4, be sure that the requirements you identify as "show stoppers" are truly critical.

Update the ratings on the user, technical, and vendor requirements, if needed, to ensure that they reflect the latest information received. Summarize the vendor evaluations on a table that shows the overall ratings of each vendor. Include at least the following:

- User requirements overall rating
- Technical requirements overall rating
- Vendor requirements overall rating
- Vendor qualification
- Costs
- Summary of strengths
- Summary of weaknesses

When preparing for the final selection meeting, steering committee members should review the technical assessment of alternatives, user assessment of alternatives, and vendor qualification forms. During the meeting, the committee reviews each of the alternatives and then discusses each member's preference and the reasons for it. The committee should discuss the alternatives and preferences until a consensus is obtained. Document the reasons for the selection.

For many companies this level of rigor in evaluating systems is sufficient. Others might want to further reduce the risk of making a poor decision. For example, one company bought a discounted single-user license for six months so that it could have a manufacturing execution system (MES) on site for further evaluation. A MES is essentially part of an electronic batch record. The MES documents (or the operator inputs) information concerning the manufacturing process, such as weights of raw materials and values of parameters (e.g., temperature and pressure), at different points in the process.

During the six-month license period, the production manager and QA learned more about the system's capabilities, estimated the effort required to implement the system, and quantified the potential savings from using the system. At the end, the project team decided to delay the purchase of an MES system. The team's vision for production automation included automatically downloading new revisions of batch records from a document control system to the MES. The team decided to implement a document control system first and then to take another look at MES systems in light of the integration requirements.

| Medatech 5.6 | Summary of Vendor Evaluations |

The table below summarizes the evaluations made by Doc and the selection committee.

Evaluation or alternatives	Vendor A	Vendor B
User requirements' overall average	3.45	3.9
Technical requirements' overall average	3.35	4.15
Vendor requirements' overall average	4.5	3.5
User satisfaction (e.g., references, demos)	3.75	4.5
Vendor qualification	Qualified	Conditionally qualified
Costs	Higher	Lower
Summary of strengths	■ Solid established company ■ Superior quality system ■ Better organized support function ■ Large installed base ■ Satisfactory functionality	■ Superior usability ■ Newer functionality ■ Less expensive ■ Web-based, modern technology
Summary of weaknesses	■ More expensive ■ Older technology	■ Younger company ■ Higher risk of future financial problems ■ Fewer implementations

REVIEW KNOWN DEFECTS

If you plan to purchase a high-risk system, one final check (i.e., a review of known bugs) should be made before management is asked to approve entering into contract negotiations.

As discussed in chapter 1, all systems are released for sale with known defects. Normally, only a small number of the defects found after the software is in use get repaired. Request the vendor to allow you to review a list of known defects for the application. Many software companies have such lists available over the Internet. If you discover defects that make the system unfit for use at your company, either select another application or get a money-back guarantee from the vendor that the defects will be repaired within a reasonable period of time.

If the vendor refuses to allow you to review the known defects before purchasing the software, negotiate a contractual arrangement that will allow you to review the known defects after purchase. The contract terms should allow you to return the software at no cost if critical defects are identified and not repaired within a reasonable period of time (e.g., sixty days).

GET MANAGEMENT APPROVAL TO NEGOTIATE A CONTRACT

Management approval for systems often involves two steps: an approval to proceed to negotiate a contract and approval of the terms of the contract.

Prepare a proposal to gain management approval to negotiate a contract. The proposal could take the form of deliverable 3.5, the System Selection Report. Presumably, management agreed with the importance of your system during phase 1, when the computer system project proposal was approved. What management needs to know now is that the concept is still viable, an acceptable solution has been identified, and the approximate cost and the time and resources are needed for implementation. Therefore, the request to proceed with a contract should include:

- The system mission statement
- A summary of the selection process
- Your conclusion as to why a specific system should be purchased and the reasons why it's preferred over others

---

Medatech 5.7 — Review of Known Defects

Medatech informed vendor B that it had been selected pending a review of known defects. Doc explained to the sales representative that document control systems were considered high-risk because if they failed in some key aspects, Medatech could lose control of the design, manufacture, and/or testing of its products. For that reason, Medatech needed to determine if there were any known defects in the application that would make the system unusable for the company. If such defects were present, Medatech needed a commitment from the vendor to have the defects repaired before the contract was signed. Doc asked for a session during which Tec would review known bugs of high severity with a representative of the vendor's development or support organizations.

Vendor B's sales manager requested a copy of Medatech's critical requirements and had the manager of customer support review them. The sales manager assured Medatech that there were no known defects that would interfere with the application's ability to meet critical requirements. Nevertheless, vendor B's sales manager refused to allow Medatech to review the known defects list without having signed a contract. The companies agreed that a review would take place within thirty days after signing the contract, and that if any known defects prohibited the application from meeting any of Medatech's critical requirements, the vendor would have sixty days to repair the defects or void the sale. The list of critical requirements would be attached to the contract.

- The high-level ratings of the applications (for COTS and configurable applications) on user, business, and technical requirements as well as any other dimensions of critical importance
- A comparison of the applications on out-of-pocket costs, and the time needed from internal resources to successfully implement the system
- A summary of the vendor qualification process for the selected software vendor
- Identification of any special contractual terms that must be negotiated and the reasons why they're important

Before approving the contract negotiations, management should verify that all the critical deliverables up to now have been completed and approved, including, as appropriate:

- Computer system project proposal
- Initial risk assessment

Medatech 5.8	Management Approval to Negotiate a Contract

The selection committee prepared a system selection report following the description in deliverable 3.5. The project team met with the electronic document management system (EDMS) steering committee to present the report and asked for approval to proceed with contract negotiations. The vice president of manufacturing pointed out that the project team hadn't determined how much the system would shorten the manufacturing turnaround time. (Recall the vision statement: "Medatech is implementing an EDMS system to speed manufacturing turnaround time through direct online access to drawings, assembly instructions, and test procedures from the manufacturing floor.") The project team was asked to examine the question, and the meeting was adjourned.

Doc determined that Medatech would save three days on the manufacturing cycle if necessary forms could be printed by manufacturing employees from the EDMS system instead of requesting them from document control, and if the necessary drawings could be viewed online using an appropriate viewer.

The project team reported Doc's findings to the steering committee and contract negotiations were approved.

- User requirements
- Technical requirements
- Selection plan
- Vendor qualification form
- User assessment of alternatives report
- Technical assessment of alternatives report
- System selection report

NEGOTIATE A CONTRACT WITH THE APPLICATION VENDOR

For applications, negotiations can include:
- Price for a number of licenses:
  - ☐ Concurrent server licenses
  - ☐ Client licenses
  - ☐ A site license

- The warranty period
- Annual maintenance fees
- Training
- Implementation services
- Validation protocols
- Support terms
- Conditions for the return of the software (e.g., a review of critical defects)

Smaller, less expensive applications usually are sold as a commodity with a fixed price. Contracts are negotiated for larger, more expensive applications. As a negotiator, you have more leverage with smaller software companies because your sale is more important to them. In addition, such companies are more motivated to make concessions if you'll sign the contract before the end of the quarter or their fiscal year. Keep in mind that, although getting a larger discount is always attractive, a rush to consummate the deal shouldn't be allowed to justify a failure to adequately evaluate the system or resolve all contractual issues.

With the exception of shrink-wrap software, applications are priced based on the number of licenses purchased. The pricing schemes vary considerably. Client-server applications might be priced only on the number of concurrent users of the server software, or on both server and client licenses. The cost of the initial licenses is often discounted (i.e., the license fee per user might be less when the system is first purchased than when additional licenses are purchased later on). However, if you can get the software company to agree to allow you to purchase additional licenses during the first year at the same price, you can save money. Only a few licenses will be needed during phases 4 through 7 (before implementation). In addition, if the application is rolled out over time, you'll need fewer licenses during the initial implementation period.

Many companies will grant a money-back guarantee warranty period so that the software can be returned if you aren't satisfied. If your vendor doesn't have such a warranty, ask for one. Try to negotiate the length of the warranty to extend through phase 7—qualify the system.

Maintenance fees are paid for ongoing support of the product and upgrades. Such fees are paid annually, and the first payment is rolled into the initial purchase price. The clock should begin ticking not on the purchase date but after the warranty period. Support during the warranty is included in the initial purchase price.

The terms of the support agreement usually aren't negotiated, aside from a possible discount. That's why the company's support practices must be carefully evaluated dur-

Medatech 5.9   Contract Terms

The director of purchasing negotiated the contract with the close involvement of Doc and Tec. The corporation's lawyer reviewed the contract for legal terms. The agreement included the following negotiated terms:

- A copy of the source code shall be placed in escrow to be released to Medatech if the vendor goes out of business or no longer supports the application.
- The initial contract will include two concurrent server licenses at a 25-percent discount from list price. Additional licenses can be purchased during the following twelve months at the same discount price.
- The vendor will assist Medatech in reviewing the known defects within thirty days after signing the contract. If any known defects prohibit the application from meeting any of Medatech's critical requirements (list attached to the contract), the vendor will have sixty days to repair the defects or void the sale.
- The vendor won't have the access required to download software fixes into Medatech's system.

ing the selection process. It's important, however, to control the way in which software fixes and upgrades are delivered. As described in chapter 10 in the discussion of phase 8—use in the production environment—changes to validated systems must be controlled. Consequently, automated online updates to an application can't be permitted. An update or fix must be received, tested in a controlled environment, validated, and then installed in the operational environment.

Finally, to safeguard your investment in the system, it's important to include a contractual requirement that the vendor place a copy of source code in escrow. The contract should grant you access to the escrow copy if the vendor goes out of business or no longer supports the application. You would then have the right to use and modify the source code as needed within your business. Each time a new revision of the application is released by the vendor, a copy should be placed in escrow. Software escrow companies provide these services.

PURCHASE NEEDED HARDWARE AND SYSTEM SOFTWARE

Revising Technical Requirements

When technical requirements are developed, consideration should be given to compatibility with existing hardware and system software. Once the application is selected, the technical requirements must be revised according to the technical requirements of the application and the equipment needed to support the desired level of performance. If it's a client-server application, requirements might need to be revised for both the server(s) and clients. Considerations in revising the technical requirements include:

- Changes to user requirements
- Server requirements for the application based on estimates of transaction volumes and parameters provided by the software developer
- Versions of the system software for which the application is certified
- Database software requirements of the selected application
- Communication and network requirements based on estimates of network traffic and the vendor's experience with the application
- Requirements for ancillary software, such as viewers and browsers

Selecting Hardware and System Software

Based on the revised requirements and their own expertise, IT personnel will select the needed hardware and software. In addition to technical requirements and specifications, as well as any work done to qualify the manufacturer, selection considerations include:

- Cost
- Warranty terms
- Existing relationships with vendors
- Track record of vendors for performance, quality, reliability, and support
- Vendor qualification

Purchase Hardware and System Software

The contract negotiations for hardware and system software focus on cost, warranty, and/or service terms. As mentioned in the section on negotiating contracts with soft-

Medatech 5.10	Purchase of Hardware and System Software

In Doc's organization, the application server, database server, system software for both servers, and database software were manufactured by vendors that were previously approved for those products. The servers were purchased at a discount under a volume agreement with a distributor.

A new printer was purchased that would be dedicated to printing official hard copies. The manufacturer was qualified through its ISO 9001:2000 registration and the completion of a vendor survey.

ware vendors, it's important to control the way in which software fixes and upgrades are delivered. Because the system will be under change control, automated online updates to system software can't be permitted.

Ideally, you want to work with the actual equipment that will be used in the production environment starting in phase 4—design solutions to issues. As your organization works with the system through phases 4, 5, and 6, you'll get some indication of the response time and performance of which the system is capable and perhaps an early warning of potential problems. Companies that will be using a second smaller, less expensive server for testing potential changes and training users will often delay the purchase of the production server until phase 6—prepare for use.

SELECT INTEGRATORS AND CUSTOM SOFTWARE DEVELOPERS

The criteria for selecting system integrators and custom software developers are somewhat different. You might need to hire a system integrator to configure your system, modify it, or integrate it with other systems. If you plan to purchase these services from the application vendor, include in your audit of that company an examination of their methodology and practices for customization and integration services. If you'll be hiring a third party, it's important for custom developers to have some experience with the type of system you want them to build. If an integrator is being hired to modify or integrate a specific system(s), it's important that they're experienced with the specific systems they'll be working with.

It's unusual for an organization that provides customization and integration services to follow a defined life cycle. Many developers of custom software create what's

Medatech 5.11	Integration and Customization Needs

Medatech is planning on having a stand-alone system that won't be integrated with other systems or customized.

described in chapter 1 as "handcrafted" software. Appendix C describes how the nature of the development methodology affects the probability of a system failure. If the system poses moderate or high risk, contract negotiations with custom software vendors and integrators must include an agreed-upon life cycle for developing custom code (including integration code). Life cycle activities recommended for moderate- to high-risk custom systems are described at the end of chapters 6, 7, and 8. Some additional sources of information on what to include in a development agreement are:

■ The IEEE development life cycle[22]
■ The IEEE Standard for Software Verification and Validation[23]
■ Capers Jones' list of development activities that are most effective in identifying defects. The list is presented in his book, *Programming Productivity,* and in exhibit 5.1[24]

It's highly recommended that you include the development agreement or requirements for development practices in your contract with the custom software vendor and/or system integrator. Capers Jones suggests specific terms that can be included.[25] The EC Commission Directive requires "a formal agreement including a clear statement of the responsibilities of that outside agency" whenever an outside agency is used to provide computer services.[26]

SUMMARY OF PHASE 3 DELIVERABLES

Table 5.4 summarizes the deliverables from phase 3 and identifies when each deliverable is applicable.

Table 5.4	Phase 3 Deliverables

Phase 3 deliverables	Definition and explanation	When applicable	Deliverable references
Technical assessment of alternatives (see deliverable 3.1)	Data comparing alternatives in their ability to meet technical requirements. What constitutes adequate documentation depends on the risk level of the system and could range from a simple memo to extensive documentation of the evaluation of the alternatives.	All systems except for applications developed using database packages	Highly recommended
User assessment of alternative applications (see deliverable 3.2)	Data comparing alternatives in their ability to meet user and vendor organizational requirements along with documentation explaining why the top choices are preferred. What constitutes adequate documentation depends on the risk level of the system and could range from a simple memo to extensive documentation of the evaluation of the alternatives.	All systems except for applications developed using database packages	Highly recommended
Vendor audit report (see deliverable 3.3)	The audit report summarizes the findings of an audit and records any nonconformities discovered during the audit.	A report is prepared for all audits that are conducted.	CDRH 6.3
Vendor qualification report (see deliverable 3.4)	Documentation of the process used to qualify the vendor, the information found, the decision reached, and any corrective actions. The extent of the qualification process and documentation depends on the risk level of the system. The documentation includes audit reports and reports on the review of known defects, if appropriate.	All systems except applications built with database packages	21 CFR 820, Section 50 a; ISO 13485, Section 7.4.1; CDRH 6.3; EC Annex 11, No. 5 requires evaluation of the vendor's quality system but doesn't require a report
System selection report (see deliverable 3.5)	This report summarizes the selection process and documents the reasons for the selection that was made. The report is submitted with the request for management approval to proceed with the purchases.	All moderate- and high-risk systems except applications built with existing database packages	Recommended
Hardware and software purchase agreements and documentation; quality agreements for contracted services	Includes specifications sheets for product purchased and all contracts and support agreements	As appropriate	21 CFR 820, Section 50 b; ISO 13485, Section 7.4.2; EC Annex 11, No. 18

Chapter 6

Phase 4: Design Solutions to Issues

For commercial off-the-shelf (COTS) systems, five major activities must be performed during phase 4—design solutions to issues. These are:

■ Bringing the purchased systems into the company

■ Integrating the system with other systems

■ Addressing outstanding issues regarding meeting user requirements, mitigating risks, and achieving compliance

■ Preparing the validation plan, including defining criteria for when the system is acceptable for use

■ Designing needed configurations (see note 1)

For custom systems, a computerized system specification is created, the structure of the software is designed, and a high-level test plan is created.

This phase begins when the hardware and software are received into the company. Asset identification tags are placed on the hardware, and the software is secured. The system is set up as a test environment so that it can be used for the activities of this and the next phase.

System interfaces and/or integrations with other systems are established and informally tested. (Note that if custom software is required to create the interface, those programs must be developed in a manner similar to custom systems.)

Often, a COTS system isn't an ideal match to user requirements and, as discussed in chapter 1, you must presume that it contains defects. To address requirements that aren't met and risks associated with system failure, the project team must determine which requirements the system isn't capable of meeting and conduct a detailed risk analysis of the system. Mitigations are planned to address deficiencies. Mitigations can include changing user requirements, placing limitations on system use, making software changes, and developing manual processes to supplement system weaknesses. The effort required to develop and implement risk mitigations and to make accommodations for systems that don't meet requirements highlights the importance of defining requirements in advance and selecting a system that meets your requirements and has built-in mitigations.

A validation plan is prepared for most systems to describe the approach to be taken with the validation and what activities will be included. The plan describes the system, implementation and validation strategies, validation activities, a high-level validation test plan, responsibilities, and the criteria for accepting the system. The plan also identifies the life cycle deliverables that will constitute the validation record. Simple and/or low-risk systems might not require a validation plan. In such cases, the information can be included in a validation protocol (see note 2). The project plan is revised, as appropriate, to include the planned activities, and the configuration of the application is designed.

For custom systems, the developer designs the system and prepares a high-level test plan. During phase 5, the custom system is coded and tested by the developer and then released to the organization. Once the custom system is delivered by the developer, the project team will perform the other activities of this phase that are described for COTS systems, such as integration, risk analysis, mitigation planning, and preparing the validation plan.

BRING THE PURCHASED SYSTEM INTO YOUR ORGANIZATION

Take possession of the purchased system. Tag the hardware with equipment or asset numbers following your organization's asset management procedures. Keep the hardware in an appropriately secure facility. The European Community (EC) Commission Directive on medicinal products advises that attention be paid to the "siting" of equipment in suitable conditions where extraneous factors can't interfere with the system.[1] What must be done depends on the environment and risks associated with such interference.

Secure the software received on media in an appropriate location, and control it as the master. Make and secure a master of software that was received electronically. Install the hardware and software and set up a test environment so that the project team can work with it during this phase and phases 5 and 6.

This is an appropriate place to clarify the types of environments that will be discussed during the next four phases: development environment, test environment, validation environment, and production environment. This discussion is summarized in table 6.1. When applications are developed, the developer ordinarily will use a type of workstation or server and a type of operating system that's conducive to development activities. This combination of hardware and software is called the "development environment."

After the application is purchased—or, if it's a custom system, after final testing is complete in the development environment—the application is brought into the organization and installed. Because the purpose of this installation is to informally test the system while learning how to use it and to create needed integrations, this installation is referred to as a "test environment." The copy of the application used in the test environment is a "test instance." The test environment (i.e., the hardware and system software used in this instance) should be representative of the hardware and system software that will be used when the system is installed for production or operational use. Production use means the use of the system in manufacturing or producing a product. Operational use means using the system to conduct business or operating a process that's not part of production. Because processing performed in the test environment won't be used for official production, any measurement instruments that are part of the system needn't be calibrated at this point. However, all required calibrations will have to be performed prior to formal validation testing during phase 7.

When you're ready to begin the formal validation testing, your information technology (IT) function will create a hardware and system software environment (the "validation environment") that's identical or as close as possible to the system configuration that will be in place when the system is used to perform work (i.e., production or operational use). This copy of the application software, called a "validation instance," is used for conducting part of the validation testing.

When you're ready to use the system in production or operations, another environment, the "production environment," will be set up. The copy of the application used in production is called the "production instance."

After validation is completed, three environments are normally kept: the production environment, a test environment (post-validation), and a training environment. After validation, the test environment is used to test changes as part of the change control process. The training environment is used to train new users. At times, the environments are set up so that they use the same server and system software but different copies of the application software and different data storage areas. In other cases, the different environments essentially are clones of the production environment using separate but identical hardware and copies of the software.

Before the system is released for production or operational use (i.e., during phases 4 through 6), problems that are discovered while using the system are reported to the IT department, which tracks and resolves them. That department must keep records describing the problem, noting the solution, and documenting any changes that were made to the system to solve the problem. When the problem is fixed, all necessary changes are made to documents that have been developed to that time, such as user or technical requirements, risk assessment documentation, mitigation plan, system specification, user and administrative procedures, and training materials.

INTEGRATE THE SYSTEM
WITH OTHER SYSTEMS AS NEEDED

If integration with other systems is required, the integration will be designed during this phase, and created and informally tested during phase 5.

Medatech 6.1 | Receive the Application Software

The manufacturer of the electronic document management system (EDMS) system that Medatech purchased sent the company a copy of the application on CDs. Tec installed the application on a server that's currently used to run Medatech's enterprise resource planning system. Once Medatech is ready to perform the validation testing, Tec will purchase a new server for the EDMS application that will be kept in the computer room.

The technical and user documentation were copied from a CD to a secured folder on the network. Read-only privileges were assigned to those who might need to refer to the documentation.

The CDs for the EDMS are kept in a locked cabinet in the computer room.

Table 6.1	Definition of Environments and Instances		
Environment name	**Definition or uses**	**Name of the copy of the application in the environment**	**Restrictions**
Development environment	The hardware and system software used to develop the application	N/A	Used at the developer's location for creating one or more applications
Test environment (prior to validation)	An installation of hardware, system software, and the application used to informally test the system and integrations (phase 4 and 5) and for preparing to use the system (phase 6)	Test instance	Use of the environment is uncontrolled
Validation environment	An installation of hardware, system software, and the application used in validation testing	Validation instance	Use of this environment is limited to conducting validation testing. Changes to the environment must be made using a formal change control process or a variance.
Production environment	An installation of hardware, system software, and the application used to conduct the tests of the system while in actual operations, used in the production of product or the performance of other controlled work	Production instance	Use of this environment is limited to conducting formal validation testing and production and/or operational use. Changes to the environment must be made using a formal change control process.
Training environment	An installation of hardware, system software, and the application used after the validation is complete to train employees.	Training instance	The training instance must work in a manner identical to the production instance. Changes are made in parallel with those made in the production instance.
Test environment (post-validation)	An environment used to test system changes as part of the change control process	Test instance (post-validation)	The post-validation test environment must be as close to the production environment as possible to ensure that test results reflect how the system will operate in the product environment.

Individuals with technical knowledge of the systems to be integrated design the integrations, including data and/or commands that are transferred between the systems. The nature of the integration will depend on the systems; how data can be exported and imported; if immediate, real-time updates are required; or if updates will be performed periodically.

Several key questions should be answered to facilitate integration:

- How must the programs and/or applications work together?
- What are the transactional relationships between systems? What data or commands must be shared?
- When do data need to be transferred? Will certain events or conditions trigger the need for exporting data? For example, a plant operator will be paged only when the plant alarm is triggered.
- Will a database need to be scanned at certain intervals for additions, changes, and deletions? For example, if a human resources database needs to be periodically checked for changes such as the inactivation of personnel who have left the company, or changes in reporting relationships, a nightly update on changes to personnel status may be sufficient.
- Are the systems to be integrated compatible (e.g., can the commands or data exported from one system be used by the second system, or is reformatting or translation needed)?

Another type of integration is using one system and/or application in conjunction with another. For example, many document control systems provide the option of using different browsers for opening document files. Engineering drawings might be stored in their native .dwg format or converted to an image file and viewed using a browser. The browser software is integrated with the document control system so that when you click on a file, the document control system automatically uses the preferred browser for that type of file. This type of integration is generally accomplished through configuration tools but might require some custom programming.

The integration will be re-created when the validation and production environments are created. Document the information needed to re-create the integration and verify that it has been done properly. The documentation should include the steps to be performed and any technical information that will be needed.

IDENTIFY AND DESIGN SOLUTIONS TO REQUIREMENTS DISCREPANCIES

After the system is brought into your company and integrations are worked out, two questions must be answered:

- What must be done to close the gaps between your requirements (including requirements to meet regulations) and how the system works?
- How do you manage the risks associated with system failures?

These questions are answered through two steps: a detailed analysis to identify the issues (i.e., a requirements discrepancy analysis and a risk analysis) and planning mitigations, to the extent practical, to address the issues. The discrepancies between requirements and system capabilities are resolved before the risk analysis. Resolving discrepancy issues can take several forms, including deleting or modifying some requirements, and modifications to the system. Changes like these should be known at the time of the risk assessment.

Correct Discrepancies Between User Requirements and System Capabilities

Care must be taken to select a system that meets your requirements. However, the match between your requirements and the system could be less than ideal for at least four reasons. First, your business situation might call for a preferred but uncommon way of performing tasks. Second, other considerations (e.g., the ability to meet technical requirements, vendor organizational requirements, and system cost) are taken into account during the selection process. Third, systems are designed based on the software developers' concepts of how the process should to be automated. Fourth, the system can be ideally suited for certain industries but not yours.

Three options are available for aligning requirements with system capabilities:

- Modify the system.
- Change the requirements.
- Adjust the process of using the system with a change to the requirements.

A drug manufacturing example can be used to illustrate these three approaches. The drug manufacturer wants to build a new plant to manufacture one of its drugs. The drug is manufactured in a reactor. When the raw materials are mixed in a reactor, a chemical reaction takes place and creates the drug. The reaction gives off heat, and a cooling jacket that surrounds the reactor keeps the reactor and its contents from getting too hot. Software will control the temperature of the coolant and its circulation through the jacket. One potential failure of this system is that the software fails to keep the temperature from getting too high. An excessively high temperature will cause the pharmaceutical compound to decompose and create byproducts that are dangerous. If the adulterated batch is discovered, it will be discarded at a loss of $100,000. If a high level of byproducts isn't detected and the product is sold, the byproducts could lead to serious injury for those taking the drug.

The system is designed with an alarm that sets off horns and flashing lights when the temperature in the reaction exceeds a predetermined set point. If an operator is present when the alarm is activated, he or she knows to manually control the temperature. However, for this manufacturer one of the user requirements is that the plant can be safely operated unattended at night and during the weekend. Because the alarm for elevated temperature can only be noticed if an operator is on site, this requirement isn't met.

The first option is to modify the system. In this case, software that will automatically page an operator when the alarm is triggered can be integrated with the system. The software will place a call to an operator when a predetermined temperature is reached. If the temperature is low enough, the operator can get to the plant in time to take control of the reactor. Once paged, the operator is required to place a call to the system to confirm that the page has been received. If a reply isn't received by the system within a few minutes, the next operator on the list is paged. This process is repeated until an operator or supervisor responds to the page. With the pager software, a batch of product will then be contaminated with decomposed material only if the software fails to control the temperature and the system fails to notify an operator; thus, the requirement is met.

The second option is to change the user requirement to match the system capability (i.e., drop the requirement that the plant can be operated unattended). The plant will be operated only during working hours.

The third option is to make a change in how the system is used in conjunction with a requirements change. A procedural change can be made to require that an operator be present at all times when the reactor is in use. In addition, the requirement of operating the plant unattended would be dropped.

When modifying or deleting a requirement, change the requirements document and all other documentation that cites the requirement. Changes to the business process must be incorporated into the company's procedures for the business process and the system user procedures. User procedures are developed during phase 6—prepare for use.

Options for Meeting 21 CFR Part 11 Requirements

Many applications don't meet the Food and Drug Administration's (FDA) regulations for electronic records and electronic signatures as specified in 21 CFR Part 11, also known as Part 11.[2] The objective of Part 11 is twofold: to ensure the integrity of electronic records and to ensure that electronic signatures are trustworthy, reliable, and can't be readily repudiated by the signer. (The question of when Part 11 applies is discussed in chapter 3.)

Systems that aren't designed to meet Part 11 requirements ordinarily fail to meet the following requirements:

- Audit trails on creating, changing, or deleting records, and the preservation of the previously recorded information[3]
- Authority checks to ensure that only authorized individuals can create, alter, or delete a record[4]
- Operational checks to enforce sequencing[5]
- Linking required signatures to an electronic record[6]
- Securing records from unauthorized changes[7]

There are five strategies for achieving Part 11 compliance that range from reverting to a paper system to adding functions to the computerized system. None of these strategies is attractive because each one involves either reverting to some use of a paper record or making changes to the system. Of course, it's better to avoid the situation by selecting a system that's Part 11-compliant. However, in case you have to purchase a noncompliant system or must bring existing systems into compliance, here are the five strategies:

- Use a paper system (i.e., no automation).
- Only use a computer to create the paper record.
- Use a hybrid system (i.e., creating and/or managing a record both electronically and manually). For example, an electronic record could be created, printed, and then reviewed and approved manually. After approval, both the electronic record and the signed paper copy are used as an official record. If you plan to use a hybrid system, clearly specify in an approved procedure when the electronic and paper portions can and can't be used.
- Modify the software to achieve compliance.
- Implement noncomputerized solutions to the unmet Part 11 requirements.

The strategies for complying with Part 11 requirements will be illustrated with a database created by an employee for receiving material and performing incoming material inspection. The company is a manufacturer of medical devices. The following data are stored in the incoming material inspection database:

- Part identification and lot number
- Person receiving; date received
- Expiration date of the material
- Incoming inspections performed
- Incoming inspection observations and data

- Person inspecting
- Date inspected
- Record of the release of the raw material, including name of the person releasing the material and the date released
- Quality status of the material at any point in time after release (e.g., quarantined, rejected, or approved)

The company plans to use the system to:
- Determine if a raw material had been released.
- Verify that the expiration date hasn't been reached when the material is given to production for use in manufacturing.
- Verify an "approved" quality status of a raw material when it's disbursed to production for use in manufacturing (i.e., the material isn't in quarantine or hasn't been rejected).
- Trace a defective part back to a supplier.
- Meet the FDA requirements to document the acceptance of incoming materials for medical devices.[8]

The incoming materials database system doesn't meet any of the Part 11 requirements included in the previous list.

The first option for achieving compliance with Part 11 is simple: Don't use the electronic system. Use paper-based records and handwritten signatures for all aspects of creating, approving, storing, and retrieving the record. Obviously, with this approach all the benefits gained from automation are gone. With the incoming inspection database, you'd switch to a paper-based receiving system. The process would include a receiving form, incoming inspection form signed by the inspector, a material release form signed by quality assurance (QA), and a place to store these paper records.

The second option is to make the computer system incidental to the quality record, (i.e., use the electronic system to create a paper record, and then use the paper record). Electronic forms can be filled out using the software, and then printed. Once printed, the completed form can be reviewed and signed. The paper record is used exclusively thereafter. With the example of receiving incoming materials, the three forms could be filled out on a computer: receiving form, incoming inspection form, and the material release form. The completed forms would be printed and signed. The signed forms become the quality records. The forms completed on the computer aren't used for any regulated activities.

The third option is a hybrid system, part electronic and part paper. If an electronic system can't meet a requirement, then the activities needed to meet it are performed using paper records. In almost all hybrid systems, the record is created on a computer, printed, and approved by a handwritten signature on the printout. The difference between this and the second option is that with a hybrid system, the electronic form is treated and used as an electronic record. A procedure should be written to control both the electronic and paper components of the hybrid record, including:

- Control of the process of creating the paper record from the electronic file
- When and how the hybrid record is reviewed and approved
- Control of the electronic record from the time the paper record is printed
- Control of the paper record from the time the record is signed
- How changes get made to both portions of the record if a correction is necessary

With the hybrid approach to the receiving database, the receiving forms would be filled out online, printed, reviewed, and then signed to release the product. Once they're signed, the electronic database would be updated to change the status of the material to "released." Both the electronic and paper records could be used thereafter. For this scenario to meet the Part 11 requirements, a way must be found to verify that the person who has created, changed, or deleted an electronic record was authorized. In addition, if an audit trail is required by a predicate rule, the name of the person performing the activity, and the time and date of the transaction, must be recorded. The hybrid system, however, would remove the electronic signature requirement.

The fourth option is to modify the software to build in audit trails, operational checks to enforce event sequencing, authority checks to ensure that the person performing the action is authorized, and electronic signatures. Many consulting companies will help you build these capabilities or provide software programs to include in your system that will enable it to meet Part 11 requirements. Companies that provide tools and consulting services for Part 11 compliance can be found on the Web.

A fifth option is to apply nonsoftware solutions to solve the nonconformances. The FDA guidance document on Part 11 allows nonsoftware means of achieving the objectives of some of the Part 11 regulations.[9]

For audit trails, the guidance states that persons must comply with all applicable predicated rule requirements related to documentation of time, or sequencing of events, as well as any requirements for ensuring that changes to records don't obscure previous entries.[10] The guidance document also suggests that other methods can achieve the intent of audit trails: "Even if there are no predicate rule requirements to document, for example, date, time, or sequence of events in a particular instance, it may nonetheless be important [based on system risk] to have audit trails or other physical, logical, or procedural security measure in place to ensure the trustworthiness and reliability of records."[11]

Table 6.2 provides examples of noncomputerized alternatives for complying with Part 11 requirements. Note that the FDA hasn't expressed a view on these suggestions, but they comply with the intent of the Part 11 guidance. Any company following these suggestions must be able to justify the use of the nonsoftware solution based on the four considerations mentioned in the guidance document.[12]

■ The solution must be in compliance with the relevant predicate rules—for example, with the current good manufacturing practices for medical devices requirements for receiving incoming materials:

"Receiving acceptance activities. Each manufacturer shall establish and maintain procedures for acceptance of incoming product. Incoming product shall be inspected, tested, or otherwise verified as conforming to specified requirements. Acceptance or rejection shall be documented."[13]

Table 6.2	Noncomputerized Solutions to 21 CFR Part 11 Compliance
Part 11 requirement	**Noncomputerized solutions**
Audit trails of actions that create, modify, or delete electronic records or electronic signature information (Part 11, Sections 11.10 e and 11.50 b)	■ Manually record changes to electronic records in a log. ■ Print the original record and make handwritten changes. Sign and date. Change the electronic record. Print, sign, and date. Retain records. ■ Use either of the first two options and add the signature of a witness. ■ Create and link a separate electronic record of the change. Have an electronic signature on the separate record. Apply appropriate control over both parts of the record and the link.
Use of operational system checks to enforce permitted sequencing of steps and events, as appropriate (Part 11, Section 11.10 f)	■ Define and control the sequence procedurally (GAMP SIG, 6.5.7) ■ Manual check of the sequence based on date and time data for the transactions. For example, such a review might be part of a batch review.
Use of authority checks to ensure that only authorized individuals can use the system, electronically sign a record, access the operation or computer system input or output device, alter a record, or perform the operation at hand (Part 11, Section 11.10 g)	■ Create a noncomputerized audit trail using any of the methods described above for requirements listed in Part 11, Sections 11.10 e and 11.50 b. An authority check can be performed by a witness to the action, by quality assurance (QA) during an internal audit, or by QA during the normal review of the records—for instance, during the batch review. ■ Place the database in a network folder with controlled access; assign write access to users with appropriate authority. ■ Place the database on a stand-alone workstation with both a computer and screen log on. Physically secure access to the computer.

Medatech 6.2	Requirements Discrepancies and Risk Assessment

The project team compared the electronic document management system (EDMS) functionality to the user requirements. There are three important requirements that the system can't meet:

- A full-text search of documents by key words
- Automatic selection of reviewers based on the types of documents that are included in the change request
- Placement of a watermark that states "uncontrolled copy" on documents that are printed from the system

The following is a synopsis of the Medatech's risk analysis on the two most critical potential EDMS failures. This discussion is summarized in the table beginning on page 158. Note that this summary includes the results of the nine-step risk process for risk analysis and evaluation, the effect that the planned mitigations are expected to have, an adjustment made to the likelihood of system failure assuming the validation testing is successful, and an evaluation of the residual risk. These topics are addressed in the first half of this chapter. This example is best used if it's referred to while different aspects of the risk evaluation, mitigation, and residual risk evaluation are covered in the text.

For its detailed risk assessment the team used the FMEA method and scales described in this chapter.

As reported in Chapter 5 (see Medatech 5.5), Vendor B received a conditional pass on the vendor audit. Quincy conducted a follow-up audit and verified that all issues had been addressed. The project team assigned the level of "probable" for the likelihood of failure of the EDMS system.

Two of the EDMS functions that have the highest risk associated with failure are:

- Failure of controls that prohibit a change to documents without going through an approval process. If this aspect of the system fails, changes could be made to any document, including specifications, product drawings, bills of material, manufacturing methods, and test methods.
- Failure to automatically open the current revision of a document when a search is performed

Extensive noncompliances could result from a failure to control the ability to change documents. If documents can be changed without approval, then all aspects of the quality system that rely on approved procedures, work instructions, and product information are undermined. As a consequence, multiple major nonconformances would result. Those aspects of the quality system that would fail to meet regulatory requirements include design control, production and process controls, quality testing and acceptance activities, labeling and packaging control, servicing, and document control. The severity level for multiple major nonconformances is "catastrophic."

Because Medatech's product could result in death if the product malfunctioned or failed in certain ways, a severity level of "catastrophic" was assigned to EDMS failures that could directly affect the product.

The team made its best judgment of the effect the mitigations would have on the likelihood of the harm occurring and therefore on the residual risk. (The residual risk is the risk that remains after the effect of mitigation.) The team

(continues)

Medatech 6.2	Requirements Discrepancies and Risk Assessment
	(continued)

assumed, for the time being, that the validation results would be supportive. Further, the team members judged that positive validation results would enable them to change their assumption about the likelihood of a system failure from "probable" to "occasional."

The first harm that could occur if controlled documents were changed without approval was the creation of multiple nonconformances with regulations. For example, as soon as a controlled drawing for a part was changed without approval, two nonconformances would occur, one with the design control regulations and another with the document control regulations. Additional aspects of the quality system would collapse, such as production and process controls, and quality testing. Controls weren't present at Medatech that would catch limited unauthorized changes, although eventually the company would discover that employees had been using unauthorized revisions of documents. From a compliance perspective, team members decided that there weren't sufficient safeguards to lower the likelihood of a system failure causing multiple nonconformances; thus, they were unwilling to reduce the likelihood of the harm occurring from the "probable" level. The risk level with a likelihood of harm value of probable and a severity classification of catastrophic is "high" (table 6.7). The risk had to be mitigated, or the risk would have to be justified in a risk to benefit analysis.

Tec recommended that employees use electronic image files (such as PDF renditions) rather than native mode files. He pointed out that employees wouldn't be able to change a PDF electronic master even if the system failed and allowed them to save back the document.

If the system was configured so that users could only view image files, two failures would have to occur for documents to be changed without being approved: an EDMS system configuration that allowed non-image files to be viewed, and an EDMS failure that allowed a change to a non-image file to be saved without approval. The probability of these two "probable" failures happening at the same time is considered to be "occasional," without taking into account an assumption about validation results. If a successful validation is assumed, the estimate of the likelihood of a system failure can be reduced from "probable" to "occasional." The simultaneous occurrence of the failures at the occasional level is judged to be "remote." The risk level with a catastrophic harm and a remote likelihood is "moderate," with the recommendation of "mitigation is strongly advised." (See table 6.9.) Thus, the team decided to require that PDF or other image files be viewed by users instead of documents in their native mode. Further reduction of the risk was seen as impracticable.

The team realized that files can't be accessed from the EDMS file structure. The EDMS system kept the document files in a secure vault that couldn't be viewed or accessed from the server directory structure. In addition, the file structure in the vault wasn't displayed to the user.

Concerning the second harm, creating bad product as a result of unauthorized changes, Quincy pointed out that for a product to be made with unauthorized changes to parts, the following would have to happen: the system would have to fail and permit unauthorized changes, the drawings and bills of material

(BOMs) would have to be changed, the modified parts would have to have been purchased, the parts inspected at incoming inspection against a changed specification, used in manufacturing, and then function according to a revised product specification to pass final inspection. This scenario would require the modification of several documents without approval and without anyone who was working with the part noticing a difference. With these possible ways in which an unauthorized change could be detected, the team felt that the likelihood of the system failing, and someone changing the documentation without notice, would be remote.

Using table 6.9, the team determined that the risk level associated with the remote likelihood of a catastrophic harm occurring was "moderate." The recommendation is "mitigation is strongly advised." The team assumed that the validation testing would confirm that the changes can't be saved back to the system. Assuming that a sufficient validation is conducted and the results are supportive, the likelihood of a software failure can be lowered to "occasional," which would place the likelihood of the harm occurring at the "improbable" level. Using table 6.10, the risk level associated with the improbable likelihood of a catastrophic harm is "moderate," and the recommendation is to mitigate if practicable. The team then needed to determine if further mitigation was practicable. The team had already decided to only permit users to view image files. When image files are used, the user will not have the capability to change the file. If the EDMS system is configured to only display image files, the same two errors must occur that were discussed in the previous example, namely a failure of the system so that non-image files were presented to the user, and a failure that allowed a changed document to be saved back. With a successful validation, the likelihood of

each failure is "occasional" and the combination is "remote." In addition, as pointed out, multiple documents have to be changed and go undetected for product to be built and pass inspection with the wrong part. So the likelihood of product being shipped as a result of unauthorized changes is judged to be very improbable. The risk level is "low" and no further mitigation is needed.

The second most serious potential system failure is presentation of a down revision of a document or drawing to a user as the current revision. Two potential harms were identified. First, the product could be tested against an old test method, fail, and then be rejected. The potential harm is scrapping $300,000 worth of material that actually was within the current specification. Following exhibit 6.2, this loss is at the "critical" severity level. The existing mitigation in this instance is the procedure for dispositioning nonconforming material by the material review board (MRB). The procedure requires the MRB to investigate the cause of the discrepant material. For the material to be scrapped, the system would have to fail to present the current revision of the procedure, and the MRB would have to be negligent and not have checked if the proper revision of the test had been used. This combination was rated to be at the "remote" likelihood level, assuming a successful validation. With a severity level of critical and a remote likelihood, the risk is "moderate," and the recommendation is "mitigate if practicable," following table 6.9. A further mitigation is possible, but it will be discussed in chapter 7's Medatech 7.2 to illustrate the review of residual risks.

Second, the product could pass when tested with a down revision of the test procedure when in fact it should have been rejected. The potential harm is the death of a patient. For this to happen, the product would have to be made

Medatech 6.2	Requirements Discrepancies and Risk Assessment
	(continued)

with an obsolete part, the software would have to fail and present a down revision as the current revision, quality control (QC) would have to fail to verify that it was using the latest revision of the test method, and when quality assurance performed a lot release, it would have to fail to verify that QC had used the correct revision of the test procedure. The simultaneous occurrence of four events (with likelihoods of failure of probable, occasional, occasional, and occasional, respectively) is seen as very "improbable." The risk level of a catastrophic event happening at a likelihood level of very improbable is "low," and further mitigation isn't needed (see table 6.10). Note that a further mitigation is possible, but it will be discussed in the next chapter (see Medatech 7.2).

Items Selected from Medatech's Detailed Risk Assessment

Hazard or failure: Documents are changed without approval.
- **Harm:** Product specifications, bills of material (BOMs), test methods, etc. can be changed without approval, resulting in the noncompliance of multiple aspects of the quality system, e.g., design control, production and process controls, quality testing, and document control

    Severity: Catastrophic

    Controls against system failure and ways to prevent harm after failure: No other aspects of the quality system would detect changed documents; a document user would have to detect that there was an unapproved change. Documents are stored by the EDMS system in an internal database (called a vault).

    Likelihood that harm will occur: Probable. This rating is based only on the assumption about the likelihood of a software failure.

    Risk level: High

    Additional mitigations planned: Configure the system so that users can only view image files (e.g., PDF) of the items. Two failures are then required: a failure of the EDMS system to only allow image files to be viewed, and an EDMS failure that allows a change to a non-image file to be saved (probable X probable = occasional). Further, a successful validation will justify lowering the likelihood of an EDMS failure to "occasional," in which case the probability of failure is "remote."

    Likelihood that system will fail with additional mitigation(s): Remote

    Risk level after mitigation(s) (residual risk): Moderate

    Notes on what to test or validate assuming the presence of mitigations: Test to verify that users are only able to view image files of items. Test the ability to save back changes to opened documents. Verify that the documents can't be located from the server file structure.

Harm: Product specifications, bills of material, and test methods can be changed without approval, possibly resulting in a product failure that could result in death.

Severity: Catastrophic

Controls against system failure and ways to prevent harm after failure: For changes to result in a modified product, the following is required: the software would have to fail (probable), drawings and BOMs would have to be changed, modified parts would have to be purchased, and final product would have to pass QC tests.

Likelihood that harm will occur: Remote. The likelihood of the software error and that such changes would go unnoticed is "remote."

Risk level: Moderate

Additional mitigations planned: Configure the system so that users can only view image files (e.g., PDF) of the items. Two failures are then required: the failure of the EDMS system to only allow image files to be viewed, and an EDMS failure that allows a change to a non-image file to be saved (probable X probable = occasional). Further, a successful validation will justify lowering the likelihood of an EDMS failure to "occasional," in which case the probability of failure is "remote." In addition changes to multiple documents would have to go unnoticed. With everything combined, the team felt it was quite unlikely that such harm would occur.

Likelihood that system will fail with additional mitigation(s): Very improbable

Risk level after mitigation(s) (residual risk): Low

Notes on what to test or validate assuming the presence of mitigations: Test that image files are presented. Test the ability to save back changes to opened documents. Verify that the documents can't be located from the server file structure.

Hazard or failure: A down revision of a document is mistakenly presented to a user as the current revision.

Harm: Product could be tested against an old spec or with an old method, resulting in the rejection of a good lot valued at up to $300,000.

Severity: Critical

Controls against system failure and ways to prevent harm after failure: The materials review board (MRB) is required by procedure to investigate discrepant material.

Likelihood that harm will occur: Remote. The system would have to fail; assuming a successful validation, the likelihood is "occasional." The MRB would have to be negligent (occasional). The combination of both is "remote."

Risk level: Moderate

Additional mitigations planned: None

Likelihood that system will fail with additional mitigation(s): N/A

Risk level after mitigation(s) (residual risk): N/A

Notes on what to test or validate assuming the presence of mitigations: Test that the current revisions are presented to users.

(continues)

Medatech 6.2	Requirements Discrepancies and Risk Assessment (continued)

Harm: Product could be tested against an old spec or with an old method, resulting in the acceptance of a bad lot leading to a death.

Severity: Catastrophic

Controls against system failure and ways to prevent harm after failure: QC is required by procedure to verify that the correct revision of the test method was used. QA is required to verify that the proper revision of the test method was used when it releases the lot.

Likelihood that harm will occur: Very improbable. The combination of a "probable" likelihood of a system failure, the product being made with an obsolete part (occasional), the failure of QC to verify that it had the correct revision (occasional), and the failure of QA to verify at final release that QC used the correct revision (occasional) is quite improbable.

Risk level: Low

Additional mitigations planned: None

Likelihood that system will fail with additional mitigation(s): N/A

Risk level after mitigation(s) (residual risk): N/A

Notes on what to test or validate assuming the presence of mitigations: Test that the current revisions are presented to users.

Additional requirements are given in the following clause concerning acceptance records:

"Each manufacturer shall document acceptance activities required by this part. These records shall include: 1) The acceptance activities performed; 2) the dates acceptance activities are performed; 3) the results; 4) the signature of the individual(s) conducting the acceptance activities; and 5) where appropriate, the equipment used."[14]

- The risk of failure must be acceptable. This should be demonstrated through a documented risk assessment.
- The solution won't affect product quality and safety.
- The solution will preserve record integrity throughout the record's life.

Medatech 6.3   Mitigation of Requirements Discrepancies and Risk

The project team has planned the following mitigations to correct the discrepancies between user requirements and system functionality and to reduce the risk associated with the high-risk items. Keep in mind that in the worst-case sce- nario a product failure for Medatech could result in death. If Medatech's product didn't involve such a high safety risk, some of the mitigations that they chose to perform wouldn't be needed.

Mitigations for Requirement Discrepancies and Risk		
Issue to be addressed	Mitigation	Responsible person
Requirements not met by the system		
The system doesn't have a full-text search of documents that are in the electronic document management system (EDMS) by key words. Documents can be searched by words in the title and/or any of the attributes that describe the document, such as part number, originator, owner department, and product.	Replace the user requirement for full-text search capabilities with two requirements: ■ Ability to use words to search document titles ■ Ability to search for documents by attribute information	Doc
The system isn't able to make an automatic selection of reviewers based on the types of documents that are included in the change request.	■ Delete the requirement for the automatic selection of reviewers. ■ Modify the document control process so that a representative from the document control department identifies the reviewers to whom a change request will be routed.	Doc
The system isn't able to place a watermark that states "uncontrolled copy" on documents that are printed.	■ Remove this requirement. ■ Change the document control process so that the document control deptartment stamps controlled copies in red ink with the words "controlled copy."	Doc
Items requiring risk reduction		
Controls that prohibit changing a document without going through an approval process could fail.	Validate that the controls work. Configure the system so that users only view image files.	Val
A down revision of a document is presented to a user as the current revision.	Validate that the current revision is presented.	Doc

Document the Mitigations and Prepare a Mitigation Plan

Document the solutions to the discrepancies between the system and requirements, including regulatory requirements. It is sufficient to write a memo to file that includes what the discrepancies were and how they were resolved. If the mitigations are complex to develop or implement, prepare a mitigation plan for implementing and evaluating the mitigations. A mitigation plan is similar to all other plans for addressing business issues; it includes the actions to be performed, the people responsible, and timeframes. Complete the remedial actions during the next phase.

MITIGATE THE RISK ASSOCIATED WITH SYSTEM FAILURES

The Need to Manage Risk

There are as many reasons for controlling the risks associated with a computer system failure as there are potential failures that can cause moderate to serious harm of any type. Risk management is a safeguard against a loss due to system failure, including but not limited to the cost of poor product quality and the liability for any injury to, or death of, product users. Poor product quality can result in scrapping the product or reworking it. If customers discover defects during use, the company will incur warranty and service expenses, and possibly the loss of customers and market share. The potential liabilities and costs associated with the serious injury or death of a person using the product are well known.

Risk management also is an important business practice to maintain and protect the company's assets. Faulty computer systems could lead to damaged or destroyed equipment, destruction of intellectual property or records, and theft of company secrets. Keep in mind that a system failure not only refers to a down system or functionality that doesn't work properly but also to wrong, contaminated, or lost data.

Finally, computer system risk management is about maintaining business continuity and effectiveness. A system failure can disrupt the business, cause work to be redone, or hamper productivity. Finding and resolving the cause of a computer system problem distracts employees from their jobs and increases IT support costs.

From a regulatory perspective, the management of risk is focused on what regulators care about, the safety and efficacy of the product, and the accuracy and reliability of quality records. If you're going to use your risk assessment as input to your decision on how to handle the validation, you need to include these dimensions of harm in your risk analysis. Of course you can add any additional dimensions you wish.

The effort to manage and control risk should be commensurate with the potential cost of a computer system failure. A detailed risk analysis isn't necessary if the initial risk analysis (done during phase 1) has documented that the system is low-risk. For moderate- and high-risk systems, risk management begins with including safeguards against system failure in the user or technical requirements (phase 2) and selecting a system that has the appropriate safeguards (phase 3). During phase 4, you analyze the system you obtained and identify the risks associated with its failure, and then develop further ways to control the risks as needed. In phase 5, you implement mitigations that are formally tested for effectiveness in phases 6 and 7. See appendix B for a complete view of the risk management steps throughout the RiskVal life cycle.

The GAMP Forum has recognized the importance of managing risks to quality records, and has developed a guide for "a risk-based approach to compliant electronic records and signatures." The guide presents a risk management process and recommendations for how to manage risk with records that have different levels of impact on product safety.[15] The Gamp guide addresses how to manage systems in regard to the impact of its quality records on product quality and safety. However, the Guide recognizes that such an approach is only one concern, and that the management of computer system risk should address "overall undesirable outcomes that may occur independently of whether records are involved."[16] This volume is written from this overall perspective of system risk. Refer to the GAMP guide for a detailed listing of records with different risk levels, hazards, and procedural and technical controls for managing risks.

Nine-Step Risk Assessment Process

Risk assessment involves identifying potential system failures and hazards, estimating the risk associated with the hazard or failure, and determining if something must be done to control or reduce the risk. A nine-step risk assessment process, developed by Business Performance Associates (BPA), is presented here.[17] These steps correspond to steps two, three, and four of ISO 14971:2000.[18] The BPA process for software risk assessment is based on the failure modes and effects analysis (FMEA) and ISO 14971:2000.

Risk assessment requires identifying potential failures and assessing the risk associated with each. (Risk evaluation takes the next step of determining if something should be done to reduce the risk.) There are three common methods of risk analysis.[19] In appendix A, a method brief is provided for all three methods: method 4.1, failure mode and effects analysis (FMEA); method 4.2, fault-tree analysis; and method 4.3, hazard analysis and critical control points (HACCP). In appendix C, the methods are compared and recommendations are made as to when each is best suited. The first method, FMEA, is the most common and can be used to assess risks associated with any computer system. Consequently, the BPA process is an adaptation of it.

The nine steps of the BPA process for software risk assessment and evaluation follow. Record the results of the steps on a risk assessment sheet such as that shown in exhibit 6.1. The exhibit illustrates how to record the results from each step of the assessment. Review the exhibit at this time to become familiar with the type of information that's recorded on a risk evaluation form. As the example is discussed through the nine steps, the entries in the table shown in exhibit 6.1 are explained.

1. Determine a likelihood of failure for the software.
2. Identify the potential hazards or failures associated with the system.
3. Identify the various types of harm that could result from the hazard or failure.
4. Assign a severity level to each potential harm.
5. Record the controls that are in place to prevent the failure, or enable the system or your organization to identify the failure and prevent it from causing harm.
6. Assign a likelihood that the harm will occur.
7. Determine the risk level of the potential failure or hazard as high, moderate, or low, taking into account the controls that are in place.
8. Record on the risk assessment form information regarding what to include in the validation testing of the system, such as control and detection mechanisms that manage risk.
9. Evaluate the risk level and determine if action is required to reduce it.

1. Determine a Presumed Likelihood of Failure for the Software

Software that's developed on an ad hoc basis by a developer writing code and conducting undocumented testing is considered too error prone to be used, with only one exception. If you conduct extensive formal validation testing, you might determine that low-risk systems developed without any defined methodology are suitable for use.

Software that's developed without a formal development method or without using multiple defect prevention and detection methods is assigned the highest likelihood of failure rating, "frequent." During a risk evaluation of software, set the likelihood of software failure at the frequent level if any of the following is true:

- The software was developed without any defined methodology.
- A defined methodology was used, but it included only a few defect prevention or detection methods.

■ You haven't conducted an audit or collected information on the vendor's development process through some other means.

This approach is taken based on guidance provided in ISO 14971, Gamp 4, and an FDA guidance document on medical device software. ISO 14971, Annex E, Section E.4.3 reminds us that both hardware and software can contain systematic errors.[20] That is, the way that the hardware or software is manufactured will result in a failure when certain conditions occur. The standard points out that it's difficult to estimate the likelihood with which a systematic failure will occur. It recommends that, when it's not possible to estimate the likelihood of systematic failures, an initial assumption be made that the systematic failure will occur at an unacceptable rate.[21] The Gamp 4 guide makes a similar recommendation: "The likelihood [of software failure] default value of 'High' should be assigned unless there is strong documentary evidence of a high quality development process for the software under review."[22] And finally, an FDA guidance on software contained in medical devices states: ". . . we recommend that you base your estimation of risk for your Software Device on the severity of the hazard resulting from the failure, assuming that the failure will occur."[23]

The scale used in this book for the likelihood of a software failure is presented in table 6.3. Five levels of likelihood are defined. For other likelihood scales, see the references in note 3. The likelihood of the software failure is set at frequent under the conditions explained previously. If an adequate development methodology was used to develop the software, you can set the likelihood of software failure at the probable level. Using the probable likelihood level still assumes a relatively high probability of failure that requires mitigation in many situations. With a "Probable" likelihood level, risks must be mitigated if the severity of harm is catastrophic or critical (see table 6.7). If the risks can't be mitigated, a documented risk-to-benefit analysis must be conducted

Table 6.3	Scale for the Likelihood of a Software Failure That Will Result in the Occurrence of Harm
Likelihood level	**Definition**
Frequent	High probability of occurrence
Probable	Moderate probability of occurrence
Occasional	Will occur occasionally
Remote	Unlikely to occur
Improbable	Probability of occurrence is so remote that the event isn't expected to occur during the use of the item.

to determine if the benefits justify taking a risk that such serious harm will occur. If the severity of harm is "moderate," mitigation is strongly advised, and if it's "marginal," the risk is acceptable.

As will be described, the likelihood scale presented in table 6.3 is also used to estimate the likelihood that harm will occur because of a software failure. When evaluating the likelihood of harm, you must take into account the effects of controls and mitigations.

If you have some experience in software development and wish to assign a likelihood of a software failure level based on development activities, appendix C will provide guidance. It explains some of the research that relates development methods to the quality of software and presents a likelihood-of-failure scale based on development activities.

Most people don't have the background to do a detailed audit of a software development process. For that reason, it's recommended that the likelihood of software failure be assigned at the frequent level.

However, you can estimate the likelihood of software failure at the probable level if enough defect detection and prevention methods were used when the software of interest was developed. Conduct an audit or determine by some other means what development activities, including defect detection and removal methods, were used to develop the software of interest (see chapter 5). To use the probable level, the vendor's defect

Table 6.4	Typical Defect-Removal Techniques Versus Methods Used by Best-in-Class Companies	
Level of defect removal	**Static analyses performed**	**Testing**
Average	■ Informal design reviews by developers ■ Code-desk checking by developers	■ Subroutine tests by developers ■ Unit tests by developers ■ New function tests by developers ■ Regression tests by developers ■ System tests by developers ■ External beta tests by clients and users
Best in class	■ Requirements inspections—clients, developers, software quality assurance (SQA) ■ Design inspections—designers, developers, SQA ■ Code inspections, designers, developers, SQA ■ Test inspections, testers, SQA ■ Independent audits, SQA, audit specialists	■ Subroutine tests, developers ■ Unit tests, developers ■ New function tests, test specialists, SQA ■ Regression tests, test specialists, SQA ■ Performance tests, test specialists, SQA ■ Integration tests, test specialists, SQA ■ System tests, test specialists, SQA ■ External beta tests, clients, users

detection practices should be equivalent to those listed in table 6.4 for an average organization. If in doubt, assume that the software will fail at the frequent level. Here's the justification. Capers Jones reports that the U.S. average for software development effort involves six test stages (given in table 6.4) and is successful in removing about 85 percent of the defects before the software is shipped to users. He notes that out of 1,500 projects he studied, 62 percent had a defect removal efficiency of 85 percent or higher. Table 6.4 presents the typical defect-removal activities Jones reports for organizations that achieved the average defect removal efficiency of 85 percent. The practices that Jones reports for the best-in-class organizations, which average 98 percent defect-removal efficiency, are also listed.[24]

Note: The study of software quality hasn't progressed to the point where the likelihood of a failure can be accurately predicted based on software development methods. The tables provided here represent my best judgment and advice based on a general understanding of the research on software quality. Readers must make their own judgments on all aspects of risk analysis and evaluation.

Caution must be taken with custom software because ad hoc development is common in the world of custom development. The assumption that custom software was developed without using a documented methodology that was consistently followed is generally accurate. As recommended in chapter 4's discussion of vender qualification during phase 2, you should include requirements for software development in your contract with a custom developer.

Once validation testing is completed, you might be able to adjust the likelihood of failure level for the software. Although it's not possible to conclude, based on testing alone, that the system will never fail, it might be possible, through validation testing, to reduce your estimate of the likelihood that the system will fail in the execution of the functions that you have tested. More guidance is provided later in the chapter on when and how to adjust the likelihood level based on the validation results.

2. Identify the Potential Hazards and Failures Associated With the System

The system owner, with the help of knowledgeable people, draws up a list of all the potential system failures and hazards associated with system use. Potential failures should include errors that could be made either by a defective system or by users. Draw on the user and technical requirements for determining potential failures, or work from a description or understanding of what the system does. Annex D of ISO 14971:2000 lists examples of possible hazards.[25]

3. Identify the Various Types of Harm That Could Result From the Hazard or Failure

Steps three through eight are often performed in a meeting that includes the project team and additional individuals who understand the potential system failures or their impact. An individual who's experienced in conducting risk assessments may facilitate the meeting. During the meeting, the team takes one potential failure or hazard and performs steps three through eight for that item. The team continues until all the potential failures or hazards have been assessed. The results of these steps are recorded in a risk assessment table such as the one given in exhibit 6.1.

The drug manufacturing plant example will be used to illustrate the risk evaluation process. If the temperature rises too high in the pharmaceutical plant reactor, the drug will decompose. As a consequence, more byproducts will be produced, and if a person consumes them, serious injury could occur. Quality control (QC) tests are performed to identify the level of byproducts in the drug. If the level is too high, the batch will have to be destroyed; a loss of a batch is valued at $100,000. The plant example will be

---

Exhibit 6.1	Risk Assessment Form

Note: The values given in this form follow the discussion in chapter 6. The likelihood of a software failure is assumedd to be "probable."

**Pharmaceutical example: risk assessment
before taking into account the effect of validation testing**

Hazard or failure: Temperature is too high during off hours (and alarm not heard)
  Harm: Loss of batch, $100,000
  Severity: Moderate
  Controls against system failure and ways to prevent harm after failure: None
  Likelihood that harm will occur: Probable
  Risk level: Moderate
  Additional mitigations planned: Integrate pager system to have operator paged when the alarm is triggered
  Likelihood that system will fail with additional mitigation(s): Occasional (failure of temperature control times failure of the pager software)
  Risk level after mitigation(s): Moderate
  Notes on what to test and/or validate assuming presence of mitigations: Validate software control of temp. and validate pager notification of operator

Hazard or failure: Temperature is too high during work hours (local alarm)
  Harm: Loss of batch, $100,000

discussed in steps 4 through 8. The discussion is summarized in the risk assessment form given in exhibit 6.1. The exhibit serves two purposes, to summarize the discussion of the example and to illustrate how to create a record of the risk assessment. The record will become a part of the risk assessment report (deliverable 4.1).

In step 3, you identify the consequences of failures of the computer system. For example, there are two potential consequences if the automated pharmaceutical plant fails to control the temperature of the reactor: serious injury to people taking the drug and the loss of the batch. Keep in mind that if you intend to use the risk analysis as a determinant of the rigor and intensity of your validation effort, you need to include in your analysis any consequences of a failure on the safety and efficacy of the product, and the accuracy and reliability of quality records.

4. Assign a Severity of Harm Level to Each Potential Harm
Exhibit 6.2 provides scales on the severity of harm that you can use in your analysis.

Severity: Moderate
Controls against system failure and ways to prevent harm after failure: The alarm
Likelihood that harm will occur: Occasional (failure of temp. control times failure of the alarm)
Risk level: Moderate
Additional mitigations planned: None
Likelihood that system will fail with additional mitigation(s): N/A
Risk level after mitigation(s): N/A
Notes on what to test and/or validate assuming presence of mitigations: Validate software control of temp. and the alarm

---

Hazard or failure: Temp. is too high during work hours
Harm: Serious injury from byproducts of decomposition
Severity: Critical
Controls against system failure and ways to prevent harm after failure: The alarm and the QC test
Likelihood that harm will occur: Improbable (failure of temp. control, alarm, and QC test)
Risk level: Low
Additional mitigations planned: None
Likelihood that system will fail with additional mitigation(s): N/A
Risk level after mitigation(s): N/A
Notes on what to test and/or validate assuming presence of mitigations: Validate software control of temp. and the alarm

Exhibit 6.2	Severity of Impact Scales

Injury to users or operators:
Catastrophic: Potential for one ore more deaths
Critical: Serious injury. Permanent impairment, or surgery needed to avoid permanent impairment.
Moderate: Potential minor injury or nonserious injury
Marginal: Less than minor injury

Product performance:
Catastrophic: Product not operable, which leads to catastrophic harm level
Critical: Product is inoperable or ineffective, which leads to a critical-level harm for the user or operator.
Moderate: Operability and/or effectiveness are degraded.
Marginal: User might notice some change in product performance that might be an inconvenience or annoyance, but there are no functional problems with the product.

Customer dissatisfaction:
Catastrophic: Product in the market must be recalled. Loss of market share greater than $1 million in profit.
Critical: User is very dissatisfied and likely to switch to a competitive product. Loss of market share less than $1 million profit.
Moderate: User is moderately dissatisfied.
Marginal: User is likely to be annoyed.

Economic loss:
Catastrophic: Intolerable downtime, loss of productivity, equipment, or completed work costing greater than $1 million.
Critical: Downtime, loss of productivity, equipment, or completed work costing between $500,000 and $1 million
Moderate: Downtime, loss of productivity, equipment, or completed work costing between $10,000 and $500,000
Marginal: Downtime, loss of productivity, equipment, or completed work costing less than $10,000

Noncompliance:
Catastrophic: Undermining of multiple aspects of the quality system and creating multiple major nonconformances
Critical: A major nonconformance; the breakdown of a quality system element that results

in the probable shipment of nonconforming product that can lead to critical harm
Moderate: A major nonconformance that only indirectly affects the quality of the product
Marginal: A minor nonconformance

Harm to records:
Catastrophic: Catastrophic loss of, or corruption of, records, data, or programs that can't be recovered
Critical: Loss of access to quality records for an intolerable period of time
Moderate: Loss of records, data, or programs that can be recovered by information technology (IT) with difficulty
Marginal: Loss of quality records that can be easily recovered by IT

Loss of company intellectual property:
Catastrophic: Company intellectual property becomes readily available to competitors.
Critical: Limited inappropriate access to confidential information
Moderate: Inappropriate access to confidential information by company employees
Marginal: Inappropriate access to limited confidential information by company employees

Major and minor nonconformances are defined as follows:
- A major nonconformance is the absence or total breakdown of a quality system element in meeting a requirement. Included are nonconformances that would result in the release of a nonconforming product, or would render process or product controls ineffective.
- A minor nonconformance is a breach of the quality system that's not likely to result in the failure of a quality system element. The nonconformance wouldn't result in the release of nonconforming product or loss of control of product or processes. Minor nonconformances might involve a limitation or weakness of a quality element that, despite the limitation, achieves the purpose intended by the regulation or standard. For example, calibrations are appropriately performed, and decals are placed on each piece of equipment that give the last date of calibration and the next calibration date. However, decals don't identify the person responsible for the calibration.

You can modify the scales to fit your situation, or if you want to develop a different scale, the section on developing a severity of harm scale in appendix C will help.

Different organizations will be concerned about different types of consequences from system failure. Companies that manufacture products used by or on humans probably will be concerned about product safety. This is particularly true of the biomedical industries that are regulated by a government agency. Companies are also concerned about maintaining and enhancing the effectiveness of the business. For most organizations, a failure of a computerized system will affect productivity and business continuity, though the type of loss suffered will differ from company to company. Seven types of harm are depicted in table 6.5 along with examples.

Severity of harm scales are listed in exhibit 6.2 for each of the seven types of harm presented in table 6.5. To differentiate two levels of high severity, four severity levels are used in accordance with the Institute for Electrical and Electronics Engineers (IEEE) standard for Software Verification and Validation, Annex B, and military standard 882C.[26, 27] When the business implications of a failure are taken into account in addition to potential harm, it's useful to use a four-level scale. The FDA has defined three levels of concern related to the safety of medical devices. The bottom two levels of the severity scale used in exhibit 6.2 are equivalent to the lower two levels of the FDA scale. In essence, exhibit 6.2 splits the FDA's highest level into two. The death of one or more

Table 6.5	Types of Harm Associated with Computer System Failures

Type of harm	Examples
Injury to users or operators of products as the result of a failure of a manufacturing or quality system	■ If an automated welder doesn't create proper welds, parts of a medical device might separate once implanted in the body. ■ If an automated test instrument miscalculates the strength of an active ingredient in a drug, the person taking the drug might suffer from an overdose.
Product performance deterioration	■ Software on an X-ray machine fails and radiation isn't emitted. ■ Bar code scanners in a warehouse fail to read bar codes, greatly limiting the usefulness of the automated warehouse system.
Customer dissatisfaction and market share loss because of poor product performance, dissatisfied customers, or tarnished reputation	■ DSL is slow and at times not working, so customers switch to another provider. ■ An automatic teller machine network is down for 48 hours due to a software failure.
Economic loss due to equipment damage, loss of productivity, loss of product, or work performed	■ A software crash in a loan application system results in representatives being unable to process loans for several hours. ■ An error in calculating the effectiveness of a drug during clinical trials leads to canceling a project in its fifth year of development.
Noncompliance with regulations, directives, or standards, such as the cGMPs, Quality System Regulations, 21 CFR Part 11, Medical Device Directive, and ISO 13485	■ Inability to trace the distribution of products to customers or distributors, or inability to trace defective parts to finished lots of product ■ Errors in judgments of product quality due to the malfunction of automated test equipment
Harm to company records and (for regulated companies) required quality records and noncompliance with Part 11	■ Records used for the release of a product lot are lost, and as a result, data aren't available to justify the release. ■ Manufacturing records are lost because of a system overwrite, resulting in a nonconformance unless the product is scrapped. ■ No audit trail on changes to quality control test results
Loss of intellectual property	■ Controls on a network firewall fail and allow access by intruders. ■ Controls on hidden company secret plans fail, and access is given to all employees.

individuals is listed at the catastrophic level, and serious injury at the critical level. The FDA scale groups both death and serious injury into one level.[28] The definitions of the FDA levels are:

- "Major—The level of concern is major if a software failure could result in the death or serious injury to the patient and/or operator, or if it indirectly affects the patient and/or operator (e.g., through the action of a care provider) such that incorrect or delayed information could result in death or serious injury of the patient and/or operator."
- "Moderate—The level of concern is moderate if a software failure could result in nonserious injury to the patient and/or operator, or if it indirectly affects the patient and/or operator (e.g., through the action of a care provider) where incorrect or delayed information could result in nonserious injury of the patient and/or operator."
- "Minor—The level of concern is minor if software failures wouldn't be expected to result in any injury to the patient and/or operator."

Rate the severity of the potential harm, and record the value in the risk assessment table. If a potential failure or hazard doesn't have an associated harm that's at least at the marginal level, it shouldn't be included in the risk analysis. Record all types of the potential harm from a failure. The reason for this is that mitigation might control one type of potential harm, but not other types of harm that could result from the same failure. This is illustrated in the pharmaceutical plant example. The QC tests will help prevent adulterated product from being sold to patients, but they won't mitigate the risk of a failure that results in the bad batch. Thus, both the potential harm of injuring patients and the loss of $100,000 (because the product must be discarded), have to be included in the analysis. The harm associated with serious injury to patients is at the critical severity level, while the harm associated with the destruction of the batch is at the moderate level.

5. Record the Controls That Are in Place to Prevent the Failure, or Enable the System or Your Organization to Identify the Failure and Prevent It From Causing Harm
Controls include things such as:
- Error messages
- Warnings to the operator or user that alert them to the failure
- Alarms
- Actions taken by the system to stop the process or system
- Tests for failures

- Safeguards against hazards
- Hardware or software redundancy so that other units continue processing when one unit fails
- Dual processing and a comparison of results
- Dual copies of database such as those produced in ARRAY V systems

Continuing with the pharmaceutical example, the following three scenarios illustrate how to take into account the presence of factors that deter the occurrence of a failure, or the harm that might occur from a failure. In each case, it's assumed that a decision hasn't yet been taken to integrate a pager with the system.

- *Situation 1:* The system fails to control the temperature when the plant is in use during off hours. The presence of the alarm is negated because no operator is present. This situation is treated as if there were no controls beyond the system's control of the temperature. It's further assumed that the adulteration of the batch is detected and the product, valued at $100,000, is destroyed.
- *Situation 2:* The system fails to control the temperature during working hours. In this case the alarm is a control because presumably it will be noticed and acted on. Thus, a loss of a batch is presumed to occur only if the system fails to control the temperature and to activate the alarm.
- *Situation 3:* The effect of the QC test will be taken into account on the likelihood of a system failure affecting the heath of the person taking the drug. This situation also is assumed to occur during working hours. If the system fails during working hours, three failures are required for the patient to be harmed: the system has to fail to control the temperature and to activate the alarm, and the QC test has to fail to identify the batch as adulterated by the byproducts. In this case, the controls that are in place to safeguard against the harm of injuring a patient include the alarm and the QC test.

6. Assign a Likelihood That the Harm Will Occur

The likelihood that harm will occur is based on the likelihood that the system will fail, and the likelihood that any controls in place will fail at the same time. Record the likelihood of harm on the risk assessment form.

In the pharmaceutical example, the developer was audited and, based on the audit report, the likelihood of software failure was given a value of probable.

Use the statistical multiplication rule for estimating the affect of a control or mitigating factor (i.e., the probability of events happening simultaneously is the product of the probability of their independent occurrences). To use this principle, it's assumed that the one event doesn't cause the other. For example, when evaluating the likelihood that the pharmaceutical plant software will fail to control the temperature and sound the alarm, it's assumed that one failure doesn't cause the other. If the same software failure were to cause both a failure to control the temperature and activate the alarm, then the alarm would be useless.

The second pharmaceutical plant situation provides an example. The failures to control the temperature and trigger the alarm both have a likelihood of failure of probable. The likelihood of both of them happening at the same time is the product of the two probable levels. Because the scale is qualitative and not quantitative, you have to judge the likelihood level to which the product corresponds. To take a conservative approach, assume that the product of the two probabilities places the likelihood of the double failure resulting in harm at the occasional level.

7. Determine the Risk Level of the Potential Failure or Hazard to be High, Moderate, or Low, Taking Into Account the Controls That Are in Place

The risk tables given in this section can be used. Record the risk level on the risk assessment form.

Let's look at a situation in which there are no additional controls or mitigations beyond the software function being evaluated, a situation with one additional control or mitigation, and another situation with two additional controls or mitigations.

A good example of the first situation is the original temperature control problem at the pharmaceutical plant. If the system fails to control the temperature when the plant is unattended, the alarm would have no value in preventing the reactor from overheating. When the situation was discovered later on, the batch would have to be destroyed. The loss of a $100,000 batch is at the moderate severity level according to the severity scale.

Table 6.6	Risk Levels and Recommended Actions for Potential Failures and Hazards at the "Frequent" Likelihood Level		
Severity of harm	**Risk level**	**Recommendation**	
Catastrophic	High	Disqualify vendor; don't use software.	
Critical	High	Disqualify vendor; don't use software.	
Moderate	High	Disqualify vendor; don't use software.	
Marginal	Moderate	Mitigate if practicable.	

Table 6.7	Risk Levels and Recommended Actions for Potential Failures and Hazards at the "Probable" Likelihood Level

Severity of harm	Risk level	Recommendation
Catastrophic	High	Mitigate or justify use.
Critical	High	Mitigate or justify use.
Moderate	Moderate	Mitigation strongly advised.
Marginal	Low	None. Risk is acceptable.

Table 6.8	Risk Levels and Recommended Actions for Potential Failures and Hazards at the "Occasional" Likelihood Level

Severity of harm	Risk level	Recommendation
Catastrophic	High	Mitigate or justify use.
Critical	Moderate	Mitigation strongly advised.
Moderate	Moderate	Mitigate if practicable.
Marginal	Low	None. Risk is acceptable.

Table 6.9	Risk Levels and Recommended Actions for Potential Failures and Hazards at the "Remote" Likelihood Level

Severity of harm	Risk level	Recommendation
Catastrophic	Moderate	Mitigation strongly advised.
Critical	Moderate	Mitigate if practicable.
Moderate	Low	None. Risk is acceptable.
Marginal	Low	None. Risk is acceptable.

Table 6.10	Risk Levels and Recommended Actions for Potential Failures and Hazards at the "Improbable" Likelihood Level

Severity of harm	Risk level	Recommendation
Catastrophic	Moderate/low	Mitigate if practicable/None. Risk is acceptable.
Critical	Low	None. Risk is acceptable.
Moderate	Low	None. Risk is acceptable.
Marginal	Low	None. Risk is acceptable.

Use table 6.7 to determine the risk level for failures with a probable likelihood of harm. The likelihood that the system will fail and result in the loss of a batch is at the same level as the likelihood of the software failure (i.e., probable). Using table 6.7, the risk is found to be at the moderate level, bordering on high. (The recommendation columns in tables 6.6 through 6.10 will be discussed in step 9.)

Now consider instances where there's one control or mitigation in place in addition to the software being analyzed. The second pharmaceutical plant situation provides the example. Recall that the failures to control the temperature and trigger the alarm both have a likelihood of failure of probable. The likelihood of both failures happening at the same time is the product of the two probable levels. In the prior step, we estimated the product of the two probabilities to be at the occasional level. To determine the risk level for events at the occasional likelihood level, use table 6.8. The severity level of the lost batch is at the moderate level, and so the risk level is at the moderate level. The risk level is moderate without the alarm, but it borders on high. With the alarm, the risk level still is moderate but borders on the low-risk level.

The risk level is determined in a similar fashion when there are two controls or mitigations in place to reduce the likelihood of a software failure. The third situation with the pharmaceutical plant involves the likelihood that an adulterated batch of pharmaceuticals will pass the QC tests and be shipped. Three failures have to happen: The system has to fail to control the temperature and fail to activate the alarm, and the QC test has to fail to detect the product as adulterated. The probability of all three failures occurring for the same batch is the product of the likelihood ratings of the three events. Both software failures happening at the same time have a likelihood level of occasional, and the likelihood of a QC test failure is judged to be remote. The product of the three is estimated to be at the improbable level. Table 6.10 is used to determine the risk level. Because the severity of the consequence to a patient using an adulterate drug is at the critical level, the risk level is set at low.

8. Note on the Risk Evaluation Form Information Regarding What to Include in the Validation Testing of the System

The validation testing should include the system function that might fail (e.g., the ability of the system to cool the reactor) and any functions built into the system to prevent the failure or alert a user of the failure (e.g., the alarm).

9. Evaluate the Risk Level and Determine if Action Is Required to Reduce the Risk

The risk level should be evaluated to determine if the risk is unacceptably high and must be reduced.[29] Use the following guidelines. They've been incorporated into tables 6.6 through 6.10:

■ If the risk associated with a failure is high, action must be taken to reduce the risk level.

■ Moderate risks must be lowered to the extent that's practicable, from both a technical and economic perspective.[30] Failures that are moderate risk, but where the moderate rating borders on high, are more of a concern than moderate risk failures that are close to the low-risk level. This is because the ratings are judgments and could be in error. A greater effort should be taken to reduce the risk for moderate-risk items that border on high, than for those that border on low risk.

■ If the risk level is low, no action is needed.

Tables 6.6 through 6.10 contain recommendations; these have the following meanings:

■ *Mitigate or justify use.* This recommendation is given for the high-risk level. Risks at this level are unacceptable and must be reduced. If reduction isn't possible, a risk-benefit analysis must be conducted. Risks at this level, at least in regard to human health and well-being, should be reduced even at considerable cost.[31] If the risks aren't justified based on the benefits, the system, or its use as related to the high-risk failure, must be discontinued.

■ *Mitigation strongly advised.* This recommendation is made when the risk level is moderate but borders on high. Because the estimates might be in error, a determined effort should be made to reduce the risk level. However, if further reduction of risk isn't practicable, a risk-benefit analysis is strongly recommended.

■ *Mitigate if practicable.* ISO 14971 indicates that practicability should be examined from both technical feasibility and economically practicable viewpoints. Technical practicability refers to the ability to reduce the risk regardless of cost. Economic practicability means the ability to reduce risk without making the product an unsound economic proposition.[32]

■ *None. Risk is acceptable.* No action is required.

You can determine the need to mitigate the risks associated with the three pharmaceutical plant scenarios by going back again to the tables 6.6 through 6.10 for the five levels of likelihood that the failure will result in the occurrence of harm.

The first scenario described a failure of the pharmaceutical plant to control temperature during off hours. The likelihood of harm is assumed to be probable based on the assumed likelihood of a software failure. The loss of a $100,000 batch is at the moderate severity level. Using table 6.7, the risk was found to be moderate, bordering on high. Again looking at table 6.7, you'll see the recommendation "mitigation is strongly advised." Because the risk borders on being high, it's recommended that determined actions be made to reduce the risk. (Mitigations are discussed in the subsequent section.)

The second scenario involves the pharmaceutical plant during normal working hours. Under those circumstances, the presence of the alarm works as a control to reduce the likelihood that a software failure will result in bad product. Because two failures have to happen simultaneously, the probability of a software failure ruining a batch is reduced to occasional. Using table 6.8, the risk level was determined to be moderate. In this case, the recommendation is to mitigate, if practicable.

With the third scenario, in which a patient takes an adulterated drug, the severity level for serious injury is critical. The likelihood of the three failures was judged to be improbable. The risk level here, based on table 6.10, is also moderate, and the recommendation is to mitigate, if practicable.

Plan Mitigations to Reduce Risk

If a risk must be controlled or reduced, a mechanism (i.e., mitigation) must be created that will do one or more of the following:

- Reduce the likelihood that the system will fail.
- Provide a way to prevent the failure from causing harm once the system failure has occurred.
- Reduce the severity of harm associated with the failure.
- Increase the probability of detection.

Three approaches are available for reducing the risk associated with system failure. In order of effectiveness they are:

- Modify the system so that the failure is prevented, the frequency of the failure is reduced, and/or the ability to detect the failure before it can have an impact is improved.
- Introduce protective measures in the process of using the system.
- Provide instructions and training to the user to prevent an operator error or an injury.[33]

When evaluating options for how to mitigate risks, include an assessment of the risks associated with the potential failure of each option.[34]

The pharmaceutical plant can be used to illustrate the mitigation of a risk through a change to the system. With the plant unattended, the alarm that helps mitigate the risk of system failure during working hours will be of no use during off hours. Introducing a pager that will notify an operator when the overheating alarm is triggered can help manage the risk of a lost batch. The pager will allow an operator to come to the plant and use manual controls to cool the reactor before the batch is lost. With the pager in place, the probability that the batch will be lost is the product of the probability of a failure of the software that controls the temperature (i.e., occasional) and the software that sends the page (also occasional). The resulting probability is remote. The risk level is now low in the moderate range, lower than it is without the mitigating power of the pager.

Both the planned mitigation and the likelihood that the system will fail with the mitigation are recorded on the risk assessment form (see exhibit 6.1).

The database created for receiving and inspecting incoming material will be used to further illustrate the options for risk reduction. There are many potential failures of this system and/or its users. One simple example is an operator error in entering the expiration date. If the date entered is sooner than the expiration date assigned by the material's manufacturer, the material that's still good could be discarded. A more serious error would be that the true expiration date had been reached, but the material is used because the erroneous value indicates that the material may still be used. If the likelihood of the failure is occasional and the harm associated with the failure is catastrophic, the risk would be high.

As mentioned previously, the most effective approach to reducing risk is to modify the system so that an error won't occur.[35] Some general examples of system modifications include:

- Building in checks so the system won't accept an incorrect data format (e.g., not allowing an alpha value in a numeric field)
- Creating warning messages that will be displayed if a calculated value is out of an acceptable range, and not allowing the value to be acted upon
- Rewriting modules that have high failure rates (if the risk level is based on a history of defects in the code)

With the incoming materials database, several modifications could be made to the system to help reduce the frequency at which an incorrect expiration date is entered. First, the system could be modified so that it will only accept the correct date format in the expiration date field. The system could also prohibit entering a date that was earlier than the date on which the value is entered. Alternatively, the system could require that the date be entered twice and that the two values be identical.

If your system can't be modified, or if you're not interested in making such changes, the second most powerful option to reduce risk is to introduce a manual safeguard against a system or operator failure, or against the failure having an affect. In the case of entering expiration dates, a procedural requirement can be set to have a second person review the data entered for accuracy before data entry is completed. The GAMP guide on a risk-based approach to compliant electronic records provides an extensive list of procedural and technical controls for reducing the risk to record integrity.[36]

The third and least effective technique for reducing risk is to instruct and/or train the user to reduce the likelihood of an operator error. In this case, users can be trained on how to enter the date into the field and cautioned to do so carefully because of the potential risks associated with an error.

Record the following information on the risk assessment form given in exhibit 6.1:

- The planned mitigation
- Likelihood that the system will fail with the mitigation
- Mitigations that must be tested during validation testing

Up to this point in the risk management process, potential system failures have been identified and mitigation actions have been planned to reduce either the likelihood or effect of a failure. During phase 5, construct solutions to issues, the mitigations are built and informally tested to determine whether they're effective so that they can be improved if necessary or another action taken. In addition, any residual risk can be reduced, if necessary. As part of the validation testing (during phase 7, qualify the system), the effectiveness of the mitigations is formally tested, if possible.

Adjustments to the Estimates of the Likelihood of Failure Based on Validation Testing

When planning the mitigations, it might be helpful to think ahead to the effect of the validation. A successful validation could allow you to lower the assumption of the failure rate of the system, and thus make further mitigation unnecessary. An estimate of the likelihood of failure was either set at the frequent or probable level based on information, or the lack thereof, of the development methods used for the software. Or, a level was set based on a scale that you developed following the discussion presented in appendix C. After the validation, you need to ask if the findings of the validation testing support your assessment of the probability of software failure. Does your assumption, or estimate, need to be reexamined? Validation results that show numerous system failures could indicate that the assumed likelihood of failure might have to be increased.

On the other hand, the validation results might indicate that the likelihood of failure is lower than initially expected. If the assumption of the likelihood of failure needs to be changed, update the risk assessment accordingly. For example, if you set the likelihood of a software failure at the probable level based on your information, and extensive validation testing revealed no defects, you would be justified in lowering the likelihood of a software failure to the occasional level. If defects were found that are at the major or critical level, as defined later in this chapter, reducing the likelihood level to occasional wouldn't be merited. In fact, the likelihood of software failure might be raised to frequent. If numerous major or critical defects were found, the acceptance criteria, including the judgment of the project team on the system's viability, should be used to determine if the system could even be used.

Before reading the following discussion on how to reduce the estimates of a likelihood of failure, it's important to keep in mind that validation testing has several purposes. The first is to verify that the system works in your technical environment. The system might work perfectly in the development environment, but not work well with your hardware, system software, management tools, and database software. A second purpose is to verify that the configurations you have made are suitable to your use of the system. The third purpose is to determine if there are software defects that affect your ability to use the system to operate your business process. Even if you've determined through your vendor audit that the software was built using an advanced engineering life cycle that set the probability of failure at the remote level, the validation testing is appropriate for the first two reasons. This is especially the case with high-risk systems.

Before you make an adjustment to the likelihood of failure level based on your validation results, you should evaluate the appropriateness of such an action. Was the assumption of the likelihood of failure you made before the validation testing (called the "initial likelihood level" here) based on concerns about the system's development or its ability to work properly in your environment? If the initial likelihood rating was based more on the system's ability to work in your environment, then tests in your production environment (or an equivalent) would provide justification for lowering the likelihood level.

If, however, your rating was based on the vendor's development methods, you must determine how much your testing will add to the effectiveness of the testing that's already been done. For example, normal validation testing isn't extensive enough to lower the likelihood of failure level from the remote to the improbable. The reason is that in setting the level of failure at remote, you've already determined that the software is of a high quality. The developer has created the software using extensive defect prevention and detection methods. Your tests probably won't exceed the testing that's already been done, and, therefore, your results don't add additional information about the quality of the software. Such results wouldn't provide justification for reducing the likelihood of failure to the improbable level. However, the validation testing is still worthwhile because of the assurance you gain that the system will work for your intended used in your environment.

Let's return to the pharmaceutical plant example to illustrate the effect validation testing can have on the system risk level. The validation testing didn't uncover any major or critical defects, and the team believes that it's justified in reducing the probability of failure from probable to occasional. Exhibit 6.3 shows the revised risk assessment.

Recall the first situation, the potential loss of a batch of pharmaceuticals because of a system failure to control temperature during off hours. Before validation, the likelihood of the failure at the software level is assumed to be probable, and with a moderate severity level for the loss of product, the risk level was moderate. The recommendation was "mitigation strongly advised." The likelihood of failure is reduced to occasional based on the validation results. The severity of harm for the loss of the $100,000 batch remains moderate. To determine the risk level, use table 6.8, which is for the occasional likelihood of failure level. The risk level is moderate, and the recommendation is "mitigate if practicable." If the pager was put in place, the likelihood of failure with this mitigation is the product of the likelihood that the system will fail (i.e., occasional, based on the validation results) times the likelihood that the operator will not be paged (also occasional). The product of two occasional likelihood levels is assumed to be remote. The risk level of having to destroy the batch when the pager is used as a mitigation is found, from table 6.9, to be low. No further remediation is needed, the risk is acceptable.

In the second scenario, the failure of the system during working hours was analyzed. The assessment before taking into account validation tests made the assumption that two failures at the probable level would have to occur (i.e., the system would fail to control the temperature, and the alarm would fail to be activated). The risk level was determined to be moderate, with the recommendation to mitigate, if practicable. If the likelihood of the two failures is changed to occasional, their product is estimated at the remote level. The risk level is now low.

In the third situation, the software would have to fail to control the temperature, the alarm would have to fail to be activated, and the QC test would have to fail to detect the contaminated batch. The analysis before validation concluded that the risk level was

Exhibit 6.3	Risk Assessment Adjusted for Validation Results

**Pharmaceutical example: risk evaluation
after taking into account the effect of validation testing**

Hazard and/or failure: Temperature too high during off hours (and alarm not heard)
Harm: Loss of batch, $100,000
Severity: Moderate
Controls against the system failure and ways to prevent harm after the failure: None
Likelihood that harm will occur: Occasional (failure of the temperature control software)
Risk level: Moderate
Mitigation plans: Integrate pager system to have operator paged when the alarm is triggered
Likelihood that the system will fail with the mitigation: Remote (failure of temperature control times failure of the pager software)
Risk level after mitigation: Low
Notes on what was tested and/or validated assuming the presence of the mitigations: Validated software control of temperature. Validated pager notification of operator.

Hazard and/or failure: Temperature too high during work hours (local alarm)
Harm: Loss of batch, $100,000
Severity: Moderate
Controls against the system failure and ways to prevent harm after the failure: The alarm
Likelihood that harm will occur: Remote (failure of temperature control times the failure of the alarm)
Risk level: Low
Mitigation plans: None
Likelihood that the system will fail with the mitigation: N/A
Risk level after mitigation: N/A
Notes on what was tested and/or validated assuming the presence of the mitigations: Validated software control of tempurature. and the alarm

Hazard and/or failure: Temperature too high during work hours
Harm: Serious injury from by-products of decomposition
Severity: Critical
Controls against the system failure and ways to prevent harm after the failure: The alarm and the quality control test
Likelihood that harm will occur: Improbable (failure of tempurature control, alarm, and quality control test)
Risk level: Low

Mitigation plans: None
Likelihood that the system will fail with the mitigation: N/A
Risk level after mitigation: N/A
Notes on what was tested and/or validated assuming the presence of the mitigations: Validated
   software control of tempurature and the alarm

low. No further mitigation was needed. After validation the likelihood of each of the
two system failures is estimated at occasional, and the likelihood of the QC test failure
remains at remote. The product of the three is still at the lowest level, the improbable
level. The severity level is critical, and the risk level remains low.

Summary of the Effect of Mitigations and Validation Testing on Risk Levels

To simplify risk analysis and estimating the effect of mitigations and validation testing on the risk level, table 6.11, a summary table, has been created. It summarizes how
mitigations and validation can reduce the risk level of the system or the function, and
presents recommendations regarding further mitigation based on the level of risk that
remains (i.e., the residual risk). This summary is based on two assumptions. First, that
the software was developed using typical defect prevention and detection methods (see
table 6.4), and that therefore the likelihood of failure before validation is presumed to
be "probable." Second, that the mitigations have a likelihood of failure before validation also at the probable level. If a mitigation is more or less effective than what's assumed, make appropriate adjustments.

The cell for "Catastrophic" harm and "Two mitigations; validated software and mitigations" requires explanation. Two options are given for the risk level "moderate/low
residual risk." Two options are also given for the recommendation "mitigate further if
practicable/no additional mitigation needed." If the combination of the mitigations is
strong enough, or there are more than two mitigations, select the low-risk alternative.

Prepare the Risk Analysis and Evaluation Report

The results of the risk assessment are summarized in the risk analysis and evaluation
report. The report includes a description of the risk analyses and evaluation. Risks that
require further mitigation are identified. The report will be revised and extended as the

additional risk management steps are taken during the remaining phases of the RiskVal life cycle. See deliverable 4.1 in appendix A for a description of the risk analysis and evaluation report. Summarize the risk assessment findings in the results section. Attach the risk assessment form (illustrated in exhibit 6.1) to the report as an appendix.[37]

PLAN THE VALIDATION

Prospective, Concurrent, and Retrospective Approaches

There are three fundamental approaches to validation based on the timing of the validation vis-à-vis when the system is implemented: prospective, concurrent, and retrospective validations.[38]

With prospective validation, acceptable system performance is demonstrated before a failure can harm product, people, or business assets (i.e., before it's used in a production environment). ISO 13485:2003 requires prospective validation of computer software, changes to the software, and changes to how the software is used.[39] It's also the approach taken in this book. Prospective validation is superior to concurrent and retrospective validation from both a risk management and safety perspective. In addition to failing to manage risk from the first moment a system is used, the concurrent and retrospective approaches have another major weakness if such validations are attempted as an afterthought: The records and documentation needed to evaluate system performance are frequently missing or inadequate.

The second approach is concurrent validation. Although prospective validation is preferable, concurrent validation can be used to validate systems that are already in use. The steps to be taken as part of the concurrent validation are specified in the validation plan. Concurrent validation involves the following steps, as appropriate, based on the nature of the system and its risk level:

1. Prepare a validation plan, including acceptance requirements.
2. Document all the hardware and software components of the system, including upgrades, bug repair patches, and any other modifications that have been made so that the current configuration is known (see deliverable 6.1).
3. Qualify vendors.
4. Collect documentation from completed life cycle steps.
5. Create requirements documents if they're not available (see chapter 4).

Table 6.11	Summary of Residual Risk Levels After Taking Into Account Mitigations and Validation			
Impact severity level	**Risk level with no mitigations and not validated (i.e.,"probable" likelihood of failure)**	**Residual risk levels and recommendations for further mitigation**		
		No mitigations; validated software	**One mitigation; validated software and mitigation**	**Two mitigations; validated software and mitigations**
Catastrophic	High risk Mitigate or justify use Validate as high-risk system	High residual risk Mitigate or justify use	Moderate residual risk Further mitigation strongly advised	Moderate/low residual risk Mitigate further if practicable/no additional mitigation needed
Critical	High risk Mitigate or justify use Validate as high-risk system	Moderate residual risk Mitigation strongly advised	Moderate residual risk Mitigate further if practicable	Low residual risk No additional mitigation needed
Moderate	Moderate-risk Validate as moderate-risk system	Moderate residual risk Mitigate if practicable	Low residual risk No additional mitigation needed	Low residual risk No additional mitigation needed
Marginal	Low-risk Validate as low-risk system	Low risk No mitigation needed	Low risk No additional mitigation needed	Low risk No additional mitigation needed

6. Review performance data, such as trouble reports and bug repair history, for known issues, and prepare a report. The analysis of system performance is retrospective validation, as described below. Some records are available at times, but retrospective validation isn't possible because the system hasn't been used long enough, or performance records either haven't been properly kept or are incomplete. As part of a concurrent approach, whatever information is available ought to be reviewed to identify any problems that haven't been resolved.

7. Analyze and prepare a report on the system's maintenance. If maintenance isn't current, perform required maintenance.

8. Conduct a risk assessment taking into account your knowledge of system performance, and take the steps needed to reduce risk. Test any changes made to the system; record the tests and the results.

9. Evaluate the performance of the system in real time long enough to verify that the system performs according to requirements. The evaluation isn't less rigorous than

a prospective validation performed on the same system, and includes performing IQ, OQ, and PQ validation tests. Guidance for performing IQ, OQ, and PQ tests on existing systems is provided in the chapters on phases 7 and 8.

10. Create a traceability matrix that links data and/or test results to requirements.

11. Evaluate the system's fitness for use and prepare a validation final report (see deliverable 8.3 in appendix A). As a result of the evaluation, the system can be released as is, modified to correct problems, or discontinued.

12. Take actions to correct any problems uncovered during the evaluation. If changes to the system are made, the effectiveness of the changes needs to be verified before the changes are implemented in the production environment. If the system fails to meet the acceptance criteria, the critical issues must be resolved before the system can be released as a validated system.

13. Release the system as a validated system and place it under change control (phase 8) or discontinue use.

Retrospective validation is the third approach. This approach is possible when organizations are required to justify the continued use of existing systems that have been inadequately documented and tested for validation purposes.[40] The system is validated entirely based on past performance without any additional testing or monitoring of the system. From the perspective of FDA regulations and ISO 13485, retrospective validation is itself a nonconformance because systems are to be validated prior to their use. Because retrospective analysis is performed after the system has been in use, this approach provides no initial protection against the risks of system failure, and therefore has much less business value than a prospective validation.

Retrospective validation is only possible under two conditions. First, if performance records have been carefully kept of all reported problems for a long enough period of time to demonstrate that the system reliably meets requirements. The records of problems need to include those reported by users, such as through the help desk, and those discovered by the IT or other technical staff. The nature of the problem has to be described as well as the current status. Second, retrospective analysis alone is sufficient only if users can determine whether or not the system is functioning according to *all* requirements. If the failure of the system to meet some requirements can only be detected through testing, then some concurrent testing must be added to the analysis of past performance. The combination of a retrospective analysis and testing is discussed below.

The following steps are taken in retrospective validation:

1. Prepare a validation plan.
2. Document all the hardware and software components of the system, including upgrades, bug repair patches, and any other modifications so that the current configuration is known (see deliverable 6.1).
3. Collect documentation from completed life cycle steps.
4. Create requirements documents if they're not available (see chapter 4).
5. Analyze and prepare a report on the system's performance history, such as issue reports and bug repair history.
6. Analyze and prepare a report on the system's maintenance.
7. Conduct a risk assessment based on the record of performance and take the steps needed to reduce risk.
8. Evaluate the system's fitness for use and prepare a validation report. The system can be released as is, modified to correct problems, or discontinued.
9. Take actions to correct problems, if problems were uncovered during the evaluation. If changes to the system are made, the effectiveness of the changes needs to be verified before the changes are implemented in the production environment. If the system fails to meet the acceptance criteria, the critical issues must be resolved before the system can be released as a validated system.
10. Release the system as a validated system and place it under change control (phase 8) or discontinue use.

A combination of concurrent testing and an analysis of retrospective data may provide a stronger test than either of the two separately. For example, a medical device company needed to validate a COTS quality control system it used for a year-and-a-half to process change orders, authorize rework, record variances, and manage training records. At least a hundred of each of these types of transactions had been performed prior to their validation. Fortunately, the company recorded every help desk request made by employees and how their issues were resolved. The company also logged every bug that was reported to the software vendor, how the bugs were fixed, and every change made to the system. At the time the validation was started they knew that only one issue remained unresolved.

Keep in mind that the purpose of validation is to demonstrate that the system will reliably function to meet user requirements. Hundreds of transactions in which the system performed correctly provides very strong evidence that the system is meeting requirements, much stronger evidence than a few OQ and PQ tests can provide.

However, we must be cautious in using retrospective data for two reasons. First, not all malfunctions are easily detectable by the users. Three examples include: the analysis of data, recording audit trail data, and security controls. If no one checked to see if calculations were made correctly, errors may go unnoticed. If the audit trail data were never checked, no one would know whether the system was consistently recording the correct data. If everyone followed the rules for logging onto the system, no one would know if unauthorized users were able to log on.

Second, a retrospective analysis doesn't include a systematic testing of failure conditions or system misuse (e.g., operator mistakes, error conditions, or attempted inappropriate uses of the system, including uses that would result in a corruption or loss of data or the violation of regulatory requirements). All of these ought to be tested at least for high-risk systems.

Consequently, even if there are excessive amounts of performance data, some testing has to be added to the retrospective validation if performance data aren't available regarding how well the system meets each requirement. The combination of the concurrent and retrospective validation approaches is far more common than retrospective validations.

Performance data ought to be analyzed in a systematic manner. Every system failure, user issue, and change to the system ought to be examined to identify system and user failures. Frequent user failures ought to be addressed by changing the system to make it more user-friendly, or by improving user training. With system errors, first check to see if they've been corrected. If not, they're recorded as a nonconformance and must be fixed or considered when you determine if the system meets your system acceptance criteria (discussed later in this chapter). If the system error has been repaired, there are two ways we can determine if the repair has worked. First, we can test the system to determine if the system is working and if the fix has created any other problems. Second, we can look at the performance of the system after the fix has been made. If the system worked properly for a year after the fix, the performance demonstrates that the fix worked. It the system had only been used for a few transactions after the fix, we may not be able to definitively state that the fix was effective. A rule needs to be created that defines when the system has been used enough after a fix to determine if it was effective. If the system is used frequently, a month may be sufficient.

The results of the performance analysis need to be reported, including:

- A description of the performance data that was reviewed, including the timeframe over which the data were collected
- A summary of the analysis of the performance issues, including how the issues were classified and any rules developed for the analysis, such as the criteria for declaring that a problem has been successfully repaired

■ A discussion of the results, including user errors, problems identified that are unrelated to requirements, problems that were related to requirements, and a discussion of open issues, including of the effect of open issues on the system's ability to meet requirements

The combination of concurrent validation and retrospective validation follows the steps for retrospective validation, with the addition of direct testing of system performance related to its ability to function appropriately in ways that can't be detected by the users.

Common Validation Practices for Types of Systems

In planning the validation, determine what approach to take to validate your system and what to include in the validation. Table 6.12 presents information on how the validation of different types of systems is commonly approached and how to handle equipment, such as networking equipment, printers, and workstations, that's shared by different applications.

Items that are shared across applications, such as servers, printers, and database hardware and software, can be handled in several different ways.

First, the item can be included in the validation of one of the systems that uses it. If the validation testing covers how the item is used by all the applications, it's qualified for use with them all. If the tests are limited to how it's used with that one application, the item will have been qualified only for those uses. Additional uses of the item by other applications will have to be validated when those applications are validated. For example, suppose that a printer is used by several systems that haven't been validated. When the first system is validated, you demonstrate that the printer is able to print normal office documents. The printer is qualified then only for that use. If the printer is used by the next application to be validated to print engineering drawings and photographs, it has to be qualified for those additional uses. Of course, you always have the option to look ahead in the first validation and qualify the printer for normal office output as well as engineering drawings and photographs.

Second, shared items can be considered as part of the infrastructure and qualified with the infrastructure. Requirements need to be defined for the item, including how it must work with all of the applications that will use it. The device's ability to meet those requirements can be tested as part of the infrastructure qualification. In our example, the printer would be qualified to print office documents, drawings, and photographs. This amounts to the same testing as would be done under the first option.

Table 6.12	Validation Strategies for Types of Items

Type of item	Example	Validation strategy
Infrastructure items shared by different systems	Corporate infrastructure, including shared servers and data storage devices, communication lines, communication devices, shared input and output devices (e.g., printers), firewall, and network management tools	Options for an infrastructure: ■ Full qualification as an independent system ☐ Characterize the infrastructure components using infrastructure diagrams. ☐ Verify the correct installation of all devices. ☐ Run tests to verify that all components are operating properly. (For example, pinging all devices over all communication lines to verify connectivity.) ☐ Place the infrastructure under change control. ☐ Hardware and software that perform critical infrastructure functions such as archiving, backup and restoring, and the firewall can be validated as part of the infrastructure validation or as separate items. ■ Qualify each infrastructure component by an installation qualification (see chapter 9) and place it under change control. Infrastructure connectivity, communications, and functioning of devices are tested when validating the applications that use the infrastructure.
Network items dedicated to a system	Subnetwork of communication lines, routers, controllers, and microwave towers used in an automated plant	■ Consider the network items as part of the system. ☐ Verify proper installation and operability of each device. ☐ Place the network under change control. ☐ Test the network items as part of the application validation by using the subnetwork while performing functionality and data-integrity tests.
Dedicated server	Server used solely for an application such as an enterprise resource planning system	■ Document configuration. ■ Verify proper installation and the operability of all items (e.g., communication and memory cards) that are added to the manufacturer's basic configuration.
Dedicated printer	Printer attached to a test instrument	■ Consider the printer as part of the system. ☐ Print samples of reports and other output and verify that printing is accurate (e.g., printer drivers are appropriate for the material being printed).
Shared printer	Printer on a corporate network used in conjunction with a variety of applications	Options: ■ Qualify the printer with a system. ■ Qualify the printer with the infrastructure. ■ Qualify the printer as a stand-alone device. ■ Install and test the printer following a qualified procedure. ■ Add the printer to an application or the infrastructure using the change control procedure. *Note:* See the discussion in the text on shared items
Dedicated workstation	Workstation used in conjunction with a laboratory instrument, such as high-pressure liquid chromatography (HPLC)	■ Consider the workstation as part of the system. ☐ Document the configuration, including important information such as bios version and machine addresses. ☐ Verify proper installation of the workstation and all software, including applications. Verify that specifications are met. ☐ Test indirectly as part of the application or instrument (use the workstation for all system testing).
General-use workstations	Workstation used by a quality assurance	■ Ordinarily, general-use workstations aren't validated or placed under change control. They're initially configured following a

Type of item	Example	Validation strategy
	employee for a number of applications (e.g., an electronic document management system, quality control test results database, incoming inspections, and training databases).	general procedure such as the desktop and laptop setup procedure described in chapter 8. Newly validated applications are installed on a workstation following a procedure or installation protocol (see chapter 9). The company information-technology policy controls employee modifications to the workstation, such as loading additional applications. ■ To verify that the workstation configuration is appropriate for use with a validated system, validation testing for a new application is performed using a workstation that meets the minimal hardware configuration requirements and has the full configuration of software that's normally loaded on a general workstation. ■ If you decide to qualify workstations and place them under change control, the following is required: ☐ Confirm that the configuration meets requirements. ☐ Record important information, such as the bios version. ☐ Verify proper installation of the workstation and all software, including applications that are part of the standard corporate configuration.
Complementary software used in conjunction with an application	A viewer used with a document control system to view engineering drawings or other specialized files	■ Verify proper installation. ■ Verify proper integration of the complementary software with the main application (for example, when opening a file the viewer application opens). ■ Test only aspects of the complementary software that are used in conjunction with the main application. The degree of testing is dependent upon the risk associated with failure.
Programmable logical controllers	Devices that control mechanical operations, such as opening or closing valves when directed by an application or in response to a sensor signal	■ Validation testing must include verifying that the controller performs the appropriate actions in response to the signals sent by the application and/or sensors. ■ Test at least all programmed actions that can affect the quality of the product.
Sensors, detectors, and other measuring instruments	■ Electronic balances that feed readings to an application ■ Thermocouples ■ Status detectors (e.g., open or closed valves)	■ Sensors that are programmed for binary (i.e., on/off) detection must be tested to verify that they appropriately detect the conditions. ■ Instruments that measure only a value on a scale (and don't manipulate the data) need only to be calibrated to ensure that their measurements are accurate.
Integrated systems	When one system communicates a command or data to another system, such as when a human resources database sends personnel actions to a training database	■ The systems can be validated separately or together. Critical aspects to testing the integration include: ☐ Ability of each system to receive and appropriately process data and commands from the other ☐ Ability to send data and commands to the other system at the appropriate times and/or under appropriate conditions
Lab equipment that processes information (i.e., the output includes an analysis and not just raw data)	■ HPLC ■ Differential scanning calorimeters ■ Thermographic analyzers	■ Verify correct installation ☐ Perform an analysis of a known standard and compare the results with the expected results ☐ Include all the data analyses that you'll perform with the software ■ Alternatively, perform the same chemical tests and data analyses in other ways and compare results. ■ Test data security for stored data. If data are exported to a network server or other application, test data communications.

The difference is that the printer is qualified with one or more applications, or with the infrastructure.

Third, shared items can also be qualified as stand-alone items. For example, a printer can be qualified using an IQ to verify proper installation and that the printer meets technical requirements. An OQ can be used to verify that the printer is capable of printing the anticipated types of documents.

Efficiencies can be gained if a procedure for installing and testing a type of item can be qualified. If such items are installed and tested following the procedure, then they don't need to be qualified. A procedure is qualified by including it in a qualification. Once proven to be effective, the procedure can be used to install and configure other items of the same type without formal IQs and OQs. For example, qualification protocols can be written and executed to qualify a printer. If the qualification protocols are written to include the steps outlined in an installation and test procedure for a printer, that procedure is proven to be correct if the qualification tests are passed. Once the method is proven, it can be followed without a formal protocol, and with only minimum testing. For example, the qualified procedure can be followed to install and configure the printer. The procedure ought to include some simple tests that confirm that, as installed and configured, the printer can successfully print a test word processing document, a drawing, and a photograph.

If a new shared item is added, without using a qualified procedure, to a validated system, or qualified infrastructure, there are two options. The item can be qualified under change control or by using protocols (e.g., by using an IQ to verify proper installation and the meeting of technical requirements, and an OQ to verify required functionality).

Determine the Types of Qualifications to Include

Three types of qualifications are introduced here so that they can be discussed within the context of the validation plan. The information regarding these qualifications is summarized in table 6.13. A piece of equipment, a process, or a computer system is "qualified" when objective evidence has been generated demonstrating that the system meets defined requirements or a specification. The installation qualification (IQ) is the process of collecting evidence that the system has been properly installed and that components of the system meet technical requirements.

Operational qualification (OQ) is the process of collecting evidence that the system has the capability and capacity to meet user requirements. The OQ test is performed in the validation environment and is completed prior to the system's use in any way that could affect product quality or quality records. To validate the system, you must demonstrate that it works as expected when it's used in production or operations as part of an automated process. The verification of the system's effectiveness during production is called the performance qualification (PQ). These three types of qualification will be discussed extensively in chapters 9 and 10.

Every validation will include some type of installation qualification regardless of the type of system and its risk level. The IQ is the fundamental basis for all validation testing. The system must be installed properly and meet its technical requirements for you to have confidence that the results of subsequent tests are valid reflections of how the system will operate when used in the production environment.

Some degree of OQ is required for all systems because, at a minimum, you must demonstrate that the system is capable of operating. The type and extent of the OQ testing will depend on the type of system and its risk level. If little OQ testing is required, the IQ and OQ can be combined into an I/OQ. As Technical Report 18 points out, whether the qualification of proper installation (i.e., the IQ) is done concurrently or separately from the qualification of proper operation depends on the specific application.[41]

The need for a PQ will be discussed in regard to four situations. These scenarios are summarized in table 6.14 and discussed in the following paragraphs:

Table 6.13	Types of Qualifications		
Qualification type	**Environment in which qualification is conducted**	**Requirements or specification**	**Purpose**
Installation qualification (IQ)	Validation environment and, later, the production environment	Technical requirements as written in the system specification developed in phase 6	Used to verify that the validation instance meets the technical requirements. Also used to check the installation in the production environment.
Operational qualification (OQ)	Validation environment	User requirements (functional specification if it's a custom system)	Verify the system's capability and capacity to meet user requirements in a test environment
Performance qualification (PQ)	Production environment	User requirements (functional specification if it's a custom system)	Verify that the system meets requirements for how it should function in the production or operational process

- The system controls some aspect of manufacturing.
- The validation environment is identical to the production environment.
- The validation environment isn't identical to the production environment, and the system isn't used in manufacturing.
- Test or lab equipment is used to conduct a variety of tests, such as for the purity of pharmaceutical products.

In the first situation, the system controls some aspect of manufacturing. Ordinarily the system is qualified by means of an IQ and OQ. The qualification would involve tests of the capability and capacity of the system as a stand-alone unit. Then it would be tested as part of a production process, using a PQ to establish that the system works effectively as part of the process. Usually three lots of product are manufactured; these are called validation lots. The product is tested to ensure that the automation has worked properly, but the product can't be used with humans or animals unless and until the validation results demonstrate that the system meets the requirements. If the automation meets the system acceptance criteria, including the requirement that the product manufactured is within specifications, and the validation final report is approved, the system is released for production. The validation lots can be used for humans or animals if the system is approved (without changes) and the product meets the requirements for its release.

In the second situation, the validation environment and the production environments are the same. The OQ and PQ can be combined because the PQ would be identical to the OQ. When this is the case, the protocol should be referred to as an "O/PQ." If the validation is going to include an O/PQ instead of a separate OQ and PQ, include this fact in the validation plan and provide a justification. An application used to manage calibration records provides a good example. The validation (OQ) and production (PQ) environments would be identical if the calibration system is installed on the same server, uses the same network that would be used when the system is made operational, and uses an equivalent workstation. In addition, only a few operators would be accessing the system at once when the calibration system is operable. Such "stress conditions" (i.e., a few simultaneous users) can easily be included in the OQ tests. One set of tests can be developed and executed that will demonstrate that the calibration system meets user requirements. Even if the tests were conducted on test data rather than actual calibration data, you can easily make the claim that the system will operate in an identical manner with actual calibration data.

An O/PQ is appropriate when each of the following conditions are met:

- The O/PQ tests all user requirements, which need to be tested, including how the system will be used in actual production or operation.

- The technical environment in which the O/PQ tests are executed is the same as the technical environment for the production environment. This would be the case if the O/PQ testing were done using the same hardware and software that would be used in production. Care must be taken when there are slight differences, especially in the operating systems. The application might function differently even with different revisions of the same operating system.
- When the load and other stress conditions are the same between the O/PQ and the production environment. The system might work well with one user conducting O/PQ tests, but not so well when multiple users are simultaneously using the system, or when the system is used at a remote location.

When the O/PQ is successfully completed and a validation final report is approved stating that the system is ready for operational use, the system can be released. The O/PQ is typically conducted using test data identical to the actual data that the system will process. When the O/PQ is completed and the validation final report is approved, the test data are deleted or a new instance of the system is created for production use.

In the third situation, the system isn't used for manufacturing product, and an O/PQ isn't appropriate because of differences between the validation environment and the conditions of actual use (e.g., the number of concurrent users). The OQ testing would be conducted using infrastructure devices (e.g., servers, data storage devices, the network) that are as close as possible to those that will be used during operations. The more the validation and operational environments are different, the greater the likelihood that the functionality and performance obtained in the validation environment won't be the same as how the system works in the operational environment. In this scenario, the system is released for operation use when the system meets the OQ acceptance criteria, and an approved OQ protocol report states that the system is ready for production use. However, the validation isn't complete until the planned PQ tests are complete and a validation final report is signed. The following conditions should be set for using this approach:

- The OQ tests all of the user requirements that need to be tested in the validation environment.
- The validation environment is reasonably close to the operational environment.

A document control system provides an example. After completing the OQ protocol report, the system is released for production use. A new instance (or a clone) of the system is created for operational use. Documents are approved and viewed while performing work. However, at the same time, some or all of the transactions are verified for accuracy, and the system is monitored for problems. If the system is found to be malfunctioning in a significant way, appropriate actions are taken. Such actions might include suspending the use of part or all of the system while the defect is repaired and erroneous data are corrected.

The fourth and final situation involves equipment that's qualified, and the procedures for using the equipment are validated. For example, some types of laboratory equipment will be used to perform a variety of tests. High-pressure liquid chromatography equipment (HPLC) is used for testing the purity of different pharmaceutical products. An IQ and OQ must be performed to provide objective evidence that the HPLC is capable of performing accurate analyses. Then each test method for determining the purity of a product must be validated as a test method. Any qualified HPLC can be used during the method validation; after the method is validated, any qualified HPLC can be used to perform that test method. In other words, each HPLC is qualified, and each test method is validated.

In this book it's assumed that IQ, OQ, and PQ are preformed separately.

PREPARE A WRITTEN VALIDATION PLAN

Although the life cycle presented in this volume is a total integration of system implementation and validation, validation is viewed as a distinct process by some regulatory and standards organizations, and by many field auditors for such agencies and registrars. The validation plan serves as the document that defines the validation from the perspective of meeting regulatory requirements and industry standards. It documents the validation approach, activities, roles, and responsibilities. The plan identifies the life cycle activities that will be preformed and the required deliverables from those activities through phase 8, use in a production environment. The specific tasks to be performed will be dictated by the type of software, the software life cycle being followed, and the system's risk level. The validation plan defines the relevant prerequisites, the deliverables that will be created, and the approval requirements for the deliverables. Approval of the validation plan is one vehicle for authorizing system-specific variations to the life cycle. The life cycle deliverables form the validation record for the system.

It's important to note that with the approach taken here, the validation plan includes all the life cycle activities that will be performed because validation and implementation are integrated into one process. When validation and implementation aren't totally integrated, the validation plan will include all of the validation activities performed

Table 6.14	Using Performance Qualification and Releasing Product Created During Performance Qualification Testing		
Situation	**Does system directly affect production quality?**	**Types of qualification**	**Product (i.e., system output) release or use of PQ transactions**
System used in manufacturing	Yes	Installation qualification (IQ), operational qualification (OQ), and performance qualification (PQ)	Validation lots. Released for use with humans if the system passes the system acceptance criteria and the product meets final release criteria.
System not used to produce product, and validation environment is identical to the production environment	No	IQ, O/PQ (combined OQ and PQ)	Transactions created during the O/PQ are test data and aren't valid operational data. A new instance of the system is created after the validation final report.
System not used to produce product, and validation environment is different than the production environment	No	IQ, OQ, and PQ	Transactions conducted during the PQ are considered valid unless determined to be in error.
Qualification of lab equipment used for product testing and validation of test method	Yes	I/OQ, or IQ and OQ	Qualification tests aren't performed on actual product. OQ tests typically are performed on standards and the results evaluated against expected results for the standard.

with an emphasis on the validation testing that will be performed in phase 7, qualify the system, and phase 8, use in a production environment.

The validation plan is the starting point for internal and external auditors who want to verify that the system has been appropriately validated because it lays out the logic of the intended validation and defines required activities and associated deliverables. If the auditor accepts the logic presented in the plan, then the audit simply involves verification that the activities have been appropriately performed and documented.

The validation plan is a different type of document than the project plan. The validation plan defines the strategy for validating the system, identifies the activities that will be performed, and provides the logic for what will be done. Project plans normally focus on a timeline for completing tasks and are used to manage the project. Because of the validation plan's content, it's recommended that organizations—even those that aren't required to validate their systems—create a validation plan for complex implementations and moderate- to high-risk systems. Such a document will provide a written description and justification for the implementation as well as a high-level test plan. A validation plan might not add value when you're validating simple or low-risk systems such as stand-alone lab equipment and simple applications built from database packages.

Validation Plan Content

Deliverable 4.2 describes the content of a validation plan.[42] However, there are a number of decisions that are recorded in the validation plan that must be discussed here, including:

- Scope of the validation
- System description
- Validation strategy
- Implications of the risk assessment on the life cycle and validation activities
- System release for production
- System acceptance criteria
- Revalidation requirements
- System revalidation requirements
- Risk management plan

Scope of the Validation

The scope of the validation usually is identical to the scope of the system defined in phase 1 and described in the system project proposal (see the discussion of phase 1, conceptualize, in chapter 3). Hardware and software that's used solely by a system or application is considered part of the application's system, including servers, communications hardware and software, data storage devices, input and output devices, workstations, and application software. Items that are shared across applications can be validated with a system, as part of the infrastructure, or qualified separately as an independent item. See table 6.12 and the related discussion above.

System Description

At a minimum, the validation must contain a high-level description of the major hardware and software components of the system so that the system and its limits can be adequately identified. The EC Commission Directive on medicinal products requires a written system description. Beyond identifying the system's major hardware and software components, the content requirements stated in EC Annex 11, item 4, add a context to the system that's very useful in planning the validation:

"It should describe the principles, objectives, security measures, and scope of the system and the main features of the way in which the computer is used and how it interacts with other systems and procedures."[43]

If such a description already exists, perhaps in a system specification, it could be referenced.

EC Annex 11, item 4 also requires that the system description be kept up to date.[44] It's best that the system description be incorporated into the system specification that will be written during phase 6. Once the validation is complete, the validation plan won't be revised, so it's not an adequate domicile for the system description over time. The system specification will be kept up to date as hardware and software changes.

Validation Strategy

The validation strategy is the approach that you take to the validation. Technical Report 18, Section 4.7.1 points out that the specific approach to be used in validating a computerized system should be described in the validation plan.[45]

The validation strategy includes the following:

- Identifying the validation as prospective, concurrent, or retrospective. If not prospective, justify. Indicate if the approach is different for different parts of the system.
- Types of qualifications that will be included. The following possibilities were discussed above: IQ, I/OQ, OQ, O/PQ, and PQ. Include a justification for what you select.
- Timing for validating different parts of the system.
- Validating the system as a whole or as a group of subsystems. The system can be divided into subsystems that are qualified individually, and then the integration of the parts can be validated as a total system. Although customary for large systems, this isn't a required approach.
- General impact of risk level. State the rigor with which the validation activities must be conducted based on the risk level of the system (discussed in the next section).

One aspect of the strategy for a prospective validation involves the timing of when various computer functions will be validated in relation to when modules of the system will be implemented. Validation testing of all the functionality can be completed before any part of the system is used, or the testing can be staged in parallel with the implementation of system functionality. Consider, for example, two different scenarios for implementing a document control system. In one, the entire system will be used when it becomes operational. In the second scenario, the organization will limit system use to document access during the first year, and then introduce using the system to create and approve change requests. With the second scenario, the company has the option of validating all system functions before the system is used, or waiting to validate the functions of creating and approving change requests until just before those functions will be used.

There are three advantages to performing all of the validation testing before using any part of the system. First, if a defect is discovered that makes the system unusable before it's placed into use, it's easier to change systems. Second, some systems are sold with a ninety-day warranty period during which the software developer will provide field support in resolving issues, or the system can be returned. Third, the task of creating and managing validation documentation is easier when it's all done at once. For example, test methods need to be approved and reports written only once instead of twice or more.

On the other hand, waiting to test system functionality until it will be used also has advantages. Some of the costs of developing and executing tests can be delayed, and the time taken to put the system in use for the initial implementation can be shortened.

Implications of the Risk Assessment on Life Cycle and Validation Activities

The validation plan should specify how the risk level of the system will be taken into account during the validation process. First, the effect of the system risk level on the life cycle activities must be defined. As has been pointed out throughout the discussion of this life cycle, whether a life cycle activity must be performed, and the level of rigor associated with conducting and documenting the activity, are dependent upon the risks associated with system failure. Recommendations on which life cycle activities to perform based on the risk level are given in exhibit 12.1.

Concerning the first consideration—the life cycle activities to be performed—a table can be placed in an appendix of the validation plan that lists all the life cycle activities that must be performed for that system and the associated deliverables. In addition, any needed discussion of specific activities can be placed in body of the plan (see deliverable 4.2's "Validation Activities" section).

To address the second consideration, the rigor of the validation activities, a general statement can be made in the validation strategy section regarding the rigor with which

Table 6.15	Intensity and Rigor of Validation Activities Based on Risk		
Type of activity	**System risk level**		
	High	**Moderate**	**Low**
Project plans	Plans are written at a level of detail necessary to ensure complete and appropriate execution of tasks. In general, approval involves all project team members.	Plans will be prepared that identify the tasks to be performed and include additional details that identify the important actions that must be performed as part of critical tasks. In general, approval involves all project team members.	Project plans might be informal and undocumented.
Methodologies used during validation (e.g., risk analysis methods, system maintenance, user support)	Methodologies for performing important activities are documented in approved procedures or protocols.	Methodologies for performing important activities are documented in approved procedures or protocols.	Methodologies can be used based on high-level descriptions of how to conduct the method. Approved procedures aren't necessary.
Documentation or records of activities performed	Documentation of activities takes the form of formal reports. Required signatures for the reports are specified in the validation plan. Enough information will be provided on what was done and how to enable an independent evaluation of the validity of the results. The results will be summarized at a high level. Data are attached and reviewed by a designated individual. Calculations may be independently performed by two people.	Document activities in formal reports. Required signatures for the reports are specified in the validation plan. Enough information will be provided on what was done to independently evaluate the validity of the results. The results will be summarized at a high level. Data are attached and reviewed by a designated individual.	Documentation of activities might take the form of memos signed by the author (instead of formal reports). The information provided can be limited to a high-level description of what was done, a high-level summary of the results, and a conclusion. The data are retained for future reference and/or auditing.
OQ and PQ testing	Thoroughly test high-risk functions, including abnormal and failure conditions. (More details are provided in table 9.5.) Test moderate risk functions under normal conditions. Test low-risk functions if configurations or modifications were made, or if an error can't be readily identified (e.g., a calculation).	Test moderate-risk functions under normal conditions. (More details are provided in table 9.5.) Test low-risk functions if configurations or modifications were made, or if an error can't be readily identified (e.g., a calculation).	Test low-risk functions if configurations or modifications were made, or if an error can't be readily identified (e.g., a calculation). (More details are provided in table 9.5.)

the activities will be performed and documented. Rigor is defined in the IEEE standard on verification and validation as the formality of the methods used for the activities and the recording of their results.[46] Guidelines for formulating such statements are provided in table 6.15, but you must interpret them for your situation. For additional suggestions on how to modify the rigor of validation based on risk, see Gamp 4, appendix M3.[47]

System Release for Production or Operational Use

The validation plan must specify when the system can be used in the production and/or operational environment for performing work. If the validation testing isn't complete when the system is released for production or operational use, the plan must specify the conditions under which product generated by using the system can be released for use with humans or animals. The timing of the release of the system for operations is directly related to the strategy regarding testing in the operational environment (i.e., the PQ). Table 6.14 describes when the system can be released for production under the four PQ strategies.

System Acceptance Criteria

System acceptance criteria are critical. These are standards that must be met once the validation testing is completed in phase 8 for the system to be deemed suitable for use and the validation complete. The system acceptance criteria are set before the validation testing is begun and shouldn't be changed once the test results are known. If the results of the tests don't meet the system acceptance criteria, the change control system must be used either to change how the system will be used or to repair the system. Give careful thought to system acceptance criteria when you formulate them.

The easy answer to system acceptance criteria is to state that all requirements must be met; after all, they *are* requirements. However, given the nature of software, such system acceptance criteria will be difficult to meet. If you consider the circumstances under which the system truly won't be useful or shouldn't be used, in all likelihood the acceptability will depend on which requirements aren't met and/or the nature of the defect.

Four levels of defects are defined in table 6.16. These are similar to those developed by IBM, circa 1956.[48] Notice that the classification of the defect is tied to both the criticality of the user requirement and severity of harm that's associated with the failure.

The first system acceptance criteria should be that there are no critical defects related to an intended use. A system shouldn't be used if, under certain circumstances, it will crash, corrupt critical data, or affect the quality of products to the extent that they must be rejected. In addition, all critical requirements should be met.

In chapter 4 it was recommended that requirements be classified as critical, important, and nice to have. Recall the description of a critical requirement: "Absolutely required for an intended use the first day of production. The system can't be used for an intended use if this function isn't present or doesn't work properly; such a defect must be fixed before the system can be used for the intended use. The system isn't worth purchasing and installing for the intended use if this feature or function is missing or malfunctions."

Given this definition, if any critical requirement isn't met, the system shouldn't be used for the relevant intended use. One example of a critical requirement for a document control system is secured access to document files. If anyone could make changes to the files, or replace or delete them, then the system isn't workable as a system for using controlled documents. Another intended use is the electronic signoff of change requests. If the system failed to send the change request to the proper reviewers, the system wouldn't be suitable for approving change requests. However, the system could

Table 6.16	Defect Classifications		
Defect classification	**Definition**	**Criticality of user requirement**	**Severity level of harm associated with a failure**
Critical defect	Any defect that causes a down system, harm of any type at the catastrophic or critical levels, would result in the corruption of critical data, or an unfilled critical requirement	Critical requirement	Catastrophic or critical
Major defect	Any defect that results in an error with, or inoperability of, an important function, causes harm at the moderate level, or results in the inoperability of important functionality, or in the nonfulfillment of an "important requirement"	Important requirement	Moderate
Minor defect	Any defect that's immaterial to the functioning of the system or the quality of the data and leads to an unfilled "nice to have" requirement	Nice-to-have requirement	Marginal
Cosmetic defect	Any defect that's immaterial to the functioning of the system or the quality of the data and is unrelated to any specified requirements	N/A	N/A

still be appropriate for other intended uses, such as viewing controlled documents, if the critical requirements related to those uses were met.

A second acceptance criterion can be formulated for major defects (i.e., defects that result in an error with, or inoperability of, important functionality or the nonfulfillment of an important requirement). Important requirements are those features and functions whose failure doesn't render the system unusable for an intended use, but whose failure significantly lessens the value and effectiveness of the system. An example can be sited regarding the intended use of managing the change-control process. An important requirement may be the ability to search bills of material (BOMs) to find where a part is used. This is called a "where-used search." A BOM is a list of parts and the quantity of each that are needed to build a product. If a part is discontinued, the organization will have to change all of the BOMs that include the part. A where-used search is more effective than human memory for locating where the part might be used, especially is there are a large number of BOMs. However, if the system's where-used-search capability isn't working properly, the system can still be used for managing change control.

There are two options for a system acceptance criterion related to important requirements. The first is to not set an allowable number of failures on important functions. Instead, specify that the project team will determine if and how the system can be used, given the specific failures that have been identified. The concern isn't only the number of defects that you've found but the likelihood that additional latent defects exist that you haven't yet found. If the system has twenty important functions, and three of the functions can't be used because of failures, the team must determine if the system should be used without those functions and whether the system has so many defects that the software's quality should be questioned. Is it worth the risk of additional failures in the future? The answer could depend on the system's risk level. The second option for an acceptance criterion is to set a maximum number of failures of this type that can be allowed, for example, no more than three.

The third system acceptance criterion can be set for minor defects. These are related to problems with minor functionality or "nice to have" requirements. Nice-to-have requirements are characterized in chapter 4 as "the absence or loss of this feature or function will have little effect on the system's effectiveness and value." An example of a minor defect is the failure of the system to sort the change requests by date opened on an administrative report. A second example is the failure of the system to automatically attach a PDF version of a document to a change request when that document is listed on the change request as a reference document for informational purposes. As with major defects, there are two options for an acceptance criterion: specify that the project team will determine if and how the system can be used, given the specific defects, or set a limit on how many minor defects will be permitted.

An acceptance criterion isn't recommended for the number of cosmetic defects that are permitted. Cosmetic defects are issues or defects that are immaterial to the functioning of the system or the quality of the data and unrelated to any specified requirements. An example is the format of a report or a misspelling on a screen. Because these defects are trivial from the perspective of system functionality and data integrity, it's recommended that an acceptance criterion not be set to avoid having to reject the system based on cosmetic defects.

A fourth acceptance criterion is recommended related to user satisfaction. Users must be satisfied that the system will be an effective tool in meeting their requirements. Some organizations ask a panel of users to make a subjective judgment of whether they believe the system is performing to their expectations. Is the system sufficiently easy to use? Is the response time fast enough? Is the system an efficient tool for getting the job done or does it take longer than necessary?

User revolts against systems aren't unusual. If people refuse to use the system or find ways to get around the weaknesses of the system that undermine needed process controls, the system won't be effective. Here are some real examples in the realm of document control. The manager of a document control staff of a pharmaceutical company believed that the new document control system was too difficult for her staff to learn and that many operations took longer to perform with the system than they did manually. Concerns were raised to management, and the system was reviewed. The manager's concern was a contributing factor to canceling the project.

At a medical diagnostics company, an administrator was asked to load documents and data manually into a new system. She found it difficult and believed that many of the required data fields were pointless for her company. As a result, she ignored the task, and, after six months, had loaded only two documents. Employees at a remote facility of a third company downloaded and used copies of controlled documents from their desktops because it took up to a half hour to access a document over the network.

A fifth acceptance criterion can be formulated around the team's judgment of the suitability of the system. The team should look at the big picture and decide if the system is a good fit for the organization. Considerations can include:

- The nature of specific failures
- The team's confidence that the system will consistently perform to requirements
- User excitement and satisfaction with the system
- The system's performance

- System supportability
- Technical difficulties identified by IT

Additional system acceptance criteria can be added related to the business value of the system. Such criteria go beyond "does the system work as intended" and require the system to be a business success. At this point, the team comes back full circle to the vision formulated during phase 1 and asks if it's been realized. Some questions that these additional criteria address are:

- How well do the system and the process of which it's a part meet the vision that energized the organization to implement it?
- Are the users excited and supportive, or do they have reservations about the system? Will they embrace the system and make it successful?
- How heavy of a burden is the support and use of the system on the organization? Are those costs justified based on the gains from the system?

The system acceptance criteria can vary by the system risk level. For example, the number of defects that are permitted at each level might vary by the risk level of the system. An alternative for factoring risk into the system acceptance criteria is to vary the number of defects that's acceptable by the risk level of the specific function in question. For example, you might not tolerate any major defects on high-risk functions and permit multiple minor defects on low-risk functions.

Revalidation Requirements

Once the validation testing is complete, the system must be controlled so that it remains in a validated state (i.e., because changes are controlled and the necessary maintenance is performed, sufficient objective evidence is present to sustain confidence that the system will reliably function to meet requirements). Changes include adding, modifying, or deleting any system component. Two of the major tasks in maintaining a system in a validated state are to protect it from unintended changes, and to ensure that the system will continue to be reliable after intentional changes. To manage intentional changes, a change control process is developed to evaluate the effect of potential changes on the system and approve making the changes. The activities done to test the change and its effect on other parts of the system are called "revalidation." Preparing a change control process is discussed in chapter 8, and using the process is discussed in chapter 10.

The requirements for the revalidation of a system are defined in its validation plan. There are three possible approaches. In option 1, the validation plan states that the revalidation requirements for the system are the same as those specified in an approved software validation procedure. In option 2, the most commonly used approach, the validation plan states that the revalidation tests will be defined and approved as part of each change request. There are two major drawbacks to defining qualification tests for each change. First, additional time is necessary to consider what testing is appropriate whenever a similar change is made, and, second, it's difficult to be consistent in the revalidations performed over several years.

Option 3 addresses these drawbacks. The revalidation tests for certain types of changes are defined in advance and recorded in the validation plan. Whenever such a change is made, the revalidation testing is done, as described in the validation plan, as part of the change-control process. For example, you might specify in your validation plan what tests will be done when memory cards and communication cards are replaced.

Revalidation isn't required if a change is made following a qualified procedure for making such a change. Recall the printer example discussed earlier in this chapter. If a qualified procedure is followed for adding a printer, revalidation of the system isn't required. The procedure will include a qualified test to verify proper installation and functioning of the printer.

System Revalidation Requirements

System revalidation involves performing another complete validation of the system. The validation plan should specify the conditions under which a complete system revalidation must be performed. Either the plan can specify that system revalidation will be performed as required in an approved procedure, such as the procedure on the computer system life cycle, or the plan can list system revalidation conditions specific for the system. The following are examples of circumstances that might be identified as triggering a system revalidation:

- Changes that are made to the system are so extensive that it's not practical to design specific tests for each change. This might be the case when the software developer issues a major new release of the system, and is certainly the case if the developer changes the hardware or software architecture of the system (e.g., if the developer rewrites a client-server application in HTML).
- Major changes to the operating environment, hardware, or software (e.g., a change to a new server operating system)
- Changes are made to the database structure, or a central part of the application, and the ramifications of the changes to the system aren't certain.

DEVELOP A RISK MANAGEMENT PLAN

A plan is made for carrying out the remainder of the risk management procedure for this system. Include the following in the plan:

- A summary of the risk management activities performed as part of the RiskVal life cycle up to this point (see appendix B)
- The risk level of the system. This is equal to the highest risk from a single failure, or the risk posed by a combination of potential failures if that combination is higher than the risk associated with a single failure. For example, the highest risk from a single failure might be at the moderate level, but because the system poses many risks at a moderate level, the overall risk might be considered high.
- When management will review the risk management activities. This review can take place during a phase review (e.g., at the end of phase 6, prepare to use).
- Criteria for risk acceptance. Define criteria for when the risk will be acceptable. Examples include:
  - ☐ Risk analysis indicates that the risk falls in the broadly acceptable range. With such risks, risk control needn't be actively pursued.
  - ☐ The risk analysis indicates that the risk is moderate, but further reduction of risk is impractical.
  - ☐ The aspect of the item that presents the hazard or potential failure meets industry standards.
  - ☐ The aspect of the item that presents the hazard or potential failure meets specific technical requirements that have been set to mitigate potential risk, such as fault-tolerance.
  - ☐ Identification of mitigations to be implemented or a reference to where the mitigations are identified.

- The plan for assessing the effectiveness of the mitigations. The two common methods are special studies to measure the effect of the mitigations and verification as part of the OQ or PQ testing. Effects that are intangible or too difficult to measure can be estimated by professional judgment, though this practice isn't recommended with high-risk situations. More concrete mitigations, whose effect can be measured, should be used instead.
- Actions to be taken in the remainder of the RiskVal process to manage risk, including deliverables associated with the steps (see appendix B).

DESIGN CONFIGURATIONS

Configurations may have to be set for the hardware, system software, the database, and the application. The technical manual for the application ought to provide instructions on how to configure the hardware, system software, and database for the system to function properly. The appropriate configurations ought to be set when the system is installed in the test environment so that it replicates how the system will be configured in the operational/production environment. When you prepare the IQ (see chapter 9), include statements to verify the correct configuration.

Many applications allow you to adapt the system to your business by setting application configurations. Such configurations range from administrative options to customized functionality. Table 6.17 provides some examples. Configuring the system might be as simple as changing default settings for basic options to using tools to create complex functionality such as workflows. Workflows are a sequence of auto-

(continues on page 214)

| Medatech 6.4 | Validation Plan |

The project team worked together to write Medatech's validation plan following the method outlined in deliverable 4.2. Val led the effort. The following is the team's concept of the hardware that will be used by the system. The electronic document management system (EDMS) server software will run on a dedicated server that also will hold the database containing document information and electronic masters of the documents. The server is part of the company network that's used for e-mail and other business applications. The client software will be installed on workstations that users have at their desks. These workstations will comply with the standard configuration requirements (i.e., they'll have at least the minimum required memory, speed, disk capacity, and applications that are part of the standard configuration). Engineers will also be able to open the EDMS from within their computer-aided design (CAD) software. The document control department uses a dedicated printer for creating hard copy masters, including top-level views of drawings. Employees are able to print forms when needed, using the company printer that's closest to their desks.

Here's how the team addressed some of the more difficult issues in its validation plan: The scope of the system, and therefore the validation, includes the dedicated server and its software, the dedicated printer in document control, and the EDMS software. The system doesn't include other network equipment or software, or the employee workstations. Tec and Val have already qualified the network as a separate system. Using the change control process, Tec will treat the addition of the EDMS system dedicated server and system software as a change to the network. Tec's staff has been using a defined process for desktop and laptop setup (see chapter 8) and for configuring workstations; however, the process hasn't been documented yet. Tec's information technology policy (see chapter 3, deliverable

(continues)

Medatech 6.4	Validation Plan (continued)

1.1) controls the type of software that employees may load onto their workstations. The dedicated printer will be tested as part of the validation. The project team will create a procedure for printer setup and driver verification (see chapter 8) that Tec's staff will use to verify that the printers used throughout the company are suitable for printing forms from the EDMS.

Doc's strategy for the EDMS rollout is to load all the existing documents into the system and permit employees to use the system to view controlled documents and print forms from the beginning. After the users are used to the system, estimated at about twelve months, Doc will begin to have employees create and submit change requests via the system. At that time, he'll begin to have reviewers review and approve the change requests via the system. During the first year, document control will create the change requests themselves, print them, and have them approved as a hard-copy record.

The team's validation strategy is to perform a prospective validation—(i.e., the appropriate validation testing will be completed before the EDMS is used for performing work and approving change requests). The validation process, system implementation, and risk management activities are integral to each other and integrated into one process. The entire system will be validated before any part of the system is used for conducting work, including using electronic signatures for approving change requests.

As discussed in Medatech 6.2, the system's risk level is high. Because of this, the project team will pursue the life cycle and validation activities with the level of rigor recommended in table 6.15 for high-risk systems.

The team will consider the EDMS ready for viewing documents during production if the operation qualification (OQ) acceptance criteria are met. The OQ will test all the system functions that will be used, all risk mitigation measures, security and authorization functions, and administrative functions. The OQ tests will be conducted using a validation instance of the system created on the corporate infrastructure. All the tests that must be conducted to ensure confidence that the correct version of the correct document is opened by the system must be done during the OQ.

The performance qualification (PQ) will be conducted immediately after the OQ, and it will be limited to how the system will be used during phase 1 (i.e., primarily for viewing documents). For this phase, the team decided to use the confirmation approach to the PQ; using the dual system for viewing documents wasn't considered practical. (The various approaches to the PQ are explained in chapter 10.) In its validation plan, the team included a description of the approach to be taken in the PQ. More information on Medatech's PQ is given in chapter 10, but here's a summary:

■ Direct verification of all high-risk functions under normal operating conditions
■ Direct verification of all risk mitigation functions built into the software
■ Direct verification of all risk mitigations created by the project team
■ Monitoring of problem reports for six weeks
■ Meeting with user representatives after six weeks to identify any difficulties with the system

■ Conducting an audit of the document control process after six weeks to confirm that the execution of the document control process is compliant with the user procedures and regulations

Any product manufactured during the time of the PQ can be released for use with humans if those products pass the quality control tests and meet the product release criteria.

As mentioned above, the OQ testing, including electronic approval of engineering change orders (ECOs), will be completed before the system is used for viewing documents. When it's time to introduce electronic approval of ECOs during phase 2 of the implementation, Doc will submit a change request. There are two options for testing the electronic approval of the change requests: a dual system approach and a confirmation approach. (The approaches will be discussed in chapter 10.) With the dual system, ECOs would be approved electronically and on paper before the changed documents are released for use. With the confirmation approach, the accuracy of the information about the electronic ECOs and signatures would be confirmed by the people who created the ECOs and signed them. With both the dual system approach and the confirmation approach, all functions related to electronic records and signatures would be verified, including the creation of the record, attachment of electronic signatures, creation of audit trails, and inability to remove the electronic signature. If Doc had decided to introduce electronic approval right from the beginning, these tests would have been part of the PQ conducted when the system was first validated.

The project team formulated the following system acceptance criteria that the EDMS must meet to confirm that the system is suitable for use in the production environment for viewing documents, and to close the validation of the system.

■ For loading existing data, 80 percent or more of the total number of data points must load through the legacy load process, and 100 percent of all data points must be accounted for, within the log files, as either loaded or an error. All samples taken of parts or bills of material, documents, and the change requests are 100 percent accurate.
■ No unresolved critical defects
■ Not more than two unresolved major defects that leave an important requirement unmet
■ No more than eight unresolved minor defects related to nice-to-have requirements
■ Any number of cosmetic defects is permitted.
■ A majority of the user representatives indicate that in their judgement the system functions as expected and in a manner suitable to meet the business and regulatory goals of the document control process.
■ The project team believes that the system is suitable for meeting the document control process objectives, and the residual risk associated with the system is acceptable.

The requalification testing to be performed in regard to a change will be specified on the change control form for that change.

Partial or complete revalidation will be performed when any of the conditions specified in the "validation requirements for computer systems" procedure are met.

mated process activities and approvals that can be determined dynamically based on the situation. For example, an application might route service requests to appropriate departments. With some systems, an administrator creates workflows by using system tools to produce a graphical depiction of the routing process. Intelligence can be included in the configuration. For example, if the call-center service representative codes a problem as an application problem, it will get routed to software support, but, if it's

Table 6.17	Examples of System Configurations	
Type of configuration	**Examples**	**Design activities performed during this phase**
User classifications	■ Creating groups of users ■ Setting access and functional roles and privileges for each group of users	Determining: ■ What groups of users will be created ■ What privileges the members of each group should have
Security	■ Setting the source from which the time and date will be read for time-and-date stamps ■ Setting length of idle time before the system logs off a user ■ Setting the number of failed logon attempts allowed before the system deactivates the user ■ Setting notification paths for alerting the system manager for attempted security breaches	Determining the: ■ Source for the time-and-date stamp ■ Length of idle time ■ Number of failed logon attempts allowed ■ How the system manager will be alerted to attempted security breaches
Database	■ Naming of variables and setting variable type (e.g., date) ■ Setting the format for a data field (e.g., date formats) ■ Defining the capacity of tables used to store data and options for what happens when the tables are filled	Defining: ■ Variables ■ Formats for data fields ■ Database table sizes and what to do with new data if a table is full
Functionality	■ Creating workflows for tasks such as routing documents for review and routing trouble reports to departments ■ Setting values at which an alarm will be sounded when a temperature or pressure exceeds allowed limits	■ Design the workflow, routing sequence, choice points, and rules for how the routing should be done ■ Determining the alarm set points
Reports	■ Configuring reports created by the software developer, such as by selecting information to be included in reports and formatting the reports ■ Creating additional reports	■ Designing what will be in the reports and the format
System management options	■ Network communications ■ Setting printer drivers ■ Establishing user accounts ■ Allocation of storage space to users ■ Partitioning hard drive space on a computer	Determining: ■ What communication protocols are needed ■ What printer drivers are needed ■ Storage space settings ■ Sizes of partitions

identified as an operating system or hardware problem, the information will be routed to desktop support.

Obviously, it's necessary to configure a system properly for it to meet requirements and perform reliably. Some of the configurations, such as database values, are set by IT with input from the user, while someone from the user community decides upon configurations that affect functionality and access privileges. Most configuration errors of user functionality are visible to users—for example, an error in a workflow that routes service requests to the wrong department. However, other configuration errors might not be visible. For example, while validating a document control system, a diagnostics company discovered that the data tables used to save audit trail information had no more free space. From that moment on, the audit trail data wasn't recorded. The software developer had created default settings for the size of the data tables that were far too small for the document routings that the company had created. If the validation testing hadn't been performed, this problem probably wouldn't have been discovered until the audit trail was checked to answer a security question, and the needed data wouldn't have been there.

Configurations are designed during this phase. Table 6.17 illustrates what designing configurations might mean for various types of configurations. For example, if a workflow is to be developed for an IT support center, a flowchart can be developed to describe the routing of different types of issues through the organization. If the configuration involves creating a report, the report is designed during this phase. Determine, for example, what the report will include, and how the information will be formatted. During the next phase, the configurations are built into the system, informally tested, and documented so they can be reset or built again during the installation in the validation and production environments.

Configurations can be recorded as appropriate. Several alternatives are possible, including: a memo to file, placing the configurations in installation instructions, or incorporating the configurations and settings in the IQ protocol, as discussed in chapter 9.

REVISE THE PROJECT PLAN

As stated in chapter 3 in the discussion of the phase 1, a project plan is needed if the system is large, complex, or of moderate to high risk. The major benefits from a project plan stem from better project management.

- A project plan will provide a basis for estimating the resources that will be needed for the project.

- The plan will identify activities that are on the critical path. Managing the completion of critical path items will help the project team control the total time taken to complete the project.
- Defining the sequence of the activities in advance will help avoid any rework that would be needed if the activities were performed out of sequence.
- Tasks that can be performed in parallel will be identified, and time frames will be developed for coordinating the completion of the tasks.

If a project plan was drafted during phase 1, it probably will need to be revised now that a specific system has been obtained and remedial actions have been identified. If a plan wasn't developed during phase 1, the team can determine, based on a clearer vision of what needs to be done, whether preparing a plan will add value.

PHASE 4 ACTIVITIES FOR EXISTING SYSTEMS

Most validations of existing systems are performed using concurrent or retrospective validation approaches. The third, less frequently used option, is to stop using the system for production and to conduct a prospective validation as if the system were new.

With concurrent validations, a test environment is established if testing can't be performed in the production environment. A separate test environment may be set up to avoid introducing fictitious test data into existing quality records. In addition, tests of abnormal conditions or ways in which the system might be caused to violate regulatory requirements, fail, or crash can be disruptive to the on-going work being performed in the production environment by employees.

When a test environment is set up, it should match, to the extent possible, the current production environment. The closer the test environment is to the current production environment, the more likely it is that the test results from the test environment will be indicative of how the system is performing (or will perform) in the production environment. The configurations set for the test environment for the hardware, system software, and database software ought to be as close as possible to those being used in the production environment given any differences in the system components used in the two environments. You want to avoid having the system fail the OQ validation tests because of something in the test environment that's different than what exists in the production environment.

Ideally, the application will be set up in the test environment to match the configurations in the production environment. If the two copies of the application are identical, then you'll be testing the application as it will be used in the production environment. At times a company will set up a separate test environment and then purposefully change the configuration of the application before conducting the OQ tests to test modifications to the system. These configurations may be developed during phases 4 through 9. How to address these changes will be discussed in chapter 10.

All other phase 4 activities are performed for existing systems as they are for new systems.

PHASE 4 ACTIVITIES FOR CUSTOM-DEVELOPED SYSTEMS

The flowchart in figure 6.1 depicts the RiskVal life cycle for custom systems. During phase 4 prime, the developer of custom systems designs the system and prepares a high-level test plan. During phase 5 prime, the custom system is coded and tested by the developer and then released to the organization. Once the developer delivers the custom system to the user organization, the project team will perform the phase 4 activities that are described for COTS systems in this chapter, such as integration, risk evaluation, mitigation planning, and preparation of the validation plan. Phase 4 is followed by the phase 5 activities for COTS systems described in chapter 7. During phase 6 the activities for custom systems are the same as for COTS systems.

With custom systems, a number of activities are performed as needed, based on system complexity and risk level. The following list is appropriate for moderate- and high-risk systems; low-risk systems might not require each activity. The activities include many of the most effective defect-detection and -prevention practices discussed in chapter 5 that are appropriate for this phase, and the software testing and quality assurance activities described in Technical Report 18, Section 4.5.[49, 50] For a complete discussion of the activities related to the development phase of the software engineering life cycle, consult the references provided in note 4.

■ A software project risk analysis is performed to identify and address the aspects of the software project that pose significant risks to on-time completion, development cost, and quality of the software.

■ A functional specification is created to specify how the system will function to meet each user requirement.

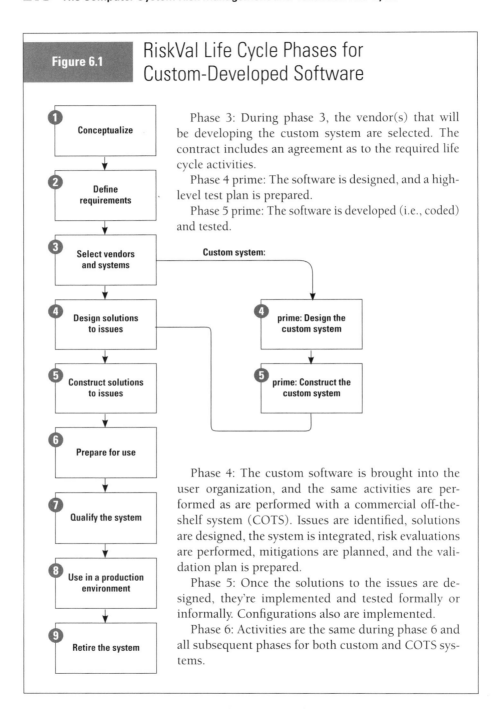

Figure 6.1

RiskVal Life Cycle Phases for Custom-Developed Software

Phase 3: During phase 3, the vendor(s) that will be developing the custom system are selected. The contract includes an agreement as to the required life cycle activities.

Phase 4 prime: The software is designed, and a high-level test plan is prepared.

Phase 5 prime: The software is developed (i.e., coded) and tested.

Phase 4: The custom software is brought into the user organization, and the same activities are performed as are performed with a commercial off-the-shelf system (COTS). Issues are identified, solutions are designed, the system is integrated, risk evaluations are performed, mitigations are planned, and the validation plan is prepared.

Phase 5: Once the solutions to the issues are designed, they're implemented and tested formally or informally. Configurations also are implemented.

Phase 6: Activities are the same during phase 6 and all subsequent phases for both custom and COTS systems.

- A traceability matrix is constructed to correlate each user requirement to a functional specification.

- A high-level design of system modules and functionality is created and documented.

- Detailed designs are created of the logic, program structures, configurations of modules, and the data flow between modules, and the designs are documented. The individuals who created the designs check them, and others review the designs to find and remove defects.

- A detailed risk analysis is performed after the detailed design is written. This risk analysis is different than the software project analysis mentioned in the first bullet point on this list. The objective of software hazard analysis is to identify safety-critical parts of the software, perhaps even down to the module level. During the analysis, the changes to help prevent or mitigate failure of safety-critical parts of the system are determined. This evaluation may lead to changes in the design (e.g., to incorporate fault-tolerant design techniques), development methods to add more rigor in methods and controls, or testing to perform more extensive testing. Any needed changes are also made to the requirements. See *Advances in Safety-Critical Systems— Results and Achievements from the DTI/EPSRC R&D Programme in Safety-Critical Systems* for a discussion of the application of the fault-tree and HAZOP (HAZard and OPerability) risk analysis techniques to software under development.[51]

- A traceability matrix is constructed to map the functional specifications to the detailed design to ensure that all functional requirements have been included, and that software engineers who will correct defects in the future know which module performs which function.

- A high-level test plan is constructed to define an approach to testing that matches the modular design of the system and includes testing of integrated system functions. The test plan is reviewed.

- A phase review is conducted to ensure that all phase 4 activities are complete and that proceeding to phase 5, construct solutions to issues, is appropriate.

If you're managing developers of custom systems and/or integrators, your job includes monitoring their work and deliverables to ensure that they're following an appropriate development life cycle. In chapter 5's discussion of phase 3, select vendors and systems, it's recommended that your contract with integrators and custom developers include a description of the development life cycle activities they must perform. Review the vendor's deliverables to audit its performance against your agreement. Request corrective action if the required activities aren't performed in a manner that's acceptable to you.

SUMMARY OF PHASE 4 DELIVERABLES

Table 6.18 summarizes the deliverables from phase 4 for COTS software and configured business systems, and identifies when each deliverable is applicable.

Table 6.18	Phase 4 Deliverables		
Phase 4 deliverables	**Definition and explanation**	**When applicable**	**Deliverable references**
Integration documentation or procedure	Information on how the system has been integrated with other systems so that the integration can be verified as part of the installation qualification (IQ), tested in the operational qualification (OQ), and repeated if the system must be rebuilt	All systems that are integrated with other systems	Highly recommended
Risk assessment and evaluation report (see deliverable 4.1)	Detailed risk assessment based on the severity and probability of harm from failures or hazards of the actual system purchased or (for custom systems) built	All moderate- and high-risk systems, unless a detailed risk assessment has already been completed	CDRH, 6.1; ISO 14971, Sections 4.4 and 5
Mitigation plan	A plan for mitigating risks that must be reduced and addressing any requirements or regulations that aren't met by the system (e.g., 21 CFR Part 11). A separate mitigation plan is created only if needed to implement and evaluate the mitigation.	If needed	ISO 14971, Section 6
Validation plan (see deliverable 4.2)	Documentation of the validation approach and activities, including the deliverables from the life cycle that will become part of the validation report. The plan also defines responsibilities and sets criteria for accepting the system.	All systems except simple and/or low-risk systems	Highly recommended
Documentation of system configurations	Hardware and software settings needed for the system to function properly, and functionality that must be created using system tools to meet requirements. A separate report can be prepared, the configurations can be documented in a procedure or the system specification, or the instructions can be included in installation instructions.	Systems that require configuration. Configurations can be included in a separate report, the system specification, installation instructions, or IQ.	Mandatory when necessary to meet requirements
Revised project plan	A plan that describes the tasks to be performed, the person responsible, and the timeline	As needed	Highly recommended

Chapter 7

Phase 5: Construct Solutions to Issues

The phase 5 objective for commercial off-the-shelf (COTS) systems and configured business systems is to fix the problems identified in the previous phase (i.e., to execute the mitigation plan, formally or informally test the effectiveness of the mitigations, and to further reduce, if necessary, the residual risks associated with potential failures and/or hazards). (See note 1.) A mitigation report is prepared if formal testing is conducted.

If the risk associated with a potential failure is still high, but can't be further reduced, a risk-benefit analysis is performed to determine if the potential benefits from using the system outweigh the risks associated with failure. This process of risk mitigation is similar to the process described in ISO 14971 and the Food and Drug Administration (FDA) guidance document on the use of COTS software in a medical device.[1, 2]

With configured systems, the configurations designed during phase 4 are also set or built. The configurations are documented, as is the process of building configurations so they can be re-created if needed. In the case of existing systems, the configuration settings in the system are documented. The documentation can

---

Chapter Highlights

be recorded in a separate document, incorporated into the system specification prepared in the next phase, or incorporated into the installation qualification (IQ) written during phase 7.

At the end of phase 5, the system should be set; all the needed mitigations should be in place. During phase 6, the final preparations for installation and use are made. After the testing is completed during phase 7, the system will be used.

Although phase 5 could involve little or no activity for COTS systems, the activity for custom systems is far more extensive because code is written and tested following a defined process for software development. At the end of the software development process, the developer reviews the test results and the status of known defects, and determines if the system is ready for release to the customer. Once the software vendor releases the custom software, it's brought into the organization. The activities of phase 4—Design solutions to issues, and phase 5—Construct solutions to issues, that are described for COTS systems are performed on the custom software.

IMPLEMENT THE MITIGATION PLAN

In phase 4 a mitigation plan was developed for COTS and configurable systems to lower risk and/or meet requirements. Three approaches were identified:

- Modifying the system to prevent failure, reduce its frequency, and/or improve the ability to detect the failure before the harm occurs
- Introducing protective measures in the process of using the system
- Providing instructions and/or training to the user to prevent an operator error

During this fifth phase, the mitigation plan is implemented. System changes are made. Processes are modified; instructions and training are prepared. The mitigations are documented as indicated in table 7.1.

TEST THE EFFECTIVENESS OF THE MITIGATIONS

Before the system is formally tested in phase 7—Qualify the system as part of the validation testing, you want to know how successful the risk reduction efforts will be.[3, 4] During phase 5, the mitigations are built and formally or informally tested to see how well they work. If such tests reveal that the mitigations are ineffective or

Table 7.1	Document Mitigations Made to the System
Change made to:	**Document the change by:**
User requirement	Revising user requirements. Revise, as needed, all documents in which the changed requirement is quoted or referenced. For example, if a requirement is deleted from the documented user requirements, modifications might have to be made to the computer system project proposal, the detailed risk assessment, a mitigation report, system user documentation, traceability matrices, and training materials.
How the system will be used	Revising user procedures or including notes in the project file so that the user procedures written during the next phase will reflect the changes
User warning in software	If the software presents the warning to the user, modify the software as appropriate and document the warning in the user manual. Create a new software master that includes the modification.
User warning placed in the work environment	If a warning is to be placed on a piece of hardware or in the work environment, document the content of the warning and verify that the warning has been posted as part of the installation qualification in phase 7.
User instructions	Revising the user instructions or documenting the instructions that must be provided. Place a note in the project file to include the instructions in the user procedure created during the next phase.
User training materials	Revising the training materials or documenting the training that needs to be provided. Place a note in the project file to include the training in the materials created in the next phase.
Software	Inserting comments into the modified programs that explain the changes made and their reasons. Revise all testing plans, system documentation and traceability matrices as needed.
Hardware	Revising documentation that describes the system configuration. Include this in the system specification written during the next phase.

inadequate, corrections can be made, including developing alternative or additional mitigations. If you wait until phase 7 to determine the effectiveness of a mitigation, you might discover too late that the system will have to be modified for further risk reduction. During phase 6—Prepare for use, procedures are written and training is prepared. Thus, if the system fails the validation tests, fixing the problem then will involve reworking procedures and training materials as well as the validation protocols.

Formal, documented evaluation of the effectiveness of the mitigations can be performed during this phase or as part of the validation testing performed during later phases. Formal testing involves a written test method, recording the findings, and preparing a mitigation report as described in the following section. If formal testing is done during this phase, the testing of the mitigation might be reduced in, or eliminated from, the validation testing. The most common practice is to informally test the effectiveness of the changes at this phase and to formally test them during the validation testing.

Regardless of whether formal testing is conducted at this stage, sufficient testing must be performed, if practical, to determine if the mitigations have been successful, and if changes to the system work effectively without a negative effect on other parts of the system.

The approaches to verifying the effectiveness of the mitigations are different for the three risk-mitigation approaches described in the previous section.

Test System Modifications

When modifications to the system are necessary, any of the following kinds of changes can be made:

- Part of the hardware can be changed.
- Application programs can be modified.
- New programs can be added, and configurations can be changed.
- Additional software can be integrated with the system to add new functionality or security.

System changes are tested either formally or informally during this phase. Test the modifications and determine if they've had an adverse effect on other parts of the system. Develop test cases and determine if the system is effective in performing the programmed functions.

Recall the example of the incoming materials database from chapter 6. Possible modifications to the system to reduce the frequency of entering the wrong date included modifying the system so it would: only accept the correct date format in the expiration date field; prohibit the entering of a date that was earlier than the date on which the value was entered; and require that the date be entered twice and the two values compared. If the system was modified to implement one of these solutions, the system should be tested to determine if the modification works. A more complex mitigation was suggested with the pharmaceutical manufacturing example (i.e., to integrate an application with the manufacturing control software so that the operator would be paged if the alarm was triggered). Once the integration is complete, perform at least informal tests to determine if the systems have been properly integrated.

Test Process Modifications

Determining the degree to which a procedural change will reduce the likelihood of a failure is difficult, and is ultimately determined by a professional that must take into account the capabilities of those performing the task, motivational factors, and managerial controls. In the example of entering expiration dates into an incoming materials database, a possible mitigation was to set a procedural requirement to have a second person check the accuracy of the date before data entry is completed.

The modifications to the procedure will be ineffective in reducing risk if they're poorly designed, or if the user fails to perform the new actions or performs them incorrectly. The success of a procedural change can be partially addressed by asking a few future users to perform the procedural steps in a test mode. Observe how the procedure is performed, evaluate the results of the work, and discuss the users' experiences with them. Such a test will help determine if the users performed the modified procedure as designed and if the modified procedure will meet the mitigation objectives. In addition, the feedback obtained will provide insight into possible operator errors and will help you understand how easy the modified procedure is to use. Operators might neglect to perform a procedural step if they feel it's too time-consuming or cumbersome.

One technique for promoting and monitoring the use of a method is to maintain records of performance. Have the operator record if a step was performed or not, or any data or information that was created during the step. Through reviews or audits of these records, quality assurance (QA) or management can determine if the step is being completed. Feedback can be provided to those who are forgetful, and disciplinary action can be taken if required.

Evaluate Warnings, Instructions, and/or Training

The third approach to reducing the likelihood of a hazard or failure is to provide warnings, instructions for use, and/or user training.

Formal testing of the effectiveness of providing information to mitigate risk is possible through controlled studies; however, the cost of conducting such research will make it impractical unless instructions, warnings, and training are necessary to reduce a high risk.

One way to informally determine the effectiveness of warnings, instructions, and training is to work with some individuals who are typical of the target user group. Train them, or provide them with the warnings and instructions in the same manner that the user will receive this information. Ask these individuals to perform the related operations and evaluate their use of the system either through observations or an evaluation of the work they performed.

If formal or informal assessment isn't performed, professional judgment should be used to estimate the extent to which the warnings, instructions, and/or training will reduce the likelihood of a hazard or system failure.

Prepare a Mitigation Report

If formal testing has been performed, document the tests and results in a mitigation report such as the one described in deliverable 5.1 in appendix A. If the evaluation at this phase is based on informal testing, a mitigation report isn't prepared because the mitigation will be formally tested as part of the validation testing. If the assessment is based solely on professional judgment, which might be the case with procedural modifications, warnings, and training, the judgments are documented in a revision of the detailed risk assessment and evaluation report.

EVALUATE THE RESIDUAL RISK

Revise the risk assessment and evaluation report based on your formal or informal assessment of the effectiveness of the remedial actions. Modify the risk ratings as appropriate—adjust the likelihood that the system will fail, the likelihood that a failure will result in harm, and the severity of harm—and revise the risk level. If the risk associated with any potential hazard or failure is still high, determine if additional mitigations are possible. Repeat the steps of designing a mitigation, implementing it, testing its effectiveness, reassessing the risk level, and revising the risk assessment and evaluation report.

If the risk associated with any potential hazard or failure is moderate, determine if further reduction is practical. Practicality should be judged from the perspective of technical and economic feasibility.[5] Document your assessment in a revision of the risk assessment and evaluation report.

Potential failures with associated low risk needn't be reduced further.

Once the mitigations are designed and evaluated, the overall risk that remains must be determined.[6, 7] Document the overall residual risk in deliverable 4.1, the risk assessment and evaluation report. If the risk is high, determine if further risk reduction actions are possible; if they're not, perform a risk-benefit analysis to determine if the benefits justify the risks associated with potential failures. Document the risk-benefit analysis in the risk assessment and evaluation report. Note that from the perspective of user or patient safety, a high safety risk can only be justified with a high benefit to

| Medatech 7.1 | Implementation and Testing of Mitigations |

The project team implemented the mitigations to the extent possible at this time. Medatech table 7.1 shows what actions were taken. Doc revised the user requirements and circulated the document to the other team members for signing. Incorporating the changes to user and

document control processes will be included in the procedures written during the next phase.

No formal testing of the effect of mitigations was performed at this time, so no mitigation report was necessary.

Medatech Table 7.1 Implementation and Testing of Mitigations

Mitigation	Implementation actions	Mitigation effectiveness test	Mitigation report
Mitigations for requirements not met by the system			
Replace the user requirement for full-text search capabilities with two requirements: ■ Ability to use words to search document titles ■ Ability to search for documents by attribute information	Revision of the user requirements	Review and approval of user requirement changes by the project team	No
■ Delete the requirement for the automatic selection of reviewers. ■ Modify the document control process to include a document control representative who will identify the reviewers to whom a change request will be routed.	■ Revise the user requirements ■ The requirement that document control will identify reviewers will be put in the user procedures during phase 6.	Review and approval of user requirement changes by the project team	No
■ Remove the requirement for printing a watermark that reads "uncontrolled copy." ■ Change the document control process so that the document control department will stamp controlled copies in red ink with the words "controlled copy."	■ Revision of the user requirements ■ The requirement that controlled copies will be stamped with the words "controlled copy" in red ink will be added to the user procedures when they're written during phase 6.	Review and approval of user requirement changes by the project team	No

(continues)

Medatech 7.1	Implementation and Testing of Mitigations (continued)		

Mitigation	Implementation actions	Mitigation effectiveness test	Mitigation report
Mitigations for risk reduction			
Validate that the controls work for prohibiting changes to documents without going through an approval process	N/A. The risk assessment report was revised in the last phase to record the need to verify that the security which protects files from unauthorized changes works	None. Effectiveness testing will be included in the validation testing	No
Configure the roles and privileges so that access to down revisions is limited to the few people who need such access.	Identify the configurations that are required to set privileges to access down revisions.	Test to verify that setting the privileges controls access to down revisions.	No

users or patients. A high risk to users and/or patients can't be justified based on a high economic benefit to the company. If the risk can't be justified, high-risk projects must be terminated.

CREATE AND TEST CONFIGURATIONS FOR CONFIGURABLE SYSTEMS

With configured systems, the configurations designed during phase 4 are set or built, informally or formally tested, and documented. For example, if a workflow has been designed for routing information technology (IT) problems through an organization, the workflows are created in the system and informally tested. If the configurations involve, for example, creating a report on the average time taken to approve a change to a document, the report is built in the system. Informal testing of the report would involve verifying that the visual display of the report and the printed report include the desired information in the correct format. The reports may also be reviewed by those who will be creating and/or using them to gauge user satisfaction.

Instructions on how to set or create the configurations must be documented so that the configurations can be reset, built, or installed when the system is installed for validation testing, or reinstalled at a later time (e.g., after a crashed system). For example, the information entered into the document control system to create the report on the

(continues on page 232)

Medatech 7.2	Evaluation of Residual Risks

After the mitigations, the team reviewed the risk assessments to evaluate the residual risk. Because the mitigation actions weren't formally tested, the team made its best judgment on the affect its actions would have. Team members assumed for the time being that the validation results would justify changing their assumption about the likelihood of a system failure to "occasional."

The project team reviewed all the risks for all the potential hazards and failures it had identified. The team realized that it could reduce the residual risk for one item, QC using a down revision of a test method to pass a lot that didn't meet a new specification. They could configure the system so that QC personnel wouldn't be able to see down revisions. With the addition of this mitigation, the residual risks were judged to be low enough to be acceptable for all potential hazards and failures.

The risk assessment report also was revised to reflect the new mitigation (i.e., not allowing QC to view down revision documents) and the team's conclusions regarding the residual risk. If the results of the validation were to reveal a number of defects, the team would review its assumptions regarding the likelihood of a software failure and its risk assessment in light of the validation results.

The risk analysis items that were discussed in Medatech 6.2 are presented in the following table with the addition of the mitigation of prohibiting QC personnel from viewing down revisions.

Evaluation of Residual Risks

Hazard or failure: Documents are changed without approval.

- **Harm:** Product specifications, bills of material (BOMs), test methods, etc. can be changed without approval, resulting in the noncompliance of multiple aspects of the quality system (e.g., design control, production and process controls, quality testing, and document control).

    Severity: Catastrophic

    Controls against system failure and ways to prevent harm after failure: No other aspects of the quality system would detect changed documents; a document user would have to detect that there was an unapproved change. Documents are stored by the EDMS system in an internal database (called a vault).

    Likelihood that harm will occur: Probable. This rating is based only on the assumption about the likelihood of a software failure.

    Risk level: High

    Additional mitigation plans: Configure the system so that users can only view image files (e.g., PDF) of the items. Two failures are then required: a failure of the EDMS system to only allow image files to be viewed, and an EDMS failure that allows a change to a non-image file to be saved (probable X probable = occasional). Further, a successful validation will justify lowering the likelihood of an EDMS failure to "occasional," in which case the probability of failure is "remote."

(continues)

Medatech 7.2	Evaluation of Residual Risks (continued)

Likelihood that system will fail with additional mitigation(s): Remote

Risk level after mitigation(s) (residual risk): Moderate

Notes on what to test or validate assuming the presence of mitigations: Test to verify that users are only able to view image files of items. Test the ability to save back changes to opened documents. Verify that the documents can't be located from the server file structure.

Harm: Product specifications, BOMs, and test methods can be changed without approval, possibly resulting in a product failure that could result in death.

Severity: Catastrophic

Controls against system failure and ways to prevent harm after failure: For changes to result in a modified product, the following is required: the software would have to fail (probable), drawings and BOMs would have to be changed, modified parts would have to be purchased, and final product would have to pass QC tests.

Likelihood that harm will occur: Remote. The likelihood of the software error and that such changes would go unnoticed is "remote."

Risk level: Moderate

Additional mitigations planned: Configure the system so that users can only view image files (e.g., PDF) of the items. Two failures are then required: the failure of the EDMS system to only allow image files to be viewed, and an EDMS failure that allows a change to a non-image file to be saved (probable X probable = occasional). Further, a successful validation will justify lowering the likelihood of an EDMS failure to "occasional," in which case the probability of failure is "remote." In addition changes to multiple documents would have to go unnoticed. With everything combined, the team felt it was quite unlikely that such harm would occur.

Likelihood that system will fail with additional mitigation(s): Very improbable

Risk level after mitigation(s) (residual risk): Low

Notes on what to test or validate assuming the presence of mitigations: Test that image files are presented. Test the ability to save back changes to opened documents. Verify that the documents can't be located from the server file structure

Hazard or failure: A down revision of a document is mistakenly presented to a user as the current revision.

Harm: Product could be tested against an old spec or with an old method, resulting in the rejection of a good lot valued at up to $300,000.

Severity: Critical

Controls against system failure and ways to prevent harm after failure: The materials review board (MRB) is required by procedure to investigate discrepant material.

Likelihood that harm will occur: Remote. The system would have to fail (probable), and the

MRB would have to be negligent (occasional). The combination of both is "remote."

Risk level: Moderate

Additional mitigation planned: Set user privileges so that QC personnel can't view down revisions.

Likelihood that system will fail with additional mitigation(s): Improbable. Two system failures at the occasional level—after validation—are needed (a down revision is mistakenly presented, and a permission error that allows a QC person to view down revisions). Plus the MRB would have to be negligent.

Risk level after mitigation(s) (residual risk): Moderate

Notes on what to test or validate assuming the presence of mitigations: Test that the current revisions are presented to users. Test that user privileges do not allow QC users to view down revisions.

Harm: Product could be tested against an old spec or with an old method, resulting in the acceptance of a bad lot leading to a death.

Severity: Catastrophic

Controls against system failure and ways to prevent harm after failure: QC is required by procedure to verify that the correct revision of the test method was used. QA is required to verify that the proper revision of the test method was used when it releases the lot.

Likelihood that harm will occur: Very improbable. The combination of a "probable" likelihood of a system failure, the product being made with an obsolete part (occasional), the failure of QC to verify that it had the correct revision (occasional), and the failure of QA to verify at final release that QC used the correct revision (occasional) is quite improbable.

Risk level: Low

Additional mitigations planned: Set user privileges so that QC personnel can't see down revisions. This additional mitigation isn't needed for this potential harm, but it's added to the system to further mitigate the potential loss of a lot given in the previous example.

Likelihood that system will fail with additional mitigation(s): Very improbable

Two system failures and three human errors must occur. System errors are: A down revision is mistakenly presented and a privilege error to allow a QC employee to view the down revision. Each is at the occasional level — after validation. Human errors are: The product will have to be made with an obsolete part (occasional), QC failing to verify that they are using the correct revision and QA failing to verify that QC used the correct revision.

Risk level after mitigation(s) (residual risk): Low

Notes on what to test or validate assuming the presence of mitigations: Test that the current revisions are presented to users. Test that user privileges don't allow QC users to view down revisions.

average time to approve a change to a document must be documented so that an identical report can be created in the future. After the validation process begins and during operational use, any changes to the configuration will be made and recorded through the change control process (see chapter 8). The documentation on the configurations will be revised.

Test the configurations to verify that they're correct. Ordinarily, the testing is informal (i.e., test protocols aren't written and executed, and a report isn't prepared). If information about the testing must be documented, a memo can be prepared and entered into the project files. The validation testing will include formal testing to verify that the configurations have been correctly created and function to requirements.

The documentation of the configurations can be recorded in a separate document or incorporated into the IQ during phase 7—Qualify the system.

PHASE 5 ACTIVITIES FOR CUSTOM SYSTEMS

Part of managing custom developers and/or integrators is to monitor their work activities to ensure that they're following an appropriate development life cycle. In chapter 4, it's recommended that your contract with integrators and custom developers include an agreed-upon development methodology or life cycle. Technical Report 18 points out that using a structured software quality assurance system will help ensure that the completed deliverables are in compliance with written specifications, standards, and practices, and thereby increase the chance for success in meeting the product requirements.[8] Review the vendor's deliverables for correctness and to audit its performance against your agreement. Request corrective action if the required activities aren't performed in a manner that's acceptable.

The development activities described in this section are recommended for moderate- and high-risk custom software development. You should determine with your software developer which of the activities are needed if your system is low risk. The activities described below include the most effective defect detection and prevention practices discussed in chapter 5, and the software testing and quality assurance activities described in Technical Report 18.[9, 10] The references provide more sources on the activities related to the development phase of the software engineering life cycle.[11-15]

Custom software is coded following agreed-upon coding conventions; comments are placed in the programs to facilitate support. The mitigations designed to control the risks of a custom system are built into the system as it's coded. Code that will be repeated in the system is created, thoroughly reviewed and tested, and placed in a secure location so that it can be reused in other places. The developer reviews his other programs. Modeling or prototyping during development helps ensure that the development efforts are aligned with the users' expectations. A panel of developers, including some who didn't write the code, formally inspects the programs for logic, structure, commenting, and correctness. Versions of the code are controlled with a configuration management process and/or tool. A traceability matrix is constructed to map programs to the detailed design to ensure the system is developed as designed. System documentation is written on the technical aspects of the system, and user documentation is prepared on how to use the system.

The developers, or test engineers, create a detailed test plan that's reviewed. To ensure that sufficient testing is performed, two traceability matrices are created, one linking the tests to the functional specification, and the other linking the tests to the user requirements. Individual programs are tested (unit tests), and tests are performed on how programs work together (integration tests). System testing is also performed that verifies the system functions effectively as a whole. Both structural verification and functional testing are performed. Structural verification includes the code inspections mentioned in the previous paragraph and a detailed examination of the program logic to verify that it meets the requirements. Functional testing involves tests of the application's functionality by comparing system outputs from tests with expected outputs. Testing the effectiveness of the mitigations is integrated into the testing of the system.

When the custom system involves hardware and software, all the parts are combined (or integrated), and a final set of tests are conducted at the developer's location to ensure that the integrated system works. The company for which the custom system is built (i.e., the user) reviews the results of the tests and determines if it will permit the system to be brought into the company. This final set of system tests is sometimes called a "factory acceptance test" (FAT). Technical Report 18 states that if the user has the appropriate involvement with the FAT, it might not have to repeat some of the tests on its site. The important thing to note is that the report is referring to the special circumstances where the exact hardware and software components that were assembled at the developer's site are relocated to the user's facility:

> If the FAT is conducted, according to protocols approved by the user, if the test results are documented properly and reviewed and approved by the user, and if it can be demonstrated that the items being tested will not change during shipping and installation at the user's site, it may not be necessary to repeat certain tests during the qualification of the system."[16]

Defects identified during the development process (including testing) are logged and repaired. Appropriate tests are conducted to verify that the defects have been repaired and that other parts of the system haven't been negatively affected by the changes. The test results and defect repairs are reviewed, and a decision is made as to whether the system is ready to be brought into the company for informal testing and integration.

Once the custom software is brought into the organization, the phase 4 and phase 5 activities that are described for COTS systems are performed, including:

- Bring the system into the organization.
- Integrate the system with other systems.
- Identify and resolve any discrepancies between user requirements and the system.
- Perform a detailed risk assessment.
- Plan mitigations.
- Plan the validation.
- Prepare a written validation plan.
- Implement the mitigation plan.
- Test the effectiveness of the remedial actions.
- Evaluate the residual risk.

SUMMARY OF PHASE 5 DELIVERABLES

Table 7.2 summarizes the deliverables for phase 5.

Table 7.2	Phase 5 Deliverables		
Phase 5 deliverables	**Definition and explanation**	**When applicable**	**Deliverable references**
Mitigation report (see deliverable 5.1).	A report that describes the actions taken to mitigate risk and system weakness in meeting requirements and regulations. In addition, it documents investigations and studies performed to determine the effectiveness of the remedial actions.	If formal testing of a mitigation is performed	ISO 14971, Section 6.3 a
Revised risk assessment and evaluation report	A revision of the risk assessment and evaluation report that was created during phase 4. (see deliverable 4.1).	If mitigations have been implemented	ISO 14971, Section 6.3 b
Update to documentation of configurations	Revision, update to, or creating documentation of system configurations (see chapter 6).	Systems that require configuration	Highly recommended

Chapter 8

Phase 6: Prepare for Use

During phase 6 the project team learns about the system and gets ready to use it. The system owner and his or her staff learn the system so that they can prepare user procedures, training materials, and, during phase 7, validation tests. The information technology (IT) department prepares the procedures that it needs to support users and maintain the system in a validated state. The IT staff that will support the users learns how to operate and support the system (see note 1).

The structure of the system is captured in a system specification that identifies the components of the system and the requirements for each component as specified in the technical requirements created in phase 2.

Those who are responsible prepare user procedures and training materials.

Generic IT procedures are written if they're not in place, including procedures for system security, support, backup and restore, data archival, disaster recovery, maintenance, calibration (if applicable), change control, and printer setup and driver verification (if the organization wants to use such a procedure instead of qualifying each printer). If the generic procedures aren't sufficient for a specific system, then system-specific procedures are developed. Such procedures are critical to keep the system under change control and maintained in a validated state (i.e., a state in which there's objective evidence that the system meets requirements).

At the same time, the tests to be included in the validation testing can be drafted and checked. Preparing the test protocols will be discussed in chapter 9, but the test protocols can be developed while the activities of this phase are carried out.

During phase 6, the system is informally tested as the activities for this phase are performed; any defects that are discovered are tracked and addressed.

By the end of phase 6, the project team and other designated individuals should be finished exploring how the system works and how they want to use it.[1]

During phase 6 commercial off-the-shelf (COTS), configured business, and custom systems are all on the same path again. The activities and deliverables are the same for each.

CREATE A SYSTEM SPECIFICATION

By the end of phase 6, all the components of the system should be known, the system assembled, and a preliminary test of the system configuration performed.

Once the configuration is set, create a system specification. This includes a system description, a complete listing of the hardware and software components, and a complete listing of all hardware and software configurations, including configurations of the applications so that it will function as desired. Include the specifications and/or technical requirements for each component.

The system description contained in the validation plan can be incorporated in the system specification because it contains all the information needed for a description in the system specification. In addition, the system specification is kept up to date even after the validation is complete and thus would meet the requirement of the European Community (EC) Commission for a system description that's kept current.[2]

The system specification also includes a listing of all of the components that must be separately installed to create the system and the specifications, or technical requirements, for each component. The system specification becomes the authoritative description of the system at the detailed level. It includes the model and version numbers of all components so that an identical system can be built as needed. For software, include any service packs or defect patches that have been installed. For highly reliable commodity items, such as cabling, record the specification without manufacturer information. When you treat an item as a commodity item, you're implicitly asserting

---

Medatech 8.1   System Specification

Tec created a system specification that was a list of all of the components of the system rather than a configuration diagram. The network was defined as a separate system and was qualified by Tec and Val (see Medatech 6.4). Tec's specification included the manufacturer's name, model or product number, and product revision for the following components:

- Server (to perform as the application server, Web server, and database server)
- Server communication cards
- Server operating system software
  - ☐ Service packs
  - ☐ Patches

- Array V disc drives
- Database software
- Dedicated printer for the document control department
  - ☐ Printer drivers

- Application software
  - ☐ Server software
  - ☐ Service packs
  - ☐ Patches

- Internet browser
- Software for creating image files from native-mode files of documents and drawings

---

that an item from one manufacturer can easily be substituted with another from a different manufacturer without a change in the probability of a failure. If this assumption isn't true, don't treat the item as a commodity item and specify the manufacturer of the item to be used.

The system specification also includes all hardware, system software, and database software configurations required by the application developer for the effective operation of the system.

Finally, the specification includes application configurations set by administrators to enable the system to function as desired in business processes. These configurations are the most valuable part of the system specification. Specifications that are based on a technical requirements document, or a vendor's technical documentation are generally not nearly as difficult and time consuming to re-create as configurations for complex routings, transactions, and/or reporting.

The specification can take the form of a tabular listing of components and/or a system diagram, sometimes referred to as a "system hardware configuration diagram." Often, both a list of components and diagrams are used because the diagrams show the communication links between the components of the system. See deliverable 6.1 in appendix A for a more complete description of the system specification.

LEARN HOW TO USE THE SYSTEM

The Need to Learn the System

Training is provided at this point for two groups of users. First, the system owner, other members of the project team, and key users who have roles to play during this phase learn to use the system. The purpose of the training is to provide the background needed for the following tasks: writing user and administrative procedures, preparing training materials for users and administrators, and preparing the validation tests. Needed familiarity with the system is best obtained through formal training from the application vendor. However, if such training isn't available or desirable, some individuals might have to teach themselves so that they can develop training materials.

The other group that must be trained is the personnel who will support those who are working with the system during this phase and the personnel who will be performing the validation testing during the next phase. At lease one person from the user organization and one from technical support must have in-depth training with the system to serve as the company's experts.

Tracking and Resolving Problems

Problems that are identified with the system must be tracked and resolved. Those working with the system must bring to the attention of the project team any problems that are experienced while using the system. An appropriate team member determines if the difficulty is due to a software defect, a discrepancy between how the system functions and a requirement, or an operator error.

Either the system owner or project team leader must track and resolve problems that are discrepancies between the system and requirements.

The IT department is the appropriate function to track and resolve system defects. The personnel in IT might choose to use the same problem tracking system they'll use to track software defects and hardware failures once the system is used in production. (A problem-tracking and -resolution process is identified later in this chapter as a required procedure to maintain the system in a validated state.) Problems that IT can't resolve are referred to the appropriate vendor.

If the resolution of the problem requires modifications to documents, the appropriate project team member should track the resolution until all required changes have been completed. For example, if a user requirement is deleted, that action might require modification of the computer system project proposal, user requirements documentation, the detailed risk assessment, a mitigation report, system user documentation, and training materials. If drafts of the validation test protocols have been started, modifications might also be required to the operation qualification (OQ) and/or performance qualification (PQ) protocols, as well as the matrix that traces requirements to test protocols. If a change isn't made completely throughout the documentation, problems of inconsistencies will occur later in the life cycle. For example, consider the situation in which a requirement has been removed because the system is not capable of meeting it. If tests related to that requirement aren't removed from the draft OQ protocols, the system will fail during the validation testing.

WRITE USER AND APPLICATION ADMINISTRATIVE PROCEDURES

Write User Procedures

User procedures are written to ensure that trained users appropriately perform work with the system. In addition, some user procedures are written because regulatory bodies require procedures for the functions that are being performed with the system. For example, the Food and Drug Administration (FDA)'s Quality System Regulations mandate that procedures be established and maintained for controlling the documents that are required by that regulation.[3]

When preparing user procedures, document how the business process is to be performed with the system. Write user procedures at the level that states what must be done rather than at a detailed level that describes how to perform each task. For example, a document control procedure for an electronic document management system

(EDMS) will have statements such as, "Create a change request by completing the change request form in the EDMS system." In preparing user procedures, assume that the person following the procedures has been adequately trained in how to use the system (e.g., in how to open the change request form and input the required data). If the individual forgets how to find and open the change request form, he or she can refer to their training materials, user's manual, or ask a document control staff member for help. A procedure tells an individual what they must do with the system to perform a business task; the user's manual tells them how the system works and how to use it to perform tasks.

The user procedures should also provide instructions for making choices. For example, if there's a data field for "type of document" in the change request form, definitions and instructions should be provided on the document categorization scheme so that everyone who completes the change request form will correctly categorize the documents they're attaching. If documents are misclassified, they might be sent to the wrong reviewers for approval.

Different user procedures might be needed for users who perform different tasks. For example, one procedure might be written for the users of document control systems who only need to open documents. Another procedure might be needed for reviewers, and still another for the document control staff who processes the change requests.

Table 8.1 lists some of the types of information that are typically given in a user procedure.

Prepare Alternative Arrangements for Down Systems

Prepare alternative arrangements for systems that must be operated even when the automated system breaks down; such arrangements are often called "contingency plans." These procedures are required by the EC pharmaceutical regulations.[4] The time required to bring the alternative arrangement into use should be related to the urgency of the need to use it. The EC regulation uses a recall procedure as an example, and states: ". . . information required to effect a recall must be available at short notice." The procedures to be followed if the system fails or breaks down should be "defined and validated."

Alternative arrangements could be either alternative system arrangements or alternative user procedures. When system availability is critical, organizations will often design the hardware to minimize system downtime. Examples include having a second server or group of servers that would take over the processing if the server failed;

Table 8.1	Information Typically Provided in User Procedures

Type of information	Document control examples
What activities to perform, including any required sequence of steps	The actions that must be carried out to create and submit a change request
Instructions on making choices	Instructions for document control staff on what reviewers to assign to different types of documents
Identification of quality records	Quality records from the document control process include the change request form and electronic signatures associated with approval or rejection of the request.
Limits on creating, modifying, and deleting quality records	Document control personnel can delete change requests only when the request is cancelled by the originator or rejected by a reviewer.
Checks of the accuracy of critical data entered manually by reviewers (EC Annex 11, No. 9)	Document control verification that an employee who created a change request entered the correct reviewers
How to generate accurate and complete copies in both human-readable and electronic form (21 CFR Part 11, Section 11.10 b), including printed copies of stored data (EC Annex 11, No. 12)	Printing change request data, including electronic signatures
Contingency procedure for a down system (EC Annex 11, No.s 15 and 16)	How to perform the work related to the system when the system is temporarily not functioning
Required qualifications for using the system and how the qualifications will be verified (Part 11, Section 11.10 i)	Prerequisites for using the system, for example, the completion of user training
Approval process for assigning user privileges (Part 11, Section 11.10 d; EC Annex 11, No. 8), and a statement of what privileges should be assigned to different types of users	■ The process for authorizing the assignment of, or change to, the privileges for an individual (e.g., a manager must submit a signed request for an employee to be given reviewer privileges) ■ A list of the access privileges assigned to different types of users (e.g., a read-only user, reviewer, and document control administrator)
System security policies and practices	■ Requirement for how often users must change passwords ■ Steps users are expected to take to prohibit unauthorized access during the periods of time the user is away from his or her workstation ■ A policy on not sharing passwords ■ Policy and procedures on assigning another employee approval power by proxy
The meaning of electronic signatures (Part 11, Section 11.50 a 3)	A reviewer's electronic signature on a change request means that the reviewer is approving or rejecting the changes to the documents attached to the change request and the disposition of the existing parts as indicated on the request
Reports that must be generated and/or data that must be exported	Document control reports on the number of change requests processed in a month and the average length of time for approving or rejecting each request

having a hot standby server ready to switch to if the system fails; making identical copies of data on two data storage devices at the same time; and having multiple communication paths between devices. The validation must include the following as appropriate:

- Automated process of switching to a backup device
- Manual process of switching to a backup device
- Recovery of data that might have been lost when the system was down
- Reinstating the failed system
- Transferring data from the backup system to the primary system (if the backup server uses a different data storage device than the main server)

Another option is to develop a manual process that can be used if the system fails. Such a manual procedure would specify how the data would be collected, recorded, and saved; how operations on the data would be performed; and how the data and transactions would be entered into the system once it becomes available.

Write Application Administrative Procedures

Application administrative procedures define the tasks that must be performed by an administrator to manage the use of the system. There are two types of administrators for some systems: an application administrator and a system administrator. The application administrator manages the aspects of the system that relate to users and the business functions of the system. The system administrator manages the technical aspects of the system, such as the database, operating system, network communications, and the hardware. An exception to this general split of responsibilities generally occurs if the organization uses Microsoft's Active Directory feature of Windows. Active Directory can be used to assign users to groups, and to grant groups of users different privileges in different applications. When Active Directory is used in this manner, the system administrator controls the assignment of user privileges instead of the application administrator.

The reasons for preparing and using administrative procedures are consistent and correct administration and meeting regulatory requirements. 21 CFR Part 11, for example, requires that procedures be in place for some administrative tasks, as does the EC Commission's directive for medicinal products.[5, 6] Table 8.2 presents some of the application administrative tasks that might be included in an application administrative procedure.

Table 8.2	Information Typically Provided in an Application Administrative Procedure
Type of information	**Document control examples**
User administration (21 CFR Part 11, Section 11.10 d; EC Annex 11, No. 8)	■ Adding new users ■ Deactivating users who have left the company ■ Changing users' group membership ■ Assigning access privileges ■ Verifying that users of various types meet the prerequisites ■ Verifying the identity of a reviewer before assigning an initial password ■ Assigning user names that are unique
Security administration (Part 11, Section 11.300)	■ Procedures for checking logs on unauthorized attempts to enter the system ■ Instructions on when to reinstate a user who has been de-authorized by the system ■ Electronically de-authorizing lost, stolen, missing, or otherwise potentially compromised tokens, cards, and other devices that bear or generate identification code or password information ■ Issuing temporary or permanent ID replacements using suitable controls
Requirements and procedure for testing devices that bear or generate identification codes or password information to ensure that they function properly and haven't been altered in an unauthorized manner (Part 11, Section 11.300 e)	N/A (Such devices aren't normally used with document control systems.)
Training requirements (21 CFR 820, Section 25 b; Part 11, Section 11.10 i; EC Annex 11, No. 1)	Training required to be an application administrator
Controls over the distribution of, access to, and use of documentation for system operation and maintenance (Part 11, Section 10 k 1)	Control of CDs that contain administrative functions

DEVELOP TRAINING MATERIALS

If the system isn't properly used, the data entered or created might be in error and the business functions that are automated might be misused. Users must be properly trained to ensure that the results produced by the system are accurate and reliable.

User training needs to meet two different goals: to develop skills in using the system, and to communicate how to perform the business process with the system. With a document control system, for example, reviewers need to learn how to use the system

Medatech 8.2	Preparation of Training Materials and User Procedures

The Medatech electronic document management system (EDMS) project team asked the EDMS vendor to train the team and a few other individuals on basic user skills. Doc's document control specialist served as the user expert for the system. After the on-site basic users' training, Doc and the specialist attended the vendor's course for document control administrators to learn how to perform administrative functions and gain a deeper understanding of the system.

Doc's document control specialist created some fictitious change requests and took them through an approval process so that some documents were in the system for others to access. She also assigned IDs and temporary passwords to everyone who had been trained. Employees who were trained began to log on to the system and prepare for its use.

Doc and the specialist reviewed the vendor's basic users' training and decided that it would be too expensive for the vendor to train all of the employees. They decided to create a training program for the common user, who would use the system to view documents, and a second training program for reviewers, who would approve or reject documents online.

The specialist drafted user and administrative procedures.

Tec worked with the system to become familiar with it. He was primarily concerned with the training that would be needed by the information technology (IT) professionals who had to support the users. Tec sent one of his staff members to the EDMS vendor's system administration class and appointed that person the IT expert for the EDMS.

Because Doc and his staff were the subject matter experts, Tec and Doc decided that the document control specialist would be the first line of support for the EDMS users. If the document control staff couldn't help a user, they would report the problem to the IT system expert. If the IT expert couldn't resolve the problem, she would contact the EDMS vendor for help.

Tec decided he would use network administration software to monitor the use of the EDMS system and the amount of network and server resources the system consumed. He'd followed the EDMS vendor's recommendations when he purchased the server. Tec's preliminary data indicated that the server would have enough capacity to easily handle the anticipated volume of transactions. Tec was concerned about the network. He'd observed some preliminary signs that response times got longer during periods of peak use. Response time would be formally monitored during the performance qualification and an evaluation made at that time.

Tec also reviewed the database table default settings, and he and Doc estimated the number of records that might be created. The default sizes were increased.

and what to do specifically as part of the business process of approving documents. These two objectives can be achieved in the same training session if the company develops training that integrates the two objectives (e.g., "How to use our EDMS system to review and approve our documents.")

The second option is to split the training objectives and provide two independent trainings. You can first train users on how to use the system and then train them on how to use the system as part of your business process. Training on the former can be taught by a variety of parties: your organization, the software vendor, and third parties either at your location or in a public seminar. The training on how to use the system within your business process, however, will be specific to your company. It must be developed and provided by your company or an individual who works under your direction. Training that's developed by your company should be tested through pilot sessions.

PREPARE INFORMATION TECHNOLOGY PROCEDURES

Information technology processes and methods should be created to ensure that validated systems will continue to perform reliably. These procedures range from protecting the system from unauthorized use and modification to restoring data that's been lost or corrupted. A list of examples is provided in table 8.3.

If IT actions and management is required that's unique to the system, system-specific procedures may be needed. Examples include client installation, database management, backup and restore, calibration, system maintenance and configuration, and security. Changes to validated systems must be approved and controlled to keep the system in a validated state. This is addressed in the next section. However, routine adjustments and modifications of a system needed to maintain performance can be defined in a system maintenance and configuration procedure. If the procedure is incorporated and tested as part of a validation protocol (e.g., an IQ or OQ), those activities can be performed, following the procedure, without going through the change control approval process.

The IT support and other IT services can be contracted to a third party. As pointed out in the EC Commission Directive for pharmaceutical products, Annex 11, the agreement developed for such services should be formalized. The agreement should include a clear statement of the responsibilities of the third party.[7]

Table 8.3	Recommended Information Technology Procedures

Title	Purpose	Topics to include
Backup, archive, and restore (cGMP, 211.68 b; EC Annex 11, No. 14)	To provide a procedure for backing up, archiving, and restoring data, programs, and applications	■ Process for completing backups ■ Frequency of incremental, complete, and historical backups ■ Review of backup logs and actions to be taken when part of the backup has failed ■ Systems that require special backup procedures ■ The process and frequency of moving data from database tables and placing it in another location (an archive) ■ Process for recovery
Network adds, changes, and deletes (Annex 11, No. 8)	To describe the process for adding users to the system and assigning user privileges, changing user information and privileges, and deactivating users	■ Management requests for adding, deleting, or modifying a user profile ■ Adding a new user to the network and e-mail ■ Assigning, canceling, or altering access privileges to controlled network directories ■ Assigning, cancellation or altering access privileges to applications if not included in the application administration procedures ■ Employee review of information technology (IT) policies, including electronic signatures ■ Password management ■ Configuration of workstations shared by multiple employees
Disaster recovery and contingency plans (Annex 11, No. 16)	To provide a plan for how the data collected by automated systems will be collected manually in case of a down system, and to provide a process for restoring computer capability following a down system or disaster	■ Contingency plans for when equipment or a system that is managed by IT fails or breaks down (e.g., database server used to store data generated by lab equipment). (Owners of individual systems are responsible for contingency plans for their systems.) ■ Contingency plans for load balancing and management when one or more components of the network are down ■ Restore of the network after a power failure ■ Restore of a server that will not boot ■ Restore of a server when a critical component has been corrupted ■ Restore of the network and computer room after a natural disaster
Logical and physical security (21 CFR Part 11, Section 11.10 c and d; Annex 11, No. 13)	To establish actions for securing company information from internal or external attacks	■ Physical security to limit access to network servers and communication equipment ■ Security for remote access to the network (e.g., firewall, encryption) ■ Anti-virus practices
System support (Annex 11, No. 17)	Establish a system for supporting end-users in the effective use of computer resources. The procedure includes the process for recording and analyzing	■ Criteria for what systems IT will support ■ Requirements for the development of custom software ■ Troubleshooting issues ■ Recording issues ■ Classifying issues ■ Referring issues to management and vendors

Title	Purpose	Topics to include
	errors to enable corrective action and/or managed change control (required by EC Annex 11, No. 17).	■ Resolving various types of issues ■ Tracking issue resolution ■ Installing solutions as part of corrective action or change control
System maintenance	Establish the generic process for maintaining computing resources. A separate maintenance and configuration management procedure is prepared for the infrastructure and each system.	■ Preventive maintenance and calibration ■ Maintenance contracts with vendors ■ Methods used to monitor network load and failures ■ Adding and expanding RAM ■ Data storage management
Printer setup and driver verification	Establish a protocol for verifying that a printer is capable of printing accurate representations of electronic data, records, and reports.	■ Requirements for installing a new printer ■ Tests to verify that a printout is an accurate representation of electronic files
Desktop and laptop setup	To set up desktops and laptops so that all needed software is installed and configuration requirements of controlled software are met	■ Preparation of employee workstations ■ Minimum hardware configuration for a workstation ■ System configurations needed for compatibility with the company network and the individual's needs ■ Applications that form the base software configuration and optional applications, and how to install these applications, or references to installation instructions
Other system-specific procedures	To provide procedures for IT activities that are specific to an application	More than one procedure might be needed to cover topics for specific systems such as: database management, system maintenance and configuration, backup and restore, calibration, and security.

CREATE A CHANGE CONTROL PROCESS

Making one change that has a detrimental effect on the system can waste the resources spent to carefully select, validate, and implement a system. The regulations that required that a system be validated also require that changes be validated before approval and issuance.[8–10] The change control process is the mechanism for making sure that the system remains in a validated state (i.e., that it continues to function reliably after a change is made). Systems are placed under formal change control when the validation testing begins with the execution of the IQ during phase 7, and systems remain under change control until the system is retired in phase 9. Changes are approved, tested, and implemented in a controlled manner.

In addition, the change control forms log the changes that are made outside of normal maintenance and configurations management. These records can provide valuable information when troubleshooting new problems. The system is first defined in the system specification, installed, and verified following the IQ. After changes have been made, the change control records provide the incremental information on the system needed to reconstruct how it evolved to its current state. The change control records also capture the testing done on the changes before their implementation in the operational and/or production environment.

As part of the change, all necessary changes are made to system documents. If a change is made during the validation, the system documentation that must be changed can include user or technical requirements, the risk assessment, mitigation plan, system specification, user and administrative procedures, and training materials. If the change is made after the validation is complete, the change to documentation could

---

Medatech 8.3	Information Technology Procedures

Like most relatively small and young companies, Medatech had a number of information technology processes in place that it used but only a couple that were documented in procedures. Tec had already approved procedures for backing up and restoring the servers, and for logical and physical security. He and his staff decided to write new companywide procedures for:

- System support
- Disaster recovery
- Network adds, changes, and deletes
- System maintenance
- Printer setup and driver verification
- Desktop and laptop setup

Tec used the system support procedure to support the people who were learning how to use the system. He recorded, tracked, and resolved problems with the system. Although the change control process wasn't formally used until the commencement of the installation qualification, Tec kept the team involved in any decisions concerning changes to the system. Changes, such as installing a patch to fix a software defect, were tested and recorded so that the same changes would be installed in the validation instance and production environment. Tec prepared two procedures specifically for the electronic document control system (EDMS):

- EDMS maintenance and configuration
- EDMS backup and restore procedure

include the system specification and/or configuration diagram, technical system documentation, user and administrative procedures, training materials, and the risk-assessment report.

Three types of changes can be identified:

- *Administrative.* A change that doesn't involve how the system functions, has no affect on data integrity, and has no potential to affect integrated systems or business processes. These changes can be made outside of the change control process if they're described in an approved procedure that's been qualified through executing an approved protocol, such as an operation qualification (OQ) protocol. The changes are controlled by the qualified procedure.

- *Fix.* A change that addresses a problem with the system. A fix has the potential to affect data integrity or how the system functions. A fix also could affect other systems, equipment, or processes.

- *Enhancement.* An improvement of the system, usually through the addition of functionality or upgrading equipment. An enhancement can affect data integrity, system output, business processes, other systems, or equipment.

Fixes and enhancements are made following an approved change control procedure such as that described in deliverable 6.2.[11] Some administrative changes can be made outside the change control process, while others must be made through the change control process. Application administrative changes are changes made to the current configuration of the application, or to create new functionality using configuration tools.

For example, assume that a workflow for approving procedures was validated at the same time a document control system was. Also assume that the capability to modify a workflow was captured in an application administrative procedure and validated, but the ability to create a new workflow was neither described in a procedure nor validated. Changes to the workflow for approving procedures can be made without change control approval if the changes are made following the validated methods described in the application administrative procedure. When a new workflow is required—for example, to approve engineering drawings—the change control process must be used because creating a new workflow is outside the scope of the original validation. The changes can be either application administrative changes or system administrative changes.

A change control process involves the following:

- A description and assessment of the change, a risk assessment, and a decision on whether to proceed

- The evaluation of the change in a test environment
- Qualification testing of the change prior to installation for production use to verify that the change is defect-free and there's no negative effect on data integrity and system functionality
- Implementation of the change for production use
- Post-change impact analysis

The change-control process described here and in deliverable 6.2 is but one way of meeting the requirements of a managed change-control process.

Establish a Change Control Board

The change control board evaluates and approves or rejects a proposed change. Evaluating a proposed change involves the efforts of the same functions that comprise the project team. The system owner evaluates the value of the change from the user perspective and will have some insight into how a particular change might affect other functionality. The IT function, of course, assesses technical issues related to the system, the implementation of the change, and any maintenance and support requirements. The validation and/or quality assurance (QA) function(s) reviews the planned validation testing and related protocols, if any, and will review the executed protocols (i.e., test records) from the perspective of validation requirements prior to the board giving the approval to implement the change. The QA representative will also consider any changes from the perspective of quality system requirements.

Ordinarily, a single change review board reviews all changes to all systems. Alternatively, a different change review board can be set up for each system. In the latter case, the board consists of the project team for the system. The advantage of having the same board review changes to all systems is consistency across systems. The advantage of having a different board for each system is that board members will know the system and will be better able to evaluate changes to it.

Prepare a Change Request

Whoever initiates the request begins by completing a change request form (see deliverable 6.3) and submitting it to the change control board.[12] The request includes:

- A description of the change and all the documentation that must be modified as part of the change, including user procedures and training materials

- Affected systems and subsystems
- Any new moderate or high risks that the change introduces and any planned mitigations of those risks
- The justification for the change—why it's worth the cost and effort
- Planned validation testing of the change itself and revalidation of other aspects of the system that might be affected
- Planned implementation steps
- Planned monitoring of the installation after the change

Review and Approve the Request

Board members review the request and determine if the change should be made. Each member records his or her observations and concerns on the change request form, including any steps that should be taken or requirements that should be met that haven't been included in the request. Board members also record any additional moderate or high risks that they think the change will introduce. Once the members have recorded their reactions, the board meets to discuss and approve or reject the request. The board reviews the change for possible risks associated with the change. Determine the harm that can be associated with a failure of the changed item on the same dimensions of harm as were included in the detailed risk assessment. Estimate the probability that the system will fail and that the failure will cause harm. Derive a risk value. Determine if mitigation is necessary; if so, include the implementation of the mitigation in the change request. Document the risk analysis on the change request form.

Install the Change in a Test Environment

A test environment is created that's identical to the current configuration of the system. Usually, a test environment is kept current with the configuration used in the production environment. Prepare installation instructions, or an installation protocol for the fix or enhancement. Protocols are approved as required by the computer system validation procedures. Install the change by following the instructions given in the change request, vendor instructions, or the protocol; if a protocol is executed, it becomes the installation record and is kept as part of the change control record. Also install any mitigations that are part of the change package.

If the verification of the change is simple, verification instructions can be included in the change request, or combined with the OQ in an I/OQ if OQ qualification is needed.

Conduct Validation Testing

The change is tested in a test environment before it's implemented in the production environment. The test should:

■ Verify that the change is effective in correcting the problem or addressing the issue (e.g., if functionality is changed, the test should verify that the new functionality works properly).

■ Verify that the mitigations work as anticipated in reducing the probability of risk.

■ Determine if the change has had an adverse effect on other system functionality.

■ Determine if data integrity has been adversely affected.

If the tests to be performed are simple, they can be included in the change request and approved with it. If they're extensive or complex, a protocol is prepared and approved following your company's computer system validation procedures. If the testing is done based on instructions provided in the change request, a report is prepared after the changes are executed. If a protocol is executed, it's approved and maintained as a record. If necessary, a protocol report is prepared following the description given in chapter 9.

Implement the Change in the Production Environment

The change control board reviews the results of the validation tests and determines if the fix or enhancement functions properly and whether it will negatively affect other aspects of the system. The board's approval will authorize the installation of the fix or enhancement in the production environment.

Users are notified of the change or trained as appropriate in advance to the installation.

The change is installed in the production environment following the instructions given in the change request, vendor instructions, or the protocol; if a protocol is executed, it becomes the installation record and is kept as part of the change control record. Tests are conducted in the production environment if specified in the change request. Any deviations from the planned installation are documented, approved, and filed with the change request. The board reviews all deviations from the expected test results; appropriate actions are taken and documented to resolve any issues. (The handling of deviations in test results will be discussed in more detail in chapter 9.)

Amendments to the change request can be submitted to the board anytime during the processing of a change request. Once the change has been implemented and production testing is complete, a new change request needs to be submitted if further changes are needed. Amendments should include a description of the change that's requested and the reasons for the change. The board approves the amendments.

As part of implementing the change, updates are made as needed to documentation, including the system specification and/or configuration diagram, technical system documentation, user procedures, training materials, and the risk assessment report.

Post-Change Impact Analysis

It's difficult, if not impossible, to determine in advance the full effect of every change to a system. As part of the change control request, the change review board determines if the change and/or system must be monitored after it's implemented. Simple changes that clearly have limited effect might not require monitoring. A change to a part of the application that performs multiple functions or is used by multiple parts of the application should be monitored. The type of monitoring and the duration is determined as part of the change request review. Monitoring normally involves paying close attention to issue reports on new problems that occur within several weeks of the change. Determine if the change could have caused the problem.

Emergency Change

An emergency is defined as a situation where an immediate change is required to:

- Prevent product quality, safety, or integrity from being jeopardized
- Maintain personnel safety
- Address an urgent regulatory compliance issue or business need
- Restore proper operation to a system or a critical component of a system

To speed the process of implementing the change, it's approved and directly implemented. Validation tests and, if needed, protocols are prepared and executed after the implementation. If difficulties are uncovered, actions are taken to correct the situation.

PHASE 6 ACTIVITIES FOR CUSTOM SYSTEMS

At the end of phase 6 of the RiskVal life cycle, the activities for custom systems and COTS systems are once again aligned.

Medatech 8.4	Change Control Procedure

Quincy and Tec developed a change control procedure for computer systems following the method outlined in deliverable 6.2. A change control board was established that would review changes to all validated computer systems. The board included Quincy, the head of quality assurance; Tec, the head of information technology; and Val, the validation specialist. System owners would participate in discussions about, and the approval of, changes to the systems for which they had responsibility. This meant that Doc would meet with the board whenever changes were considered to the electronic document management system.

Table 8.4	Procedures Created During Phase 6 If Needed

Phase 6 deliverables	Definition and explanation	When applicable	Deliverable references
Information technology procedures: ■ Backup, archive, and restore (see cGMP 211.68 b and EC Annex 11, No. 14 for backup requirements) ■ Network adds, changes, and deletes ■ Disaster recovery and contingency plans ■ Logical and physical security ■ System support ■ System maintenance (optional) ■ Printer setup and driver verification ■ Desktop and laptop setup (optional) ■ Other system-specific procedures (e.g., client installation)	Procedures needed to maintain a system in a validated state. Most of the procedures listed here are generic (i.e., they can be used for many applications and/or systems). If a system requires a unique process, a separate procedure is written for it. For example, a generic backup-and-restore procedure will cover most of the items on a network; however, if a system requires a unique process for backup and restore, an additional procedure is written for that system.	All systems as appropriate	Part 11, 11.10 c, d, i, j, k; 21 CFR 211, Section 68 b; EC Annex 11, No. 8, 13, 14, 16, 17
Change control procedure (see deliverable 6.2) and change request form (see deliverable 6.3).	A procedure that defines the process used to make controlled changes to a validated system, and the form used to request and approve the change	All validated systems	21 CFR 820, Section 820.70 i; ISO 13485, 7.5.2.1; EC Annex 11, No. 11 Part 11, 11.10 k 2

During phase 6 COTS, configured business, and custom systems are all on the same path again. The activities and deliverables are the same for each.

SUMMARY OF PHASE 6 DELIVERABLES

Table 8.4 summarizes the procedures created during phase 6 if they don't already exist; these documents will be used for all computer systems. Table 8.5 lists the phase 6 deliverables that will be created for each computerized system.

Table 8.5	Summary of Phase 6 Deliverables Created for Each Computer System		
Phase 6 deliverables	**Definition and explanation**	**When applicable**	**Deliverable references**
System specification (see deliverable 6.1)	A specification for the system that includes a system description and lists all hardware and software components, their hierarchical relationships, and requirements for each component. A diagram showing the hardware components of a system and their connectivity can be included.	Recommended for low-risk systems that are complex or that will change relatively often, and moderate- to high-risk systems	EC Annex 11, No. 4 (system description)
User procedures	User procedures define how the system is to be used by end-users.	Low-risk systems if predicate rules or quality system standards require	Required if covered by a predicate rule or quality system standard; highly recommended with other systems
Application administration procedures	Administrative procedures define how the system is to be managed by application administrators	All systems with administrative functions	21 CFR 820, Section 25 b; 21 CFR 11, Sections 11.10 d, i, j, k 1 11.300; EC Annex 11, No. 8
Contingency procedure	Alternative arrangements for systems that need to be operated in the event of a breakdown	All systems that can't have down time	EC Annex 11, Nos. 15 and 16
Training materials	Manuals and other materials needed to train users and administrators. Such materials may be purchased or developed by the company	All except systems where training isn't needed	Highly recommended

Chapter 9

Phase 7: Qualify the System

During phase 7, the system is tested in a validation environment before it's installed in the production environment during phase 8. The testing, called qualification, demonstrates that the item (e.g., piece of equipment, software program, or computer system) has been properly installed and is capable of meeting a relevant set of requirements. (See note 1 for the difference between qualification and validation.) If a system uses the same network and/or servers as other applications, the qualification is usually split into application qualifications and infrastructure qualifications.

Qualifying a system or application begins by creating a validation instance of the system. The system includes the application software, other software used only in conjunction with the application, infrastructure resources dedicated to the application (such as data space), and hardware dedicated to the application that's not considered part of the infrastructure. Such dedicated hardware could include input, output, and communication devices. The application is installed following a documented procedure, and infrastructure devices used by the system are configured to provide the application with the resources it needs.

Proper installation of the system is verified, as is the ability of the hardware and software to meet the technical requirements, by executing an approved installation qualification (IQ) protocol. The system IQ verifies that the system hardware and software are properly installed, configured, and have the capability and capacity to support the application. Prior to beginning the IQ, the person executing the protocol confirms that all measurement equipment (e.g., test instruments) is calibrated, and maintenance is up-to-date for all instrumentation and equipment. A report is prepared on executing the IQ protocol. It includes a summary of the results, problems encountered (i.e., discrepancies between actual and expected results), how the problems were resolved, and a conclusion regarding the readiness of the system for operational qualification (OQ) testing (i.e., the system meets the IQ protocol-acceptance criteria). The executed IQ protocol is attached to, or referenced in, the IQ report.

The OQ is performed following an approved protocol. This should include tests for user requirements and an evaluation of the users' ability to understand and correctly interface with the system. Supportive operations used by the system to perform the functions mandated in the user requirements are also tested. A traceability matrix is prepared that maps where in the OQ each user requirement and supportive operation is tested. As the protocol(s) is executed, discrepancies between expected results and actual results are written up as variances. The resolution of each variance is documented and approved. Changes to the user requirements, software, infrastructure, or dedicated hardware to resolve problems are performed under control of the variance or an approved change control procedure (see chapter 8). An OQ report is written that includes a summary of the data collected while executing the OQ protocol, a discussion of the variances and their resolution, and a conclusion regarding the ability of the system to reliably meet requirements and perform supportive operations. The executed OQ protocol(s) are attached to, or referenced in, the OQ report.

Validation packages provided by software vendors can be invaluable in speeding the validation process, though caution must be applied. To use these tests for validating a system, it's necessary to verify first that the tests adequately cover all requirements. The adequacy of the vendor's tests can be evaluated by creating a matrix that traces user requirements and required supportive operations to the OQ tests. It might be necessary to develop and execute supplemental tests.

The infrastructure is divided into two categories: providing automated services and providing the underlying hardware and software platform that hosts both infrastructure services and applications. Services provided by the infrastructure can play a critical role in safeguarding systems, preserving data integrity, and providing network communications. The infrastructure platform can include, but isn't limited to, network equipment, shared servers, a database management system, and input and output devices.[1]

The infrastructure platform might need to be qualified, depending on the risks associated with its failure. As is the case with hardware and system software that's dedicated to an application, the infrastructure platform is qualified using IQs and OQs to demonstrate that the infrastructure devices, system software, and ancillary software provide the capability and capacity specified in requirements.

Risk analysis also is used to determine if an infrastructure service needs to be qualified and the extent of qualification required. This book recommends that the risk be assessed based on the potential effect of a service on product quality and the criticality of the service for compliance, data integrity, security, and business efficiency and continuity. An infrastructure service is qualified through an IQ for the hardware and software that provide the service and an OQ which demonstrates that the service functions as required.

With configured business systems, configurations are created before the IQ and verified using the IQ. Functionality created through the configuration is tested during the OQ and as part of the performance qualification (PQ) in phase 8, if appropriate.

Custom systems are treated in the same manner as commercial off-the-shelf (COTS) systems; that is, the proper installation of system components that meet technical requirements is verified, and the system is tested in a validation environment.

INTRODUCTION

Validation testing normally involves an IQ, OQ, and PQ. Qualification means verifying that the item, service, or infrastructure meets relevant specifications or requirements. There are no absolute lines to be drawn between these three types of testing.[2] This chapter discusses the IQ, which is used to verify that a system meets the technical requirements defined in the system specification and is properly installed. The OQ, which is also discussed in this chapter, verifies that the system has the capability and capacity to meet user requirements throughout all anticipated operating ranges.[3] With custom software, the OQ verifies that the system meets the requirements defined in the functional specification (see note 2). The performance qualification (PQ), which is discussed in chapter 10, confirms that the system meets user requirements in the actual production environment.

Food and Drug Administration (FDA) regulations don't require any specific protocol. Rather, the language allows the individual validating the system to determine how to structure the qualification and validation activities, but an approved protocol must be used. In addition, the results of the activities need to be documented. Here's the exact language: "...the manufacturer shall validate computer software for its intended use according to an established protocol. All software changes shall be validated before approval and issuance. These validation activities and results shall be documented."[4] With the RiskVal life cycle, the mandate to use established protocols is met with the IQ, OQ, and PQ, as appropriate based on the nature of the item and the associated risks.

From a regulatory perspective, validation testing of COTS systems can be limited to parts of the system that must be used to meet user requirements that are related to production or quality systems (see note 3). For example, if you don't plan to use the electronic signature function of an electronic document control system, you don't have to gather objective evidence either in a validation environment (i.e., an OQ) or production environment (PQ) that the electronic signature functions work properly. If you decide later to use electronic signatures, that can be validated under change control.

When a system is validated, the system IQ is used to verify that the hardware as well as the system and ancillary software dedicated to the application provide the capability and capacity needed for the application to work effectively. Take, for example, a situation where controlling the temperature of a chemical reaction is critical to worker and consumer safety. The infrastructure equipment and system software used to control the temperature need to be treated as high-risk items in the validation. The communication with and control over the programmable logical controllers (PLCs) that circulate the coolant in the reactor need to be thoroughly tested. Hardware and system software that's dedicated to an application are qualified as part of the application validation. The IQ for the automated manufacturing system will be used to verify that the PLCs and the communication equipment used within the plant meet the technical requirements and that the equipment has been properly installed. The OQ and PQ performed on the automated manufacturing system will verify that the PLCs are appropriately controlled under normal and abnormal conditions by the manufacturing system. During the OQ (validation environment) and PQ (in a validation or production environment), tests are conducted to establish that the system can meet user requirements. The OQ and PQ will have to go beyond direct testing of user requirements and include tests of supportive operations used by the system to perform the functions related to the user requirements.

Supportive operations are used by a system to accomplish what the organization wants it to do (as defined in the user requirements) and therefore must operate effectively for the system to be reliable. The requirements for supportive operations are what others in the validation field call "functional specifications." For example, suppose a user requirement for a document control system states that only authorized reviewers can approve a change request using an electronic signature. Some of the supportive operations that must be verified in addition to the direct approval of a change request are:

- An authority check to determine if the user has the authority to approve the change request
- An error message that appears if the individual isn't an approved reviewer
- Storage of the electronic signature information in a secure location that can't be changed
- Association of the electronic signature with the electronic record of the approval in such a manner that the two will always be displayed together

The required supportive operations may be identified in a separate document (also known as a functional specification) or included in the user requirements if the user has sufficient understanding of how the application works. If the supportive operations aren't written as a separate document or included in the user requirements, include tests of the supportive operations in the OQ protocol as part of the testing of the functions they support. The specifications and/or requirements for the supportive operations are included in the OQ's expected results statements. Note that the RiskVal life cycle doesn't require supportive operations (also known as functional specifications) to be identified in a separate document. Too often, organizations struggle with trying to determine if a requirement is a user requirement or a supportive operation. Don't waste time and resources trying to differentiate between the two. If the system must perform the function or operation, include it either with the user requirements, in a document dedicated to supportive operations, or simply test it as part of the performance of the function it's supporting.

Testing supportive operations is very important. If these operations don't work properly, the high-level system functions that correspond to the high-level user requirements won't work properly. The testing of supportive operations will be addressed more extensively in the discussion of the OQ later in this chapter. The IQ and OQ for systems and/or applications will be discussed in the first half of this chapter.

As mentioned in chapter 6, the network, shared servers and system software, database equipment and software, and input and output devices used by multiple applications can be qualified as part of the infrastructure rather than as part of an integrated computerized system.

The infrastructure can also provide services needed to safeguard data and applications. When we think of using computer systems, we think in terms of an application being used to perform an action based on some data or information. However, records of the actions that are performed often need to be kept to document what happened and the outcome of the actions. Under such circumstances, the automation needs are extended from the performance of an action to the preservation of the data used, a record of the action performed, and the results. Hardware and software that aren't part of the application and/or system can be used to meet these additional needs. Here again, this book applies the same simple rule: If a service, including the hardware and software used to provide it, is limited to one application, include the service, hardware, and software in the validation of the application. If the service, including the hardware and software used to provide it, serve more than one application, include them in the qualification of the infrastructure.

This chapter introduces the terms "infrastructure platform" and "infrastructure services."

The infrastructure platform is the underlying hardware and software components that must be present and functioning for network communications and applications to work. It includes but isn't limited to equipment and software such as servers and system software, database equipment and software, input and output devices, and routers, switches, hubs, and communications software used in network communications.

Infrastructure services are the functions performed by the infrastructure hardware and software to safeguard systems, preserve data integrity, and provide network communications. Infrastructure services include, for example, backup and restore services, firewall services, network communications, and control of access to the network, network drives, and applications.

The importance of the services as well as the hardware and software that support them is determined by a risk analysis of the services. The results of the analysis are used to determine what's appropriate for the qualification of each service and the infrastructure platform.

The second half of this chapter discusses how to qualify both the infrastructure services and platform.

Many approaches can be used to obtain the needed objective evidence that an application performs to requirements and that records and applications are protected. As long as the objective is achieved, any approach can be used. The approach presented here is to define a system as an application and dedicated hardware and software. Validating the system includes qualifying the dedicated hardware and system software as having the capability and capacity to support the application, including providing services for it. If hardware and software supports only a single system, this book recommends that its support be qualified and/or validated as part of the system.

Infrastructure functions that are, or will be, performed for more than one application are considered to be infrastructure services. The hardware and software used by more than one system, or to provide infrastructure services to more than one application, is considered the infrastructure platform. Granted, this distinction is arbitrary, and hardware and software dedicated to a single application could also be considered part of the infrastructure platform. Items are separated into either a system or infrastructure solely for presenting a simple criterion for determining when to include hardware and system software with a system validation.

In short, the guidelines used in this book are:

- If hardware and system software perform functions for only a single system, include them in the system validation.
- If the infrastructure hasn't yet been qualified, include shared hardware and system software in the infrastructure qualification.
- If the infrastructure has been qualified, and new common hardware and system software or infrastructure services are introduced, introduce them under change control to the infrastructure.

Table 9.1, which will be discussed extensively in this chapter, describes how these guidelines flow into specific protocols.

PREPARE THE INSTALLATION QUALIFICATION PROTOCOL

IQ Objectives

The IQ ensures that an appropriate foundation is in place for running applications and infrastructure services. System IQ protocols for hardware and system software that support a single application have the same objectives, content, and format as infrastructure IQ protocols used for hardware and system software that support multiple applications or infrasturcture services. An IQ contains a detailed description of the components of the installed system or infrastructure, including all configurations. An IQ also includes a statement of all specifications and/or requirements so that the actual

Table 9.1	System and Infrastructure Protocols

To obtain evidence that:	Protocols to use
The dedicated hardware and software meets technical requirements for the system and is installed and configured properly.	System installation qualification (IQ)
The application can meet user and supportive operations requirements for performing the regulated work in a validation environment.	System operational qualification (OQ)
The application and infrastructure services combined work effectively as used in the automated process for doing work in the production environment.	System performance qualification (PQ)
Hardware and software used by more than one application meet technical requirements for the applications, are installed and configured properly, and perform basic operations.	Infrastructure IQ and OQ
The hardware and software needed for infrastructure services meet technical requirements for the services and are installed and configured properly.	Infrastructure service IQ
The infrastructure services work properly.	Infrastructure service OQ

hardware and software and their configurations can be compared to the specifications. The IQ can be used to install an identical system if necessary.

The IQ has several objectives:

■ Identify each hardware and software component of the system that's individually installed.

■ Verify that each component has been completely and correctly installed.

■ Verify that each component meets relevant technical requirements as defined in the system specification.

■ Verify that all configurations for hardware, system software, and ancillary software used for infrastructure services have been appropriately set.

■ Verify that all configurations for the application software have been appropriately set.

■ Verify that all IT procedures needed to control and maintain the system in a functional state are approved and implemented.

IQ Protocol Content

An IQ protocol is written and approved before it's executed. (A protocol is executed when the actions stated in the protocol are performed and required data regarding the results of the actions are recorded.) The requirements for the IQ protocol content include general requirements for all qualification and validation protocols (IQ, OQ, and PQ) as well as requirements specific to IQ protocols. Technical Report 18 identifies both the general requirements and requirements specific to each type of protocol.[5] The deliverables presented in appendix A include both the generic and specific protocol requirements; see deliverable 7.1 for the IQ, deliverable 7.3 for the OQ, and deliverable 8.1 for the PQ.

Information that should be included in all qualification protocols includes:

- Objectives of the tests
- Specific method to be used for each test
- Expected results of the tests
- Data to be collected regarding the actual results
- How the data are to be collected and reported
- Protocol-acceptance criteria. These are used to determine if the item being evaluated is acceptable (i.e., if it passes the qualification tests).
- Review and evaluation procedures that will be used to determine if the protocol-acceptance criteria were met.[6]

Content specific to the IQ versus an OQ or PQ is also described in Technical Report 18 and includes verification that:

- All important aspects of installing the hardware and software adhere to the system specification.
- Proper versions of the programs have been installed.
- There are appropriate user manuals.
- There are appropriate as-built drawings (or equivalent documentation about the system).
- There are appropriate calibration reports for instruments.
- Appropriate backup copies of the software exist.[7]

Deliverable 7.1 provides more information about the IQ's content.

IQ Test Section

The IQ test section is where the installation of each component of the infrastructure or system is verified, and information for identifying each unique device or piece of equipment is recorded. Most systems involve many different types of items, such as servers, system software, the application, ancillary software, and dedicated input and output devices. With IQs for such systems, the protocol's test section can be broken down into subsections. For each test subsection (e.g., the IQ for the server), prepare the following:

- An objective
- A list of required materials and equipment
- Acceptance criteria for the verifications in that subsection
- A verification part in which the proper installation of an item, as well as whether the item meets the requirements, are evaluated. This component will be referred to as the "Installation verification part" of a test section in subsequent discussions; it's illustrated in figure 9.1.
- A conclusion about the results. Make a concise statement of what's demonstrated by the successful passing of the tests contained in the subsection.

If the IQ protocol test section isn't subdivided, the test section involves only the verification of the proper installation of components and whether the specification is met. This corresponds to the fourth bullet point in the list above, for parts of a test subsection.

To verify the installation of each device, optional feature, optional component, software, and all configurations, identify each component by name, its model or part number, and its revision level, as appropriate, in the installation verification part of the test subsection. If serial numbers or company part numbers have been assigned, these should be recorded in the installation verification part when the protocol is executed to unequivocally identify what was installed at the time of the IQ. Exceptions to this principle are communication cables and network interface cards that are treated as commodity items. The types of network interface cards and cables are identified in the installation verification part, but the manufacturer and model aren't specified in advance. The MAC addresses of the network interface cards are recorded during the IQ.

If requirements define either an acceptable range along a dimension, or a binary state (e.g., a feature is turned on or off), in the installation verification part of the test section state the range or the binary state as a required specification in the "expected results" column. The person executing the IQ will record the actual value as the "actual results" and indicate whether the expected results were met (i.e., the value is within the specification range, or the binary state is as expected). Exhibit 9.1 provides an example. On line number two, the expected result for central processing unit (CPU) speed is between 1.8 and 2.8 GHz. The actual speed gets recorded in the "actual results" column. If requirements haven't been set, write the infrastructure IQ protocol so that the expected result is that the device is installed, and instruct the person executing the IQ to record critical information about the device. With a server, for example, write the installation verification part of the test section to confirm that the server has been installed, and instruct the person executing the IQ to record the CPU speed in the space provided.

One way to structure the verification part of the IQ test subsection is illustrated in exhibit 9.1.[8, 9] Note that the installation doesn't include everything that might be verified about a server (see table 9.2 for additional items). The table shown in exhibit 9.1 has columns for:

- Stating the test item number
- Identifying the item being qualified (e.g., server processor and memory)

| Exhibit 9.1 | Installation Verification Part of an IQ Test Section |

The following table is an example of the verification part of an installation qualification (IQ) subsection for a server. See table 9.2 for additional items that should be verified in such instances.

No.	IQ item	Record login account ID	Procedure	Specification or expected results	Actual result	Initial date
1	Server processor and memory	Logon with an ID for a server manager. ID used:	Record the number of CPUs and the type and serial number of each.	2 Intel Xeon CPUs	Processor 1: Type: Serial No.:	
					Processor 2: Type: Serial No.:	
					Processor 3: Type: Serial No.:	
					Specification met: ☐ Yes ☐ No	
2	CPU speed and cache size	Logon with an ID for a server manager. ID used:	Record the speed and cache size of each CPU	1.8 GHz to 2.8 GHz, at least 512 KB cache	Processor 1: Speed: Cache size:	
					Processor 2: Speed: Cache size:	
					Processor 3: Speed: Cache size:	
					Specification met ☐ Yes ☐ No	
	Conclusion re: server installation	All tests of the configuration meet expected results. The server processor and memory are properly configured.			☐ Yes ☐ No	

- Stating the type of logon account ID the tester is to use and providing a space for the tester to record the actual ID being used (you must be logged on as the correct type of user to perform the dictated actions)
- Instructions and actions to be performed by the tester (i.e., the procedure)
- The specification or expected results. Provide a range of acceptable values, if appropriate.
- Recording the actual results obtained and an evaluation by the tester as to whether the specification was met
- The tester's initials and the date the results were recorded

The table in exhibit 9.1 also provides an example of a conclusion that can be drawn if the actual results meet all the expected results.

A System or Application IQ Protocol

A validation instance of an application must be prepared for performing the OQ and, at times, for the PQ. The validation instance is an operating copy of the application on a server and/or workstation with its own dedicated data space. The validation instance and the hardware and software used to run it are called the "validation environment." This is created so that the validation testing can be performed with a copy of the application that's free of random data or test cases leftover from employees who were learning how to use the system and/or preparing training materials, procedures, or test cases. Such data and transaction remnants might interfere with the validation testing. When OQ tests are performed, actual results that the system produces are compared to the expected results. For example, if you search for a type of document to test the search capability, you'll specify beforehand what documents should appear in the search results. If other documents are in the system from previous use, they might appear on the search results, and although the system is functioning correctly, the actual results won't match the expected results.

The validation environment could involve a completely separate system, including separate hardware and system software, database storage, and a separate instance of the application. In addition, needed configurations of the hardware, system software, database, and application have to be set. Alternatively, the validation instance could involve a separate instance of the application that uses the hardware and system software set up when the test instance was constructed. In the latter case, configurations are still needed so that the application software can have access to infrastructure resources, store and access data, communicate with other software and users, allow users access,

(continues on page 271)

Table 9.2	Examples of Items Included in Installation and Operational Qualifications for the Infrastructure Platform	
Type of item	**Examples of items included in the IQ**	**Examples of items included in the OQ**
Server	■ Processor central processing unit (CPU) (e.g., type, physical quantity, logical quantity, speed, cache size) ■ RAM quantity and type ■ Motherboard basic input/output system revision (if needed) ■ Firmware revision ■ Removable media device type ■ Power supply quantity and type ■ Power supply voltage and amperage ■ Local console access (e.g., device type, server identifier, connector type, console cable and/or port ID) ■ Remote console access (e.g., type, server identifier, connector type, cable/port ID, management utility)	■ Record the average CPU usage over a specified time. ■ Record the average physical memory usage during a specified time. ■ Insert formatted media into bootable media device and determine if the device can read it. ■ Disable one power supply and determine if the server continues to operate without interruption. ■ Login to server's out-of-band remote console.

Network connectivity	■ Identifiers (e.g., server host name, alias, directory service, fully qualified domain name, operating system domain name)
	■ Network interface cards:
	  □ Type
	  □ Quantity
	  □ MAC addresses
	  □ Connect speed and duplex mode
	  □ Default gateway IP addresses
	  □ Subnet mask
	  □ Preferred DNS server
	  □ Enabled protocols
	  □ Port locations
	■ Network interface cards configuration (e.g., number, fail-over, configuration)
	■ Communication protocol name and version
	■ Communication software service packs and patches
	■ Server-specific configuration settings for communication software
		■ Log onto the network server and determine if the server being validated can be found from the server being used.
		■ Verify that shared server resources are shown and are accessible.
		■ TCP/IP connectivity: ping each accessible IP address from a network PC.
		■ Record the time to resume network connection after breaking a link.

Data storage	■ Storage type (e.g., direct attached, networked)
	■ Storage partition configuration
	■ Storage controller:
	  □ Quantity, type, and model
	  □ Communication protocol
	  □ Firmware version
	  □ External cable
	  □ Management utility name and version
	■ Storage physical partition configuration, capacity of each partition, RAID type, and hard drive ID
	■ Storage logical partition configuration, drive letter, volume label, and description
		■ Record the connection status for each volume
		■ Verify that the storage management utility displays the virtual disk(s), storage container(s), and/or meta-device(s)
		■ Verify that hard drives are hot-swappable without interruption

(continues)

Table 9.2	Examples of Items Included in Installation and Operational Qualifications for the Infrastructure Platform (continued)	
Type of item	**Examples of items included in the IQ**	**Examples of items included in the OQ**
Operating system (OS)	■ OS name and version ■ OS service packs and patches ■ License type and number of licenses ■ Server-specific configuration settings ■ Operating system security groups	■ Log in to the server console as a user from each user group. ■ Verify that the user possesses the assigned privileges and only the assigned privileges.
System management service	■ Server management utility name and version ■ Server management configurations ■ Change-detection software name and version ■ System monitoring software name and version	■ Log in to the server management utility and determine if the configurations recorded by the server management utility are correct. ■ Change the configuration and verify an accurate adjustment by the software. ■ Change a test file stored in an appropriate location and verify that the change has been detected by the change detection software.
Application software	■ Application name and version ■ Service packs and patches ■ License type and number of licenses ■ Client software name and version	■ Log in to the application using the name and password for the super-user provided by the software vendor.
Web services	■ Web server software name and version ■ Service packs and patches ■ License type and number of licenses ■ Web browser software name and version ■ Web browser configurations	■ Log in to the Web service as a user from each user group. ■ Verify that the user possesses the assigned privileges and only the assigned privileges.
Database management software	■ Application name and version ■ Service packs and patches ■ License type and number of licenses ■ Database table size	■ Log in to the database system console as a user from each user group. ■ Verify that the user possesses the assigned privileges and only the assigned privileges.
Data input devices	■ Equipment name and version (e.g., terminals, scanners, bar code readers, magnetic strip readers, environmental monitors, test instruments, etc.) ■ Software name and version ■ Service packs and patches ■ License type and number of licenses	■ Power up the device and confirm that the device reaches a ready state. ■ Log in to the terminal services system console as a user from each user group. ■ Verify that the user possesses the assigned privileges and only the assigned privileges.
Data output devices	■ Equipment type and model (e.g., printers) ■ Software name and version ■ Software service packs and patches	■ Power up the device and confirm that the device reaches a functional state.

Type of item	Examples of items included in the IQ	Examples of items included in the OQ
Devices controlled by output	■ Equipment type and model (e.g., programmable logical controllers, alarms) ■ Software name and version ■ Service packs and patches ■ License type and number of licenses	■ Power up the device and confirm that the device reaches a functional state.
Backup and restore service	■ Backup server type and model ■ Backup software name and version ■ Server recovery utility name and version ■ Service packs and patches ■ License type and number of licenses ■ Back up and restore operational and maintenance procedures.	■ Create backup of a server and reconstruct the server from the backup.
Security service	■ Physical security measures ■ Anti-virus software name, version, and configuration settings ■ Server firewall security name, version, and configuration settings. ■ Service packs and patches ■ License types and number of licenses	■ Attempt to access the system using an unauthorized account. ■ Verify that an error message appears and that the system administrator is notified. ■ Enter incorrect passwords. ■ Verify that the account deactivates after a predetermined number of tries. ■ Attempt to add an unauthorized data stream into the system (e.g., add an HPLC without authorization). Verify that the data stream is rejected. ■ Verify that the latest updates have been loaded.
Final preparation	A procedure has been developed for managing and controlling the server's internal clock, and its time is periodically synchronized with a National Institute of Standards and Technology-traceable time source.	N/A

and so that system management and monitoring software tools can be used with that instance of the application.

When the validation instance is created, configure the application, including any functionality that's created with the tools provided with the application, such as approval routes. Install any programs with which the application must be integrated and/ or set the configurations needed for communication between the validation instance of the application and other systems with which it must interact. Set up validation instances of the applications with which the system is integrated if you can't test the integration using the existing instances of those applications.

The validation instance can be converted later into the production instance of the system, thereby making it unnecessary to perform another separate installation. You can establish a validation instance using the same hardware and system software and infrastructure services as will be used to operate the system once it's validated. After the validation testing is done, the test data and transactions can be purged from the system and the validation environment transformed into the production environment. Such a validation environment is advantageous because the IQ and OQ testing will be performed in a technical environment that's very close to the environment in which the system will be used. However, such a validation environment will still differ from the production environment in one significant way: Only transactions related to the validation are being performed. The system isn't being used to transact business, as it will when the validation environment is converted to the production environment. Consequently, system stress due to the volume of transactions is likely to be higher in the production environment.

The IQ for an application or specific system consists of verifying that the validation instance meets the system's technical requirements and is properly configured. The best approach to writing the IQ is to use the system specification developed during phase 6 if it incorporates the technical requirements. Recall that the system specification lists the components of the system and all relevant specifications for each component. Simply write a statement in the installation verification part of the test section for each component that's installed. State each specification for the component as a separate expected result. Provide a space for recording the actual value for the device as well as a space for checking if the specification is met. Exhibit 9.1 provides an example.

If a system specification wasn't prepared, use a list of the system components or take an inventory of them. The technical requirements defined during phase 2 will provide the specifications for at least some of the components.

The system and/or application IQ includes the following items:

- Configuration of the shared hardware and system software needed for successfully operating that system (e.g., server parameters, communication settings, data space, and access privileges)
- All dedicated equipment and its configuration, including servers; data storage devices; input, output, and communication devices; measurement instruments; and dedicated subnetworks
- All system software that's needed to support only the application and isn't considered part of the infrastructure (e.g., interface protocols between integrated systems)
- All application-related software, including server, database, Internet, and client software, as appropriate, and all configurations of such software
- All other applications used by the application being installed and validated. During the IQ, the system must be set up so that it can be operated to the extent called for by the intended uses and user requirements. For example, if a document control

system is being validated, the software it uses must be installed as needed on the server, Web, and workstations that will be used. This might include browser software for accessing the Internet, viewer software for opening image files, and e-mail software for sending messages to reviewers.

- All configurations of the application needed for it to function appropriately in the user processes (e.g., user groups, classes of objects, and workflows)

Risk-Based Considerations for the IQ

The IQ is the most basic aspect of validation, and it provides a foundation for all subsequent validation testing. The IQ has the same content regardless of the infrastructure's or system's risk level.

IQ Prerequisites

Define in the IQ protocol the prerequisites that must be met before it can be executed. One prerequisite should be that all the deliverables that should be completed to this point in the life cycle for an application have been completed and appropriately approved. The list of deliverables would include, as appropriate:

- User requirements
- Technical requirements
- A completed specification, system description, or as-built drawing
- Validation plan
- Current risk management documentation, including the risk assessment, mitigation plan if needed, and any risk mitigation reports
- Documentation on how the system is, or will be, configured. This includes hardware and system software configurations as well as application configurations.
- Change control procedure
- Information technology (IT) procedures needed to support the system and maintain it in a validated state
- Training records for IT staff training
- Appropriate warranties and/or support agreements with external service providers
- Appropriate technical and user documentation at the location of use for all hardware and software. The documentation must be kept in a secured location. Information that's available online should be downloaded and secured, if needed, to preserve the information for the lifetime of the system. Internally-created system documentation must be complete, approved, and under revision control.[10] Verifying the existence

of the documentation can be included in the installation verification part of the IQ test section instead of the IQ prerequisite section.

■ Records that all required calibration and maintenance is current for items included in the IQ

■ Backup copies of all software

Additional items that can be included in the prerequisites section are:

■ Completing all risk mitigation activities

■ Performing required site preparation work, if any

■ Setting any needed environmental controls

■ Taking any needed security measures

IQ Protocol-Acceptance Criteria

The protocol-acceptance criteria are based on the system specification developed during phase 6, which includes the technical requirements from phase 2.[11] IQ protocol-acceptance criteria usually include requirements such as:

■ All prerequisites have been met.

■ Technical specifications are met for all components. If a specification isn't met, a variance form was completed.

■ All variances are resolved. (Ways in which variances can be resolved are discussed later in this chapter.)

■ All test equipment used in executing the IQ was properly calibrated prior to commencing the IQ, and copies of the calibration records are attached to the executed protocol.

■ All personnel involved with executing the protocol were properly trained. Copies of their training records are available for review.

■ All personnel who entered data into or signed the protocol have also signed the signature log given in a protocol appendix or the company's signature log.

■ All supporting documentation (e.g., screen prints and reports) collected while executing the protocol is logged in an appendix and attached to the executed protocol

IQ Protocol Approval

The protocol's author, the project manager or team leader, IT, the validation representative, and quality assurance (QA) approve the IQ protocol.

MANAGING AND EXECUTING PROTOCOLS

The guidance on managing and executing protocols given in this section applies to all types of protocols (IQ, OQ, and PQ) for all types of computer systems (individual systems as well as the infrastructure).

Control and Modification of Protocols

If your organization has a procedure for controlling protocols, it should be followed. In many organizations the document control function controls the signed master of protocols and issues controlled copies for use in the RiskVal life cycle. The following guidelines are presented for organizations that have no experience managing controlled documents. Other approaches may be equally effective.

If a protocol must be changed after it's been approved but before executing the protocol, revise it and approve the revision. Indicate the revision status on the document.

If the protocol must be changed after the execution of it has begun, prepare an amendment to the protocol, approve it, and add it to the back of the protocol and all copies of it. The approvers of the amendment are the same individuals who approved the protocol. Some companies prefer to make all changes by means of amendments and don't ever revise the document once it's been approved.

Include the following in the amendment or on an authorization form attached to the amendment:

- An amendment number unique to that amendment as well as an amendment revision number. You can assign a unique number by making the amendment number equal to the protocol number and using a sequential number as a suffix for the amendment number (e.g., 1234-01).
- A number for each page of the amendment (e.g., one of two, two of two)
- A cross-reference to the material in the protocol that the amendment changes; list all sections where the amendment applies.
- The change to the protocol
- Reason for the change
- A space for the originator's signature and the date the amendment was written
- Signature spaces for the approvers

When the amendment is approved, don't revise the protocol. Instead, hand write a cross-reference to the amendment at all points in the protocol where the amendment applies. Insert such cross-references in each copy of the protocol that's being used. Date and initial each cross-reference.

Guidelines for Good Records

It's critical that regulated organizations follow good record-keeping practices as described in exhibit 9.2.[12] Failure to appropriately document and authenticate findings might result in an invalidation of the findings. If the validation isn't valid, not only will you have to complete the validation again, the results achieved by the system will be considered unreliable. Product might be prohibited from human use, or it might have to be retested because the systems used in its manufacturing and/or testing can't be considered to have been properly validated.

Resolving Variances

There are two types of variance. The first is a discrepancy between what the protocol stated should be done and what was actually done during the protocol execution. This type includes situations where the protocol can't be followed because it's in error. The second type of variance is a discrepancy between an actual result of a test and the expected result. Either type of variance can occur when executing an IQ, OQ, or PQ. Table 9.3 presents several causes of variances and provides examples of variances for each cause. The examples are typical of the types of variances found when executing OQ and PQ protocols.

With the exception of some protocol errors, each variance must be fully documented in a variance report; see deliverable 7.2.

There are three reasons for documenting variances and their resolutions, even when they will be resolved before you finish executing the protocol. First, the project team members are given the opportunity to make their own assessments of the seriousness of the problem, provide input into its resolution, and verify that the problem has been resolved. In instances where the person performing the protocol fixes problems without reporting them to the team, the team members are unaware of the problems that were encountered and can't offer an opinion about the adequacy of the solution that's taken.

For example, the person executing an OQ for a document control system installed at a pharmaceutical company recorded that the system crashed four times in performing a step before the step was performed successfully. Because the step was performed successfully on the fifth try, the person didn't report this incident as a problem. However, a system crash should be reported as a variance. Four system crashes at the same

(continues on page 279)

Exhibit 9.2	Good Record-Keeping Practices

Protocols are completed in keeping with good record-keeping practices. Although these principles are basic for those who are familiar with them, they must be stated for the uninitiated so that simple errors don't invalidate the completed protocol as a validation record. Poorly kept records can result in having to repeat the testing.

Recording data and observations

■ Record any data on the protocol neatly and legibly, using indelible blue or black ink. Write the information in the space provided. If the space is insufficient and a comments section is provided on the same page, indicate with an asterisk at the end of the material written in the provided space that additional information is provided in another location. In the comments section, write an asterisk, identify the item or line number that's being continued, and complete recording the information. Alternatively, provide the additional information on a blank page and attach it to the protocol. Number the page in sequence with the protocol pages. At the end of the information written in the space provided in the protocol, provide instructions to see the added page.
■ Don't write on the back of a single-sided record.
■ Don't use abbreviations unless they're defined or commonly used and understood.

Working with and recording numbers

■ Use a leading zero when recording a value below 1 (e.g., 0.025).
■ Perform the rounding of numbers to the appropriate number of significant figures only at the end of a calculation and not at each step.

Dating and initialing entries

■ The person who made the entry on the protocol must date and initial, or sign, the entry if so directed by the protocol.
■ Write the date only in the defined format.
■ Don't use shortcuts such as writing ditto marks instead of the date or your initials.

Attaching material

■ The protocol might require the collection and preservation of supporting documentation that provides evidence of the proper functioning of the system and/or of system failures. Examples include printing a screen shot of information displayed on the screen, printing a report, and output printed by instruments.

(continues)

Exhibit 9.2	Good Record-Keeping Practices (continued)

- Label the material so that it can be identified; include a description of the item and the test step that required it to be collected. Enter a name of the item in a log of supporting documentation. Number the items in the log and write the log number on the item as part of the label. Initial or sign and date all supporting documentation. Affix supporting material to the protocol.
- If small pieces of paper, such as a printout from an instrument, are to be preserved, paste the material onto the protocol in a space provided or onto a page the same size as the protocol pages. Don't attach material to the back of a single-sided record. Sign the pasted material across an edge so that the signature is partially on the smaller paper and partially on the page it's pasted onto.

Indicating that the record has been completed
- Cross through any unused spaces with a single line. Write the date and your initials along the line.
- Number the protocol pages and any attachments as page 1 of 2, 2 of 2, etc., as needed.

Correcting an error
- Draw a single line through the error so as not to obliterate the original value.
- Write the correct value in close proximity to the crossed-out original value.
- Initial, or sign and date, all corrections.
- If the reason for a correction isn't obvious, record the reason alongside the correction. Where there's insufficient space next to the correction, place an asterisk next to the correction and annotate the reason in the margin or a comments section elsewhere on the page.
- If the employee responsible for the original entry is unavailable, the responsibility for any corrections lies with the supervisor or manager.
- If part of the protocol has to be repeated because of a problem or error, keep the original copy of the protocol intact. From the master, make a copy of the protocol steps that must be repeated. Repeat the steps and record the results on the new copy. Attach the copy to the variance form.

Adding missing data or dates
- If an entry or date was omitted in error and the recorded information is verifiable, record the value and add "performed on (date), recorded on (date)," and initial and date the entry with the current date.
- If the employee responsible for the original entry is unavailable, the responsibility for any additions lies with the supervisor or manager.

Table 9.3	Sources of Variances

Causes of variances	Examples
Protocol error. An error in the protocol, either in the directions of how to perform a step or in the expected results	■ The protocol states to click "Close" to close a window, but the screen has an "OK" button instead of a "Close" button. ■ An expected result statement in the protocol states that the "new person" window closes, but the actual name of the window that opened was "new user." ■ The protocol gave incorrect search instructions for finding a document.
Setup error. Faulty preparation for the test (e.g., not setting up the system in a way that's needed to perform the tests or not inputting needed test data)	■ The test assumes that a user has been established in the system with certain privileges that haven't been assigned. ■ Data that's presumed to have been put into the database wasn't loaded in advance of performing the test.
Tester error. A mistake made in operating the system or in following the protocol	■ A data entry error ■ Clicking on the wrong item ■ Performing a step or activity incorrectly ■ The person performs more actions than specified at a step, (i.e, the tester got ahead of the test and achieved results for subsequent steps). ■ The tester skipped a step.
System failure	■ An incorrect value is calculated. ■ A transaction doesn't occur or occurs incorrectly. ■ An individual is able to perform a transaction that should have been blocked for a certain type of user. ■ The system fails to issue a command to a device under certain conditions, or the device fails to respond.

step should be considered a major issue that requires substantial investigation. If the person executing the protocol is given the sole discretion to determine the severity of a failure and what should be done to prevent future occurrences, as was the case in this example, failures that others might consider serious problems could pass without being addressed.

The second reason for documenting variances is to have a record of the number of problems that were encountered during the validation and their severity. You use the variances to judge the quality of the software, as a test of your assumptions about the likelihood of failure made in the risk assessment, and as a basis for corrective action. If many of the variances are due to operator error, for example, then the user training should be improved. As another example, the following comment appeared in an IQ protocol where variance forms weren't used: "Several errors occurred when trying to print." The nature of the errors wasn't indicated, nor was documentation provided in the form of screen shots or printouts. The notes on the protocol went on to indicate that the problem had been resolved, but the nature of the problem and the solution wasn't disclosed. This limited information is insufficient for determining if any future occurrence of a printing problem is a reoccurrence of the same problem or a new one. The team can't determine if the same solution will work again, or if the problem hasn't been completely resolved.

The third reason for documenting variances and their resolutions is to ensure that proper change control is exercised during the validation testing. Once validation testing starts, the system is under change control. Any changes that are made to the system must be tested before implementation so that additional problems aren't created. In the printer example above, there's no record of how the problem was fixed and no documentation of how the fix was tested before it was implemented.

There are several possible causes of a printer malfunction. One could be a software error that requires a modification to the software. Another cause could be a configuration setting in the printer, which can be easily changed but should be recorded in the system configuration for future reference. Another possibility could be that the printer was off-line, in which case the printer ought to be brought online. This action should be noted in a variance form. The IQ or installation instructions for installing a printer should be amended to include the steps of bringing the printer online, or verifying that it's online before executing the printer tests.

Errors in protocol test instructions may be corrected on the protocol without completing a variance report as long as the correction doesn't affect the nature of the test or the expected results. Such errors include typographical errors, simple errors in procedural steps, and simple errors in expected results. Each correction is initialed and dated by the individual making the correction and a representative of the QA or validation function. The latter may be the person who's responsible for reviewing the executed protocol.

When a variance report is required, stop the execution of the protocol and complete the report. A blank form can be provided in an appendix to the protocol, or a form can be provided in conjunction with a validation procedure. See deliverable 7.2 for a discussion of the information that should be included on the form.[13] Attach the approved variance reports to the variance report appendix in all protocols to which they apply.

A single variance report can handle multiple occurrences of identical error conditions. Each occurrence of the error must be recorded, initialed, and dated by the observer in the executed protocol(s) at the procedural step where it occurred. Each occurrence must be listed in the variance report.

Five ways of resolving variances are given in table 9.4 along with examples and an indication of when the resolution should be performed. After the variance has been resolved and the variance report approved, continue executing the protocol. The permissible resolutions must be defined in an approved validation procedure, approved validation plan, or the protocol being executed. For example, if you want to be allowed to repair software defects during the validation testing, you must state that such changes to the system are permissible. Of course you must also indicate any requirements that will control such actions (e.g., the change control process must be used for software

Table 9.4	Options for Resolving Variances

Resolution of the variance	Examples of variances	When the resolution is performed
Repeat the test.	Tester error	After the approval of the variance form
Modify the protocol to correct an error.	The protocol instructions for conducting a document search are in error.	A change to the protocol is authorized in the variance. The protocol is changed immediately, the failed test is repeated, and the testing is continued.
Correct the system setup to match what's required to perform the test.	Incorrect privileges are assigned to a user during the system setup.	A change to the system setup is authorized in a variance. The setup is changed immediately, the failed test is repeated, and the testing is continued.
Modify the system to correct an error in the system.	■ During the installation qualification (IQ), a system component is out of a specified range. ■ A configuration is wrong. ■ A software defect is found for which a patch is available from the vendor.	■ If a correction is critical for subsequent sections of the protocol, the execution of the protocol can be suspended until the correction is made. The failed test is repeated after the correction, and testing is continued. ■ If the change doesn't have to be implemented immediately, it can be made anytime before the report is prepared for that protocol.
Modify user requirements to eliminate a particular use of the system.	The requirements can be modified to eliminate the ability to use the system for the electronic approval of documents.	A change in requirements to resolve a variance can take place anytime prior to preparing the validation final report. Requirement changes are made through the change control process. Other documentation must be changed to be consistent with the revised requirements (e.g., traceability matrix, risk assessment report, and PQ protocol).
No action is taken, and the variance remains open throughout the validation.	If a system error isn't serious enough to create a problem for using the system, the variance can be left open (e.g., a report doesn't include some information that's important but not critical).	The variance is categorized in the validation final report as "open" and considered when a judgment is made regarding whether the system acceptance criteria have been met.

changes). If a type of resolution hasn't been approved in advance, the variance must be resolved in another manner or left open and the testing continued. Too many open variances might result in the rejection of the system. After the entire protocol has been executed, all open variances are evaluated against the protocol acceptance criteria. If criteria aren't met, the system must be rejected. Modifications not permitted during the execution of the protocol can then be made and the execution of the protocols repeated.

All changes made to the user requirements, software, infrastructure, or dedicated hardware must be made following requirements defined for resolving variances, or by means of an approved change control procedure (see chapter 8). This includes changes made to correct variances. If the change control procedure is used, a copy of the change control record is kept with the variance.

PERFORM THE INSTALLATION QUALIFICATION

This section applies to infrastructures as well as systems and/or applications.

Install, Calibrate, and Perform Maintenance on Equipment

Install all hardware and software components that haven't been installed. Installation instructions can be handled in one of two ways: Manufacturer instructions can be used, or a procedure can be created. The procedure might direct the installer to use a certain set of manufacturer installation instructions. If a procedure is written, approved, and followed for the installation, successful IQ and OQ tests can be used to confirm that the procedure is correct. In the future, the procedure can be used to install equipment without having to go through a change control process. The procedures can include a statement to perform the installation according to the manufacturer's instructions and then provide a reference to the instructions. Examples include the installation of servers, storage devices, and printers.

The IT department must keep records of how the components were installed (e.g., what version of the manufacturer installation instructions were used). Record any configurations, settings, or adjustments that must be made during the installation. Configurations are recorded for three reasons:

■ If the system is installed again, the new installation will be identical to the first.

■ To troubleshoot problems in the future

■ To enable efficient and orderly system management. These configurations, settings, and adjustments are identified in a document such as a memo, a procedure, and/or an IQ.

The difficulty a medical diagnostic company encountered when installing a new revision of a system administration tool illustrates how neglecting document configurations can lead to inefficiencies. The IT technicians attempted to install the new revision by writing over the existing tool, expecting the install to take about twenty minutes. After a full day of frustration, they discovered that when the existing version of the tool was installed, the installer configured the software so that it wouldn't permit itself to be overwritten. This configuration wasn't documented, and the person who installed the original version of the system had left the company.

Before the IQ is conducted, take the normal precautions to ensure that equipment and instruments function properly. Calibrate all instruments that must be calibrated and make sure that all maintenance is up to date.[14] Prepare the system by defragmenting the hard drives, if needed, and synchronizing the server's internal clock time and date with a controlled, well-defined standard.

Execute the IQ Protocol

A protocol is executed when the actions stated in the protocol are performed and required data regarding the results of the actions are recorded.

Obtain a copy of the signed protocol for recording the data collected while executing the protocol. Keep the approved protocol as a master in case the protocol needs to be executed again in the future. Approved protocols are often kept by the document control function, in organizations that have one. The copy of the protocol that was signed is kept as the master. Copies are made as needed for executing the protocol.

The person executing the protocol will record the results of the actions performed and other requested data, and write the date and his or her initials or signature by entries as required by the protocol.

In regulated industries QA will check the executed protocol and sign it as a reviewer. QA will check that:

- The entire protocol has been executed, and the tester(s) has dated and initialed entries as required by the protocol.
- Data and information has been recorded properly.
- Changes to the protocol made during test execution were done according to the rules defined in the protocol or a validation procedure.

Medatech 9.1 | ## Installation Qualification Development and Execution

Doc purchased a software validation package from the selected vendor. Because he and the team had prepared their own validation plan and had their own procedures for the process, including variances and amendments, Doc rewrote the introduction to the validation package to be consistent with their procedures and validation plan.

Tec used the system specification that he'd developed to compare his system to what was included in the software vendor's installation qualification (IQ) protocol. Some additional items had to be added. Before submitting it for review, he and his staff performed a dry run of the execution of the protocol. Refinements were made in the protocol, and it was submitted for approval.

Tec created a new instance of the application and database for the validation testing and then executed the IQ. No variances were encountered.

- A variance form has been correctly completed as required for discrepancies.
- Required materials have been placed in the protocol appendices.

Prepare a Protocol Report

Write a protocol report when the protocol has been executed and the variances to be addressed prior to writing the report have been completed and signed. This report summarizes the results achieved while executing the protocol and concludes whether the system meets the protocol-acceptance criteria.[15] Normally before a subsequent qualification can be executed, a report must be approved for each prerequisite qualification that indicates the qualification has been successfully completed and the protocol-acceptance criteria have been met. For example, the OQ can't be begun until the IQ report has been approved.

The protocol reports for IQs, OQs, and PQs all contain the same type of information; see deliverable 7.4.[16] The important content includes a:

- Summary of findings
- Summary or listing of all variances
- Discussion of the effect of each open variance on the ability of the system to reliably meet requirements
- Conclusion as to whether the system meets the protocol-acceptance criteria

Attach the completed protocol to the report, or reference the protocol in the report. The complete protocol includes all the variances and supportive information placed in the appendices.

The individuals who approved the protocol also review and sign the report. This normally includes the report author, system owner (for the OQ and PQ), IT (at least for the IQ), QA (for all reports), and validation (all reports).

Normally the system will be deemed acceptable if the system acceptance criteria are met. However, it's possible that so many problems occurred and were fixed while executing the protocol that the team must conclude the system isn't acceptable because the software is either unreliable or not properly configured. If a protocol report is signed stating that the system isn't acceptable, the system can't be used for the related functions, and perhaps not at all. The issues must be addressed, and the protocol must be executed again.

PLAN THE OPERATIONAL QUALIFICATION

Objectives of the Operational Qualification

The OQ has two general objectives. The first is to establish the capability and capacity of the system to perform the functions needed to meet its intended uses and defined requirements before the system is used to perform real work. This first objective is accomplished by obtaining documented objective evidence that the system performs to functional requirements through all anticipated operating ranges.[17]

Some explanation of this first objective is needed. First, the system is tested before its use for real products and real data to discover problems before a system failure can result in harm. This is the main reason for a prospective approach as discussed in chapter 6. Problems can be discovered and evaluated, and corrections and mitigations made to prevent and control system failures and associated harm. Second, the system is tested in the validation environment for the reasons mentioned above (i.e., so that other activity and data won't interfere with the testing or produce unexpected results). Third, "anticipated operating ranges" refers to a range of values that a parameter or a variable could have when the system is being used. Fourth, in establishing that the system is capable of performing the automation needed for it to meet the intended uses and requirements, all the supportive operations performed by the system in conjunction with a use or function must be shown to perform appropriately for moderate- and high-risk functions. These supportive operations are how the system accomplishes what you want it to do and therefore must operate effectively for the system to be reliable. For example, a user requirement for a document control system is that authorized reviewers can approve change requests using electronic signatures. Some of the supportive operations that would have to be verified in addition to the direct approval of a change request are:

- An authority check to determine if the user is allowed to perform the function
- An error message that appears if the individual isn't an approved reviewer
- Storage of the electronic signature information in a secure location that can't be changed
- Association of the electronic signature with the change request in such a manner that the two will always be displayed together

What's considered a supportive operation will depend upon the detail provided in the user requirements. For example, if the inability of one reviewer to change or replace another reviewer's approval or rejection of an engineering change order (ECO) isn't explicitly mentioned in the user requirements, it must be considered a supportive operation.

The OQ's second objective is to verify that user procedures are accurate and complete. This objective is partially accomplished by verifying that user procedures have been approved. This approval is usually covered in the OQ protocol prerequisites section. In addition, the OQ tests should mimic the use of the system as required in the user procedures to test if the system can be used to perform the procedure.

Items to Include in the OQ for Dedicated Hardware and System Software

The following are examples of the general types of testing that's performed during the OQ for hardware, system software, and ancillary software dedicated to the system being validated. (A discussion appears later in the chapter on how to qualify infrastructure hardware and software used by multiple applications.) Note that the list below isn't exhaustive. Specific examples are provided in table 9.2.[18]

- Verification that communication links between system components are operable, including input and output devices both on location and at remote sites. For example, a requirement for the infrastructure would be that every PC attached to the network is able to communicate with the e-mail server. During the infrastructure OQ, the e-mail server can send a signal to each workstation device to read its Internet protocol address and confirm that the conductivity has been established.
- Verification that input devices are capable of recording or reading data and uploading it to the infrastructure

- Testing that the system responds appropriately to adverse conditions, such as a failure of a central processing unit, disk drive, or network connection
- Confirming that security devices work, such as the firewall, antivirus software, and access control
- Determining if some aspects of the system software (e.g., load balancing) operate effectively
- Verifying the correct operation of tools for database management (e.g., setting up data spaces) and the simultaneous storage of data in two locations as a precaution against data loss from a disk crash
- Establishing baseline measures for the utilization of system resources (e.g., CPU and storage) during the operation of the system without user initiated transactions. The baseline is useful for performance monitoring, diagnosis, and trouble-shooting once the infrastructure is in use.
- Establishing the effectiveness of IT procedures for maintaining and configuring the hardware and software that is dedicated to the system, and for infrastructure services used only by the system, such as procedures for:
  - ☐ Adding, modifying, and inactivating users, and assigning user privileges
  - ☐ Backing-up and restoring
  - ☐ Archiving data
  - ☐ Maintaining and configuring the system

IT procedures developed for maintaining the system during operations and protecting data from corruption need to be qualified. Such qualification can be completed under separate IQs and OQs. For example, if a special process is used for backing-up and restoring a system, that process needs to be qualified. An IQ can be prepared and executed to establish that the backup-and-restore hardware and software have been properly installed and configured. An OQ can be used to verify that backups are properly made and to provide objective evidence that the system and/or part of its data can be restored from the backup.

In a similar manner system maintenance and configuration processes ought to be qualified. An OQ can be used to demonstrate that changes of predetermined types can be made successfully following a maintenance and configuration procedure, and that the change doesn't have an adverse effect on the system. Once a procedure for maintenance and configuration management has been qualified, changes can be made without obtaining prior approval (i.e., without using a change control request).

An example of an OQ test procedure item for a server is provided in exhibit 9.3.

Exhibit 9.3	Operational Qualification Test Section

The following table is an example of part of the operational qualification of a server.

IQ item	Record login account ID	Procedure	Specification or expected reslut	Actual result	Initial date
Measure average CPU usage	Log on with an ID for a server manager. ID used:	Record the average CPU usage during 10 minutes, expressed as a percentage of total CPU capacity	Average CPU usage < 75%	Actual CPU usage as a percent of total CPU capacity: Specification met: ☐ Yes ☐ No	

Items to Test in an OQ for an Application or System

Areas to consider for the OQ are:

- *Functionality.* The ability to perform transactions, operations, and processing through the defined limits of acceptable values (i.e., maximums and minimums of allowed values) in a manner that complies with specifications and requirements. Where appropriate, the ability of the system to check for the correct entry and processing of data, and the ability to have another operator confirm the accuracy of a record.[19] Appropriate issuing of error messages when data entry, functional, or operator errors are encountered.

- *Regulatory compliance.* The capability of operating in a manner that meets applicable regulatory requirements, including drug and/or device regulations, 21 CFR Part 11 and the European Community (EC) Commission directive on medicinal products[20, 21]

- *Configurations.* Performance of the system as determined by configurations set in the system

- *Access control.* The ability to secure the system from unauthorized access (see the Part 11 requirements related to access security)[22]

- *Audit trails:* For creating, modifying, or deleting critical records (as specified in Part 11 for FDA-mandated quality records and/or in the EC Commission directive for medicinal products)[23, 24]

- *Authorization.* Controls on who can perform certain actions and verification that a user has the authority to perform such actions before they're accepted by the system. Actions that must be verified include canceling, modifying, amending, or deleting an action or record in addition to initially creating the record or performing the action.[25, 26] For example, the EC directive for medicinal products, Annex 11, requires that the release of batches be limited to qualified persons and that the system identify and record the person authorizing the release.[27]

■ *Legacy data load.* The complete and accurate transfer of data and/or commands from an old system to a new one.

■ *Integration.* The ability of systems to exchange data and or commands as per requirements.

■ *File and data integrity.* Maintaining data and files without loss, corruption, or unintentional modification.[28, 29] The ability to obtain clear, printed copies of electronically stored data.[30]

■ *Ease of use of the system.* This includes clarity and simplicity of data entry, clarity and simplicity of commands and operator actions to perform transactions, and minimal screen navigation required to perform transactions

■ *Human factors.* The ability of the intended user to use the system appropriately, including such considerations as the user limitations and circumstances of use

■ *Performance.* Appropriate performance levels (e.g., response time for transactions, availability of the application, and the ability of the system to perform under peak stress conditions)

■ *Reliability.* Methods designed into the system, added to, or integrated with the system to control risks associated with failure or operator errors (e.g., error messages, alarms, data-entry restrictions, limits on options, and warnings of potential problems

■ *Operating system services.* The operating system itself doesn't need to be validated. However, the OQ testing should include tests of the application verifying that the activities the operating system performs for the application are done correctly. Tests should include all the operating system services used by the application, such as maximum loading conditions, file operations, handling of system error conditions, and memory constraints that might be applicable to the application's intended use.[31]

■ *Continuity.* Proper startup and shutdown of devices. The ability of the system to continue to function after a component failure, or to suffer only a minimum loss in the event of a system failure because of the transition to a failsafe mode. Continuity includes the proper functioning of redundant components that take over if a similar component fails, the manual or automated switching from a device or software to a backup, and the software that handles failure modes, including shutting the system down in a safe state when necessary. Also included is the ability to reinstate a failed system, transfer data from the backup system to the primary system once the primary system is reinstated, and recovering data that might have been lost when the system was down.[32–37]

Some of the testing performed by the developer at the development site can be considered part of the OQ tests. Such tests might include stress tests that are difficult to perform at the end-user site, for example tests for high volumes of data, heavy loads or stress, security, fault testing (i.e., avoidance, detection, tolerance, and recovery), and error messages, especially those that the normal user may be unaware of.[38] However, before the results from the developer's tests can be considered part of the validation, the transferability of the test results must be demonstrated. The developer's test hardware and software platform must be equivalent to the operating system used by the company.

OQ Tests for Systems or Applications

Three types of tests are described here that could be included in the OQ or PQ: boundary tests, functional tests (i.e., black-box tests), and structural tests (white-box tests).[39]

Boundary tests. Boundary tests ensure that the system performs properly at the extremes permitted during system use. For example, a requirement for a chemical reactor is that the automated controls keep the temperature at a set point, plus or minus two degrees over a temperature range from twenty to 150 degrees Celsius. In this situation, the OQ should include tests to demonstrate the system's ability to control temperature throughout the range. Tests would be performed at temperature values within the range and just below and above the two extremes. Testing at the extremes of the range is called "boundary testing" or "boundary value testing" (see note 4).

An OQ protocol for systems that control facilities, equipment, and production automation must identify:

- All important operating parameters
- The range of accepted values that the parameters may take
- Criteria for determining if the system has functioned properly during the tests of the boundary conditions[40]

Many systems don't control parameters related to physical objects or processes, but the concept of testing the performance of the system over a range of values might still apply. Examples include:

- Testing the performance of a diagnostic instrument with very low and high concentrations of the material being analyzed
- Testing the performance of the same diagnostic instrument under extreme envi-

ronmental conditions (e.g., the maximum lab temperature and humidity that the manufacturer considers appropriate for the instrument)

■ Testing the ability of the system to perform calculations on extreme values (i.e., high or low), and when a value is missing or is zero

Boundary testing might also include the boundaries of acceptable values for data entry (e.g., the value must be in a specific date format, negative values aren't acceptable, or when a value must fall within a range of, say, between 0 and 1.00). Tests of such boundaries must determine whether the system will work properly with values at the acceptable limits and whether the system won't accept values beyond the acceptable limits. Data-entry boundaries should be tested for data that's important for high- or moderate-risk functions.

Functional tests. When considering what should be tested prior to using the system, functionality is the first on the list. Does the system correctly perform the business functions you wanted to automate? Functional tests should correspond to the functionality defined in the user requirements, supportive operations, and/or functional specification. Functional testing means testing the accuracy and completeness of transactions as seen by the user without knowledge of the methods used by the computer. These tests are also called "black box tests" because they're performed without consideration of the processing logic or steps. Black-box tests consist of inputting the necessary information and using the system to perform a transaction. The results of the computer's processing are compared to expected results that are defined in advance. Because software development companies ordinarily don't share the logic used in their programming, black-box testing is a common practice in computer system validation.

If functional testing follows user procedures, the tests confirm the accuracy of the written procedures as well as the proper functioning of the system. Verification that the business process is effective in achieving its goals is usually performed as part of the PQ. However, if the OQ can be structured in a manner to provide additional information on the effectiveness of a process, that information provides additional value. The problems that are discovered can be solved before the PQ.

Functional testing includes more than just tests of business transactions and process automation. You might need to tests aspects of the system related to security, data integrity, risk and error management, and performance if they're implicitly or explicitly included in your requirements. The previous section on types of items to test in an OQ for an application or system provides a more complete list of the type of items included in OQ tests. The next section discusses how to take the system's risk level into consideration when determining what to include in the OQ.

Structural testing. Also known as "white box testing," structural testing means testing software based on the logical structure used in it. Tests are designed specifically to see if the logic designed into the system works. Using logic coded into the software, a system is programmed to process data differently, based on different conditions. To thoroughly test the software, all possible conditions, and perhaps all possible combinations of conditions, must be tested to see if the system produces appropriate results in all types of cases. Any logic in the system whose failure is associated with moderate or high risk ought to be tested. With white-box testing, test cases challenge the logic programmed into the software. Tests are also performed to verify the program's data structure, including how the database has been configured.

White-box testing should also be used to verify that custom programs used to interface systems or collect data for reporting purposes are constructed appropriately.

To design white-box tests, the test developer must have access to the detailed system design and source code.[41] Software vendors are rarely willing to provide such information. Consequently, white-box testing must be performed by the developer. Part of your audit of the developer should include how extensively it conducts white-box testing through such practices as design reviews, code reviews, and unit or module testing. If the developer hasn't performed white-box testing, the probability of failure will be higher. You might be able to make up for the developer's deficiencies by performing white-box testing yourself. You'll need a copy of the detailed design and knowledge of the source code.

From a practical perspective, conducting white-box testing of a COTS system is beyond the capability of most companies. Alternatively, you should perform sufficient black-box testing to establish that the software meets your needs. Because black-box testing is done without knowledge of how the software works, it's not possible to determine how thoroughly your black-box testing has covered how the program works. For this reason, the FDA guidance document warns that for many applications, black-box testing isn't sufficient and suggests that it might be more appropriate for you to purchase a system where the vendor has performed white-box testing.[42] Chapter 5 discusses how to qualify vendors, including ways to evaluate the development methodologies used by software developers.

Risk-Based Considerations for the OQ

As stated multiple times in this book and in the FDA's guidelines regarding validation, "The level of validation effort should be commensurate with the risk posed by the

Table 9.5	Recommended Functional Testing Under Different Risk Conditions
System risk level	**What to include in operational qualification testing**
High-risk functions	■ All applicable areas in this chapter's list of what to include in operational qualification (OQ) testing ■ White-box testing of programming logic, if possible ■ Black-box testing of high-risk functionality under normal and abnormal circumstances in which the system will be used ■ Testing error conditions, including operator mistakes that the system shouldn't allow (e.g., error-handling), and inputting erroneous data from an operator or an integrated system ■ Attempted inappropriate uses of the system in a manner that will affect product quality ■ Attempts to falsify results ■ Attempted uses of the function in a manner that would violate relevant FDA predicate rules or company procedural directives ■ Attempted uses of the system that would result in a catastrophic loss or corruption of records, data, or programs ■ Attempted security breaches ■ Testing of all supportive operations Hard evidence should be obtained to document test results (e.g., screen shots or copies of reports)
Moderate-risk functions	■ All applicable areas in this chapter's list of what to include in OQ testing ■ White-box testing of programming logic, if possible ■ Black-box testing of moderate-risk functionality under normal circumstances in which the system will be used ■ Attempted security breaches ■ Testing of the normal use of all supportive operations for the function Hard evidence should be obtained to document important test results (e.g., screen shots or copies of reports)

Low-risk functions	■ Black-box testing to:
	  ☐ Verify configurations
	  ☐ Test customizations
	  ☐ Test functions for which a system error can't be readily detected (e.g., an error in calculation)
	
	Hard evidence should be obtained to document important test results. Focus on selective evidence that demonstrates the end result is correct (e.g., a final calculation or report)

automated operation."[43] One way to implement this principle is recommended in this section. Keep in mind that you're responsible for determining what's suitable for your circumstance. The RiskVal recommendations are summarized in table 9.5.

If a detailed risk assessment of a system is performed as described in chapter 6, the level of effort associated with testing a function can be based on the risks associated with the failure of that function. If a detailed risk analysis isn't performed, then the level of testing of the functions performed by the system is based on the system risk level determined in phase 1 (see chapter 3). Testing all functions of high- and moderate-risk systems based on the system risk level is generally not practical for systems used to perform a high number of functions.

High-risk functions performed by systems obviously require the greatest amount of testing. High-risk functions and all associated supportive operations should be thoroughly tested, including tests of all normal and abnormal circumstances in which the function will be used. Table 9.5 describes additional tests of high-risk functions that ought to be performed, including error conditions, attempted inappropriate uses, attempts to falsify results, and attempted security breaches. All software logic used by high-risk functions should be tested if possible. Hard evidence of the results of the OQ tests should be collected (e.g., copies of reports and screen shots of results displayed by the system, such as an error message).

The extent of testing of low- and moderate-risk functions of systems and/or applications can be reduced from the testing performed for high-risk functions, if *one* of the following conditions is met:

■ The software is certified to operate on the hardware and software platform on which you intend to use it.

■ The system is used widely in the industry for similar purposes.

■ The vendor qualification confirms that the software was developed using an appropriate life cycle methodology to estimate that the likelihood of failure is at the "probable" level or lower. As stated in chapter 6, it's recommended that the development methodology used be at least equivalent to that listed in table 6.4 for an average organization.

The following reductions in regard to functional testing of systems or applications are recommended if the condition for reduced functional testing is met. These guidelines are recommendations only; you need to determine if they're suitable to your systems. All moderate-risk functions and associated supportive operations should be thoroughly tested for normal operational conditions. For low-risk functions and associated supportive operations, tests should be performed to verify configurations, test customizations, and test functions for which a system error can't be readily detected (e.g., an error in a calculation). Testing isn't recommended for low-risk data entry, ranges of acceptable data values, data storage, and data retrieval. See table 9.5 for additional details.

Design the OQ Tests

Before you begin writing the OQ, develop a list of all the things that must be tested. Use the list provided earlier in this chapter concerning types of items to test in an OQ for an application or system. You might also have to test the ability to cancel or terminate transactions at different points as well as the ability to process some transactions through to the end. For example, with document control systems you should test the ability to reject a change request as well as the ability to approve it. You should also test the ability to cancel a change request at various stages of processing. While processing the change request to the point at which you want to test the ability to cancel it, you can test other features (e.g., the ability to attach an engineering drawing to a change request).

Once you've identified what must be tested, arrange the potential tests into an order that can be performed sequentially by the system, following the logical paths that can be taken during processing. A flowchart of your business process would be helpful. One test will follow one choice of options, and another test will follow the path leading from another option. You might need to take many paths through the system to cover all of the tests that must be performed. Medatech 9.2 provides an example of the structure of multiple OQ protocols for a document control system.

PREPARE THE OPERATIONAL QUALIFICATION PROTOCOL

Deliverable 7.2 describes the content of an OQ protocol.[44] The contents of parts of the protocol are discussed in this section.

Prerequisites

In the prerequisites section, list the prerequisites that must be met before the OQ can be executed. The prerequisites should include, as appropriate:

- An approved IQ report
- An approved OQ protocol
- Approved procedures for application administrative and user activities or at least user procedures that are in final draft and ready for signoff
- An up-to-date traceability matrix that maps requirements to protocol tests (except for simple systems)

Medatech 9.2	Partial Design of OQ Protocols for the Document Control System

Doc created an operational qualification (OQ) test plan for the OQ with input from the project team. Because of the amount of testing that's needed, Doc decided to break the OQ down into many separate OQ protocols. The part of the plan that relates to engineering change orders (ECOs) is presented here. This example illustrates, at a high level, how OQ protocols can be structured to cover various alternative processing paths—referred to below as "approval routes"—and different functionalities. It's not intended to provide detailed information on the content of each protocol, nor does it present the full range of OQ testing needed for a document control system.

- *OQ 1 purposes.* Put an assortment of new documents into the system representing the types of documents commonly used in the company (e.g., documents, spreadsheets, presentations); test approval route one.
- *OQ 2 purposes.* Add file types not commonly used to the system (e.g., image files, digital photographs, video); test approval route two.
- *OQ 3 purposes.* Revise documents of commonly used file types; obsolesce a document by ECO action; test the lockout that prevents two changes to a document at a time. ECO rejected in first round, modified, and then approved. Verify audit trail.
- *OQ 4 purposes.* Test status of documents attached to an ECO to bring them into the system and other documents attached to the ECO for revision after the ECO is rejected and then cancelled. Test approval route three. Verify audit trails.
- *OQ 5 purpose.* Test bringing public standards into the system via approval route four.
- *OQ 6 purposes.* Add and approve nonresident documents to the system. (Nonresident documents are those that are under control and brought into the EDMS system. No electronic file is managed by the system. Examples include studies and validation reports that are a compilation of multiple documents and records, and standards for which electronic files aren't available. Test approval route five.
- *OQ 7 purpose.* Test approval route six to make administrative changes to documents.

- Completion of system setup per the requirements specified in the protocol
- Completed user-training materials
- Completed training of testers in how to execute a protocol and operate the system

Protocol-Acceptance Criteria

Technical Report 18 refers to the criterion for determining if the system has functioned properly during a test as "acceptance criterion."[45] Some organizations use the term acceptance criterion for results that should be obtained for a specific test, while other organizations use the term "expected results." In this book the acceptable values for each test are called expected results. The term "protocol-acceptance criteria" refers to higher-level criteria used to determine whether the system has met the requirements for a qualification (i.e., has met the criteria specified in the OQ protocol). In the discussion of the protocol-acceptance criteria for the OQ protocol, for example, a number of failures to pass specific tests may be permitted. The number of allowed defects at various levels of criticality can be one of the protocol-acceptance criteria. As described in chapter 6, the acceptance criteria that are formulated for the entire system are called "system acceptance criteria."

The protocol-acceptance criteria for OQ protocols must fall within the system acceptance criteria that were stated in the validation plan (see chapter 6). Recall that four classes of defects were defined: critical, major, minor, and cosmetic. If the system acceptance criteria places limits on the number of critical, major, or minor defects that are permissible (e.g., none), the numbers permitted for one OQ protocol can be equal to or fewer than the numbers allowed for the entire system.

Additional protocol-acceptance criteria include:

- All prerequisites have been met.
- Variance forms are completed as needed.
- All test equipment used in the OQ is properly calibrated before use in the test. Copies of calibration certificates are attached to an appendix.
- All personnel entering data or signing the protocol have signed a signature log in a protocol appendix or company log.
- All supporting documentation (e.g., screen prints and reports) collected during the execution of the protocol are logged in an appendix and attached to the protocol.

OQ Test Section

If the test section contains multiple subsections, each would have its own components, including:

- Objective(s)
- User requirements tested
- Materials and equipment required
- Test procedure
- Conclusion (regarding the test results)

If the test section of the OQ protocol doesn't have subsections, the test section will include only the user requirements tested and the test procedure. The objectives and required materials and equipment that are stated for the entire OQ will apply to the test section.

Examples of test procedures are given in exhibits 9.4 and 9.5. Notice that the following components are included:

- A description of the function or item to be tested. This statement is written with a moderate level of detail and intended to let reviewers and testers know what will be tested in the next few steps. A new description is stated in each row that contains the first step in testing a function or item.
- Statements, as needed, on how to operate the system to test the function or item. Such instructions are given on how to perform a test if you want a specific method to be used or, as discussed below, if the tester needs such information to operate the system.
- Specific data to be used to perform the test (e.g., "In the session context dialog box, type: 'User Penelope PDM.'"). Instructions to input specific data values are preferred when future tests depend on the values entered or if the purpose of the test is to verify data entry and accurate data retrieval. The tester can be responsible for determining what value to input as long as he or she is instructed to record the value that's used so the expected output value can be determined.
- The results that the system should obtain from performing the transactions. These are called the "expected results." The tester compares the actual results obtained with the expected results and indicates whether the expected results were achieved. For this reason, the expected results stated in the protocol must be specific so the tester can determine if the actual results are identical.
- A place to record the actual results. Information on how to record actual results is given below.
- A space for the initials of the person performing the test and the date the test was performed
- A conclusion regarding what the test results indicate (e.g., that a specific function is working properly)

When preparing the test procedures, provide the level of detail about operating the system that's appropriate based on the tester's familiarity with the system. Provide detailed instructions, keystroke by keystroke, if the tester isn't familiar with the system and might make errors if not given detailed instructions. (See the example provided in exhibit 9.4.) If you can assume that the tester knows how to perform an operation, the instructions can be given at a higher level. (See the example given in exhibit 9.5.)

Recording the actual results is critical. These form the basis for the objective evidence that the system functions as required. Resist the urge to simply indicate if the test was passed or failed instead of recording the actual results. When executing the

Exhibit 9.4	Operational Qualification Protocol Test Procedure With Detailed Instructions				
Step	**Procedural notes**	**Procedure**	**Expected results**	**Actual results**	**Initial and date**
1	Start system administration	Select Start—Programs—System Administration	Administration login window appears	Administration login window appears? ☐ Yes ☐ No	
2	Login as an administrator	In administration login window, type: ■ User: Susan Admin ■ Password: pp.SA ■ Then click OK	■ Administration login window disappears ■ Administration window appears	■ Administration login window disappears? ☐ Yes ☐ No ■ Administration window appears? ☐ Yes ☐ No	
3	Define facility attribute with a range of values	Choose Object—New—Attribute	New attribute window appears	New attribute window appears? ☐ Yes ☐ No	
4		Type the following: ■ Name: Facility ■ Description: Manufacturing location ■ Type: String	Data entered	Data entered? ☐ Yes ☐ No	
5		■ Click ranges tab ■ Then click Add	Add-range window appears with equal button set	Add-range window appears with equal button set? ☐ Yes ☐ No	
6		■ Type Facility 1 in the text box ■ Then click OK	■ Add-range window disappears ■ New attribute window appears at ranges tab; Range = Facility 1 is added.	■ Add-range window disappears? ☐ Yes ☐ No ■ New Attribute window appears at ranges tab; Range = Facility 1 is added? ☐ Yes ☐ No	
7		Click Add	Add-range window appears with equal button set	Add-range window appears with equal button set? ☐ Yes ☐ No	
8		■ Type Facility 2 in the text box ■ Then click OK	■ Add-range window disappears ■ New attribute window appears at ranges tab; Range = Facility 2 is added.	■ Add-range window disappears? ☐ Yes ☐ No ■ New attribute window appears at Ranges tab; Range = Facility 2 is added? ☐ Yes ☐ No	
Conclusion	All expected results were achieved. The "add new attribute" and "define range" functions of the system operate per requirements.			☐ Yes ☐ No	

Note: The protocol may ask the person executing it to write their initials and the date on each line, as is done in this example. Alternatively, a space may be provided at the bottom of the page where the tester can sign and date to indicate that he or she completed the entire page.

	Exhibit 9.5	Operational Qualification Protocol Test Section for Testers Familiar With the Application			
Step	**Procedural notes**	**Procedure**	**Expected results**	**Actual results**	**Initial and date**
1	Define a facility attribute with a range of values	■ Use "Susan Admin" as the administrator. ■ Password: pp.SA ■ Create a new attribute name using the following information: ☐ Attribute name: Facility ☐ Description: Manufacturing location ☐ Type: String	Facility attribute created with the description of manufacturing location and the type as string	New attribute window, ranges tab, lists; Range = Facility 1? ☐ Yes ☐ No	
2		Add two ranges to the facility attribute: Facility 1 and Facility 2	■ New attribute window, ranges tab, lists; Range = Facility 1 ■ New attribute window, ranges tab, lists; Range = Facility 2	New attribute window, ranges tab, lists; Range = Facility 2? ☐ Yes ☐ No	
Conclusion		All expected results were achieved. The "add new attribute" and "define range" functions of the system operate per requirements.		☐ Yes ☐ No	

protocol, you need to provide a statement of the actual results. The format presented in the "actual results" column in exhibit 9.4 can be used to record whether the expected result occurred. Note that for ease of use, the expected result is repeated in the form of a question. Were these specific expected results achieved? The protocol instructions should tell the tester to check "yes" if the expected results were achieved, "no" if they weren't achieved, and to record the actual results in a comment space on the page (usually in the footer).

If the expected result is a quantitative value from a calculation or a measurement, the actual value calculated or measured ought to be recorded, even if it's identical to the expected results. If the expected result is a value within an acceptable range, give the actual value and indicate if the test was passed. (See exhibits 9.1 and 9.3 for examples.) To the extent practical, record data and information so that information about whether the test was passed can be assessed by an independent reviewer or auditor. Screen shots and reports can be printed, noted on the protocol, and attached in an appendix. Objective evidence is particularly important for high-risk functions and important results of moderate-risk functions. If quantitative measures aren't made, and printouts of some type aren't possible, one alternative is to have a second person sign the protocol to attest that the actual results match the description given by the first tester on the protocol.

The FDA guidance on software validation explains that, "test procedures, test data, and test results should be documented in a manner permitting objective pass/fail decisions to be reached. They should also be suitable for review and objective decision making subsequent to running the test..."[46] FDA field auditors look for objective evidence to document test results.

The test procedures must be carefully written and thoroughly checked (preferably by performing a dry run) before the OQ is executed to ensure that the protocol doesn't:

- Instruct the tester to perform an operation incorrectly
- Erroneously state the expected results
- Contain errors that will have to be corrected during the execution of the protocol or that will require the preparation of a variance. As stated above, if the correction doesn't affect the nature of the test or the expected results, errors in protocol test instructions may be corrected on the protocol without completing a variance report. However, a large number of corrections will raise questions about the protocol's accuracy and the care with which the protocol was prepared.

The length of the OQ protocol varies considerably. It can be fewer than fifty pages or more than a couple thousand. The length depends on many factors, including:

- Scope of the application
- Complexity of the application (e.g., the number of different situations it can handle and the complexity of the logic that's applied to determine what to do)
- Risk associated with the system
- Format used in the protocol
- Level of detail given in the testing steps

As an example, an OQ for a complex document control system that had a lot of custom code was 2,200 pages long. The system also included the approval of deviations and maintaining training records. That OQ was structured into thirty separate protocols. Breaking the OQ into a number of separate protocols, each with its own purpose, helped those who were writing, reviewing, or executing the protocols to focus on the purpose of each protocol. In addition, shorter documents are easier to revise and work with and are subject to less corruption and fewer system crashes.

However, the length of the protocol isn't important. Focus instead on answering the question, "Are the OQ tests adequate in providing objective evidence that the system performs to meet user requirements throughout its operating range?"

If multiple protocols are written, special care must be taken. The proper sequence for executing the protocols must be carefully documented and followed if:

■ Later protocols are dependent upon the performances of functions, creating users, or data entry in earlier protocols.

■ If executing protocols out of sequence will create data that aren't expected to be found in protocols executed later.

Backward Traceability Matrix

Tables can be placed in the OQ and PQ protocols that indicate what requirements are being tested by each test. Such tables provide a "backward traceability matrix," (i.e., a path from a specific test back to the requirements being tested by it). A backward traceability matrix is usually organized according to test steps and can be used to answer questions about what requirement is being tested at each step. This information is valuable to reviewers because they have to evaluate if a specific test will provide adequate objective evidence that the system meets a specific requirement. A backward traceability matrix can also provide a high-level view of how a protocol is structured. Backward traceability matrices in protocols are optional, especially if a forward traceability matrix is created. A forward traceability matrix indicates the path from requirements to tests and is normally organized according to the requirements. (Forward traceability matrices will be discussed later in this chapter.) If the number of requirements and tests is limited, the forward traceability may provide an easy way to

Exhibit 9.6	Backward Traceability Matrix

The table below is the beginning of a backward traceability matrix for the administrative functions of a document control system.

Function tested	User requirements tested	Tests to conduct	Test steps
1. Add an attribute value	6.2	Add an attribute of "Facility"	1–4
2. Define attributes values	6.3		
a. A set of values can be defined to create a pick list.	6.3.1	Facility names used for pick list items	5–8
b. A default value can be set for a pick list.	6.3.2	"Facility" is used as the attribute type, and "Facility 1" is set as the default value.	9–13
3. Change an attribute value	6.4	Change "Facility 1" to "Cleveland Plant"	14–16
4. Delete an attribute value	6.5	Delete "Facility 2"	17–18

identify the requirement being tested at a step in the protocol, and thus make a backward traceability matrix unnecessary. If you have many lengthy protocols, a backward traceability matrix can be very helpful in determining what requirement is being tested at each step. Part of a backward traceability matrix is given in exhibit 9.6.[47]

Legacy Data Installation and Verification

Transferring data from an existing application or database to a new application or database is one of the most critical activities of the system implementation process. It can also be one of the most difficult. The software vendor ordinarily provides implementation support that includes loading legacy data. An example of the transfer of legacy data is moving documents, and information concerning them, from an existing database application into a new electronic document management system (EDMS).

Loading legacy data presents users with an opportunity to clean up the data before they're imported. Missing data can be added, and errors can be corrected. The accuracy of results obtained with your new system and the value you derive from it are dependent to a large extent on the accuracy of the data the system uses. If the data being changed are records that require audit trails on changes, appropriate documentation should be kept of all changes and corrections.

At least three legacy load situations are possible. First, and easiest, some new systems don't require the transfer of data from an old system because the new system can be configured to read the data from the existing database. Second, the complete database can be copied into a new or modified system. (This situation is common with system upgrades.) Third, existing data must be exported, and possibly reformatted, and then imported into a new system that has a different database structure. The data must be exported in a format that can be read either by the new application or by custom code written to translate the exported data into a format that fits the new system's database structure. The legacy data are then loaded directly into the data space of the new application, thus avoiding the effort required to enter data through the user interface.

If the OQ doesn't require the legacy data, the legacy load can be done directly in the production environment prior to the PQ. The load can be performed following written instructions and then verified as part of the PQ. Alternatively, the process of loading legacy data may be tested as part of the OQ to establish that the methodology developed will result in the accurate transfer of an acceptable percentage of the records. The legacy data are loaded in the validation environment at the beginning of the OQ when the OQ tests make use of legacy data, or if you'd like the validation environment to be close to the production environment. With the legacy data loaded, for example, you can better judge performance, such as the speed of data searches. If a production environment is set up that's different from the validation environment, the legacy data must be loaded and tested again.

The complete and accurate loading of legacy data must be verified, and that process is different for the three situations described previously. In the first situation, the new system is configured to read the data from the old database. The configurations need to be tested to verify that the correct data is being read for each data field.

For the second situation, when an entire database is copied from one system, or version of a system, to another, the completeness and accuracy of the database and its structural integrity ought to be verified. The characteristics of the database can be reviewed after the load to determine if all records have been loaded in the proper sequence.

The following are examples of what could be checked to evaluate the complete and accurate loading of a database. (These same tests can be used to verify that a database has been properly restored from a backup.) You need to decide what is sufficient for your situation.

■ Database size. Compare the number of tables of the original database to the copy.
■ Completeness of the database. Compare the number of rows in the tables and verify that all groupings are present.
■ Check the order of the data records to determine if all records are accounted for and are in the proper sequence (e.g., by examining a numeric key).
■ Run automated referential checks using the database tools. A reference is when one item refers or points to another item in a different table. A test can be run to determine if all the references have integrity (i.e., the object they're pointing to is there).
■ Verify database scripts for:
  □ *Sequence generation.* Check to see if items were generated with the correct sequential numbering (e.g., the primary key or field used to identify the item in all tables).
  □ *Triggers.* These are a set of rules that set some value from some input. A trigger ought to be present for values that the system assigns.
  □ *Auto-entry.* What to enter into blank fields.
  □ *Calculations.* These are customized, but when you check to see if the data are there, you'll be verifying the calculations.
  □ *Input validation.* Checks to see if the values input for certain fields match the type of data that ought to be input (e.g., date fields).

The following tests are recommended to verify the data's integrity:

- Select one record of each type (e.g., an engineering change request or rework record) and compare the data in the copied database to the data in the original database. You could create test records in the original database to use for the comparison, or you can select existing records that would represent the most rigorous tests.
- Verify that all attachments to a record are present (e.g., audit trails, electronic signatures, and documents)
- Verify the integrity of hot links between items

The third situation involves existing data that are exported, possibly reformatted, and then imported into a new system that has a different database structure. In such situations, you can expect to have a less-than-perfect data transfer. Therefore, you must have a method whereby the records or items (such as document files) that didn't load through the automated process can be entered manually. When testing the legacy load under these circumstances, the first task is to verify that all records and/or items are accounted for. Either the record has loaded successfully, or there's an error message stating that it didn't. For example, if there are 375 documents in your current document control system, you should be able to account for 375 records of information about documents (e.g., document number, title, originator, effective date, and revision) and the loading of 375 electronic files (i.e., documents).

Missing values and format errors can prevent a data record from loading or cause some values to load in the wrong fields. If there are a large number of error messages for records that didn't load, clean the data so that fewer records are rejected. A special character, missing data, or a misplaced blank space could cause a failure. These problems can be fixed so that the record will load successfully. Before conducting the official load, you might have to conduct many trial runs of the legacy load to verify that the software used to load the records is written correctly and to identify and correct data problems.

The second task in verifying the legacy load in which the data are loaded into a new structure is to test that the data have been loaded into the correct database fields. The records in the new system must be compared to the records from the old system to confirm data integrity. You can review 100 percent of the records or a sample percentage. A sampling plan can be developed on what you determine to be an acceptable quality level (a quality control engineer can help determine an appropriate sample size). If incorrect data are associated with high risk, either review all records or select an acceptable quality level that assumes only a few, if any, errors are acceptable.

Many of the tests and associated acceptance criteria suggested for the second situation (i.e., loading data into a database with the same structure), don't apply when the load is transferred to a database with a new structure. The structural differences are likely to result in different numbers of tables, rows and columns within tables, and references.

The legacy load protocol-acceptance criteria should be set along three dimensions when legacy data are loaded into a database with a new structure:

1. The number of records and/or items that are unaccounted for. The normal requirement is that all records should be accounted for, either as having been successfully loaded or as an entry in the error log.

2. The percent of records and/or items that must load (e.g., at least 80 percent). The percentage that you set as acceptable will depend in part on how difficult it is to manually load the records that weren't loaded in the automated process.

3. The number of errors in data records that are acceptable, if any. This number can be set at zero or derived from statistical tables based on the acceptable quality level.

Required Application Setup

When the OQ, and perhaps the PQ, is written, the protocol developer assumes that the user is capable of performing certain functions and that the application contains the data required to perform the operation. Some of these conditions can be created as the result of an earlier action performed as part of a protocol. For example, a protocol requires that a user—let's call her Sue—be created in the system and given user privileges. To do that, the tester, Mary, must be able log on as an application administrator. Before the OQ execution can begin, a user named Mary with administrator privileges must be set up in the system. As the OQ is written, it's advisable to keep track of the setup requirements for the system and to record them in a section of the protocol so that the system can be prepared for testing. If a setup requirement is missed or incomplete (e.g., if Mary is created as a user but not given administrator privileges), variances and problems will occur. Mary won't be able to create a new user, and if this situation isn't recognized as a setup error, one might erroneously decide that the administrative function isn't working properly.

System setup might be necessary along the following dimensions:

■ Establishing types or groups with specific user privileges

■ Creating users that belong to different groups or have different privileges

■ Entering legacy and/or test data

■ Establishing partially completed transactions. For example, if you wanted to test if a change request can be cancelled after all reviewers had approved the request but before document control releases the new documents, you could test this in one of two ways: by creating a change request and working it through the approval process as part of the test protocol, or by creating an approved change request as part of the system setup in preparation for executing the protocol. Then in the protocol you can directly test the ability to cancel the change request.

Prepare a Matrix That Traces Requirements to Validation Tests

A matrix that maps user requirements to the IQ, OQ, and PQ tests is one of the most important deliverables in the RiskVal life cycle. Traceability from requirements to test protocols is called "forward traceability." This matrix has four important uses:

- It can be used as an index for the protocols.
- It's an easy and effective way of determining if all items to be tested have been included in the validation testing.
- The matrix is an important tool during an audit. Having a map of where everything is tested is an easy way to demonstrate to an auditor that appropriate validation tests have been conducted. Most auditors would look at the matrix, pick out a couple of items, and then check the protocols to verify that the tests have been performed. A forward traceability matrix makes it much easier to demonstrate that you have systematic and thorough verification that the system functions to requirements.
- The forward traceability matrix also has a valuable role to play in troubleshooting. When a problem occurs in the future, the investigator might want to know how the system was tested and how it performed during the validation testing. If the system performed a function well during validation testing but is failing during production use, the differences between the two situations can be examined as a probable cause.

The ideal time to prepare the matrix is while the OQ is being drafted. In the process of creating the matrix, you can check if adequate testing has been created for all the requirements you must test in the OQ.

If the system is simple and the OQ protocol is relatively short, the traceability matrix isn't necessary because forward traceability can be achieved by going directly from the requirements to the protocol.

The forward traceability matrix can be included either in the OQ or created as a separate document. If the OQ is structured into two or more protocols, the matrix should be a separate document.

One easy way to create such a matrix is to prepare a table. Put the user requirements in one column, and in another place references to where the requirements are tested in the protocol(s).

Approve the OQ Protocol

The OQ protocol's approvers ordinarily include the project manager or team leader, the system owner, the validation representative, and QA.

EXECUTE THE OPERATIONAL QUALIFICATION PROTOCOL AND PREPARE A REPORT

Prepare to execute the OQ by setting up the required database conditions in the validation instance by either clearing an existing database of all inappropriate information or creating a new database instance. Load the test data required for the OQ and the legacy data, if appropriate. Create the users identified in the OQ and assign appropriate privileges. Complete all the prerequisites.

The protocol is executed according to the instructions given in the protocol or the methods defined in an approved procedure. As with the IQ, follow the guidelines in exhibit 9.2 for record keeping. If the expected results aren't achieved, follow the guidelines given earlier in this chapter for resolving variances.

As mentioned previously in discussing the report for the IQ, the report for each type of protocol is basically the same. Findings are summarized, variances are discussed, and a conclusion is drawn as to whether the system meets the protocol-acceptance criteria. Deliverable 7.4 provides more information on the content of the protocol report.

USE VENDOR VALIDATION PACKAGES CAUTIOUSLY

Many vendors of manufacturing and quality system applications sell validation packages that include an IQ and OQ, and some also include a PQ. Such packages can save tremendous amounts of time in developing the IQ and OQ protocols; such packages should be used if they're appropriately constructed. In general, these packages represent an honest effort by the vendor to provide adequate tests of the system. A cynic, however, might view them as only a collection of tests that the vendor wants you to run and not necessarily an appropriate assessment of the system's performance. Also keep in mind that vendors don't bear the responsibility for validation and probably aren't experts in the validation process. Therefore, use such packages of pre-prepared IQs and OQs, but do so under your control and in a manner that integrates the package into your validation process instead of letting the package replace your process.

Common Misconceptions of Software Vendors Regarding Validation

A software vendor might not have expertise in validation even if it offers a validation package. You must make your own judgment as to what's required for your validation. Remember, you're responsible for validating your system; the vendor isn't.

Here are some of the statements you might hear from a software company representative, and why they're erroneous:

- "We've already validated the system; you don't need to. You can audit our test results. In fact, we'll even issue you a certificate of validation." The software vendor you're talking with might have performed extensive tests of the system. However, such testing doesn't relieve you of the responsibility of ensuring that the system will perform to your requirements in your technical environment. You must still perform a validation.

- "The system has been validated by a customer of ours, so you won't have to." This statement is a variation on the previous one and basically asserts that if someone validates the system once, it's a validated system. Of course this statement reflects a fundamental misunderstanding of the purpose of validation, which is to obtain objective evidence that the system will function to your requirements in your environment.

- "The FDA has approved our system." The implicit conclusion to this statement is, "And therefore you don't have to worry about validation." The FDA doesn't approve or certify systems. This statement could be based on the fact that the FDA audited one of the vendor's clients, and the auditor didn't issue any findings with regard to the application or its validation. The fact that another company validated the system for its uses in its environment doesn't mean the same system will function reliably to your requirements in your environment.

- "We'll install the system and perform the validation for you." Certainly the vendor can install the application software, but the validation testing should be controlled by an independent agent (i.e., a person or organization other than the developer). This individual must fully understand the user requirements. There are several reasons for having a person who's independent of the software vendor conduct the validation:

☐ A tester from your organization is less likely to be biased in favor of the system and is more likely to be familiar with how the system should work to meet your specific requirements.

☐ The software vendor probably won't critically review the validation protocols in light of your specific user requirements prior to executing them and make appropriate changes. (Potential changes that must be made to the protocols are discussed in the next section.)

☐ An internal tester is more likely to identify issues about how the system works for your intended uses and will be able to identify situations where the system works as designed but not as you want it to work. A representative of the software company will know how the system was designed to work, but he or she won't be as familiar with your requirements as a person from your company that you've trained.

☐ It's more likely that an independent person will be objective in recording the test results.

☐ If the field service representative from the software vendor who installed the system also is executing the IQ, he or she might be tempted to fix any installation problems without creating a variance and recording the failure.

☐ If the system fails a functional test, the vendor might just fix it by changing a configuration or custom code without recording the failure and completing a variance form.

Make Vendor Validation Packages Work for You

Many vendors would have you believe that validation is simply a matter of going through the protocols and performing their tests. Unfortunately, that isn't enough. To use vendor-provided validation packages, the following actions must be performed and safeguards taken:

■ Obtain an electronic copy of the package that you can edit.

■ Prepare and approve written user requirements for your use of the system. The vendor might provide a user requirement document, but you must review it and either confirm that it matches your requirements or edit it. Find out the origins of the system and the industry expertise of the designers. Many systems are designed by individuals who are experienced only in one or two industries. Some systems are developed for a particular company and then broadened to meet the needs of companies in that or other industries. When reviewing the vendor's requirements statement, keep in mind aspects of your situation that might be unique to your organization or industry, including:

☐ Any configurations of the system to adapt it to your use

☐ Any unusual conditions of use that require performance testing, including remote users, number of users, environmental conditions, or special equipment for data input or retrieval

☐ Steps you've taken to mitigate risk

☐ Parts of the system you won't be using and don't wish to test

☐ Hardware or system software you plan to use that might not comply with the vendor's specifications

■ Does the IQ section include all the application software patches you'll need? Unless the validation package has been modified as necessary to adjust to service packs and bug fixes, negative results could be obtained solely because the validation package is out of date, and new functionality may not be tested.

■ Is the validation package current with the version of the software you're installing? At times, vendors will create a comprehensive validation package for a revision of their application—for example, revision one. Then, when they release revision two, they create an additional validation protocol for the incremental functionality and bug fixes contained in revision two. Customers who purchase these vendors' validation packages must install version one and complete the validation package for version one. Then they must install the upgrade for version two and use the incremental validation package for version two to complete the validation. The preferable way of handling an upgrade is to install both the system and upgrade, and then conduct all the tests on the upgraded system.

■ Does the validation package include adequate regression testing for new versions, service packs, and defect patches? The approach of installing and testing version one and then installing and testing version two is acceptable from a validation perspective if the validation package for version two includes adequate regression tests. These are tests on parts of the system that haven't been changed to determine if they've been affected by the revision. If you purchase a validation protocol that tests service packs and/or bug patches, determine what parts of the system might be directly and indirectly affected by those changes, and determine if tests of those aspects of the system are included in the protocol. If you can't determine what might have been affected, retest all high-risk functions and at least a selection of moderate-risk functions.

- Determine if the validation package is complete and accurate for your system. To make the vendor's package suitable for your needs, you might have to:
  - ☐ Edit the vendor's validation plan, if there is one, so that it fits your plans and approach. If the scope of your plan exceeds the vendor's, you probably will have to add to the qualification protocols. If your validation plan defines limited use of the system, you might be able to delete some of the tests in the package.
  - ☐ Modify the package to reflect your choice of what to include in the validation based on the risks associated with your use of the system.
  - ☐ Create any missing protocols; many of the validation packages don't include a PQ.

- Change sections of the protocol(s) as necessary to personalize them for your company.
  - ☐ Changes might need to be made to the purpose, scope, system description, responsibilities, and referenced documents sections.
  - ☐ Change the instructions provided for the execution of the protocols.
  - ☐ Add appendices for calibration records, signature logs, supporting documentation, or variances.
  - ☐ Change or add prerequisites.
  - ☐ Modify the protocol-acceptance criteria.
  - ☐ Modify the process to be used to report and resolve variances.
  - ☐ Add space for QA to record comments as it reviews the executed protocol.

- Modify the specifications in the IQ, including the types of hardware and system software that you'll use, to match your specifications for such items.
  - ☐ If your choice of hardware or system software is different from what the vendor recommends, consult with the vendor to determine what its experience has been with your type of products and determine if the vendor's software will work with them.
  - ☐ If the vendor's IQ allows you to write in your own hardware and system software specifications, edit the document to include your system components and related specifications prior to executing the protocol.
  - ☐ Modify the IQ to include the configurations to the hardware and software needed for your system.
  - ☐ Add IQ items for installing or verifying the installation of various patches if they're not already included.

- Modify the tests included in the protocols.
  - ☐ It's recommended that you develop a traceability matrix that maps your requirements onto the vendor's protocol as a method for determining what's included in the validation package.
  - ☐ Delete OQ tests for functions that you won't use.
  - ☐ Add OQ tests for unique aspects of your system or items not included in the vendor's protocol (e.g., reports that you've created).

- Once the modifications have been made to the vendor's protocol, approve the protocol through the same process you use for internally developed protocols. Make changes after the protocol is approved and before execution has begun by revising the document with amendments. Changes made after execution is begun are made through variances. *(continues on page 315)*

| **Medatech 9.3** | ## Preparation and Execution of the Operational Qualification |

Tec asked a consultant to write a software program to transfer existing documents and data to the new system (a process referred to as "performing the legacy load"). The program read the data in Doc's database and placed it into the appropriate fields of the new system's database. Doc's database included: document title, document number, revision level, originator, and effective date (see Medatech 3.1). The new system had additional data fields for the engineering change order (ECO) number and owner department. Rather than adding these fields to his database and transferring it to the new system, Doc decided to leave the fields blank on the legacy load. Data for those two fields would be added in the system when new documents were added and revisions were made. Before the legacy load, Doc had to separate database entries for obsolesced documents and down revisions of documents from entries for currently effective documents. He'd structured his folders for the electronic files so that there were two fold-

ers, one for the current revisions and one for all down revisions for each document number. He moved the down revision files to a completely different folder structure to segregate them more clearly from files for the current revisions.

The legacy load software was run several times in a trial mode, and rejected files were studied to determine the source of the error. The software had to be modified, and the punctuation of some of the records had to be corrected. When the percentage of successful record loads exceeded 90 percent, Doc and the consultant stopped refining the software and database.

Because security of ECO acceptance and rejection, audit trails on acceptance and rejection actions, and security on changing documents were high-risk items, Doc augmented the vendor's testing in these areas with additional tests. For example, he added a test to see if the document control department could change a document during the approval process.

The legacy load was formally tested as the

(continues)

Medatech 9.3	Preparation and Execution of the Operational Qualification (continued)

first part of the operational qualification (OQ). During the load, 92 percent of the records and documents were successfully loaded. 100 percent of the loaded records that were sampled were found to be accurate. The legacy load protocol acceptance criteria were met. The loaded data and documents were then erased, and the setup data and users needed for the other OQ tests were entered into the system.

A number of problems were encountered during the OQ, including the following:

- The database tables for the audit trail filled to capacity, and the system stopped writing audit trail data to the database. To fix this variance, configuration changes were made to the database. The installation qualification (IQ) was amended to include the database configuration so that its setting would be verified when the IQ was used to verify the proper system setup for production.

- One of the users that Doc created was supposed to have administrative privileges, but assigning those privileges wasn't included in the protocol setup requirements. Therefore, the user wasn't able to logon as an administrator. A variance was prepared, and the privileges were assigned as per the instructions in the variance form.

- The system was designed so that the administrator could control which group of employees could view down revisions of documents. The OQ testing verified that if an employee wasn't a member of the group, the down revisions and obsolesced documents wouldn't be seen on the document search results, and therefore that individual wouldn't be able to open the documents as a result of the search. However, it was discovered that the same individual could view down revisions if he or she went into the tree structure of the files within the electronic document management system and found the file of the down revision.

Tec contacted the vendor and was sent a software patch to fix the problem. He created a change request, and when it was approved, he installed the patch. Then all the tests related to privileges of group members were repeated. Tec added the patch to the system specification and wrote an amendment to the IQ to verify the installation of the patch.

When the OQ was completed, a report was prepared. Although there was still one major defect open and several minor defects, the system passed the protocol acceptance criteria. The open defects would be tracked in the problem-reporting and -tracking system until they were resolved. Software changes to correct the defects would be introduced in the system through the change control system.

QUALIFY THE IT INFRASTRUCTURE AND INFRASTRUCTURE SERVICES

As discussed above, the network, shared servers and system software, database equipment and software, and input and output devices used by applications can be qualified as the infrastructure rather than a part of an integrated computerized system. These components of the infrastructure provide a hardware and software platform for operating applications and providing infrastructure services. These services may play a necessary role in safeguarding systems, preserving data integrity, and providing network communications. This section discusses the qualification of both the infrastructure hardware and software platform and the infrastructure services (see note 5).

If you're beginning the process of validating computer systems and have an existing IT infrastructure, you can qualify the hardware and software platform that supports the business applications and the IT infrastructure services. The infrastructure will change over time in response to both organizational growth that increases transactions and organizational demands for new applications. When a new application is planned, the infrastructure configuration needed for the application is determined and included in the technical requirements. The infrastructure is modified, if needed, to support the new application. The changes to the infrastructure can include adding more hardware and/or software, expanding an existing service, and/or activating a new service. For example, some network management utilities have the ability to push software out to desktops. When you're implementing a new application, you may decide it's time to start using that feature. When a new system is added to a qualified infrastructure, the changes to the infrastructure platform and services can be made under change control (which involves qualification), or they can be qualified as part of the validation of the new application.

The infrastructure's contribution has two dimensions. The first is the collection of hardware, and the operating system and auxiliary software used to support business application software and network communications. This dimension is referred to as the "infrastructure platform." The second dimension is called "infrastructure services." Infrastructure services are the functions performed by the infrastructure hardware and software to provided a safe and effective technical environment for the operation of business applications. Infrastructure services safeguard systems, preserve data integrity, and provide network communications. These services include, but aren't limited to, the network communications (e.g., local area networks and wide area networks), file shares, backup and restore, networked storage, firewall, intrusion detection, antiviral, and authentication and authorization services. The term "infrastructure" as used here intentionally includes both dimensions (i.e., the infrastructure platform and infrastructure services). The discussion in this section provides options for qualifying both dimensions of the infrastructure.

The information provided here about infrastructure qualification isn't exhaustive. This book focuses mainly on risk management and validation of computerized systems. The discussion of infrastructure qualification is intended only to provide perspective and information on what needs to be done. How to perform the qualification isn't exhaustively discussed. For additional details on qualifying the infrastructure platform, refer to the proposed standard on network qualification developed by the Institute of Validation Technology (IVT) Network Infrastructure Qualification Committee. In the proposed standard, the infrastructure is depicted as "composed of the underlying hardware and software components that must be present and functioning in order for network communications and applications to work."[48] This definition corresponds to the RiskVal platform dimension of the infrastructure; the proposed standard doesn't discuss infrastructure services.

The infrastructure ought to be qualified for regulatory compliance, for business efficiency and continuity, and to protect high-value data and information. The list of infrastructure failures that can affect system performance is extensive and commonly recognized. They included but aren't limited to:

- Networks that fail to provide acceptable response rates
- Communication or data loss between application and devices that control manufacturing processes
- Service denial or interruption
- Data corruption and/or loss
- Viruses, worms, and other unwanted content that can change functionality or destroy computerized systems and data
- Security breaches leading to system corruption or theft of high-value information
- Faulty storage or backups that increase risk to business continuity and regulatory scrutiny
- Power failures

Historically, the qualification of the infrastructure platform was buried in the application validation effort. Infrastructure services were "implicitly qualified" as part of the overall operating environment. For example, a command was sent from a workstation to the application requesting that a report be printed. If the correct report was printed, it was taken as material evidence that the network functioned sufficiently well to be used with the application. The IVT-proposed standard provides a more sophisticated approach to qualifying the platform aspect of the infrastructure. The process includes steps similar to the RiskVal life cycle: planning, designing, building and testing, installing and verifying the network, ongoing operation, and retirement. The qualification discussed in this section of the book corresponds to the proposed IVT standard's third step (i.e., build and test), and the concepts presented for that step have been integrated into this discussion.

The arrival of infrastructure services that are highly integrated with specialized application software has boosted the role that infrastructure plays in providing system security, access control, and data integrity.

- Data security has become more complex both in terms of protecting local networks from unauthorized entry and protecting data, records, and documents from destruction by viruses, worms, and other parasites.
- Some of the functionality that was done by the application can now be done for all applications by software that's part of the server operating system. For example, Microsoft's Active Directory can be used to define groups of users and to set access privileges for each group for all of the applications that are run from the server.
- In some organizations, applications don't run on single servers. Server farms or clusters are installed, and a transaction performed by an application could be performed on any of the servers because the system software manages the server load.
- In some situations data storage is distributed to many devices, with part of the data located in the proximity of users who need it the most.
- Web-based applications are very common now. The application and user interface might reside on different servers anywhere in the world. Your access to it and transfer of accurate data and information depends upon the proper functioning of your IT infrastructure.

The purpose of qualifying the infrastructure is to verify that it has the capability and capacity to support applications and perform the operations your organization needs. For example, the qualification of the backup service involves demonstrating that the hardware and software used for backups have the capability and capacity to perform the required backups.

When to Qualify the Infrastructure

The infrastructure, or appropriate parts of it, should be qualified when:

■ The infrastructure is used to provide services needed by systems to function reliably. You can't state that an application or system will function reliably unless you have material evidence that the hardware and system software upon which it depends will function reliably. The FDA has been issuing observations of nonconformance and warning letters for inadequate control of networks and networked computer systems (see, for example, warning letter 320-01-08, January 11, 2001, published on the FDA's Web site).

■ Services are required for data integrity, such as virus protection.

■ Infrastructure failures need to be prevented and controlled to lower business risk.

■ Efficient technical management of the infrastructure is needed to support the operations of the organization.

■ A service is required by a regulation, such as backup and restore.[49–51]

■ A service must be configured to be used effectively with an application that has to be validated. Backup and restore is an example if, as mentioned above, the backup software has to be configured to backup specific files and data for a document control system at specific times. Another example is using an application deployment function for downloading bug fixes or new revisions of client software for a specific application.

QUALIFY THE INFRASTRUCTURE SERVICE

Organizations can use infrastructure services differently. Qualification of the service is entirely dependent upon the intended use. The extent of infrastructure qualification should be proportional to the overall risk associated with using the infrastructure service. Because the risk level is dependent on the intended uses, what's required for qualification will vary from company to company.

Table 9.6 provides examples of services and their uses by a medical device company. The right column states if the use is for compliance, to meet a business need, or both. The examples in the table make some assumptions about the use of the infrastructure services. These assumptions are stated in the table. These services and their uses will serve as an illustration throughout this section.

| Table 9.6 | Infrastructure Services and Their Uses |

	Service	**Uses**	**Business or compliance use**
1	Firewall	Prevents unauthorized users from accessing private networks connected to the Internet *Assumption:* All messages entering or leaving the network pass through the firewall, which examines each network packet and blocks those that don't meet the specified security criteria set within the firewall.	Business and compliance
2	Authorization and authentication (e.g., Active Directory and Windows NT security)	Active Directory (AD) provides user authorization and authentication services. AD controls access onto the network, what network drives users can access, who can log onto applications, and what privileges users have for using an application based on their assigned roles.	Business and compliance
3	Application deployment	Download application software and updates to desktops, including applications used to create quality records. *Assumption:* Using application deployment is a convenience. When it fails to work properly, it can be easily detected and corrected by manual actions.	Business and compliance
4	Backup and restore	4 a. Backup of servers *Assumption:* Quality records are stored on servers in security-protected drives.	Business and compliance
		4 b. Backup of desktops *Assumption:* Quality records aren't stored on desktops	Business
5	Virus protection	5 a. Antivirus scan of e-mail servers *Assumption:* E-mail isn't used for product-quality issues or transactions involving quality records	Business
		5 b. Antivirus scan of servers	Business and compliance
		5 c. Antivirus scan of desktops *Assumption:* quality records aren't stored on desktops.	Business
6	Virtual private network	6 a. Providing secure network access to remote authorized users	Business
		6 b. Prohibiting access of unauthorized users	Business and compliance
		6 c. Limiting the access of remote users to systems and/or directories on the network once users are inside the network	Business and compliance
7	Host mirroring for key systems for disaster recovery	Limit disruption to application availability by using hot back-up servers at different locations.	Business and compliance

(continues)

Table 9.6	Infrastructure Services and Their Uses (continued)		
	Service	**Uses**	**Business or compliance use**
8	Electronic mail	8 a. Receiving and sending e-mail outside the company *Assumption:* E-mail isn't used in conjunction with quality records.	Business
		8 b. Receiving and sending e-mail within the company	Business
9	Internet	To provide access to the Internet *Assumption:* Internet access isn't used during the normal course of business (i.e., Web-hosted applications aren't in use).	N/A
10	Help-desk system	Method by which users alert the information technology department about problems *Assumption:* This procedure is used to report difficulties with validated systems.	Business and compliance
11	Network communications	7 a. Routing information and files from a source to a destination	Business and compliance
		7 b. Printing files	Business and compliance

Determine the Infrastructure Service Risk Level

The level of effort to qualify an infrastructure service ought to be proportional to the risk associated with its failure.

As explained in chapter 6, in the risk analysis of software, the assumption is made that the software will fail at an unacceptable level. The risk level then can be determined by the severity of the consequence of a failure. From a regulatory perspective, failures of some infrastructure services may have a direct effect on product quality, record integrity, and compliance. From a business perspective, failures may also disrupt the organization's efficiency and the continuity of business operations. The severity of such an effect can be easily evaluated. For example, the failure of an antivirus service may lead to the destruction of quality records. The failure of the backup-and-restore system is itself a noncompliance as well as a potential factor in data loss. A failure of Active Directory, or the way that it's been configured, could enable unauthorized use of a system.

Some infrastructure services, such as a firewall, are more removed from applications and the data that applications generate. The failure of such services has a less direct effect on record integrity, compliance, or product quality. You must determine how a failure of such infrastructure service might affect product quality, record integrity, and/or compliance. If the firewall failed and an intruder gained access to the system, records could be altered or deleted, assuming the intruder was also able get past the network security and gain access to protected drives and folders or databases that hold such records.

The severity of harm can be assessed using severity scales as described in chapter 6. The same dimensions can be used, including product quality, compliance, record integrity and confidentiality, business efficiency, and business continuity. However, an approach that's slightly different from that used in chapter 6 will be given here as an alternative. Note that either approach could be used. Two scales will be used to determine the severity of a failure. The first is the effect on product quality. This will be taken into account separately from other concerns. The second scale takes into account the most severe effect on the following dimensions: compliance, record integrity and confidentiality, business efficiency, and business continuity. For example, if a consequence of a failure is more severe in terms of compliance than the other dimensions, the severity level on compliance is used.

The scale used for impact on product quality takes into account whether a failure can directly or indirectly affect product quality. The three levels are:

■ *High.* A failure of the service can directly affect the quality of the product (i.e., affect whether the product is correctly made, tested, or released). The effect on product quality is also considered high if a failure will provide direct unauthorized access to data or systems in such a way that product quality can be compromised or altered, or defective product can be released for use.

■ *Moderate.* The service doesn't directly affect an application used in production or testing or releasing the product, but the service can affect something that could have a direct effect on product quality.

    ☐ The effect is also considered moderate if that service as well as an additional service or application must fail simultaneously for a negative effect on product quality to occur.

    ☐ A service failure can also be categorized as moderate if the failure is easily detectable, if a procedure or automation is used to monitor for the failure, and the failure can be addressed before harm can occur as a result of the failure.

■ *Low.* The service has no direct or indirect relevance to the product being correctly made, tested, or released. Or, sufficient mitigations are in place so that multiple failures would have to occur simultaneously for product quality to be affected.

A second scale is used to factor in the effect of a failure on compliance, record integrity and confidentiality, business efficiency, and business continuity. The risks associated with a service failure are also evaluated based on how critical the proper functioning of the service is for compliance, record integrity and confidentiality, or business efficiency and business continuity. Three evaluation levels can be used:

■ *Critical.* Absolutely required. Failure to meet this requirement:
  □ Makes critical applications unable to meet their intended use
  □ Causes a serious compliance issue with the quality system regulations or Part 11
  □ Would create a catastrophic loss of, or corruption of, records, data, or programs that can't be recovered, or the loss of access to such items for an intolerable period of time
  □ Would result in an extensive loss of security for high-value information and/or sensitive business and proprietary information
  □ Would result in an intolerable loss of business efficiency or business continuity

■ *Important.* Without this service, an application is useable but loses significant value and effectiveness in regard to an intended use, or the failure results in one of the following issues:
  □ A moderate noncompliance issue with quality system regulations or a Part 11 requirement
  □ A loss of records, data, or programs that can be recovered by IT with difficulty
  □ A temporary loss of security for records or business proprietary information. Or, the failure results in a situation where access to records and/or business proprietary information is possible but requires extraordinary means.
  □ Presents a moderate reduction of business efficiency or causes a moderate disruption to business continuity
  □ Although not directly affecting an application that's critical to compliance, record, data, or program integrity, or business continuity, the service failure removes a significant control that's used to reduce risks associated with the failure of such applications.

■ *Minimal.* The absence, loss, or failure of this service will have little or no effect on a system's effectiveness or compliance. For example:
  □ Lost or corrupted quality records or high-value information that can easily be recovered by IT
  □ The failure doesn't affect the confidentiality of records or sensitive or proprietary information.

☐ The failure results in a momentary or minor loss of business efficiency and/or continuity.

Table 9.7	Risk Level as a Function of Risk to Product Quality and Service Criticality		
Criticality of the service	**Effect on product quality**		
	Low	**Moderate**	**High**
Critical	Moderate risk	High risk	High risk
Important	Moderate risk	Moderate risk	High risk
Minimal importance	None	Low risk	Moderate risk

Table 9.7 shows the risk levels associated with the infrastructure services as a function of the potential effect of the failure on product quality and the criticality of the service.

Level of Qualification Needed for an Infrastructure Service

Table 9.8 defines the level of qualification needed, based on the risk level of the infrastructure service. (*Note:* Again, readers must determine what's appropriate for their own organizations.) Obviously, if a service will have a high effect on product quality and is critical for achieving the intended use of a service, the qualification activities ought to be more extensive.

Table 9.9 explains what's included in the qualification levels.

Exhibit 9.7 provides a partial example of an infrastructure-service risk analysis from a medical device company.

Approaches for the Qualification of Infrastructure Services

Table 9.10 provides examples of how to approach the qualification of infrastructure services. These are examples and apply to how one company used the services. A risk analysis was performed; part of it is given in exhibit 9.7. To determine a risk level, the effect of a failure on product quality and the criticality of the failed service were determined. Table 9.7 was then used to identify the risk level. Table 9.8 was used to determine the nature of the qualification, the "quality system requirement (QSR) required

(continues on page 326)

Table 9.8	Level of Qualification Required as a Function of Risk to Product Quality and Service Criticality		
Criticality of the service	**Effect on product quality**		
	Low	**Moderate**	**High**
Critical	Installation qualification (IQ) and limited operational qualification (OQ) testing of services	IQ and OQ testing of normal and fault conditions	IQ and OQ testing of normal and fault conditions
Important	IQ and limited OQ testing of services	IQ and limited OQ testing of services	IQ and OQ testing of normal and fault conditions
Minimal importance	None or IQ only	IQ and limited OQ testing of services	IQ and limited OQ testing of services

Table 9.9	Levels of Qualification Activities
Qualification level	**Required qualification activity**

4. Installation qualification (IQ) and operational qualification (OQ) testing of normal and fault conditions	■ IQ and OQ of the infrastructure hardware and software, as explained about the infrastructure platform below
	■ Direct OQ testing of the ability to provide a service that meets requirements, including:
	  ☐ Normal operation of the service
	  ☐ OQ testing of the service, to the extent possible, of potential user errors or failure conditions, including:
	    ◆ Potential failures that would affect product quality
	    ◆ Potential failures that would result in serious compliance issues
	    ◆ Potential failures that would result in a catastrophic loss or corruption of records, data, programs, or other high-value information

3. IQ and limited OQ testing of services	■ IQ and OQ of the infrastructure hardware and software, as explained about the infrastructure platform below ■ OQ testing of the normal routine provision of aspects of the service that could affect product quality, compliance, records, data, program integrity, or business efficiency or continuity
2. IQ only	■ IQ of the infrastructure hardware and software
1. None	■ None, because the service is used in a support capacity that has no effect on the quality of the product, compliance, record, data, program integrity, or business efficiency or continuity (e.g., tools used for monitoring the central processing unit capacity that's being used).

| Exhibit 9.7 | Partial Example of an Infrastructure Service Risk Analysis | | | | | | | |

Services and intended uses	Nature of the hazard or failure; comments	Risk of effect on product quality	Reason for effect on quality rating	Nature of of the criticality issue	Criticality issue	Criticality rating	Qualification required for QSRs
1. Firewall							
1. Incoming and outgoing traffic is filtered based on a set of rules to control access to the network from outside the company.	Failure means firewall is down, not functioning properly, or disabled.	Moderate	If the firewall was down, a hacker would have to get a user name and password to gain access to a controlled drive where electronic quality records are stored. That drive is only protected by the security on the drive.	Compliance	Quality records could potentially be altered if the security on the drive also failed.	Important	Installation qualification (IQ) and limited operational qualification (OQ) testing of services
				Business	Hacker might be able to access proprietary data, or use company resources to hack into other systems.	Important	N/A
2. Authorization and authentication (e.g., Active Director and Windows NT security)							
2 a. Network login	Failure means people can't log in.	Low	If people can't log in, they can't use the quality system. They can't make any product.	Business	Loss of productivity and business continuity. If people can't log in, they can't use automated aspects of the quality system and must wait or use a manual backup system.	Critical	N/A
2 b.	Failure means people can log on when they shouldn't be able to.	Moderate	Once hackers got on to the network, they would have to get a user name and password to gain access to a controlled drive. Electronic quality records are stored on a drive	Compliance	Quality records could potentially be altered if the security on the drive also failed.	Important	IQ and limited OQ testing of services
				Business	Individuals would be able to access proprietary data if that's protected only by the security on the drive.	Important	N/A

(continues)

Exhibit 9.7	Partial Example of an Infrastructure Service Risk Analysis (continued)						
Services and intended uses	**Nature of the hazard or failure; comments**	**Risk of effect on product quality**	**Reason for effect on quality rating**	**Nature of of the criticality issue**	**Criticality issue**	**Criticality rating**	**Qualification required for QSRs**
2 c. Access to controlled local and network direc- tories	Failure means no access to local directo- ries (e.g., "my documents")	Low	Product infor- mation is ac- cessed through applications.	Business	Loss of productiv- ity due to inability to access "my documents." Servers are shared so that login can be given by a backup server.	Minimal importance	N/A
	Failure means people have access to controlled directories that shouldn't be accessible.	High	Electronic qual- ity records are stored on a drive that's protected only by the security on that drive.	Compliance	Quality records could potentially be altered if the security on the drive failed.	Critical	IQ & OQ test- ing of normal and fault conditions
				Business	Individuals would be able to access proprietary data.	Important	NA

qualification," based on the risk-level. The QSR required qualification was recorded for the example in the second-to-last column of table 9.10. The last column translates the QSR-required qualification for the service into specific things that the qualification needs to include. Note that your organization's risk assessment could lead to a different risk level and corresponding qualification approach.

Notice that for all services that require qualification, the qualification approach in-cludes the phrase "verification of operational and maintenance procedure in the OQ" (see the last column of table 9.10). As mentioned above, such procedures include rou-tine activities that should be performed to adjust the configurations that control the service. If the range of possible configuration values and the method of creating the configurations are tested in the OQ, the system configurations may be changed to one of these setting without getting additional approval through the formal change control process. The instructions given in the procedures are also tested in the OQ to verify their accuracy and confirm that following the procedures will achieve the intended purpose without negative side effects.

(continues on page 330)

Table 9.10	Examples of Approaches to Infrastructure Service Qualifications			
	Service	**Uses**	**Quality system requirement (QSR) required qualification**	**Qualification approach, based on the QSR required qualification**
1	Firewall	Prevent unauthorized Internet users from accessing private networks connected to the Internet. All messages entering or leaving the network pass through the firewall, which examines each network packet and blocks those that don't meet the specified security criteria set within the firewall.	Installation qualification (IQ) and limited operational qualification (OQ) testing of services	■ Verify firewall settings in the IQ. ■ Verify operation and maintenance procedure in the OQ. ■ Include firewall tests as a section in the OQ. Test that the firewall correctly screens network packets, based on the security criteria set with the firewall.
2	Authorization and authentication (e.g., Active Directory and Windows NT security)	Active Directory (AD) performs authorization and authentication services. AD controls access onto the network, and what role(s) users are assigned. AD uses the role assignment to determine what network drives users can access and what applications they can log onto. The applications use the roles to assign privileges to users.	IQ and OQ testing of normal and fault conditions	■ Verify security settings for the roles in the IQ. ■ Verify operation and maintenance procedure in the OQ. ■ Test network logon security. This appropriately allows logon and denies logon with incorrect user ID and/or password. ■ Test ability to access protected directories when users are assigned the appropriate privilege or not. Test "read only" and "write" capabilities when users are assigned the privileges or not. ■ Test ability to access all applications for which the AD controls access (also test access denial for users not assigned the privilege). ■ Test proper assignment of privileges for each application, based on group membership.
3	Application deployment	Download application software and updates to desktops, including applications used to create quality records. *Assumption:* Using application deployment is a convenience. When it fails to work properly, it can be easily detected and corrected by manual actions.	None	N/A
4	Backup and restore	a. Backup of servers *Assumption:* Quality records are stored on servers in security-protected drives.	IQ and OQ testing of normal and fault conditions	■ IQ of backup-and-restore hardware and software, including configurations.

(continues)

			Quality system requirement (QSR) required qualification	Qualification approach, based on the QSR required qualification
	Service	**Uses**		
				■ Verifiy operation and maintenance procedure in the OQ. ■ Verify complete backup of the server that has quality records on it, and the ability to restore all server content. ■ Test failure condition: Take three or four servers out of use and determine if the backup system properly indicates failure to backup the servers.
		b. Backup of desktops *Assumption:* Quality records aren't stored on desktops.	N/A	N/A
5	Virus protection	a. Antivirus scan of e-mail servers *Assumption:* E-mail isn't used to create, approve, or transmit quality records.	N/A	N/A
		b. Antivirus scan of servers	IQ and OQ testing of normal and fault conditions	■ Verify the antivirus settings in the IQ. ■ Verify operation and maintenance procedure in the OQ. ■ Test that antivirus updates are pulled down at scheduled intervals, or as available by the antivirus company. ■ Verify that the updates are included in the scans. ■ Test that antivirus scans are made at scheduled times. ■ Verify that all material to be scanned is, in fact, scanned.
		c. Antivirus scan of desktops *Assumption:* Quality records aren't stored on desktops.	N/A	N/A
6	Virtual private network (VPN)	a. Provide secure network access to authorized remote users. *Assumption:* If people can't logon, they can't use the quality system or affect product quality.	N/A	N/A
		b. Prohibiting access to unauthorized users	IQ and limited OQ testing of services	■ Verify VPN configurations in the IQ. ■ Verify operation and maintenance procedure in the OQ.

Table 9.10 Examples of Approaches to Infrastructure Service Qualifications (continued)

	Service	Uses	Quality system requirement (QSR) required qualification	Qualification approach, based on the QSR required qualification
				■ OQ testing of logon security. This appropriately allows logon, and denies logon with incorrect user ID and/or password.
		c. Limiting the access of remote users to systems and/or directories on the network once users are inside the network	IQ and limited OQ testing of services	■ Verify that users who were legitimately granted access to enter the network by the VPN have appropriate access only to systems and drives per privileges.
7	Host mirroring for key systems for disaster recovery (e.g., hot backup servers at another location)	Limit disruption of application availability by using hot backup servers	IQ and limited OQ testing of services	■ Perform IQ on the hot backup servers, including loading the applications. ■ Verify operation and maintenance procedure in the OQ. ■ Verify in the OQ that the backup servers are identical to the host server when the command is given to synchronize. ■ Verify that the hot backup will take over as the primary server under failure conditions of the host server.
8	Electronic mail	a. Receiving and sending e-mail outside the company	N/A	N/A
		b. Receiving and sending e-mail within the company *Assumption:* E-mail isn't used to create, approve, or transmit quality records.		
9	Internet connectivity	To provide access to the Internet *Assumption:* Internet access isn't used during the normal course of business (i.e., Web-hosted applications aren't in use).	N/A	N/A
10	Help-desk system	Method by which users alert the information technology department about problems *Assumption:* The method is used to report difficulties with validated systems.	IQ and limited OQ testing of services	■ Perform IQ on software used for the help desk, including any configurations (e.g., for routing problems or requests). ■ Verify in an OQ that help-desk procedures work for recording and tracking defects. Verify integrity of the defect database.
11	Network	Routing information and files from a source to a destination; printing	None	See the last paragraph of this section on page 330.

For example, a cluster of load-balanced servers may be adjusted so that one of the servers can be taken off-line for troubleshooting purposes. The OQ can confirm that the remaining servers seamlessly continue to provide the service. A second type of procedure might need to be written for using infrastructure services (i.e., how to use a service in a specific situation). An example is backup and restore. If the backup of a specific system requires special instructions, a separate procedure can be written stating those instructions. For instance, you might have a backup-and-restore procedure for backing up your enterprise resource planning system that includes configuration settings for the backup software and instructions for the operator. In an IQ you would confirm that the settings have been properly made. In an OQ, you'll verify that a complete and accurate backup can be made with the configuration settings and the instructions provided in the procedure.

In the example shown in table 9.10, the risk analysis pointed only to business risks for network failure; however, it's important to maintain adequate control of the network. For this reason, a minimum qualification can be performed even if the risk analysis shows that a network failure won't affect product quality, record integrity, or compliance. First, a procedure needs to be approved that specifies what's required for network operation, maintenance, and configuration management. The procedure should also include how network equipment diagrams are managed, and how to repair and replace components. An IQ can be performed to confirm the existence of the procedure, maintenance records, and the accuracy of the network diagrams. An OQ can be performed to qualify the preventive maintenance procedure and configuration management options. In addition, the OQ can be used to verify that repairs and the replacement of standard network components can be performed without an adverse effect on the network.

QUALIFY THE IT INFRASTRUCTURE PLATFORM

The qualification of the hardware and system software (i.e., the platform) is basically the same if the equipment, system software, and ancillary software are:

- Used for a single application
- Considered part of the infrastructure platform (i.e., used for multiple applications
- An addition to the existing infrastructure platform
- Used specifically for providing an infrastructure service

The hardware and system software used in these different situations may have different capacity specifications and technical requirements. Capacity specifications include such things as concurrent user access, total storage, CPU utilization, downtime expectations regarding scheduled maintenance, and performance benchmarks. Technical hardware requirements include such things as server make and model, number of CPUs, amount of RAM memory, storage volume and configuration, media devices, physical location, and the number and types of network cards.[52] These technical hardware requirements are driven in part by technological standards that your organization has established. How the hardware and software are configured is determined primarily by the application software requirements.

Items to Include in the Infrastructure Platform IQ

The purpose of the IQ for infrastructure equipment and software is the same as for applications (i.e., to confirm that the technical requirements are met and that each item is properly installed). The structure of an IQ used for the infrastructure is the same as the IQ structure used for an application. (See deliverable 7.1 in appendix A as well as the discussion above on the IQ content for applications.) In general, the test section of the IQ for infrastructure hardware and software must include the following types of items:

- Every hardware and system software component of the infrastructure that's purchased as a separate entity or is an option when the item is purchased. Exceptions include interchangeable items such as cables and communication lines.

- Items that are bundled together and purchased and installed as a single product needn't be verified individually.

- For prospective infrastructure qualifications, include the configurations of the hardware and system software that were set at installation and after installation as the team worked with the system during phases 4 through 6.

- With concurrent and retrospective infrastructure qualifications, include in the IQ the hardware and system software configurations of the infrastructure and any changes that will be made before executing the IQ.

- IT procedures needed to maintain the infrastructure in a controlled state, as discussed in phase 6. The verification that such procedures have been approved and implemented can be performed either in an IQ test section or as an IQ prerequisite.

If records are available of what's been installed in the infrastructure, or a system specification was prepared for the infrastructure during phase 6, use those records to create the infrastructure IQ. Infrastructure architecture diagrams that show the devices and how they're connected can also be used. If records haven't been kept as the infrastructure was built, an inventory must be taken. Items that are bundled together, purchased, and installed as a single product can be shown as a single item.

The IQs and OQs for different pieces of infrastructure equipment of the same type (e.g., servers) will be similar. The same dimensions will be included in an IQ for almost all servers, but the expected results will vary according to the specific requirements for a particular server. Consequently, developing generic protocols that can be customized for specific pieces of equipment, such as a server IQ and a server OQ, will lead to efficiency gains.

Table 9.2 provides examples of the types of items that would be included in an infrastructure IQ.

Install, Calibrate, and Perform Maintenance on the Equipment

As is the case with hardware and system software that's considered a part of an integrated system, the hardware and software must be installed before the IQ is executed. If the system involves measuring devices that require calibration, the calibration must be current before the IQ is executed. Finally, preventive maintenance must be up to date.

Items to Include in the Infrastructure Platform OQ

The purposes of the OQ for the infrastructure platform include, as appropriate:
- To verify that the infrastructure platform configuration is operating as intended (e.g., media drives, local and remote consoles, and network communication)
- To record benchmarks for utilization and performance (e.g., for basic server functions)
- To establish downtime estimates for routine and preventive maintenance
- To verify maintenance operations (e.g., inspection of error and performance logs, evaluation of available storage space, checking the integrity of disks, defragmenting hard drives, verifying the integrity of the database, synchronizing time, and creating or updating a server's backup image)

- To verify that maintenance and configuration procedures specific to a service are effective and won't inadvertently cause failures or errors (e.g., how to maintain and configure a firewall)
- To verify the efficacy and safety of maintenance and configuration procedures for equipment and software that aren't covered in a procedure related to a specific application or service. Again, servers and server software provide examples. A generic procedure for managing and configuring a server farm and database farm ought to be developed and tested, including the following:
  - ☐ Checking integrity of disks and databases
  - ☐ Defragmenting hard drives
  - ☐ Running diagnostics and performance benchmarks
  - ☐ Synchronizing time to the National Institute of Standards and Technology
  - ☐ Updating a backup image
  - ☐ Evaluating the adequacy of available storage space and making appropriate modifications
  - ☐ Using tools to balance server load
  - ☐ Reviewing error logs[53]

If any analysis has been done to determine the risk level of the infrastructure, consideration can be given to the amount of OQ testing that's done for infrastructure devices. For infrastructures used only to run low-risk applications, little or nothing can be done to confirm the functioning of devices that are less relevant to the infrastructure's overall performance. For example, with a low-risk infrastructure, you might decide not to verify that printers have printer drivers that are able to print your information accurately. Such aspects of the system can be tested informally or tested during an OQ for an application.

Table 9.2 provides examples of OQ test items for infrastructure hardware. An example of an OQ test procedure item for a server is provided in exhibit 9.3.

QUALIFICATION OF CONFIGURED SYSTEMS

With configured business systems, the configurations designed earlier in the life cycle are implemented in the validation instance and confirmed in the IQ. The configured functionality is tested in the OQ, and during phase 8 as part of the performance qualification, if appropriate.

QUALIFICATION OF CUSTOM SYSTEMS

Tests of the system, including unit and/or modular tests, subsystem tests (i.e., integration tests), and total system tests, should have been designed and performed by the developer of custom software during phase 6. These tests should include boundary, white-box tests of internal logic, and black-box tests. During phase 7, tests are performed by the user organization to determine if the system functions to meet requirements in the validation environment and then, during the next phase, in its own production environment. The test environment at the developer's facility should be as close to the user's technical environment as possible to minimize the effect of different environments.

SUMMARY OF PHASE 7 DELIVERABLES

Table 9.11 summarizes the deliverables from phase 7 and identifies when each deliverable is applicable.

The QSR requires an approved protocol for computer system validation. The FDA lists the "validation protocol used," and the "test cases and results" in its list of five documents that a manufacture ought to have from its validation efforts.[54, 55] The European Commission requires that the system be thoroughly tested and confirmed as capable of achieving desired results.[56] ISO 13485 states that documented procedures should be established for the validation of computer systems and that the results of the validation shall be recorded.[57] None of the regulations, or the ISO 13485 standard, or the FDA's guidance on software validation specifies a type of protocol that's required (i.e., an IQ, OQ, or PQ). With the RiskVal life cycle, the mandate to use established protocols is met with the IQ, OQ, and PQ, as appropriate, based on the risk level of the system.

Table 9.11	Phase 7 Deliverables		
Phase 7 deliverables	**Definition and explanation**	**When applicable**	**Deliverable references**
Calibration records	Records of the calibrations and maintenance performed prior to the installation qualification (IQ)	When equipment requires calibration	21 CFR 211, Section 68a; 21 CFR 820, Section 72; ISO 13485, Section 7.6
Maintenance records	Records of the maintenance performed prior to the IQ	When equipment requires maintenance	21 CFR 211, Section 67; 21 CFR 820, Section 70 g 1; ISO 13485, Section 6.3
IQ protocol	A protocol that defines the steps to be taken to verify the proper installation of hardware and software and that it meets requirements	All systems	CDRH 6.2; EC Annex 11, No. 7; ISO 13485, Section 7.5.2.1
IQ report (test environment)	A report that summarizes the results from the IQ protocol and states a conclusion regarding the system's ability to meet the IQ protocol acceptance criteria	All systems	21 CFR 820, Section 70 i; EC Annex 11, No. 7; ISO 13485, Section 7.5.2.1; CDRH 6.2
Operational qualification (OQ) protocol	A protocol developed to verify that the system operates, in a test environment, in accord with requirements throughout all anticipated operational ranges	All systems	21 CFR 820, Section 70 i; CDRH 6.2; EC Annex 11, No. 7; ISO 13485, Section 7.5.2.1
Traceability matrix (user requirements to protocols)	A mapping of all user requirements to test steps in the protocols. The matrix documents that the requirements are being tested.	All systems except systems with simple protocols	Highly recommended
OQ report	A report that summarizes the OQ results, including variances, and states a conclusion regarding the system's ability to meet the OQ protocol acceptance criteria.	All systems	21 CFR 820, Section 70 i; EC Annex 11, No. 7; ISO 13485, Section 7.5.2.1; CDRH 6.2
Change control records	Records of the approval and testing of changes prior to their implementation in the production environment	All systems	21 CFR Part 11, 11.10 k 2 CDRH 6.1; 21 CFR 820, Section 70 i; ISO 13485, Section 7.5.2.1; EC Annex 11, No. 11
User training records	Records of the training provided to individuals trained to execute the validation protocols	All systems	21 CFR 211, Section 25; 21 CFR 820, Section 25 b; Part 11, Section 11.10 i; ISO 13485, Section 6.2.2; EC Annex 11, No. 1

Chapter 10

Phase 8: Use in a
Production Environment

P hase 8—Use in a production environment spans the entire operational life of the system, from when it's officially installed in the production environment to when it's retired (see note 1). The purposes of this phase are to:

- Verify that the system functions appropriately in the production environment.
- Use the system in compliance with approved user procedures.
- Support and manage the system following approved information technology (IT) procedures to ensure that the system remains in a validated state.

Once the system is qualified in the test environment, it's installed in a production environment and verified using the installation qualification (IQ) protocol. Further testing, called the performance qualification (PQ), is conducted under actual operating conditions to verify that the system performs its intended functions while operating in its normal production environment. The approach taken to the PQ depends on the risk associated with the system. Options include:

- Testing functions by comparing results obtained with the electronic system with results obtained from a parallel manual system or electronic system
- Executing designed tests of program logic and system functionality
- Verifying end-result data but not testing processing steps
- Monitoring the system by reviewing system data, logs, and problem reports
- Combining any of the options

A PQ report is written and approved.

A validation final report is written that, when approved, completes the validation aspects of the life cycle.

Throughout the system's production use, it's carefully managed to ensure continued reliable performance.

- Trained users and administrators operate the system according to approved procedures.
- Security measures block the system from unauthorized use and safeguard data from unauthorized changes.
- System performance is maintained through calibration and maintenance.
- Problems are tracked and difficulties resolved using controlled methods.
- Changes are evaluated, approved, implemented, and tested in a test environment and then introduced into the production environment. The system is monitored after the change to ensure that any unexpected negative effect is detected.
- The system and the control processes are audited. The system's operating experience is evaluated through a review of problem reports and change-control records. The use of procedures that control system use or maintain the system in a validated state is audited.

When changes are extensive or system performance has degraded, a complete system revalidation can be performed.

PREPARE THE SYSTEM IN THE PRODUCTION ENVIRONMENT

New systems are installed in the production environment, and existing systems are prepared for the performance qualification.

New systems

New systems are installed following manufacturer instructions, the integration documentation or procedure developed in phase 4, and the configurations developed in phases 4 through 6. Hardware, system software, and database software are installed and configured to be as close to the test environment as possible. With a successful operational qualification (OQ), you know that the system will meet requirements in the test environment. If that environment is replicated as a production environment, it should function there as well as it does in the test environment. There are exceptions where some of the configurations need to be changed to accommodate, among other things, higher transaction volumes and differences in database transactions. The performance qualification will confirm that these changed aspects of the system are as needed to meet user requirements including response time.

The application configurations established in the test environment and tested in the OQ are created in the production environment. For some applications, the configurations are stored in an application file that can be copied into the production environment. With other applications, the configurations have to be created manually. It's a good idea to check or informally test the application configurations before the IQ is executed.

Once the production environment is created, including all of the configurations, the IQ protocol prepared in the previous phase is executed again. Because the IQ is written to confirm the test environment installation, differences between the test environment and the production environment will be identified as variances when the IQ is executed. There are two options for addressing this situation. First, a separate IQ protocol for the production environment can be prepared and approved. If this approach is taken, modify the expected results so that they match how the production environment is supposed to be configured. A second approach is to use the same protocol that was used with the test environment. Handle differences by means of variances (see chapter 6). On the variance form describe the variance (how the production environment is different than the expected results), and explain that for the production environment the actual results are appropriate.

Existing systems

With existing systems validated with a concurrent validation approach, use of the system may be continued while testing is performed in the test environment. As mentioned in chapter 6, the alternative is to perform all testing in the production system. If a test environment is established and the system is modified in the test environment, an additional complexity is encountered. In some situations, the test environment is set up to include changes desired in the production system. These changes are tested along with the rest of the system by means of the test environment OQ. Once the OQ is complete, the changes have to be installed in the production environment, and then the installation confirmed with the production IQ.

The installation in the production environment typically involves taking the application off-line and making the changes. As above with new systems, configurations, including the changes, can be made by copying and installing files from the test environment, or by creating the configurations manually in the system.

The situation is the same with the IQ as is the case with new systems that have been configured in the test environment. Discrepancies between actual results and expected results may occur due to the changes made in the test environment. The same options for resolving these variances exist: create a new IQ protocol for the production environment where the expected results are changed to match the changes in the system, or report and address the variances on variance forms.

Once the IQ report is approved, the system can be used as planned in the validation plan and the performance qualification can be executed.

PLAN THE PERFORMANCE QUALIFICATION

Objectives of the PQ

The last component of validation testing is the PQ. From a compliance perspective, the PQ verifies the ability of the system to function as required, throughout all the anticipated operating ranges, as it's used for performing work. The PQ is "performed on the total integrated computer-related system while operating in its normal environment."[1] The system is tested under normal and extreme operational conditions (called stress testing) to verify that it can perform reliably. The PQ should include an evaluation of the system users' ability to understand and correctly interface with it. Operators should be able to perform the intended functions.

The PQ can also have the broader role of verifying that using the system is an effective tool for the company's relevant automation needs. This aspect of the PQ is appropriate as a business assessment and not required from a regulatory perspective. At this point, the team comes full circle back to the vision formulated during phase 1 and asks if the vision has been realized. Questions that can be asked include:

- How well does the system and the process of which it's a part meet the business goals for which it was planned?
- Are the users excited and supportive, or do they have reservations about the system? Will they embrace the system and make it successful?
- How heavy of a burden is the support and use of the system on the organization? Are those costs justified based on the gains from the system?

As was mentioned in chapter 9, the FDA regulations don't require any specific protocol. Rather, the language allows the individual validating the system to determine how to structure the verification and validation activities, but an approved protocol must be used. In addition, the results of the activities need to be documented. Here is the exact language: ". . . the manufacturer shall validate computer software for its intended use according to an established protocol. All software changes shall be validated before approval and issuance. These validation activities and results shall be documented."[2] With the RiskVal life cycle, the mandate to used established protocols is met with the IQ, OQ, and PQ, as appropriate based on the risk level of the system.

System Release Before or After the PQ

As mentioned in chapter 6 in the discussion of validation strategy, the system is released for production after the PQ is successfully completed and the validation final report is approved. Exceptions are discussed in chapter 6. The OQ qualifies the system as capable of meeting user requirements, although in a test environment. The PQ involves collecting objective evidence to demonstrate that it meets requirements for how it's used in the automated process. Meeting requirements means that the system works as it's intended, and if it could affect the quality of the product, that the products produced meet specifications. This can be seen from the generic definition of validation used by the Food and Drug Administration (FDA): "establishing documented evidence that provides a high degree of assurance that a specific process will consistently produce a product meeting its predetermined specifications and quality attributes."[3] If the system meets requirements in the production environment, including producing a product that's within specifications, it's released for use. The next section discusses alternative ways of demonstrating that the system is effective in the production environment.

Alternative Approaches to the PQ

The four approaches that can be taken to the PQ are summarized in table 10.1 and explained in the paragraphs below.

In the first approach, called the "dual-system approach," every transaction is performed twice—once with the automated system, and once manually or with a previously validated electronic system. The results are compared. If there's a difference, the cause of the difference is investigated. If the cause is determined to be the system being validated, a variance is written. The paper records, or the records produced by a previously validated system, are the official quality records. This approach minimizes the risk of harm from a system failure. In addition, the product produced with this approach can be used with humans, assuming that the manual systems have been appropriately established and the product meets specifications.

Table 10.1	Approaches Taken in the Performance Qualification		
Approach	**Definition**	**Type of testing**	**Recommended uses**
Dual system	Each transaction is performed in a manual system as well as the automated system.	Compare the outputs from the two systems.	Possible use for high-risk transactions
Confirmation	Verification of the end-result data produced by the system during normal use	Confirm the accuracy of transactions either by confirmation or manual calculations.	High- and moderate-risk transactions
System test	Designed tests of the system are executed.	Execution of tests defined in the PQ protocol. Tests can be performed on actual or test data.	Recommended for high- and moderate-risk operations that can't be verified through end-result data
System monitoring	Monitoring of system logs, employee problem reports, and user satisfaction	Review of logs and problem reports	Recommended to be used in combination with other approaches or for low-risk systems

An example of this approach with a document-control system is the approval of documents. In addition to the electronic approval by means of the electronic document management system (EDMS), a paper change-request form would be circulated for handwritten signatures. The approvals in the system would be compared to the handwritten signatures. The dual-system approach is limited to the output of transactions and doesn't address such things as breaches of security, error messages, response times, and ease of use.

The dual system is required by the European Community (EC) good manufacturing practices for pharmaceuticals if a manual process is being replaced: "Before a system using a computer is brought into use, it should be thoroughly tested and confirmed as being capable of achieving the desired results. If a manual system is being replaced, the two should be run in parallel for a time, as a part of this testing and validation."[4] The dual-system approach is labor-intensive. Organizations that aren't bound by an EC directive could evaluate other approaches to determine if a less costly and equally effective approach is available.

The second approach, called the "system confirmation approach," involves using only the automated system and confirming the accuracy and completeness of a sample of the end results of transactions but not the intervening processing steps. This approach is less labor-intensive than the dual-system approach because a separate manual system doesn't have to be maintained. The system confirmation approach shares the same weaknesses as the dual system approach (i.e., it doesn't test or verify the operations of the system that aren't reflected in end results of transactions).

With an EDMS system, for instance, a sample of electronically approved change requests could be taken. The accuracy of the electronic signatures can be confirmed by two actions. First, by confirming that each individual whose name appears as an electronic signature did, in fact, enter an electronic signature. Second, by checking that an electronic signature is present for all reviewers, and only those reviewers, who were supposed to approve the change request. The accuracy of the information on the electronic change request forms can be checked with the individuals who entered the data. The confirmation approach differs from the dual-system approach in that there's not a parallel paper system for approving the same change requests. The confirmation approach is best suited for moderate- and high-risk transactions.

In the third approach, system test, designed tests of program logic and system functionality are executed. Some companies run all the OQ tests over again to serve as the PQ, while others perform work by using the system. Other organizations will only use system tests for operations that can't be verified by checking system output. With the system-test approach, any unwanted data or records must be deleted once you've completed executing the tests. The advantage of the system-test approach is that system operations that aren't reflected in system output can be tested.

System monitoring is the last approach and involves reviewing system data, logs, and problem reports. With this approach, the normal systems for reporting and resolving problems are used. The problems that occurred are reviewed from a validation perspective after a period of time. If this approach is taken, the PQ should cover continuous operations for a sufficient time to allow the system to encounter a wide spectrum of conditions and events so as to detect any latent faults that aren't apparent during normal activities. In addition, user satisfaction with the system can be evaluated through interviews, a questionnaire, or a focus group meeting with a panel of representative users.

The system-monitoring approach is paramount to a probationary period. System performance is also monitored on a routine basis as a part of system maintenance, but for a different purpose. When the system is monitored as part of the PQ, the purpose is to determine if the system is fit for ongoing use. When the system is monitored after validation testing is complete, the purpose is to identify and resolve problems. Because system-monitoring is a less rigorous approach, it's best used in combination with other approaches for high- and moderate-risk systems. System monitoring can also be used as a stand-alone approach for low-risk systems if a PQ is considered necessary.

Finally, any combination of the four options can be used. For example, system monitoring might be used in combination with the confirmation approach to determine how well the system performed on transactions that naturally occurred during the course of business.

Potential Tests for the PQ

As discussed above, the PQ can cover some or all of the items tested in the OQ. The difference, of course, is that during the PQ the tests are performed on a system that's used for production under real conditions, including concurrent users from various locations and transaction volumes.

The following items aren't normally covered in the OQ, but should be included in the PQ if appropriate for your system:

- Verification that the user procedures can be followed as written without deviations due to the way the automated system operates

- Employee assessments of the ease of system use and their ability to understand and use the system's output
- Employee and management assessment of the adequacy of the user training
- Verification that response times and the time taken to perform transactions under peak utilization as well as normal conditions are acceptable to the users
- Verification that the system will continue to function correctly under high stress (i.e., with a high number of concurrent users performing resource-intense actions)
- Monitoring the use of system resources (e.g., CPU and storage) while operating the system under peak utilization[5]

Items might also be added to assess the performance of the system from a business perspective. Are the gains expected from the system realized?

Risk-Based Considerations for the Performance Qualification

Low-risk systems don't require a performance qualification if sufficient evidence is obtained through the OQ that the system can function reliably. At most, the PQ should be limited either to system monitoring or confirming important transactions. Of course, you must determine what's appropriate for your own situation.

For moderate- and high-risk systems, care must be taken at least to verify that high- and moderate-risk requirements are being met in the production and/or operational environment. This can be accomplished by any of the four approaches to the PQ.

Design the PQ Tests

Depending on the approach taken, multiple tests can be conducted simultaneously with the PQ. Typically, OQs are designed to start at the beginning of the protocol and work through to the end, but some of the PQ tests can be conducted concurrently. For example, data on problem reports can be collected while multiple system outputs are confirmed. If you plan to perform parts of the PQ simultaneously, include appropriate remarks in the instructions section of the protocol. The PQ's test section can be divided into subsections of test items that must be tested sequentially. The subsections could then be coincidentally executed.

If system monitoring is part of the PQ, you must determine the length of time you'll monitor the system. Take into consideration how often the system is used. For heavily used systems that perform the same tasks repetitively, four weeks might be sufficient. If the system is infrequently used, and handles a large variety of transactions, much more time might be needed. If it's practical, you should allow enough time for the system to perform the high- and moderate-risk transactions in its full range of options at least once, if not several times.

PREPARE THE PERFORMANCE QUALIFICATION PROTOCOL

Deliverable 8.1 in appendix A describes the content of the PQ protocol. It closely parallels the content of the OQ protocol.[6]

Prerequisites

PQ prerequisites include:

■ An approved OQ report stating that the protocol-acceptance criteria for the OQ have been met

■ Approval of the PQ protocol

■ An IQ report for installing the system in the operational environment. (This is discussed in the section about executing the PQ protocol and preparing a report.)

■ A report for installing legacy data into the operational environment. The legacy data must be loaded into the operational environment. A copy of the OQ protocol that was written for the legacy load is executed. A report is written based on the data recorded in the protocol. The legacy load must meet the protocol-acceptance criteria.

■ The required users and test data are set up for the PQ.

■ Required training is complete for those executing the protocol.

■ If approved user procedures and IT procedures weren't verified as a prerequisite in a previous protocol, include them as a PQ prerequisite.

Don't include any activities or items that are prerequisites for the OQ (such as approving the IQ report from the installation in the test environment) unless the prerequisites were deferred to the PQ through a variance.

Protocol-Acceptance Criteria

You should develop the PQ protocol-acceptance criteria along the same lines as the system-acceptance criteria discussed in chapter 6, as is appropriate to your system. The PQ protocol-acceptance criteria might not encompass the full set of system-acceptance criteria, but they should match the system-acceptance criteria for whatever is relevant to the PQ (e.g., user satisfaction). The following suggested PQ acceptance criteria refer to the state of the system at the time the PQ report is written. Defects can be repaired prior to preparing the report. Some options include:

- Criteria for the legacy load in the production environment if it was done as part of the PQ. Legacy-load criteria should be related to the percent of records successfully loaded and the accuracy of the data loaded.
- Recall that four classes of defects were defined: critical, major, minor, and cosmetic. If the system acceptance criteria places limits on the number of critical, major, or minor defects that are permissible (e.g., none), the numbers permitted for the PQ can be equal to or fewer than the numbers allowed for the entire system.
- Variance forms are completed as needed.
- All test equipment used in the PQ was properly calibrated before use in the test. Copies of calibration certificates are attached to an appendix.
- All personnel entering data on the protocol have signed the signature log in the appendix or have their signature on file with the company.
- All supporting documentation (e.g., screen prints and reports) collected during test execution is logged in an appendix and attached.
- A representative sample of users are satisfied with the performance of the system.
- The project team has confidence that the system will consistently perform to requirements.

The defects referred to in the protocol-acceptance criteria list above can be identified from:

- Tests of the system (i.e., using the system test approach)
- Errors found through the dual-system or confirmation approach
- Deviations written during system use
- IT help desk problem reports

Test Section

As mentioned previously, subsections can be created in the test section to segregate tests that can be performed simultaneously. The test section can have the same structure as the OQ (i.e., each subsection would have its own components), including:

- Objective(s)
- User requirements tested
- Materials and equipment required
- Test procedure

Two examples are provided of how the test procedure can be structured.[7] Exhibit 10.1 illustrates the system-monitoring approach to verifying that a system functions according to requirements. This first example includes a table with the same format for the test procedure that appeared in chapter 9's discussion of the OQ. Exhibit 10.2 illustrates a test procedure format that can be used with the system-confirmation approach. In this example, the accuracy of information about documents, engineering change orders (ECOs), and electronic signatures fixed to an ECO are checked.

Forward Traceability

A forward-traceability matrix is also created for the PQ. It identifies where each user requirement is tested in the PQ. It has the same value as the traceability matrix for the OQ discussed in chapter 9. In fact, the traceability information for the OQ and PQ can be combined into a single matrix. As with the OQ, the forward-traceability matrix is a separate document. Ideally, it's created after the PQ has been written but before it's approved. When creating the forward-traceability matrix, evaluate if the testing identified for each requirement is sufficient.

Approve the PQ Protocol

The system owner, IT, QA, and validation approve the PQ protocol.

Exhibit 10.1	Sample Performance Qualification Test Procedure for the System Monitoring Approach			
Step	**Procedural notes**	**Procedure**	**Expected results**	**Actual results**	**Initial and date**
1	Document start date	■ Document the date. ■ Document the date in thirty days.	■ Dates documented	■ Start date: _____ ■ Date in thirty days:_____	
2	Monitor help desk for hardware problems (during thirty-day evaluation period).	■ During the 30-day evaluation period, monitor the help desk for hardware problems. ■ If any problems indicate a failure to meet requirements, complete a variance report. Attach all pertinent reports from the help desk to the variance report. ■ List variance numbers:	■ Help desk monitored for hardware problems ■ Pertinent reports from the help desk attached to a variance report ■ Hardware problems evaluated for any adverse effects on the PQ	■ Help desk monitored for hardware problems? ☐ Yes ☐ No ■ Pertinent reports from the help desk attached to a variance report? ☐ Yes ☐ No ■ Hardware problems evaluated for any adverse effect on the PQ? ☐ Yes ☐ No	
3	Monitor help desk for software problems and document as training errors or defects (during thirty-day evaluation period).	■ During the thirty-day evaluation period, monitor the help desk for software problems. ■ If any problems indicate a failure to meet requirements, complete a variance report. Attach all pertinent reports from the help desk to the variance report. ■ Evaluate the software problems for any adverse effect to the PQ by following these criteria (based on the criticality levels defined in the validation procedure): ☐ Level I or II error: stop execution and complete corrective action ☐ Level III or IV error: continue execution ■ List variance numbers:	■ Help desk monitored for software problems ■ Pertinent reports from the help desk attached to a variance report ■ Software problems evaluated for any adverse effect to the PQ	■ Help desk monitored for software problems? ☐ Yes ☐ No ■ Pertinent reports from the help desk attached to a variance report? ☐ Yes ☐ No ■ Software problems evaluated for any adverse effect to the PQ? ☐ Yes ☐ No	

Exhibit 10.2	Example Performance Qualification Test Procedure for the System Confirmation Approach

The instructions and checklists below illustrate how to create a test procedure with the system confirmation approach to performance qualifications (PQs).

Document Checklist
1. Randomly select three currently effective documents that were created or revised since the PQ began.
2. Search for each document in the system. Verify that the combination of document number and revision level is unique.
3. Print the data that identify or describe each document (i.e., metadata) from the electronic document management system (EDMS).
4. Meet with the originator of the engineering change order (ECO) and verify that the metadata are correct.
5. Record the results of the verification in the table below.

Document number	Revision	Is the combination of document number and revision unique?	Is document information correct?	Initial and date
		☐ Yes ☐ No	☐ Yes ☐ No	
		☐ Yes ☐ No	☐ Yes ☐ No	
		☐ Yes ☐ No	☐ Yes ☐ No	

ECO Checklist
1. Identify the numbers for the ECOs that were approved for each of the three documents randomly selected in the previous confirmation.
2. Search for the ECOs in the system. Verify that there is only one ECO for each of the ECO numbers.
3. Print the ECOs.
4. Meet with the originator and document control to verify that the information recorded on each ECO is correct, including the required approvers.
5. Record the results of the confirmation in the table below.

ECO number	Is the ECO number unique?	Is ECO information correct?	Are required approvers correct?	Initial and date
	☐ Yes ☐ No	☐ Yes ☐ No	☐ Yes ☐ No	
	☐ Yes ☐ No	☐ Yes ☐ No	☐ Yes ☐ No	
	☐ Yes ☐ No	☐ Yes ☐ No	☐ Yes ☐ No	

ECO Approval Confirmation Checklist

Perform the following steps for each ECO:

1. Present the ECO printed from the EDMS system to each reviewer and verify that they took the actions recorded (i.e., approved the ECO) and electronically signed the ECO at the designated time and date.

2. Record the verification in the table below.

ECO number	Reviewer	Reviewer name	Is the electronic signature correct?	Has the correct action been recorded	Are the signature, time, and date correct?	Initial and date
	1		☐ Yes ☐ No	☐ Yes ☐ No	☐ Yes ☐ No	
	2		☐ Yes ☐ No	☐ Yes ☐ No	☐ Yes ☐ No	
	3		☐ Yes ☐ No	☐ Yes ☐ No	☐ Yes ☐ No	
	4		☐ Yes ☐ No	☐ Yes ☐ No	☐ Yes ☐ No	
	5		☐ Yes ☐ No	☐ Yes ☐ No	☐ Yes ☐ No	

EXECUTE THE PERFORMANCE QUALIFICATION PROTOCOL AND PREPARE A REPORT

Prepare for Production Use and PQ Execution

Prior to executing the PQ protocol, the production instance of the application and database is set up. All configurations of the hardware and software are made. The appropriate IQ is executed and an IQ report is written for the production instance and approved.

Once the IQ report for the production instance is approved, the legacy data can be loaded. The OQ protocol for the legacy load is executed. Missing records are manually loaded, and errors in the data are corrected. A brief report is written for the legacy load in the production environment.

If the protocol-acceptance criteria for the legacy load aren't met, the legacy-load process or software must be modified and the load conducted again. Kept records for this process include:

■ The executed protocol for the legacy load that failed

■ Variance form from the failed load

- Any change-control records for changes made to the system to correct the situation
- Any revised life-cycle deliverables
- Executed protocol for the successful load
- A brief report on the legacy load

The application administrator sets up the system for the PQ testing, if needed, and for use by the users. Appropriate administrative procedures are followed. Users are trained, as needed, and training records are kept.

Executing the PQ Protocol

The protocol is executed following good record-keeping practices as described in chapter 9.

Because an evaluation of user experience and satisfaction is recommended as both a PQ and system-acceptance criterion, assessing user experience and satisfaction merits some discussion. There are several choices for getting feedback, including a written questionnaire, one-on-one interviews, and a group meeting. When deciding which method is the best for you, an important consideration is which will give you the most candid assessment of how users feel about the system. In some situations individuals might be reluctant to publicly voice positive or negative comments after others have presented opposite views. Of course, the time required and cost are also considerations.

If a user meeting is held to assess experience and satisfaction, a structured discussion is recommended. In preparing the users for the session, set the stage by reminding them of the overall plan for the system. If you've completed only the first stage of a multistage implementation, review the plan for subsequent stages. Prepare a questionnaire and distribute it in advance to the participants. The questionnaire can be used to request preparation and to guide the discussion. Both open-ended questions and rating scales are recommended. General questions can be asked, such as, "What do you most like about the system?" and "What do you like least about it?" A discussion of these questions might prompt reactions that the project team hadn't anticipated. The focus of the questionnaire and meeting should be on important user requirements that involve subjective judgments, such as ease of use, satisfaction with response time, the system's effect on work group efficiency, and their judgment of whether to continue using the system. In addition to asking for comments, provide rating scales for each item.

Medatech 10.1   Performance Qualification

The Medatech project team decided to use a combination of the system confirmation and system monitoring approaches to the performance qualification (PQ). The system was monitored for six weeks. Beginning at week five, output from the system was randomly selected for confirmation following the PQ protocol. Waiting for four weeks allowed time for the system to be used and a large selection of output to be available for random selection. During weeks five and six, the confirmation took place while monitoring continued. (The reasoning for selecting this approach is explained in Medatech 6.4 in chapter 6.)

The confirmation included verification of the following:

- The engineering change order (ECO) number assignment, accuracy of ECO information, proper routing, correct ECO action (i.e., accept or reject), and correct signatures
- The documents that were added to the system or revised, including document and revision numbering
- The completeness and accuracy of metadata for the documents

The system monitoring included:

- Monitoring issue reports for all types of problems: hardware, software, administrative, access, and security
- Determining user satisfaction with the system

The following steps were involved in conducting the PQ:

1. The electronic document management system (EDMS) system that Medatech purchased couldn't be set up in separate instances on the same server. So Tec installed a production system that was identical to the system he established for the installation qualification (IQ) and operational qualification (OQ). The IQ was executed on the production system to verify that the installation was complete and correct. A report for the production system IQ was prepared and approved.

2. Employees who were going to use the EDMS system were established in the system as users and as application administrators, when appropriate.

3. Legacy data were loaded into the system following the OQ legacy load protocol. The legacy data protocol acceptance criteria were met.

4. The PQ was executed.

5. A meeting was held with the user advisory board to assess its satisfaction with the system. Doc prepared a questionnaire that he circulated to the group in advance. During the meeting he lead a discussion on the items he'd prepared, and then opened the discussion to issues or concerns that anyone wanted to bring up.

Although one level-two defect and two level-three defects were identified during the PQ, the system met the PQ protocol acceptance criteria, and the project team judged it to be ready for use.

During the meeting, encourage all participants to present their views. At the end of the meeting, ask the group for a clear recommendation on whether to proceed with the system. Obtain a completed questionnaire from each person. After the session, the project team should meet and discuss what they learned from the users, and if the assessments meet the protocol-acceptance criteria. The team should also agree on what problem reports to open, based on the issues identified during the meeting.

RESIDUAL RISK ASSESSMENT

Update the Risk Assessment

Review the assumptions made in the detailed risk assessment during phase 4 based on the results of the validation testing. An estimate of the likelihood of failure was set either at the probable level based on an assumption about the software's failure rate, or based on the defect-prevention and -detection methods used by the vendor. Do the findings of the validation testing support your analysis of the probability of failure, or should those estimates be reexamined? Validation results that show frequent failures of the system might indicate that the likelihood of failure that was initially assumed should be increased.

On the other hand, the validation results might indicate that the likelihood of failure is lower than initially expected. If the assumption needs to be changed, update the risk assessment accordingly. If you've set the likelihood of failure at the probable level based on an assumption, as was recommended in chapter 6, extensive validation testing in which no defects were discovered would provide justification for lowering the likelihood rating to occasional. If defects are found that are at the major or critical level as defined in chapter 6, reducing the likelihood level isn't merited.

As discussed in chapter 6, you must be cautious in making any adjustments to the likelihood of system failure based on validation testing. Before you adjust the likelihood of failure level based on your validation results, you must evaluate the appropriateness of such an action. Was the assumption of the likelihood of failure you made before the validation testing (called the "initial likelihood level" here) based on concerns about the system's development or its ability to work properly in your environment? If the rating was based more on the system's ability to work in your environment, tests in your production environment (or an equivalent) would provide justification for lowering the likelihood level. If your rating was based on the vendor's development methods, you must determine how much your testing will add to the testing that's already been done.

For example, normal validation testing probably isn't extensive enough to lower the likelihood of failure from the remote to the improbable level. The reason is that in setting the level of failure at remote, you've already determined that the software is of a high quality. The developer has created the software using extensive defect-prevention and -detection methods. Your tests probably won't exceed the testing that's already been done, and therefore wouldn't provide justification for reducing the likelihood of failure to the improbable level.

In exhibit 10.3 the risk analysis example used in chapter 6 (i.e., the pharmaceutical plant) is adjusted to reflect successful validation testing. For the sake of the example, the validation results merited changing the likelihood of software failure from the assumed level of probable to the occasional level. Consequently, in the first scenario in exhibit 10.3, the likelihood that the temperature wouldn't be controlled during off hours was changed from the probable to the occasional level. The likelihood that the software would fail to page the operator when the temperature went out of range was also set at occasional, based on the validation results. The likelihood that the temperature and the pager would fail at the same time is the product of the occasional level for a failure to control the temperature, and the occasional level for a failure of the pager. The product of those two scenarios is estimated at the remote level. The risk associated with a loss of the batch (i.e., moderate severity) with a remote likelihood is low. (The risk tables in chapter 6 are used to determine the risk level.)

The second scenario in exhibit 10.3 deals with the temperature becoming too high during work hours. The likelihood of both the temperature not being controlled and the alarm not working can be reduced from probable to occasional based on the validation results. The product of these two likelihoods (i.e., remote) is the likelihood of the batch being lost because of both things failing simultaneously. The combination of a moderate level of harm and a remote likelihood of failure results in a low-risk level.

The third scenario, a serious injury to a patient, is analyzed. Such harm is at the critical level. Two mitigating factors are the alarm and the quality control (QC) test for the product's purity. The likelihood of a patient getting hurt is the product of three likelihoods. The likelihoods of the system failing to control the temperature and the alarm to sound are both considered to be at the occasional level based on the validation results. The probability of the QC test failing remains at the remote level. The product of the three is still at the lowest level on the scale (i.e., improbable).

Exhibit 10.3	Revised Risk Evaluation: Post Risk Mitigation and Validation

The likelihood of a software failure was reduced from "probable" to "occasional" after successful validation testing.

Pharmaceutical Example: Risk Evaluation After Taking Into Account the Effect of Validation Testing

Hazard and Failure: Temperature too high during off hours (and alarm not heard)

Harm: Loss of batch, $100,000

Severity: Moderate

Controls against system failure and ways to prevent harm after failure: None

Likelihood that harm will occur; post validation estimate: Occasional (failure of the temperature control software)

Risk level: Moderate

Additional mitigations implemented and tested: Integrate system to have operator paged when the alarm is triggered.

Likelihood that system will fail with the mitigation: Remote (i.e., failure of temperature control multiplied by failure of the pager software)

Risk level after mitigation: Low

Notes on validation and effectiveness of mitigations: Temperature control operated to spec. Operator paged within five minutes of the alarm.

Hazard and Failure: Temperature too high during work hours (alarm heard)

Harm: Loss of batch, $100,000

Severity: Moderate

Controls against system failure and ways to prevent harm after failure: Alarm

Likelihood that harm will occur; post validation estimate: Remote (failure of temperature control, multiplied by failure of the alarm)

Risk level: Low

Additional mitigations implemented and tested: None

Likelihood that system will fail with the mitigation: N/A

Risk level after mitigation: N/A

Notes on validation and effectiveness of mitigations: Temperature control and alarm operate to specification

Hazard and Failure: Temperature too high during work hours
   Harm: Serious injury from byproducts of decomposition
      Severity: Critical
      Controls against system failure and ways to prevent harm after failure: Alarm and QC test
      Likelihood that harm will occur; post validation estimate: Improbable (failure of temperature control, alarm, and QC test)
      Risk level: Low
      Additional mitigations implemented and tested: None
      Likelihood that system will fail with the mitigation: N/A
      Risk level after mitigation: N/A
      Notes on validation and effectiveness of mitigations: Temperature control and alarm operate to specification

Assess the Overall Residual Risk

Once the adjustments are made based on the results of the validation testing, the residual risk accumulated from the entire system must be assessed.[8, 9] The residual-risk value can be determined by projecting the overall likelihood of any high- or moderate-severity failure occurring. The residual-risk value can be determined by using the tables that derive a risk value from the likelihood of harm and its severity, as was done with individual functionality. These tables are located in chapter 6.

If any aspect of the system or the accumulative residual risk is high, the team must carefully consider if further mitigation is practical both from a technical and economical perspective. If further mitigations are practical, they can be introduced through the change-control process.

Perform a Risk-Benefit Analysis

If further mitigations are impractical, the benefits of system use should be examined to determine if they outweigh the residual risk.[10] If the analysis demonstrates that the system is worth the risk, the risk-benefit analysis is documented either separately or as part of the risk-management report.

If appropriate, prepare or reference contingency plans for responding to system failures and keeping the business process functioning if the system fails.

If the benefits don't outweigh the residual risk, then the risk remains unacceptable. System use must be stopped or limited to functions that pose less risk. The decision to disband the system should be recorded in a memo to file and stored with the life-cycle records.

A risk-benefit analysis doesn't need to be performed if the risk level is acceptable based on the criteria established in the validation plan.

Write a Risk Management Report

A risk management report is prepared to document the risk management aspects of the life cycle and to summarize the state of the system from a risk perspective.[11] Deliverable 8.2 describes the content of the risk management report.

COMPLETE THE VALIDATION PROCESS

Project Team Assessment

Once the PQ is completed and before the validation final report is prepared, the project team should review the system and determine if it should be used on an on-going basis. If your system-acceptance criteria include project team confidence that the system will consistently perform to requirements, some method of assessing team confidence is required. Even if it isn't required, a final team assessment is a good way to bring closure to the implementation process and to assess the lessons learned for future projects. Individual members' thoughts and the team's conclusions are summarized in the validation report, a memo, or a report to management.

In making its assessment, the team should take into consideration the following, as appropriate:

- The results of the validation tests, including the number of system problems that were corrected and the effect of any open variances on the system's ability to function according to user requirements

- Whether the system is stable. Did problems that were repaired resurface later on in the testing? Did new problems occur during the PQ that weren't seen when the same functions were tested during the OQ?

- User reactions. Are users excited about the system, or are they dreading having to use it? Do users see any gains from the system to themselves and the organization?

- The system's supportability. Is the IT function capable of supporting the system and its users? Can it take on the support load? Is the vendor committed to maintaining and enhancing the system?
- Compliance problems or issues
- Business gains from using the system compared against the costs of using the system
- The system's viability as your company grows and changes in the near and long term
- Residual risk

It's critical that the residual risk associated with the system be taken into account. If the validation tests show that the system isn't completely reliable, but sufficient mitigation controls are in place to reduce or minimize the harmful effects of failure, the question of whether to use the system becomes a business decision. Do the system's benefits justify the costs, including the cost of detecting and correcting errors?

The project team can decide on one of several options in making its assessment:

- A conclusion is reached that the system is ready for production use in line with intended uses.
- The team could recommend a limited use of the system, and/or use only by certain users. For example, with a document-control system, the project team can recommend that only document control use the capabilities of creating an ECO until potential users become more comfortable with the system. Full use of the system can be contingent upon addressing open variances or other contingencies.
- The team could recommend that the system remain offline until certain conditions are met.
- The recommendation also could be to stop the project and not use the system at all.

Prepare the Validation Final Report

Prepare the validation final report after the PQ report is approved. Deliverable 8.3 describes in detail the content areas of the report, so that information won't be repeated here.[12] However, the background work that must be performed in preparing to write a validation final report is listed in the bullet points below.

- Review the life-cycle process and identify any discrepancies between what was done during the validation process and what the validation plan required. Check to determine if variance forms were used to record such discrepancies and if the variances were resolved in an acceptable manner.

- Review the deliverables identified in the validation plan that were to be part of the validation record. Examine each of the deliverables to determine if it was approved by the functions listed in the validation plan or company procedures.

- Review the results of the validation tests as described in the IQ, OQ, and PQ reports. Determine how well the system met the acceptance criteria of each protocol and the system-acceptance criteria defined in the validation plan. Review all variance reports to determine if any of them are still open. Assess the effect of all open variances on the system's ability to reliably meet requirements.

- If changes were made to the system during the validation testing, review all related documentation and verify that it's been updated with the changes. For example, if a function was dropped from use because it malfunctioned, make sure that it's removed from the user requirements, procedures, training, manuals, and all other material that's intended for users. If the system configuration has changed (e.g., a piece of software is no longer to be used), verify that the system specification has been revised. Tests of discontinued functions should remain in the executed protocols, but be removed by amendment from all protocol masters.

- Review the risk management report to understand the residual risks associated with each potential hazard and failure, the overall residual risk assessment, and the risk-benefit analysis, if one has been prepared.

- Review the data related to each of the system acceptance criteria and meet with the project team, if necessary, to draw a conclusion regarding how well each criterion is met.

- Draw a conclusion with the project team regarding the system's ability to consistently meet requirements throughout its operating range. This conclusion should be based on objective evidence (including ratings from users, if appropriate) demonstrating that the system meets the system-acceptance criteria. In addition, the project team should make a recommendation regarding ongoing system use as described above.

The system owner, IT, QA, and validation approve the report. With this approval, the validation process is completed. Any outstanding issues, such as a defect that must be repaired, are logged into the issue reporting system and tracked to completion.

MAINTAIN SYSTEM EFFECTIVENESS DURING PRODUCTION USE

The ongoing effectiveness of the system depends on its appropriate use and the organization's adherence to procedures designed to keep the system in a validated state.

Ongoing System-Use Records

Records should be maintained on the activities listed in table 10.2. The business reason for the records and the regulatory references are also given in the table. More information is provided on some of the records in the following sections.

Table 10.2	Records That Must Be Created During Ongoing Use	
Record	**Business reason**	**Regulatory requirement**
User training records	■ To ensure that users are able to use the system correctly ■ To verify that a user is competent before assigning user privileges	■ 21 CFR 820, Section 25 b ■ 21 CFR 211.25 ■ 21 CFR 11, Section 11.10 i ■ EC Annex 11, No. 1
System backups	■ To be able to restore missing or corrupted files ■ To preserve intellectual property and work performed	■ cGMP 211.68 b ■ EC Annex 11, No. 14 ■ 21 CFR 820, Section 180
Calibration records	To ensure accuracy of measurements	■ 21 CFR 211, Section 68 a ■ 21 CFR 820, Section 72
Maintenance records	■ To track that the regularly scheduled maintenance has been performed to prevent system failures ■ To provide a history of unscheduled maintenance for troubleshooting	■ 21 CFR 211, Section 67 ■ 21 CFR 820, Section 70 g 1
Issue tracking and resolution records	■ To ensure that issues get resolved ■ To have a record of the occurrence of issues for troubleshooting	■ EC Annex 11, No. 17
Change control records	■ To ensure that only changes that are benign are made to the system ■ To use the change history when reconstructing the system and troubleshooting problems	■ EC Annex 11, No. 11 ■ 21 CFR 11, Section 11.10 k 2
Audit reports	To verify that the system is being used properly, including all measures implemented to manage risk	■ 21 CFR 820, Section 22 ■ General Principles, 2002, Section 6.2 ■ EC Annex 11, No. 13

Training

Ensure that system users are appropriately trained and follow user and administrative procedures. Keep training records.

System Backup

The system is backed-up as defined in the company's general backup and restore procedure, or in a procedure specifically written for the system in question. The backup and restore procedure is written during phase 6. Automated backups are rarely 100-percent successful. Care must be taken to monitor the backup records to determine what parts of the system, if any, weren't backed up. Follow the procedure for how to handle missing material, including manual backup. Backup data should be stored as long as necessary at a separate and secure location.[13]

System Maintenance

Several aspects of system maintenance are necessary for keeping the system running effectively. All system maintenance activities are either performed following a calibration procedure, a qualified maintenance procedure, or by means of the change control procedure.

- Regularly calibrate instruments used for measurement. Quality system standards and regulations require such calibration to ensure that the measurements remain accurate.[14–17]
- Conduct periodic preventive maintenance on computer hardware and instrumentation to ensure their proper ongoing operation. Quality system regulations and standards also require preventive maintenance.[18–20]
- Maintain the databases by adjusting data spaces, archiving data that must be removed from the production system, and checking the integrity of the physical hard drives.
- Optimize the performance of the hardware and software by performance tuning.
- Maintain the physical and logical security through protective measures such as safeguards on passwords, system firewalls, and virus control.

User Support, and Issue Tracking and Resolution

Providing support to users by resolving their problems is critical to ensuring that the system is effective. Problems will surface during system use that didn't occur during validation testing. These new problems can occur from any of a number of causes, such as:

- User error
- The state the system was in momentarily while being used. Such errors frequently can't be replicated in a test environment and their cause can't be identified.
- A fix to a defect that adversely affected another part of the system
- Human error in installing an enhancement or a fix to a problem
- The system wasn't designed to do what you want, in the way you want it to. Although most instances like these will be discovered during a well-designed validation, users are occasionally surprised.
- An aspect of the system being used wasn't included in the validation testing.

A process for tracking and resolving issues should have been developed during phase 6 to handle both defect repair and system enhancements. EC Annex 11 requires such a procedure.[21] The following steps, or their equivalent, should be included:

- *An issue is reported.* A user reports a problem that he or she discovered or submits a recommendation for an improvement (i.e., enhancement). If the individual can be helped immediately, the respondent resolves the issue. The call, nature of the problem, and solution are recorded in a call log.
- *Unresolved issues are escalated and logged into the problem-tracking system.* If the issue can't be resolved immediately, the individual receiving the information from the user opens an issue report. Sufficient information is obtained from the person reporting the issue for the program coordinator to determine who should perform a diagnosis. The issue report is transferred to the coordinator, who assigns the report a number and, based on the nature of the issue, routes it to the appropriate person.
- *Classifying the issue.* The person receiving the issue report from the coordinator reviews the issue to determine its nature. The coordinator classifies the issue; categories can include no problem (i.e., system functions properly), system defect, operator error, enhancement (i.e., a desired improvement to the system), and undetermined. A defect level is determined for defects. The issue classification, and defect level if relevant, trigger time frames for a response.

- *Diagnosis and solution.* A diagnosis is conducted to determine the cause if the issue is a problem, or the ramifications of the change if the issue is a system enhancement. If the person assigned to resolve the issue knows of a resolution, it's recorded in the issue report. If a solution isn't known, the issue is referred elsewhere within the organization or to the appropriate vendor. Once the solution is determined, its implementation depends on the nature of the solution. If the solution requires a change to the system or system documentation, a change request is opened. Actions that fall within qualified procedures for maintenance or configuration can be implemented when the timing is appropriate.

- *Assess the incident's risk implications.* Judge if the incident calls into question the current revision of the risk assessment and evaluation. Does the issue represent a new type of failure that hasn't been assessed? Does the situation involve a new type of harm that hadn't been anticipated? Does the incident call into question the accuracy of the estimate of the likelihood that this type of failure will occur, or that it will result in harm? Re-evaluate the risk assessment and make any needed changes. Create and implement any needed mitigations using the change control procedure. Revise the risk analysis records and report as needed.

  If necessary, the risk assessment will be expanded to include new items. The entire process of risk management must take place for the newly discovered failure; the risk level must be determined and the need for mitigations evaluated. If mitigation is required, the change-control process is used to validate and implement a change to the system. Data should be gathered on the effectiveness of the mitigation, and the residual risk determined and evaluated.

  If a failure that was previously evaluated needs to be reexamined, change the judgment that's thought to be in error and move forward through the process starting at that point. For example, you might need to start with the estimate of the severity of harm associated with the failure or the likelihood of a failure's occurrence. In other cases, the effectiveness of a mitigating action might be called into question.

- *Close the issue report.* Once the change process and other needed actions are completed, the coordinator verifies, to the extent possible, that issues have been resolved. The issue report is then closed and filed. The issue log is updated to indicate that the issue has been closed.[22]

Change Control

If changes must be made to correct problems or enhance the system, use the change-control procedure approved during phase 4. The change is first implemented in a test environment, and the system is retested to verify that it still functions as expected. The retesting must include at least the aspects and/or functions of the systems that were modified, and other aspects of the system that might have been affected by the modification. The extent of retesting is approved as part of the change request. The performance of the system can be monitored for a period of time to make sure the change didn't have any unexpected consequences.

Post-Implementation Risk Management

The organization should be alert to the nature and frequency of system failures to detect patterns and evaluate the overall assumptions made about the quality of the software. The system owner, IT, and QA must all be sensitive to patterns of problems that suggest the actual risks associated with system failures are higher than the estimated residual risks. If such a situation develops, the team must review and revise the residual-risk assessments and determine an appropriate action.

Two methods are recommended for maintaining vigilance: a) including a space on the issue report to indicate if an issue's risk implications should be investigated and requiring that the investigation to be completed before the issue report can be closed, and b) performing a periodic system review.

Periodic System Review

The periodic system review formally evaluates system reliability and performance, and determines the risk-management implications of the findings. The review is recommended only for moderate- and high-risk systems. The validation plan should address the need for, and frequency of, system reviews (e.g., once a year). The review should include an examination of issue reports for possible relevance to safety and any other dimensions of harm evaluated in the risk analysis. Based on the review and subsequent actions, the risk analysis, evaluation, and report are revised, especially if:

- Previously unrecognized hazards are present.
- Experience with the system indicates that judgments concerning the likelihood of an occurrence of harm or its severity are in error. In such instances, the risk analysis

and evaluation must be revised. Appropriate action to mitigate risk must be taken using the change-control process to introduce any system changes.

■ The risk is no longer acceptable. In this instance the situation is the same as when the residual risk is too high. Mitigations must be put into place through the change-control process, otherwise use of all or part of the system must stop. The effectiveness of the mitigations should be evaluated through the validation tests that are performed as part of the change-control process, and monitored after installation in the production environment.[23]

The periodic review should be documented in a memo to file or a report.[24]

System Audit

The system audit is an important tool for monitoring the system and the methods that were established to keep it in a validated state. The system audit's purpose is twofold: to determine if the system is still functioning in a manner that meets user requirements, and to ensure that the processes created to keep the system in a validated state are being followed. Examples of the type of things included in a system audit are given in table 10.3.

The audit should be conducted by a trained auditor who is independent of functions that manage or support the system. The auditor (along with QA, depending on the company's audit practices) feeds back to each department head relevant audit findings. The auditor prepares a report and submits it to QA for review. The auditor and QA present the findings to the managers of the audited departments and the system owner. Following the audit, QA prepares corrective action reports on nonconformances with company policy and/or procedures. The system owner reviews the audit findings and nonconformances. Appropriate departments perform root-cause analyses to determine the cause of problems and take needed action. Modifications to the system are handled through the change-control procedure.

Audits of low-risk systems are necessary only if any of the following conditions exist:

■ Compliance regulations require an audit.

■ Failure of the system would cause widespread inconvenience.

■ The system's reliability has degraded to the point where an investigation is necessary to correct the situation.

Table 10.3	System Audits

Audit dimension	Items to review or investigate
Operational effectiveness	■ A sample of the results achieved through the automation. For example, if the system is to monitor and control the pressure of a reactor, are there incidents where the pressure wasn't properly controlled? ■ Records of the review of system effectiveness. If the system output is reviewed, have the reviews found errors?
Integrity of stored data	Check stored data for accessibility, durability, and accuracy. Such checks should occur at a frequency appropriate to the storage medium being used (EC Annex 11, No. 13).
Issue tracking and resolution process	■ The number of defects reported ■ Completion of the issue report forms, including proper signatures ■ Response to and resolution of issues within the time frames established in the procedure ■ Appropriately using the change control process in conjunction with resolving an issue ■ Following issues to completion, including those referred to vendors ■ Proper storage of records ■ The average length of time required to close an issue report for different categories of issues ■ The number of open issues, their type, severity, and time open ■ The number of closed issues, their type, severity, and time to close ■ Impairments of system use because of open issues
Change control	■ Proper completion of change control forms, including the definition of required validation testing and proper signatures ■ Completion of validation tests prior to implementing in the production environment ■ Completion of change control actions in a timely manner based on classification of the issue (including defect level)
System use	The manner in which the system is used. Is the system use compliant with user and administrative procedures?
Training	Training records of application administrators, system administrators, and users
System maintenance and support	■ Availability of system support resources ■ Maintenance records
Backup and archival	■ Backup and archive records ■ Backup and archive procedures are being followed, including, when it's defined in the procedure, the manual backup of items. ■ Restores are successfully performed in a timely manner.
Performance monitoring	Performance records: ■ Does system performance meet predetermined criteria? ■ Are deviations from acceptable operating criteria investigated and appropriate action taken?
Security of records	Is the system adequately protected from physical damage, outside intruders, and damage from Trojan horses, worms, and viruses? (EC Annex 11, No. 13)
User satisfaction	The system owner and a sample of users are satisfied with the manner in which the system is meeting their requirements.

(continues)

Table 10.3	System Audits (continued)
Audit dimension	**Items to review or investigate**
Periodic review of system performance	Review records: ■ Is a periodic review of the system conducted for moderate- and high-risk systems? ■ Are appropriate records reviewed? ■ If a decision was reached that the risk assessment should be modified, was the assessment reviewed, modified, and further action taken to manage the risk?

The content of the audit report can vary with the risk level of the system. Reports for routine audits of low-risk systems can simply provide a summary of the findings and identify areas of nonconformance. Reports for moderate- and high-risk systems should also provide sufficient information about what was covered in the audit to document its thoroughness.

Broadening System Use

If the system is well received by users, they'll see more things that can be done with it. For example, if users see that a document-control system works well for electronic routing and approval of documents, they'll begin to think that it can be used for routing deviations, corrective actions, or other types of records that require review and approval. How such expansion is to be handled depends on the choice made about what to include in the initial validation.

Two options were available when planning how to validate capabilities that wouldn't be used in the initial implementation of the system: a) include all the system's capabilities in the initial validation whether you'll use them in the first implementation phase; and b) include in the initial validation only the capabilities that will be initially used and validate additional capabilities as they're needed, using the change-control process. The example used to illustrate this was the delay of electronic approval of documents until the second phase of the implementation of an EDMS system. With the first approach, electronic approvals would be included in the initial validation. With the second approach, electronic approvals would be validated under change control when the organization was ready to implement it.

Situations that involve tools provided in the application for creating functionality follow the same principle and approaches. Examples are spreadsheets and applications that allow you to create functions such as workflows. If the application's tools and a procedure for using them were qualified in the initial validation, new functionality can be created following the procedure and using the qualified tools. During the OQ, the procedure must be used to create typical functionality, and the tools must be appropriately tested. The procedure should include some type of testing of the new functionality, such as an approval route, to verify that it works as the creator intended. Most companies don't select this option; validating the tools usually requires more extensive testing than what's normally required to validate the specific functionality created.

The second option was to validate only the specific functionality created using the tools, and not the tools themselves. This approach is normally taken with database packages. The database package tools aren't included in the initial validation, but the spreadsheets or applications created with them are validated. The same would be the case with tools provided in applications for creating approval routes. The tools aren't validated, but the initial approval routes are. Functionality created after the initial validation must be validated through a separate validation, as is the case with new spreadsheets or Access applications, or change control (as would be the case with new approval routes).

System Revalidation

A full system revalidation is performed when any of the circumstances defined as requiring system revalidation in your validation procedure or the validation plan occur. The activities to be performed as part of the system revalidation are defined in a new validation plan prepared for the system revalidation. Circumstances under which full system revalidation is performed have been discussed in chapter 6.

Medatech 10.2   The System's First Year of Use

During the first six months of use, the system functioned very well. All in all, Doc and the users were quite pleased. Of course, there were some problems. For example:

- New users often found that they had to do a lot of trial-and-error fiddling with the system to find and open the documents they wanted. So the user training was expanded to allow more time for practice.
- One of the patches that was installed to fix a bug inadvertently set the auto document numbering scheme back to the vendor's default setting. As a result,

---

(continues)

Medatech 10.2 The System's First Year of Use (continued)

some documents were assigned surprising numbers. The document number configuration had to be reset to Medatech's scheme. The documents with the incorrect numbers had to be obsolesced and entered into the system again with a Medatech number.

However, a larger problem evolved after the new manufacturing facility was opened. The server and database for the electronic document management system (EDMS) remained at the original site. A dedicated communication line was set up between the two facilities. Adding connectivity from the new facility was done under change control. The time required to open a document at the manufacturing site was tested. The result of the test—a minute and one-half to open a document—was marginally acceptable. The project team recognized that the situation had the potential to get worse, but for budget reasons, management requested that the system be used as it was.

As time went on, the number of employees at the manufacturing site grew. The same communication line was used for e-mail traffic, the enterprise resource planning system, and the EDMS system. Response time and the time needed to open a document gradually increased until it became a hindrance to depend on the system for the use of controlled documents on the manufacturing floor. Appeals had been made to management, but sparse dollars were spent on more pressing company needs.

During the second periodic review of the system, Doc took a strong stand. The situation needed to be resolved. Quincy, the QA representative at the review meeting, joined Doc in insisting that the issue couldn't be deferred any longer. Doc had asked Paula, the head of production, to attend the meeting and present her point of view. The project team made the decision that unless the situation was resolved, access to the system would be denied to shop-floor computers, and Doc would set up binders of paper copies of documents and drawings for use. In the report of the meeting, Doc clearly stated that the system had become a compliance risk because employees were beginning to use inappropriate alternatives to the electronic documents.

The annual report was escalated to upper management through the quality assurance, information technology, and manufacturing chains of command. As a result, the executive committee made a budget reallocation so that Tec could purchase more servers to handle the increased demand on the system resources.

SUMMARY OF PHASE 8 DELIVERABLES

Table 10.4 summarizes the deliverables from phase 8 and identifies when each deliverable is applicable.

None of the regulations, the ISO 13485 standard, or the FDA CRDH guidance document specify a type of protocol that's required, that is, a PQ. The QSR does require an approved protocol.[25] In its list of five documents that manufacturers ought to have from its validation efforts, the FDA lists the "validation protocol used," and the "test cases and results."[26] The European Commission requires that the system be thoroughly tested and confirmed as capable of achieving desired results.[27] ISO 13485 states that documented procedures should be established for the validation of computer systems and that the results of the validation shall be recorded.[28] With the RiskVal life cycle, the mandate to use established protocols is met with the IQ, OQ, and PQ, as appropriate, based on the risk level of the system.

Table 10.4	Phase 8 Deliverables		
Phase 8 deliverables	**Definition and explanation**	**When applicable**	**Deliverable references**
Installation qualification (IQ) report (production environment)	A report on the installation of the system in the production environment	When the system is installed to create a production environment	Highly recommended
User training records	Records of the training provided to end users, administrators, and those who execute the validation protocols	All systems	21 CFR 211, Section 25 ; 21 CFR 820, Section 25 b; 21 CFR Part 11, Section 11.10 i; EC Annex 11, No. 1; ISO 13485, Section 6.2.2 e
Performance qualification (PQ)	A test protocol developed to obtain documented evidence that the system performs effectively and reliably under normal production conditions	All moderate- and high-risk systems for which any production condition is different from that of the operational qualification (OQ) test environment	21 CFR 820, Section 70 i; CDRH 6, 6.2, 6.3; EC Annex 11, No. 7; ISO 13485, Section 7.5.2.1
PQ report	A report that includes the data collected during the execution of the PQ protocol and a conclusion regarding the system's success in meeting the protocol acceptance criteria	All instances in which a PQ protocol is executed	21 CFR 820, Section 70 i; CDRH 6, 6.2, 6.3; EC Annex 11, No. 7; ISO 13485, Section 7.5.2.1
Risk management report	A report that summarizes the risk management process, including actions to implement and verify risk control measures, and an assessment of residual risk	Moderate- and high-risk systems	ISO 14971, Section 8
Validation final report	A report that: ■ Summarizes the life cycle activities ■ Identifies the deliverables from the life cycle that are part of the validation record ■ Summarizes the results of the formal testing (e.g., IQ, OQ, and PQ) ■ Addresses all variances and states a conclusion as to the suitability of the system	All systems. For low-risk and simple systems, the validation final report can be combined with a protocol report.	21 CFR 820, Section 70 i; CDRH 6.2; EC Annex 11, No. 7; ISO 13485, Section 7.5.2.1

Phase 8 deliverables	Definition and explanation	When applicable	Deliverable references
System backups	Copies of electronic files and records preserved in a secure location and used to restore damaged or deleted files or data	When backups are required or of sufficient business value. Moderate- and high-risk systems.	21 CFR 211, Section 68 b; EC Annex 11, No. 14; 21 CFR 820, Section 180
Maintenance and calibration records	Records of the maintenance and calibration of the system during its life	When equipment requires calibration and/or maintenance	21 CFR 820, Sections 70 g 1 and 72; 21 CFR 211, Section 68 a; ISO 13485, Sections 6.3 and 7.6
Performance monitoring reports	Reports of activities performed to monitor system performance. Reports are prepared following documented procedures for system management.	When the system requires monitoring to ensure proper security, operation, and/or performance	Highly recommended
Issue reports	Records of problems and their resolution, and system enhancements	All systems	EC Annex 11, No. 17
Change control records	Records of the approval and testing of changes prior to their implementation in the production environment	All systems	21 CFR 11, Section 11.10 k 2; CDRH 6.1; 21 CFR 820, Section 70 i; ISO 13485, 7.5.2.1; EC Annex 11, No. 11; 21 CFR 211, Section 68 b
Periodic system review report	A report of a periodic review conducted to formally evaluate system reliability and performance and determine the risk management implications of the findings	Moderate- and high-risk systems	21 CFR 211, Section 68
Audit reports	Reports of the results of audits performed on system use, management, and maintenance	All systems	21 CFR 820, Section 22; EC Annex 11, No. 13; ISO 13485, Section 8.2.2

Chapter 11

Phase 9: Retire the System

When the system is no longer needed, or when it's obsolesced by more advanced technology, it's retired (see note 1). Planning for the system's retirement is normally done at the same time as implementing a new system. The new system will be selected, implemented, tested, installed, and used following the RiskVal or similar life cycle.

Data preservation is often the most critical problem faced with system migration. There are several options:

- The new system can access data from the old system.
- The old system can be preserved for accessing old data while the new system is used for new data.
- Legacy data can be loaded into the new system.
- Records can be archived to non-electronic media such as microfilm, microfiche, and paper, or to a standard electronic file format such as PDF, XML, or SGML.

PRESERVING RECORDS

Objectives

Records are preserved to ensure that they're available for use during the records-retention period.[1] The record-retention period is the length of time that the record must be available for review or use. The records must be preserved in such a manner that the electronic records remain trustworthy, reliable, authentic, and continue to meet business needs and regulatory requirements.[2] Along with the record itself, information associated with the signing of the record, such as the name of the signer and the date and time of the signing, must also be preserved. The retention period is determined by company policy based on business needs and/or regulatory requirements. For example, the Quality System Regulation states, "All records required by this part shall be retained for a period of time equivalent to the design and expected life of the devices, but in no case less than two years from the date of release for commercial distribution by the manufacturer."[3]

Electronic Records Maintenance Process

Procedures and controls should be developed for the "protection of records to enable their accurate and ready retrieval throughout the records-retention period."[4] The need for such a procedure is based on regulatory requirements and/or business needs. A records-maintenance procedure might include the following:

- Acceptable alternatives for record storage (see the following section)
- Requirements for the control and monitoring of factors that might affect the reliability of records, such as storage conditions for magnetic media
- Record retrieval and access requirements and controls
- Practices to ensure the continued availability and readability of the records, including periodically accessing the records to verify that they're still readable and to determine if they should be transcribed to other media before degradation renders them unrecoverable
- Requirements and practices for creating and storing back-up copies
- Requirements for copying electronic records (e.g., to ensure that a copy is accurate and complete), a built-in error check can be used, such as a cyclic redundancy check. If such a check isn't possible, the process of creating a copy should be tested, and its accuracy should be verified.

APPROACHES TO PRESERVING ELECTRONIC RECORDS AFTER THE SYSTEM IS RETIRED

There are four ways to preserve electronic records after the application that created them is no longer in use:

1. The new system can access data directly from the old system.
2. The old system can be kept for accessing the old records.
3. The data can be moved to a different system.
4. The records can be converted to a non-electronic media or a standard electronic file format.[5]

The first approach is to use the new system to access the data directly from the old database. This approach is commonly used when a system is upgraded to a new version. In addition, some vendors have built in the ability of their system to read data directly from the databases used with other vendors' systems so that data needn't be transferred to their application.

With the second approach, preserving the system, the system used to generate the records is kept intact only for the purpose of preserving and accessing the old records. The system might even be inactive if it's accessed infrequently, but it still must be capable of working. Changes can be made to the system under change control, as long as care is taken not to modify or delete the records as a consequence of the change or impair the ability to retrieve the records. This approach might not be practical for records that must be maintained for a long time, but it's often a viable choice in the event of a short-term need.

The third approach, migration, involves moving the electronic records to a different system. This approach has been discussed several times in this book as the movement of the legacy data from a system being phased out to a new system. It's important to perform an operational qualification (OQ) on loading the legacy data (or "legacy load") to ensure that the data are transferred completely and accurately. The legacy load OQ also provides a traceable history of the data through the transition. If such a protocol isn't used, it's important to document—in the record migration report, for example—the transfer of data so that the information can be found in the future, and any problems can be diagnosed. Such documentation is especially needed if the names of the data elements are being changed or if new elements will be added to the data record at the time of transfer or in the future.

Making a distinction between a record and metadata is helpful in understanding the requirements for changes to data being transferred from one system to another. "Metadata" are descriptive data or information about the record that gives it context and meaning. For example, the record for the approval of a document includes the document, the approval record that contains the identity and signature of the approvers, and the document-effective date. Additional information (or metadata) might be available about the record that's not actually a part of the record. Examples of metadata for a controlled document might include the author's name and department, and the name of the document-control specialist who prepared the change request. When data on the controlled document are transferred from an old to a new system, new metadata might be added, some dropped, and the name of some data fields might change (e.g., from author to originator). Any changes to the metadata shouldn't lessen the reliability of the information the electronic record preserves and presents. If the official record is modified, create an audit trail, especially if it's a regulatory requirement or important for business reasons.

When records are migrated to new systems, be careful of the following:

■ The new system's print and display devices shouldn't affect the reliability of the record that's preserved and presented. For example, data in the old system might be available in a graphic display. The display might use shading or color to convey meaning or differentiate values. When the data are transferred to a new system with different graphics, the same meaning must be conveyed.

■ When transferring electronic records, care must be taken to also transfer and appropriately attach information that establishes record integrity. For example, an electronic record may have audit-trail information and electronic signatures associated with it.

■ The process of creating the record in the new system must be an entry in the audit trail.

The fourth option for preserving electronic records is to convert them to non-electronic media such as microfilm, microfiche, or paper. Records can also be converted to a standard electronic file format, such as PDF, XML, or SGML. Here again, care must be taken to ensure that the record communicates the same information that was communicated in the electronic record, and that necessary related information such as electronic signatures is appropriately preserved.

After the migration, the old records might still be kept if there's a chance that previously unknown problems with the old records or system might be discovered, or if the accuracy of the transfer must be verified for a particular data point. As an alternative, some companies will print the data from the old system so that they have a record of the data before it was transferred and a way of verifying that the transfer was properly completed.

SYSTEM RETIREMENT AND RECORD MIGRATION REPORT

A record of the retirement is recommended for all systems so that the history of the data can be traced. The report includes the following, if relevant to the situation:

- A description of the records. Type of records, their purpose, the owner department, range of dates during which the records were created, any information regarding the records' scope (e.g., records beginning with number 4575 and ending with 8934), and the dates or date range when the record-retention period will end.
- A reference to any regulation or company procedure that requires the records and/ or specifies the record retention time
- Any regulatory significance of the records (e.g., the test records were included in a new drug application)
- How the records were created (e.g., the name and version of the software used to create the records), the name and version of the operating system used with the application, and any other important information concerning the configuration of the system used to create the data
- Information about the database and its structure (e.g., a data dictionary and information about, or a map of, the structure of the database tables)
- The media and format in which the records are being stored. The hardware and software needed to extract the stored information for display or as printed records, if such information isn't obvious from the media.
- A list of copies of the records, where the copies are stored, and their media (e.g., the records have been printed and have been archived in the off-site storage, or the original paper records are available)
- A description of the changes made to the records or metadata, including global changes and changes to individual records (e.g., change of department name and record update for a new owner). Such changes shouldn't eliminate required information or affect the reliability of the information that's preserved. The changes made to a specific record must be added to the audit trail, if one is required.

SUMMARY OF PHASE 9 DELIVERABLES

Table 11.1 summarizes the deliverable from phase 9 and indicates when it's applicable.

Table 11.1	Phase 9 Deliverables		
Phase 9 deliverable	**Definition and explanation**	**When applicable**	**Deliverable references**
System retirement and record migration report	Documentation that provides a traceable history of what systems were used throughout the records-retention period and how the records were migrated	All systems	21 CFR 820 Section 180 b; ISO 13485, Section 4.2.4

Chapter 12

Minimum Validation Requirements

Many who have read this book are searching for a clear statement that identifies the minimum requirements for validation. There are several reasons for this quest. Some organizations already have existing systems that are working well but haven't been validated, and their industry regulations require validation. Other organizations want to either minimize the cost of the validation or minimize the implementation time for a new system.

Recall that the purpose of validation is "confirmation by examination and provision of objective evidence that the computer-system specifications conform to user needs and intended uses, and that the particular requirements implemented through the computer system can be consistently fulfilled."[1] Identifying the minimum requirements for objective evidence for computer-system validation is difficult.

This chapter has two objectives:

- To answer the question, "What's the minimum I must do to validate a commercial off-the-shelf (COTS) computerized system?"

- To compare the deliverables identified in the RiskVal life cycle with those recommended, or required by the Food and Drug Administration (FDA), European Community (EC) Commission directive for medicinal products, and Gamp 4.[2–5]

COTS and configured business systems will be addressed from the perspective of regulatory bodies. Keep in mind that the following is based on my reading of the regulations and guidance documents; you must make your own judgment based on the same documents and other sources with which you might be familiar. This list isn't intended to apply to custom-developed systems, which require additional documentation from the development process.

MINIMUM REQUIREMENTS FROM A REGULATORY PERSPECTIVE

Minimum Requirements—FDA

Although the FDA identifies some required documentation in its guidance document, it also states that what's sufficient depends on the risk to product quality and record integrity.[6] The application of this principle is left to the organization that's required to perform the validation and the discretion of the FDA. In the guidance document on 21 CFR Part 11, the FDA repeats the message:

> We suggest that your decision to validate computerized systems, and the extent of the validation, take into account the impact the systems have on your ability to meet predicate rule requirements. [In the preceding paragraph, the guidance states: ". . . persons must still comply with all applicable predicate rule requirements for validation..."] You should also consider the effect those systems might have on the accuracy, reliability, integrity, availability, and authenticity of required records and signatures. Even if there's no predicate rule requirement to validate a system, in some instances it may still be important to validate the system[7]

This section identifies what documentation the FDA guidance document on software validation states an organization should have.

To begin listing the minimum from the FDA's perspective, the relevant requirements stated in the FDA regulations that govern pharmaceuticals and medical devices will be identified. These regulations are called predicate rules. For example, the medical device good manufacturing practices (GMPs) state that "each manufacturer shall . . . ensure that all personnel are trained to adequately perform their assigned responsibilities. Training shall be documented."[8] It follows that training records would be required for users of computerized systems that are used to perform work covered by the regulation. The deliverables that are required by predicate rules, depending on the nature of the system, are:

- Established protocol.[9] In the RiskVal life cycle, the validation protocols are organized into installation qualification (IQ), operational qualification (OQ), and performance qualification (PQ) protocols.
- Calibration records[10, 11]
- System backups[12, 13]
- Maintenance records[14, 15]
- User training records[16–18]
- Audit reports[19]
- Validation final report[20]

Next, we can add to the list those deliverables that are required by Part 11 for systems with electronic records or electronic signatures. These deliverables include:

- Validation procedure[21]
- Information technology (IT) policy.[22] Part 11 requires a written policy that holds individuals accountable and responsible for actions initiated under their electronic signatures.
- User training[23]
- Change control records.[24] Part 11 requires change control over system documentation.

Next, we can add to the list of minimally required deliverables those identified in the FDA guidance document on software validation. The FDA discusses many activities related to validation, such as vendor audits, but its list of validation documentation that a manufacturer should have includes only five items. The corresponding RiskVal deliverables are identified in brackets. The guidance document states:

"The device manufacturer should have documentation including:

- Defined user requirements [user requirements]
- Validation protocol used [IQ, OQ, PQ]
- Acceptance criteria [part of the RiskVal validation plan or protocols if a validation plan isn't written]
- Test cases and results [IQ, OQ, and PQ protocols and protocol reports]
- A validation summary [validation final report]

. . . that objectively confirms that the software is validated for its intended use."[25]

EC Commission Directive on Medicinal Products Requirements

The EC Commission directive on the manufacture of medicinal products lists a number of requirements in Annex 11. Those that are related to validation, system use, and system maintenance are listed here. Annex 11 defines additional requirements that aren't given here, for example, requirements for specific functionality. Recall that the commission considers validation "as part of the complete life cycle of a computer system. This should include the stages of planning, specification, programming, testing, commissioning, documentation, operation, monitoring, and modifying."[26] The numbers given after the items represent the clauses of Annex 11 that are the sources of the item. The deliverables given in brackets after the items are the corresponding RiskVal procedures or deliverables.

- Training for the management and use of systems that utilize computers[27] [training materials and records]

- A written, detailed description of the system[28] [system specification]

- The user shall take all reasonable steps to ensure that the software has been produced in accordance with a system of quality assurance[29] [vendor qualification].

- Before a system using a computer is brought into use, it should be thoroughly tested and confirmed as being capable of achieving the desired results[30] [IQ, OQ, PQ protocols, and protocol reports].

- There should be a defined procedure for the issue, cancellation, and alteration of authorization to enter and amend data, including changing passwords[31] [user and administrative procedures, or IT procedure].

- Alterations to a system or to a computer program should only be made in accordance with a defined procedure that should include provision for validation, checking, approving, and implementing the change. The alteration should be approved and recorded[32] [change control procedure and records].

- Data should be secured by physical or electronic means against willful or accidental damage[33] [IT logical and physical security procedure].

- Stored data should be checked for accessibility, durability, and accuracy[34] [IT maintenance, or quality assurance (QA) audits].

- Data should be protected by backing-up at regular intervals[35] [backup procedure].

- The procedures to be followed if the system fails or breaks down should be defined and validated.[36] If a manual system is used as the contingency process, it can be included in the user procedure. If an automated process is used, the transition to the backup automated process, the functioning of the backup process itself, and the transfer back to a restored process need to be validated [contingency procedures].

- A procedure should be established to record and analyze errors and to enable corrective action to be taken. Any failure and remedial actions taken should be recorded[37] [issue tracking and reporting].

- When outside agencies are used to provide a computer service, there should be a formal agreement including a clear statement of the responsibilities of that outside agency[38] [supplier agreements].

COMBINED LIST OF FDA AND EC COMMISSION REQUIREMENTS

The total list of deliverables required by predicate rules, Part 11, the EC Commission directive, and explicitly identified in the FDA guidance document is given in table 12.2.

This section provides lists that combine the FDA and EC Commission requirements.

First, table 12.1 provides a list of the policies and procedures mentioned in a regulation. These documents should be developed in advance to define a life cycle for the risk management and validation of all computer systems. The table also provides the deliverable number for a particular brief that appears in appendix A of this book. Appendix D presents a more extensive list of the policies and procedures discussed in conjunction with the RiskVal life cycle.

Second, in table 12.2 I've included all of the activities and deliverables that are required in FDA regulations or the EC Commission's directive for medicinal products EC Annex 11. In addition, I've provided the business reasons for the deliverable. If a brief is provided on the deliverable in appendix A of this volume, the deliverable's number is provided after the deliverable's name.

Third, table 12.3 lists the records that must be created during ongoing use of a computer system after the validation is complete.

From a regulatory perspective, the minimum validation for COTS systems can be determined by selecting the items from the above tables that are required by the body or bodies that regulate your company (i.e., the FDA, EC Commission, or both). From a business perspective, the minimum is what's needed to protect your company from the risks associated with potential system failure.

Table 12.1	Software Validation Policies and Procedures Required by Regulations	

RiskVal policy procedure and deliverable number	Requirement	Requirement reference
Validation procedure (see deliverables 1.2 and 1.4)	Procedures and control shall include validation of systems to ensure accuracy, reliability, consistent intended performance, and the ability to discern invalid or altered records.	21 CFR 11, Section 11.10 a ISO 13485, 7.5.2.1
Information technology policy (see deliverable 1.3)	The establishment of, and adherence to, written policies that hold individuals accountable and responsible for actions initiated under their electronic signatures to deter record and signature falsification	21 CFR 11, Section 11.10 j
Backup, archive, and restore	Data should be protected by backing-up at regular intervals. (Annex 11)	cGMP 211.68 b; EC Annex 11, No. 14
Network adds, changes, and deletes	There shall be a defined procedure for the issue, cancellation, and alteration of authorization to enter and amend data, including the changing of personnel passwords.	Annex 11, No. 8
Disaster recovery and contingency plans	The procedures to be followed if the system fails or breaks down shall be defined and validated.	EC Annex 11, No. 16
Logical and physical security	Procedures and control shall include limiting system access to authorized individuals, and adequate controls over the distribution of, access to, and use of documentation for system operation and maintenance. (Part 11)	21 CFR Part 11, Section 11.10 c and d; Annex 11, No. 13
System support	A procedure should be established to record and analyze errors, and enable corrective action to be taken.	Annex 11, No. 17
Change control (see deliverables 6.2 and 6.3)	Alterations to a system or computer program should only be made in accordance with a defined procedure, which should include provision for validating, checking, approving, and implementing change. (Annex 11) Change control on system documentation. (Part 11)	21 CFR 820, Section 70 i; ISO 13485, 7.5.2.1; EC Annex 11, No. 11; 21 CFR 11, Section 11.10 k 2

The Minimum Isn't Always Enough

The FDA considers software validation to be "confirmation by examination and provision of objective evidence that software specifications conform to user needs and intended uses, and that the particular requirements implemented through the software can be consistently fulfilled."[39] Later on in the same guidance document, the FDA addresses the question, "How much validation evidence is needed?" The answer is that it depends upon the risk posed by the automated process:

Table 12.2	Minimum RiskVal Validation Activities and Deliverables Based on Regulatory Requirements and Business Reasons		
RiskVal activity	**Deliverable**	**Business reason**	**Regulations, standards and guidance documents that indicated importance**
Writing user requirements	User requirements (see deliverable 2.1)	User requirements are the logical foundation for demonstrating that a system is capable of meeting requirements.	General Principles, 2002, Section 6.2
Qualifying vendors	Vendor qualification report (see deliverables 3.3 and 3.4)	Software quality must be built into software. Validation testing can't find all the defects. The vendor must be qualified based on its development practices.	EC Annex 11, No. 5
Executing hardware and software purchase contracts, including quality plans and support agreements	Hardware and software purchase agreements (including service agreements)	Purchase agreements are binding contracts and warranty agreements. Services and quality requirements for services must be defined. Support terms are important to ensure that the system will remain in a validated state.	EC Annex 11, No. 18
Defining system acceptance criteria	The acceptance criteria can be given in the validation plan (see deliverable 4.2) or in a validation protocol (see deliverables 7.1, 7.3, and 8.1).	Acceptance criteria must be defined in advance to set a standard for when the system is acceptable.	General Principles, 2002, Section 6.2
Define and/or describe the system.	System specification and/or system hardware configuration diagram (see deliverable 6.1)	The specification defines technical requirements and ensures that the system has the hardware and software needed to function effectively. It provides a master list for the installation qualification (IQ) and for replicating the system.	EC Annex 11, No. 4
Define the appropriate use of the system.	Instructions on system use can be provided in a separate user procedure or in a procedure for the automated process.	Instructions for using the system within an automated process are needed to ensure user effectiveness.	EC Annex 11, No. 8
Define how to administer the system.	Application administrative procedures	Instructions for administering the system are needed to ensure user effectiveness and system security.	21 CFR 820, Section 25 b; Part 11, 11.10 d, i, j, k 1, 11.300

(continues)

Table 12.2	Minimum RiskVal Validation Activities and Deliverables Based on Regulatory Requirements and Business Reasons (continued)		
RiskVal activity	**Deliverable**	**Business reason**	**Regulations, standards and guidance documents that indicated importance**
Define how to administer the system.	Application administrative procedures	Instructions for administering the system are needed to ensure user effectiveness and system security.	21 CFR 820, Section 25 b; Part 11, 11.10 d, i, j, k, 1, 11.300
Define what to do to maintain the process when the system fails or breaks down.	Contingency procedures. If a manual system is used as the contingency process, it can be included in the user procedure.	Employees must know what to do in case the system is unavailable, even if it's to wait until the system is brought back up. If the system will be down for an extended period of time, a contingency plan will avoid stopping the business.	EC Annex 11, No. 16
Calibrate measurement devices.	Calibration records	Calibration is needed to ensure that measurements are accurate.	21 CFR 211, Section 68 a; 21 CFR 820, Section 72
Perform maintenance.	Maintenance records: Performance of maintenance during the operational qualification (OQ) can be used to qualify the maintenance process	Unscheduled and scheduled preventive maintenance are necessary to ensure that the system will continue to function effectively.	21 CFR 211, Section 67; 21 CFR 820, Section 70 g 1
Train users. If appropriate use isn't obvious from the procedures, user training is needed.	Training records	Early users who will perform the validation testing must be trained to prevent operator errors during the execution of the protocols.	21 CFR 820, Section 25 b; 21 CFR 211, Section 211.25; 21 CFR 11, Section 11.10 i; EC Annex 11, 1
Preparing and executing validation protocols and reports	Ordinarily, IQ, OQ, and performance qualification (PQ) protocols are prepared, but they can be combined and at times a PQ protocol isn't needed. (See deliverables 7.1, 7.3, and 8.1.)	The tests to be executed must be defined and written in advance with expected results. The executed protocols provide a permanent record of the tests performed and a comparison of the actual results with the expected results.	21 CFR 820, Section 70 i; General Principles, 2002, Section 6.2; EC Annex 11, No. 7
Writing a validation final report	The final report can be a separate report or it can be combined with the report for the last protocol written for the system, usually the PQ. (See deliverable 8.3.)	An approved final report closes the validation and releases the system for production.	21 CFR 820, Section 70 i; General Principles, 2002, Section 6.2

Table 12.3	Records that Must Be Created During Ongoing Use
Calibration records	21 CFR 211, Section 68 a; 21 CFR 820, Section 72
Maintenance records	21 CFR 211, Section 67; 21 CFR 820, Section 70 g, 1
Issue tracking and records resolution	EC Annex 11, No.17
System backups	cGMP 211.68 b; 21 CFR 820, Section 180; EC Annex 11, No. 14
User training records	21 CFR 820, Section 25 b; 21 CFR 211.25; 21 CFR 11, Section 11.10 i; EC Annex 11, No. 1
Change control records	21 CFR 11, Section 11.10 k 2; EC Annex 11, No. 11
Audit reports	21 CFR 820, Section 22; General Principles, 2002, Section 6.2; EC Annex 11, No. 13

"The level of validation should be commensurate with the risk posed by the automated operation. In addition to risk, other factors such as the complexity of the process software and the degree to which the device manufacturer is dependent upon that automated process to produce a safe and effective device, determine the nature and extent of testing needed as part of the validation effort. Documented requirements and risk analysis of the automated process help to define the scope of the evidence needed to show that the software is validated for its intended use."[40]

This statement raises the question of what more might be needed. Insight can be gained by looking at the items discussed in the FDA guidance document on software validation that aren't included in the list of documentation that should be created during validation. These items include the following (RiskVal equivalent deliverables appear in brackets after the item):

- A documented risk analysis[41] [initial risk assessment]
- A definition of the expected operating environment, including any required hardware and software configurations, software versions, and utilities[42] [technical requirements]
- Audit of the vendor's design and development methodologies, and the development and validation documentation generated. The audit should demonstrate that the vendor's procedures for, and results of, the verification and validation activities are

appropriate and sufficient for the safety and effectiveness of the medical device[43] [vendor qualification].

- Risk assessment and evaluation report[44] [risk assessment and evaluation report; risk management report]
- Change control records[45] [change control records]

Half of these items are required by the EC Commission directive for medicinal products, and therefore were included as part of the minimum regulatory requirements above (i.e., vendor qualification, agreements with vendors, and change control).

There are two additional items are that aren't on the minimum list of validation activities, but are necessary for systems of average or high complexity:

- *A validation plan.* This defines what parts of the RiskVal life cycle will be performed for the system in question. It also states the validation strategy, how the system's risk level will affect the rigor and intensity of the validation activities, and when the system will be released for production use. The system-acceptance criteria are one of the items on the minimum requirements list; they're normally given in the validation plan. Although the information contained in the plan can be included in the OQ or PQ for the system, it's better to define and document the validation strategy and activities much earlier in the life cycle. If the validation plan is written early in the life cycle, it can direct the life-cycle activities.
- *Traceability matrix of user requirements to test protocols.* Such a matrix ensures that all requirements are appropriately tested and provides a useful tool for internal and external audits.

Risk-management activities haven't been included in the minimum activities because the regulators have recommended, but not required, risk management. In the discussion of risk management in validation guidance documents, risk is seen primarily as a mediating factor on the rigor and intensity of validation activities, especially testing. Risk management as a way of preventing system failure or the occurrence of harm isn't the focus of regulations and guidance documents regarding COTS software used in production and quality assurance. However, the use of risk management to prevent system failure and/or the occurrence of harm is a concern with COTS and custom software used in medical devices.[46]

COMPARISON OF RISKVAL DELIVERABLES WITH REGULATORY REQUIREMENTS AND GAMP 4

Exhibit 12.1 summarizes the deliverables from the RiskVal life cycle. It identifies each deliverable and states when each is applicable, based on the risk level of the system. Keep in mind that these are personal opinions and each organization must determine for itself when it thinks each activity is needed, based on the system risk level.

Exhibit 12.1 also indicates what regulations require an activity and if the FDA guidance document on software validation discusses it. Gamp 4 is a popular guidance document for the validation of software. It was written by a group of experts from the pharmaceutical industry, but it's applicable to all regulated industries.

Risk-management references aren't included in exhibit 12.1 if they're not needed from a validation approach. The reasons for this exclusion are: 1) providing objective evidence that the system functions as required can be distinguished from controlling the risk associated with its failure; and 2) appendix B of this book provides information on how the risk-management process described in ISO 14971:2000 is integrated into the RiskVal process. If you want to determine which risk management activities to put in your organization's computer system risk management and validation process, appendix B will provide the information you need to determine which risk management activities you should add.

Exhibit 12.1 Comparison of RiskVal Activities With Regulatory Requirements, Guidance Documents, and Gamp 4

This exhibit lists the RiskVal life cycle deliverables for commercial off-the-shelf (COTS) systems and configured business systems, and indicates what regulations require, or guidance documents discuss, each kind of deliverable. Keep in mind that a referenced regulatory document might not use the same name for a deliverable, might not discuss or require all that's recommended as content in a deliverable, or might discuss an activity in more general terms. For example, neither FDA regulations nor guidance documents, nor the EC Commission's Annex 11 directive on computerized systems for manufacturing medicinal products, nor ISO 13485 require an installation qualification (IQ), operational qualification (OQ), or performance qualification (PQ). However, all the documents discuss the need to collect and document objective evidence, such as test results, that the system functions as required. The Quality System Regulation requires that established protocols be used and that all validation activities and results be documented. The IQ, OQ, and PQ protocols are the structure used in the RiskVal life cycle to meet the requirement of using approved protocols and gathering objective evidence of system performance. To determine the exact requirements or discussion about a deliverable, consult the document references.

Policy and procedure documents aren't included in the following table except for those that might be specific to a system. (For a discussion of required policies and procedures, see table 12.1.)

Here is an explanation of the table that follows:

■ Column one lists the deliverables from the RiskVal life cycle.

■ Column two indicates if the deliverable is on the RiskVal minimum list provided in chapter 12. An item falls in this category if it's required—by an FDA predicate rule, Part 11, the EC Commission directive on medicinal products, and the items identified in the FDA guidance on software validation—as a document that an organization should create during a validation. A yes is also indicated in this column if ongoing records are required when the system is used in a validated state. The references from these documents are given in column six, titled "Predicate rules; Part 11; CDRH minimum documents; Annex 11."

■ Columns three, four, and five indicate whether a deliverable is needed for low-, moderate-, or high-risk systems. If the word "All" is listed, then the deliverable should be created for all systems at that risk level (e.g., for all low-risk systems).

■ Column six gives references to where an activity or a deliverable is mentioned as a requirement in FDA predicate rules, Part 11, the EC Commission directive on medicinal products, Annex 11 on computerized systems, or ISO 13485. It also gives references to those documents that the FDA guidance on software validation indicates should be created as part of the validation.

■ Column seven adds references to the FDA guidance document on software validation if the deliverable, or associated activity, is discussed but not included in the list of documentation that should be created. These references are included to present a comprehensive view of the regulations and guidance documents. References to ISO 14971 are made if the standard identifies the deliverable as needed for risk management.

■ Column eight gives references to where the deliverable or associated activity is discussed in Gamp 4 in relation to COTS software.

Items not needed for existing systems are indicated by a footnote.

References for the documents sited in this exhibit are given in chapter 2, table 2.1.

RiskVal Deliverables Compared to Regulatory Requirements and Gamp 4

Deliverable	On the minimum list	RiskVal recommendations			• Predicate rules • Part 11 • CDRH minimum documents • Annex 11 • ISO 13485	• Predicate rules • Part 11 • Discussed in CDRH • Annex 11 • ISO 13485 • ISO 14971	Gamp 4 guidance
		Low-risk systems	Moderate-risk systems	High-risk systems			
Phase 1: Conceptualize							
Computer system project proposal (see deliverable 1.5)	Yes—High-level risk analysis	All	All	All		CDRH, 6.1—initial risk analysis	Sections 7, (ID GxP sys), 7.4.1 (risk assessment)
Computer system project plan		Complex low-risk systems	Complex moderate-risk systems	All high-risk systems			Sections 7.5; 7.5.2
Phase 2: Define requirements							
User requirements (see deliverable 2.1)	Yes	All	All	All	CDRH, 6.2	CDRH, 6.2	Section 7, 7.3
Technical requirements (see deliverable 2.2)	Yes	All except applications built with database packages (1)	All except applications built with database packages (1)	All except applications built with database packages (1)		CDRH, 6.2	Section 7.5.1
Vendor organizational requirements (see deliverable 2.3) (2)		When a long-term solution from the same vendor is required	When a long-term solution from the same vendor is required	When a long-term solution from the same vendor is required			
Phase 2 review minutes (2)		Large or complex systems	All	All			Section 6.2
Phase 3: Select vendors and systems							
Technical assessment of alternatives (see deliverable 3.1) (2)		All except for applications developed using database packages	All except for applications developed using database packages	All except for applications developed using database packages			
User assessment of alternative applications (see deliverable 3.2) (2)		All except for applications developed using database packages	All except for applications developed using database packages	All except for applications developed using database packages			
Vendor audit report (see deliverable 3.3)		A report is prepared for all audits that are conducted. (However, au-	A report is prepared for all audits that are conducted.	A report is prepared for all audits that are conducted.		CDRH 6.3	Section 7.4.3; App M2

(continues)

Exhibit 12.1	Comparison of RiskVal Activities With Regulatory Requirements, Guidance Documents, and Gamp 4 (continued)

RiskVal Deliverables Compared to Regulatory Requirements and Gamp 4

Deliverable	RiskVal recommendations				• Predicate rules • Part 11 • CDRH minimum documents • Annex 11 • ISO 13485	• Predicate rules • Part 11 • Discussed in CDRH • Annex 11 • ISO 13485 • ISO 14971	Gamp 4 guidance
	On the minimum list	Low-risk systems	Moderate-risk systems	High-risk systems			
		dits generally aren't required for low-risk systems.)					
Vendor qualification report (see deliverable 3.4)	Yes	All systems except applications built with database packages	All systems except applications built with database packages	All systems except applications built with database packages	21 CFR 820, Section 50 a; ISO 13485, Section 7.4.1 Annex 11, No. 5	21 CFR 820, Section 50 a; ISO 13485, Section 7.4.1; CDRH 6.3; Annex 11, No. 5	
System selection report (see deliverable 3.5) (2)		Not needed	All except applications built with existing database packages	All except applications built with existing database packages			
Hardware and software purchase agreements and/or documentation; quality agreements for service provision	Yes	As appropriate	As appropriate	As appropriate	21 CFR 820, Section 50 b; ISO 13485, Section 7.4.2	21 CFR 820, Section 50 b; ISO 13485, Section 7.4.2; EC Annex 11, No. 18	Sections 7.5, 7.5.2, 7.11.4, App O2
Phase 4: Design solutions to issues							
Integration documentation or procedure		All systems that are integrated with other systems	All systems that are integrated with other systems	All systems that are integrated with other systems			
Risk assessment and evaluation report (see deliverable 4.1)		Not needed it the initial risk analysis indicates it's a low-risk system	All moderate- and high-risk systems	All moderate- and high-risk systems		CDRH, 6.1: ISO 14971, Sections 4.4 and 5	Section 7.4.1; App M3

RiskVal Deliverables Compared to Regulatory Requirements and Gamp 4

Deliverable	RiskVal recommendations				• Predicate rules • Part 11 • CDRH minimum documents • Annex 11 • ISO 13485	• Predicate rules • Part 11 • Discussed in CDRH • Annex 11 • ISO 13485 • ISO 14971	Gamp 4 guidance
	On the minimum list	Low-risk systems	Moderate-risk systems	High-risk systems			
Mitigation plan		If needed	If needed	If needed		ISO 14971, Section 6	Appendix M3, Section 4.2.8
Validation plan (see delliverable 4.2)	Yes	Not needed. Relevant information can be included in an IQ or OQ protocol.	For simple applications, relevant information can be included in an IQ or OQ protocol.	For simple applications, relevant information can be included in an IQ or OQ protocol.	CDRH, 6.2— acceptance criteria	CDRH, 6.2— acceptance criteria	Sections 7.4.2, 7.5, 7.5.1, App M1
Documentation of system configurations		Systems that require configuration. A separate report may be prepared, or configurations can be included in the system specification, installation instructions, or IQ.	Systems that require configuration. A separate report may be prepared, or configurations can be included in the system specification, installation instructions, or IQ.	Systems that require configuration. A separate report may be prepared, or configurations can be included in the system specification, installation instructions, or IQ.			Section 7.6 (design specifications)
Revised project plan		As needed	As needed	As needed			
Phase 5: Construct solutions to issues							
Mitigation report (see deliverable 5.1)		If formal testing of a mitigation is performed	If formal testing of a mitigation is performed	If formal testing of a mitigation is performed		ISO 14971, Section 6.3	
Revised risk assessment and evaluation report		N/A	If mitigations have been implemented during phase 5	If mitigations have been implemented during phase 5		ISO 14971, Section 6.3	App M3
Update to documentation of system configurations		Systems that require configuration. A separate report may be prepared, or	Systems that require configuration. A separate report may be prepared,	Systems that require configuration. A separate report may be prepared,			Section 7.11.7

(continues)

Exhibit 12.1	Comparison of RiskVal Activities With Regulatory Requirements, Guidance Documents, and Gamp 4 (continued)

RiskVal Deliverables Compared to Regulatory Requirements and Gamp 4

Deliverable	RiskVal recommendations				• Predicate rules • Part 11 • CDRH minimum documents • Annex 11 • ISO 13485	• Predicate rules • Part 11 • Discussed in CDRH • Annex 11 • ISO 13485 • ISO 14971	Gamp 4 guidance
	On the minimum list	Low-risk systems	Moderate-risk systems	High-risk systems			
	.	or configurations can be included in the system specification, installation instructions, or IQ.	or configurations can be included in the system specification, installation instructions, or IQ.	configurations can be included in the system specification, installation instructions, or IQ			
Phase 6: Prepare for use							
System specification (see deliverable 6.1)	Yes	Recommended for complex systems and systems that will change relatively often	All	All	EC Annex 11, No. 4 (system description)	EC Annex 11, No. 4 (system description)	Section 7.6 (design specification)
Information technology procedures that are specific to the system	Yes	As needed	As needed	As needed	21 CFR 11, Sections 11.10 d, i, j, k EC Annex 11, No. 16	21 CFR 11, Sections 11.10 d, i, j, k; EC Annex 11, No. 16	Sections 6.4, 7.11, 7.11.5, 7.11.6, 7.11.7, 7.11.9, 7.11.10, 7.11.11, 711.12, App: O7, M9, O3, O5, O6, O8
User procedures	Yes	If predicate rules require procedures for the automated functions	All	All	If regulator(s) require procedures for functions to be performed with the system	If regulator(s) require procedures for functions to be performed with the system	Section 7.11.1
Application administration procedures	Yes	All systems with administrative functions if predicate rules require user procedures for the automated functions	All systems with administrative functions	Allsystems with administrative functions	21 CFR 820, Section 25 b; 21 CFR 11, Sections 11, 11.10 d, i, j, k, 1 11.300 EC Annex 11, No. 8	21 CFR 820, Section 25 b; 21 CFR 11, Sections 11, 11.10 d, i, j, k, 1 11.300; EC Annex 11, No. 8	Section 7.11.1

RiskVal Deliverables Compared to Regulatory Requirements and Gamp 4

Deliverable	On the minimum list	RiskVal recommendations Low-risk systems	RiskVal recommendations Moderate-risk systems	RiskVal recommendations High-risk systems	• Predicate rules • Part 11 • CDRH minimum documents • Annex 11 • ISO 13485	• Predicate rules • Part 11 • Discussed in CDRH • Annex 11 • ISO 13485 • ISO 14971	Gamp 4 guidance
Contingency procedure	Yes	All systems that can't have down time	All systems that can't have down time	All systems that can't have down time	EC Annex 11 Nos. 15 and 16	EC Annex 11, Nos. 15 and 16	Section 7.11.12
Training materials		All except systems where training isn't needed	All except systems where training isn't needed	All except systems where training isn't needed			Section 7.11.2
Phase 7: Qualify the system (3–6)							
Calibration records	Yes	When equipment requires calibration	When equipment requires calibration	When equipment requires calibration	21 CFR 211, Section 68 a; 21 CFR 820, Section 72 ; ISO 13485, Section 7.6	21 CFR 211, Section 68 a; 21 CFR 820, Section 72; ISO 13485, Section 7.6	Section 7.11.5
Maintenance records	Yes	When equipment requires maintenance	When equipment requires maintenance	When equipment requires maintenance	21 CFR 211, Section 67; 21 CFR 820, Section 70 g 1; ISO 13485, Section 6.3	21 CFR 211, Section 67; 21 CFR 820, Section 70 g 1; ISO 13485, Section 6.3	Section 7.11.5
IQ protocol and report	Yes	All	All	All	21 CFR 820, Section 70 i; CDRH 6.2 2; EC Annex 11, No. 7; ISO 13485, Section 7.5.2.1	21 CFR 820, Section 70 i; CDRH 6.2 2; EC Annex 11, No. 7; ISO 13485, Section 7.5.2.1	Section 6, 6.3
OQ protocol and report	Yes	All (see chapter 9 for what is included in an OQ for low-risk systems)	All (see chapter 9 for what is included in an OQ for moderate-risk systems)	All (see chapter 9 for what is included in an OQ for high-risk systems)	21 CFR 820, Section 70 i; CDRH 6.2 2; EC Annex 11, No. 7; ISO 13485, Section 7.5.2.1	21 CFR 820, Section 70 i; CDRH 6.2 2; EC Annex 11, No. 7; ISO 13485, Section 7.5.2.1	Section 6, 6.3
Traceability matrix (user requirements to protocols)	Yes	All systems except systems with simple protocols	All systems except systems with simple protocols	All systems except systems with simple protocols			Section 6.2, App M5

(continues)

Exhibit 12.1	Comparison of RiskVal Activities With Regulatory Requirements, Guidance Documents, and Gamp 4 (continued)

RiskVal Deliverables Compared to Regulatory Requirements and Gamp 4

Deliverable	RiskVal recommendations				• Predicate rules • Part 11 • CDRH minimum documents • Annex 11 • ISO 13485	• Predicate rules • Part 11 • Discussed in CDRH • Annex 11 • ISO 13485 • ISO 14971	Gamp 4 guidance
	On the minimum list	Low-risk systems	Moderate-risk systems	High-risk systems			
Change control records	Yes	All systems	All systems	All systems	21 CFR 820, Section 820.70i; 21 CFR 11, Section 11.10 k 2; EC Annex 11, No. 11; ISO 13485, Section 7.5.2.1	21 CFR 820, Section 820.70i; 21 CFR 11, Section 11.10 k 2; CDRH 6.1; EC Annex 11, No. 11; ISO 13485, 7.5.2.1	Section 7.11.3, 7.11.8, App 04
User training records	Yes	All	All	All	21 CFR 820, Section 25 b; 21 CFR 25; 21 CFR 11, Section 11.10 i; EC Annex 11, No. 1; ISO 13485, Section 6.2.2 e	21 CFR 820, Section 25 b; 21 CFR 25; 21 CFR 11, Section 11.10 i; EC Annex 11, No. 1 ISO 13485, Section 6.2.2 e	
Phase 8: Use in production environment (3–6)							
IQ report (production environment)		When the system is installed to create a production environment	When the system is installed to create a production environment	When the system is installed to create a production environment			
User training records	Yes	All systems	All systems	All systems	21 CFR 820, Section 25 b; 21 CFR 211, Section 25; 21 CFR 11, Section 11.10 i; EC Annex 11, No. 1; ISO 13485, Section 6.2.2 e	21 CFR 820, Section 25 b; 21 CFR 211, Section 25; 21 CFR 11, Section 11.10 i; EC Annex 11, No. 1; ISO 13485, Section 6.2.2 e	Section 7.11.2

RiskVal Deliverables Compared to Regulatory Requirements and Gamp 4

Deliverable	On the minimum list	Low-risk systems	Moderate-risk systems	High-risk systems	• Predicate rules • Part 11 • CDRH minimum documents • Annex 11 • ISO 13485	• Predicate rules • Part 11 • Discussed in CDRH • Annex 11 • ISO 13485 • ISO 14971	Gamp 4 guidance
	RiskVal recommendations						
PQ protocol and report	Yes Yes	Not needed	All systems for which any production condition is different from that of the OQ test environment	All systems for which any production condition is different from that of the OQ test environment	21 CFR 820, Section 70 i; EC Annex 11, No. 7; CDRH 6.2; ISO 13485 Section 7.5.2.1	21 CFR 820, Section 70 i; EC Annex 11, No. 7; CDRH 6, 6.2, 6.3 2; ISO 13485, Section 7.5.2.1	Section 6, 6.3
Risk management report		Not required	All	All		ISO 14971, Section 8	
Validation final report	Yes	For low-risk and simple systems, the validation final report can be combined with a protocol report	All	All	21 CFR 820, Section 70 i; ISO 13485, Section 7.5.2.1; CDRH 6.2; EC Annex 11, No. 7	21 CFR 820, Section 70 i; ISO 13485, Section 7.5.2.1; CDRH 6.2; EC Annex 11, No. 7	Section 7.1, 7.5.1, 7.10
Calibration records	Yes	When equipment requires calibration	When equipment requires calibration	When equipment requires calibration	21 CFR 211, Section 68 a; 21 CFR 820, Section 72; ISO 13845, Section 7.6	21 CFR 211, Section 68 a; 21 CFR 820, Section 72; ISO 13845, Section 7.6	Section 7.11.5
Maintenance records	Yes	When equipment maintenance	When equipment maintenance	When equipment maintenance	21 CFR 211, Section 68 a; 21 CFR 820, Section 70 g 1; ISO 13485, Section 6.3	21 CFR 211, Section 68 a; 21 CFR 820, Section 70 g 1; ISO 13485, Section 6.3	Appendix 01, Section 4.2.2., p. 233; Appendix 09, Section 2.1, p. 290
Performance monitoring reports		When the system requires monitoring to ensure proper security, operation, and/or performance	When the system requires monitoring to ensure proper security, operation, and/or performance	When the system requires monitoring to ensure proper security, operation, and/or performance			Section 7.11.10; Appendix 05
Issue reports		All	All	All	Annex 11, No. 17	Annex 11, No. 17	Section 7.11.3

(continues)

Exhibit 12.1	Comparison of RiskVal Activities With Regulatory Requirements, Guidance Documents, and Gamp 4 (continued)

RiskVal Deliverables Compared to Regulatory Requirements and Gamp 4

Deliverable	RiskVal recommendations				• Predicate rules • Part 11 • CDRH minimum documents • Annex 11 • ISO 13485	• Predicate rules • Part 11 • Discussed in CDRH • Annex 11 • ISO 13485 • ISO 14971	Gamp 4 guidance
	On the minimum list	Low-risk systems	Moderate-risk systems	High-risk systems			
System backups	Yes	All	All	All	21 CFR 211, Section 68 b; EC Annex 11, No. 14; 21 CFR 820, Section 180	21 CFR 211, Section 68 b; EC Annex 11, No. 14; 21 CFR 820, Section 180	Appendix 07
User training records	Yes	All	All	All	21 CFR 820, Section 25 b; 21 CFR 211.25; 21 CFR 11, Section 11.10 i; EC Annex 11, No. 1; ISO 13485, Section 6.2.2 e	21 CFR 820, Section 25 b; 21 CFR 211.25; 21 CFR 11, Section 11.10 i; EC Annex 11, No. 1; ISO 13485, Section 6.2.2 e	Section 6.4
Change control records	Yes	All systems	All systems	All systems	21 CFR 820, Section 70 i; 21 CFR 11, Section 11.10 k 2; EC Annex 11, No. 11; ISO 13485 Section 7.5.2.1; 21 CFR 211, Section 68 b	21 CFR 820, Section 70 i; 21 CFR 11, Section, 11.10 k 2; CDRH 6.1; EC Annex 11, No. 11; ISO 13485, Section 7.5.2.1; 21 CFR 211, Section 68 b	Section 7.11.3, 7.11.8, Appendix 04
Periodic system review summary		N/A	All	All	21 CFR 211, Section 68 b	21 CFR 211, Section 68 b	Section 7.11.13, Appendix 01
Audit reports		All	All	All	21 CFR 820, Section 22; EC Annex 11, No. 13; ISO 13485, Section 8.2.2	21 CFR 820, Section 22; General Principles, 2002, Section 6.2; EC Annex 11, No. 13; ISO 13485, Section 8.2.2	Section 7.11.13

RiskVal Deliverables Compared to Regulatory Requirements and Gamp 4

Deliverable	On the minimum list	RiskVal recommendations			• Predicate rules • Part 11 • CDRH minimum documents • Annex 11 • ISO 13485	• Predicate rules • Part 11 • Discussed in CDRH • Annex 11 • ISO 13485 • ISO 14971	Gamp 4 guidance
		Low-risk systems	Moderate-risk systems	High-risk systems			
Phase 9: Retire the system							
System retirement and record migration report		When records are migrated to a different system during the records-retention period	When records are migrated to a different system during the records-retention period	When records are migrated to a different system during the records-retention period	21 CFR 820 Section 180 b; ISO 13485, Section 4.2.4	21 CFR 820 Section 180 b; ISO 13485, Section 4.2.4	Section 7.11.14

(1) Not needed for existing systems if a system specification is prepared

(2) Not needed for existing systems

(3) 21 CFR 820 Section 70 i states that the validation should be performed according to "an established protocol"; however, it doesn't specifically identify an IQ, OQ, or PQ.

(4) The CDRH guidance document (Section 6.2) doesn't specify an IQ, OQ, or PQ but does list the "validation protocol used" and "test cases and results" as two of the documents the device manufacturer should have.

(5) EC Annex 11, No. 7, doesn't require an IQ, OQ, or PQ but does require the system to be thoroughly tested and confirmed as capable of achieving desired results.

(6) ISO 13485 states that documented procedures should be established for the validation of computer systems and that the results of the validation should be recorded (7.5.2.1). It doesn't specifically require an IQ, OQ, or PQ.

Appendix A

Phase Deliverables and Method Briefs

This appendix consists of the deliverable and method briefs for use in the Computer System Risk Management and Validation Life Cycle. The actual deliverable and method briefs follow the list.

Phase 1—Conceptualize

Deliverables:

Phase 2—Define requirements

Deliverables:

Methods:

Phase 3—Select vendors and systems

Phase 4—Design solutions to issues

Phase 5—Construct solutions to issues

Phase 6—Prepare for use

Phase 7—Qualify the system

Deliverables:

Phase 8—Use in a production environment

Deliverables:

Phase 9—Retire the system

Deliverables:
None

Deliverable 1.1	Validation Policy

Purposes: The company's validation policy is the highest-level validation document. It establishes validation principles and defines requirements for validation. Its scope includes the following types of items: equipment, facilities and utilities, test protocols, processes, and computer systems. The validation policy is formulated before any validations are conducted.

Resources Used: Reference materials used to create this deliverable include:
- *General Principles of Software Validation; Final Guidance for Industry and FDA Staff.* Center for Devices and Radiological Health, Center for Biologics Evaluation and Research, Food and Drug Administration, January 11, 2002.
- *Guidelines on General Principles of Process Validation.* Food and Drug Administration, May 11, 1987.
- R. Timothy Stein. "Validation Policy." Business Performance Associates, 2002. (See *www.bpaconsultants.com.*)

Risk-Based Adjustments: The validation policy is a general policy for the company. It will state that the rigor and intensity of the validation will vary for items of different types and risk levels.

Validation Policy Outline	
Section	**Contents**
1. Purpose	Defines the purpose of the policy
2. Scope	Defines the type of items covered by the policy. Note that a general validation policy will cover all items requiring validation, such as facilities, utilities, processes, test protocols, equipment, and computer systems.
3. Responsibility	Summarizes the responsibilities of the item owner, quality assurance, and support functions such as information technology (IT) and facilities
4. Purpose of validation	■ States the purpose of validation ■ Provides an overview of the validation process
5. When validation is performed	■ Explains validation requirements for processes and equipment used at different stages of the product life cycle (e.g., preclinical) ■ Documents when computer systems must be validated

Section	Contents
6. Requirements for validation processes	Defines the following as requirements for validation processes for different types of items: ■ Creation of a validation master plan ■ Development of validation procedures for the different types of items that further define required practices for validating each type of item ■ A validation approach, tailored to the type of item and integrated with the life cycle of the item, such as computer systems ■ Requirements for acquiring different types of items that must be validated, including vendor qualification
7. Use of validated items	■ Defines requirements for the use of validated items ■ Changes are made using a documented change control process. Descriptions of systems are kept current with changes. ■ User procedures are written. ■ Procedures are required as appropriate for calibrating, maintaining, and supporting validated items. ■ Data are backed up. ■ Proper security is maintained.
8. Validation records	■ Validation records are maintained following established procedures for record management and retention.

Preparation Tips: Develop the validation policy to meet regulatory requirements. Confer with validation experts from other companies as needed.

Nonregulated business need not prepare a validation policy. Ensuring that systems can consistently meet user requirements can be discussed in the IT policy.

Approvals and Signatures:
■ Head of quality assurance

| **Deliverable 1.2** | Computer System Risk Management and Validation Life Cycle Procedure |

Purposes: The purpose of this procedure is to define the requirements and process for developing, selecting, validating, and using computer systems to ensure that systems will function reliably within the anticipated range of operation, risks will be appropriately managed, and systems will be in compliance.

Resources Used: Use relevant internal documentation, such as the validation policy, and external guidance documents, such as:

- *The Good Automated Manufacturing Practices (GAMP) Guide for Validation of Automated Systems in Pharmaceutical Manufacturing, Vol. 4.* The GAMP Institute, December 2001.
- AAMI/American National Standard SW68, Medical Device Software—Software Life Cycle Processes. Association for the Advancement of Medical Instrumentation, Arlington, VA, 2002.
- Grigonis, George J., Edward J. Subak, Jr., and Michael L. Wyrick. "Validation Key Practices for Computer Systems Used in Regulated Operations." *Pharmaceutical Technology,* June 1997.
- IEEE 122070-1996. Standard for Software Life Cycle. Technical Committee on Software Engineering of the IEEE Computer Society, Institute of Electrical and Electronics Engineers, Inc.
- *General Principles of Software Validation; Final Guidance for Industry and FDA Staff.* Center for Devices and Radiological Health, Center for Biologics Evaluation and Research, Food and Drug Administration, January 11, 2002.
- Stein, R. Timothy. "Computer System Risk Management and Validation Life Cycle Procedure." Business Performance Associates, 2002. (See *www.bpaconsultants.com.*)

Risk-Based Adjustments: The computer system risk management and validation life cycle (RiskVal) procedure is a generic methodology. It should identify how the life cycle is used based on the risk level of the system. Information is provided throughout this book about how the risk level affects what should be done (see the tables in chapter 2, and exhibit 12.1), and the rigor and intensity with which the activities are done.

| **RiskVal Procedure Outline** ||
Section	Contents
1. Purpose	Defines the purpose of the procedure
2. Scope	Defines the types of systems covered by the procedure
3. Responsibility	Summarizes the responsibilities of the system owner, validation, quality assurance, information technology (IT), and the project team

Section	Contents
4. Computer system definition	Defines what's included in a computer system
5. Life cycle approach	Explains the purpose for taking a life cycle approach to ensuring the quality of business applications
6. Life cycle phases	Provides a section for each life cycle phase identifying the activities to be performed and the deliverables to be created for systems at various risk levels. The responsibilities of relevant functional areas are defined.
7. Use of legacy systems and exceptions	Discusses how legacy systems will be treated, including how noncompliances with 21 CFR Part 11 will be addressed
8. Appendix	Summarizes in a table the life cycle activities as they apply to off-the-shelf, configurable, and custom systems. Describes how the activities are different for low-, moderate-, and high-risk systems.

Preparation Tips: Use the life cycle as defined in this volume or another source as a template. Form an interdisciplinary team of individuals from validation, IT, and user departments who are, or will soon be, system owners for a major system. Define the life cycle phases and the major deliverables for each phase. For each deliverable, identify which function has primary responsibility, which functions must contribute, and which functions must approve each deliverable. Once the process is agreed, prepare the procedure.

Approvals and Signatures:
- Validation
- Head of quality assurance
- Head of IT
- A representative of the users, such as the head of operations

| Deliverable 1.3 | Information Technology Policy |

Purposes: The information technology (IT) policy defines the company's requirements for managing and using computer systems and the company's IT infrastructure. The requirements are developed to ensure regulatory compliance, reliability and security of communication and computing systems, and the integrity of electronic records.

Resources Used:

■ 21 CFR Part 11—Electronic Records—Electronic Signatures. Food and Drug Administration. *Federal Register,* Vol. 62, No. 54. March 20, 1977.

■ Stein, R. Timothy. "Information Technology Policy." Business Performance Associates, 2004. (See *www.bpaconsultants.com.*)

Risk-Based Adjustments: The IT policy is a general policy for the company. It defines how systems with different risk levels might be acquired, maintained, and used.

IT Policy Outline	
Section	**Contents**
1. Purpose	Defines the purpose of the policy
2. Scope	Defines the type of systems covered by the policy
3. Responsibility	Summarizes the responsibilities of IT and users
4. Responsibilities of users of company computer systems	■ The purpose of company computing resources and general policy on use of systems ■ Limits on software that employees can bring into the computing environment ■ Use of e-mail and the Internet ■ Control of login names and passwords ■ Required user training
5. Control of electronic records and signatures	■ Part 11 regulations that are relevant to the company
6. IT support	■ Help desk ■ Second- and third-level support

Section	Contents
	■ Third-party support ■ Defect tracking and repair ■ System enhancements ■ Change control
7. Network management	■ Security ■ Virus protection ■ Backup and restore ■ Maintenance ■ Response time and performance ■ Data integrity
8. System acquisition and implementation	■ Life cycle approach ■ System selection and purchasing requirements ■ Software development requirements

Preparation Tips: Document the policy that's implicit in current practices. Review and modify it based on state-of-the-art practices that are appropriate for the company. Incorporate relevant Part 11 regulations.

Approvals and Signatures:
■ Head of IT
■ Chief executive of the units covered by the policy
■ Quality assurance

Deliverable 1.4	Requirements for Computer System Validation Plans, Protocols, and Reports Procedure

Purpose: The requirements for computer system validation plans, protocols, and reports procedure provides instructions for creating the major computer system validation deliverables.

Resources Used: To create this deliverable, use relevant internal documentation, such as the validation policy, and external guidance documents, such as:

- *General Principles of Software Validation; Final Guidance for Industry and FDA Staff.* Center for Devices and Radiological Health, Center for Biologics Evaluation and Research, Food and Drug Administration. January 11, 2002.
- *The Good Automated Manufacturing Practices (GAMP) Guide for Validation of Automated Systems in Pharmaceutical Manufacturing,* Vol. 4. The GAMP Institute, December 2001.
- Stein, R. Timothy. "Requirements for Computer System Requirements Validation Plans, Protocols, and Reports." Business Performance Associates, 2003. (See *www.bpaconsultants.com.*)

Risk-Based Adjustments: None. This procedure is a generic one for validation methods. For modifications of validation practices based on system risk, see deliverable 1.2, Computer System Risk Management and Validation Life Cycle (RiskVal) Procedure.

Requirements for Computer System Validation Plans, Protocols, and Reports Procedure Outline	
Section	**Contents**
1. Purpose	Define the purpose of the procedure.
2. Scope	Define the types of systems covered by the procedure and what's included in a computer system.
3. Reference documents	List documents that are referenced in the text (i.e., documents that must be used to meet the requirements specified in this procedure).
4. Definitions	Provide definitions of terms that readers aren't expected to understand or that have a special meaning in regard to this document.
5. Responsibilities	Summarize the responsibilities of the system owner, validation, information technology, and project team.
6. Validation plan	■ Plan content requirements. ■ Plan approval requirements.

Section	Contents
7. Validation protocols and reports	■ Describe required prerequisites, content, and approval requirements for installation, operational, and performance qualifications. ■ Describe the content and approval requirements for protocol reports. ■ Describe the content and approval requirements for the final validation report.
8. Revalidation	■ Define the requirement to include appropriate revalidation as part of the change-control procedure. ■ Define the circumstances under which a full revalidation is required.
9. Concurrent validation	Describe the requirements for performing a concurrent validation for a system that's already in use.
10. Validation records	State that validation records are maintained following established procedures for record management and retention.

Preparation Tips: Limit the requirements for computer system validation plans, protocols, and reports procedure to defining the detailed requirements for these deliverables. Discuss the context of these deliverables and when they're required in the RiskVal procedure.

Prepare templates for each of these reports to make it easier for employees to create them. If the templates are available, the details of the content requirements for validation plans, protocols, and reports don't have to be spelled out in the procedure.

Approvals and Signatures:
■ Validation
■ Head of quality assurance

| Deliverable 1.5 | Computer System Project Proposal |

Purposes: A computer system project proposal provides information about the system that management needs to authorize the initiation of a formal project. Information is given on the value of the system, the risks it poses, the applicability of 21 CFR Part 11 regulations, whether the system must be validated, and the magnitude of the implementation.

Resources Used:
- A computer system project proposal form can be developed.
- Stein, R. Timothy. "Computer System Project Proposal." Business Performance Associates, 2002. (See *bpaconsultants.com*.)

Risk-Based Adjustments: The risk level of the system doesn't affect the content of the computer system project proposal.

Computer System Project Proposal Outline	
Section	**Contents**
1. System information	■ System name ■ Proposal date ■ System owner ■ Owner department ■ Project team members
2. Users	Organizations that will use the system and the approximate number of users
3. System description	Information on the type of application and supporting hardware and software. The initial system description may be sketchy until further research is conducted and decisions are made.
4. Intended uses	■ Vision statement (i.e., the major purposes for the system and the business need that it addresses) ■ Data to be input and/or captured, stored, and/or retrieved ■ Business functions to be performed with the system, including data manipulation and calculations
5. Part 11 applicability	■ Quality records required by predicate rules that are created, maintained, and retrieved ■ Electronic signatures used ■ State whether Part 11 applies

Section	Contents
6. Risk level	The level of risk associated with potential system failure
7. Planned implementation	■ Specify what types and/or groups of users will use which parts of the system, over what time period. ■ Identify, at a high level, the training that will be needed by users, administrators, and information technology staff.
8. Required validation	Describe, at a high level, what parts of the system must be validated and provide any preliminary ideas on the validation approach
9. Approvals	Signature lines

Preparation Tips: The system owner has primary responsibility for creating the document. However, if the system owner teams with information technology (IT) and validation to create the proposal, it will probably be more accurate.

Approvals and Signatures: Prior to submitting the proposal to senior management, the following functions approve the proposal:

■ System owner
■ Validation
■ Information technology
■ Business sponsor

The signatures required to approve the proposal depend upon the risk and cost. Approvals might also be required from:

■ Executive management with authority to approve projects at the cost involved
■ Quality assurance
■ The executive responsible for IT

Deliverable 2.1	User Requirements

Purposes: The purpose of this deliverable is to document users' requirements for the system.

Documented requirements are the foundation of a computer system life cycle. They're essential for meeting user needs, ensuring a system's quality, managing the risks of system failure, and validating a system's effectiveness. The user requirements document also serves as the basis for evaluating systems during selection, performing detailed risk assessment, and developing tests of the system (i.e., the validation tests).

Resources Used: Methods that can be used to develop user requirements are discussed in chapter 4. They include:
- Understanding available systems and developing requirements based on aspects of those systems that reflect your requirements
- Interviewing users to determine their needs and evaluating the importance of a possible system's features and functions
- Asking colleagues from other companies that use such systems to describe what they found important and why
- Preparing process flowcharts of current business practices
- Performing use-case analysis (see method 2.1)

Several standards and guidance document identify areas that ought to be covered by user requirements:
- Parenteral Drug Association (PDA) Committee on Validation of Computer-Related Systems. Technical Report No. 18, "Validation of Computer-Related System," *PDA Journal of Pharmaceutical Science and Technology*, Volume 49, Number 1. January-February 1995 Supplement, Appendix 1.
- *Guidance for Industry Part 11, Electronic Records; Electronic Signatures—Scope and Application*, Section 6.2. U.S. Department of Health and Human Services, Food and Drug Administration, August 2003.
- ANSI/AAMI SW68:2001. Medical Device Software—Software Life Cycle Processes, Section 5.1.2. Association for the Advancement of Medical Instrumentation, 2001.
- IEEE Standard 830-1998, IEEE Recommended Practice for Software Requirements Specification. Software Engineering Standards Committee of the IEE Computer Society, October 1998.

Risk-Based Adjustments: The user requirements' level of detail isn't driven by system risk level but rather by business and regulatory needs to define what the system must do and how it must do it. Documented user requirements are a must for good system management practices and system validation.

User Requirements Outline	
Section	**Contents**
1. Cover page	■ Title. Include the type of application for which the requirements are being developed ■ Report date ■ Report author ■ Signature lines ■ Identification of your company and, if relevant, the division conducting the selection
2. Purpose and scope	■ The type of system for which the requirements are being developed
3. Background	■ Names of the system owner and members of the project team ■ Intended uses of the system (see deliverable 1.5, Computer System Project Proposal) ■ Background information regarding the definition of user requirements, such as: 　□ Description of users 　□ Conditions of use 　□ Environmental factors 　□ System integration needs
4. User requirements	*Note:* User requirements can be organized in any manner that fits the system. This list follows the types of requirements described in chapter 4. ■ System functionality ■ Information input and output integrations ■ Performance ■ Safety requirements ■ Security ■ Physical requirements ■ Managing legacy data ■ Regulatory requirements or standards

Preparation Tips: Prepare requirements in a table. Use columns for requirement numbers, the requirement statements, and the criticality ratings. Using a table format or a spreadsheet will make it much easier to create the traceability matrix in phase 7. Assign each requirement a separate number (see chapter 4).

Approvals and Signatures:
■ Report author
■ System owner
■ Validation
■ Quality assurance
■ Other members of the project team as appropriate

<table>
<tr><td>**Deliverable 2.2**</td><td>Technical Requirements</td></tr>
</table>

Purpose: The purpose of this deliverable is to document technical requirements for a system. Technical requirements are defined to ensure that:

- The technical aspects of the system will support the ability to meet user requirements.
- Hardware and software are leveraged to the extent possible.
- The company's technical staff has the capability of supporting the system.

Resources Used: Table 4.4 presents an extensive list of the type of items that might be included in technical requirements. For a detailed description of technical requirements for workstations, servers, and infrastructure services, see, Stein, R. Timothy. "Technical Requirements Template." Business Performance Associates, 2005. (See *www.bpaconsultants.com.*)

Risk-Based Adjustments: Technical requirements don't need to be defined if the system will be used with existing hardware and system software. The technical requirements' level of detail is driven not by the system risk level but by technical and business needs to define hardware and system software.

Technical Requirements Outline	
Section	**Contents**
1. Cover page	■ Title. Include the type of application for which the requirements are being developed. ■ Report date ■ Report author ■ Signature lines ■ Identification of your company and, if relevant, the division conducting the selection
2. Purpose and scope	The type of system for which the requirements are being developed

3. Background	■ Names of the system owner and members of the project team
	■ Intended uses of the system (see deliverable 1.5, Computer System Project Proposal).
	■ Background information regarding the definition of technical requirements, such as:
	  □ Description of users
	  □ Conditions of use
	  □ Environmental factors
	  □ System integration needs
	  □ Factors that might affect system performance

Section	Contents
4. Technical requirements	*Note:* Technical requirements can be organized in any manner that fits the system. This list follows the types of technical requirements described in chapter 4. ■ Client workstation ■ Server ■ Database ■ System integration ■ Communication ■ Security ■ Network accessibility and availability ■ Internet access by users and/or the system ■ Backup and recovery ■ Data archive ■ Information technology service and support

Preparation Tips: Some organizations develop a checklist or form stating requirement options that can be checked or recorded. The requirements can also be listed in tabular form. Use columns for requirement numbers, the requirement statements, and the criticality ratings.

Assign a separate number to each requirement. The numbers will be used in traceability matrices to track requirements to steps in the test (i.e., validation) protocols. With custom systems, requirements can also be traced to design elements as well as specific programs.

Use a numbering scheme that's easy to work with and reference in other documents. The easiest format is a sequential numbering of requirements, but systems that show the organization of and relationships between requirements, such as "1.1.1," can also be used.

Approvals and Signatures:
■ Report author
■ Validation
■ Information technology
■ System owner (if appropriate)
■ Other members of the project team as appropriate

Deliverable 2.3	Vendor Organizational Requirements

Purpose: The purpose of this deliverable is to document organizational requirements for vendors that will be relied upon for long-term product support or that need specific industry expertise.

The objective of such requirements is to ensure that vendors have the expertise needed to understand the regulations placed on your industry; make a long-term, strategic commitment to the product or service; and maintain financial stability.

Resources Used: Table 4.5 presents a list of typical vendor organizational requirements.

Risk-Based Adjustments: Vendor organizational requirements aren't needed if the product to be purchased can be easily substituted, if ongoing support is available from third parties, or if there are no special product requirements related to your industry. The need for vendor organizational requirements isn't driven by other risk considerations.

Vendor Organizational Requirements Outline	
Section	**Contents**
1. Cover page	■ Title. Include the type of application for which the requirements are being developed. ■ Report date ■ Report author ■ Signature lines ■ Identification of your company and, if relevant, the division conducting the selection
2. Purpose and scope	The type of system for which the requirements are being developed

3. Background	■ System owner and members of the project team
	■ Intended uses of the system; (see deliverable 1.5, Computer System Project Proposal).
	■ Background information regarding the need for vendor organizational requirements, such as:
	  ☐ Need for a long-term vendor relationship
	  ☐ Industry-related product requirements or regulations
	  ☐ The availability of third-party provided product support

4. Vendor organizational requirements	List of vendor organizational requirements

Preparation Tips: Assign a separate number to each requirement.

Approvals and Signatures:
- Report author
- System owner
- Validation
- Other members of the project team as appropriate

Method 2.1	Use-Case Analysis

Purpose: Use-case analysis is a method of developing user requirements from users' descriptions of how they envision interacting with the system, and what functions they expect the system to perform during that interaction.

Using Use-Case Analysis in the Life Cycle		
Life cycle phase	**Use**	**Notes**
Phase 2, define requirements	Use-case analysis is used to identify user requirements.	This method is used in conjunction with other methods of developing user requirements as described in chapter 4.

Method: A use case is developed during a meeting that includes a user(s), the system owner, and others who are familiar with business systems. A facilitator works with the team as appropriate to guide it through the process. The user describes how he or she envisions using the system in a specific scenario. The interactions between the user and the system are defined, as are the functions that the system performs. Participants then extract user requirements from the use case. The scenario is varied to match other situations in which the system is used in a similar manner, and the use case is extended to those situations. Additional use cases are created with different types of users from scenarios based on how they'll use the system.

Step	Actions
Prepare	■ The process owner prepares a high-level list of intended uses of the system. The list provided in deliverable 1.5, Computer System Project Proposal, can be used or expanded. ■ Identify situations where a use-case analysis might help define user requirements. ■ Determine whom to include in each use-case session. Ask users to prepare by thinking about how they see themselves using the system to perform a task, and what they expect the system to do during that process.
Conduct a use-case session	■ Carefully explain that the purpose of the use case is to determine underlying system requirements that will be extracted from the user's description. The requirements will only be as specific as necessary to determine what the system must do and how. ■ Define an exact scenario under which the user would use the system to perform a designated task. Ask the user to describe what he or she imagines doing to perform the task with the system, and what he or she expects the system to do while in use.

Step	Actions
	■ Determine what preconditions are needed for the system to perform the functions the user describes. Preconditions include, for example, a security check to confirm that the user is authorized to perform the tasks and required data that are presumed to be in the database. ■ Determine any necessary conditions of the system after the task is completed (i.e., what has changed and what must remain unchanged). ■ Create a list of user requirements for the system that are implicit in the user's description of his or her interface with the system and its performance. Be sure to identify the underlying capability required of the system and to word the requirement at a level of detail appropriate to what the system must do. Don't get locked into defining the requirement exactly as a user imagines the system might work. Make the statement as general as possible. ■ Change aspects of the scenario to match a different situation under which a user might perform the same task. Describe the use of the system and any differences in system functioning as depicted above, and extract any new user requirements. ■ Repeat the use-case analysis as needed to cover additional uses or types of users.
Meeting follow-up	A designated person researches or clarifies any open questions. The participants reconvene if necessary to consider the new information. Alternatively, the individual researching the issues can modify the use-case analysis and review the changes with the system owner.
Report preparation	A designated person drafts the use case report. Participants review the report as appropriate.

Deliverables: Use case report

References: Wiegers, Karl E. *Software Requirements*. Microsoft Press, 1999.

Deliverable 3.1	Technical Assessment of Alternatives Report

Purposes: The technical assessment of alternatives report summarizes how well the alternative solutions meet the technical requirements. The term "solution" includes the entire system, that is, the combination of the application and the system software and hardware that would be used to operate the application. An "alternative solution" is the combination of one of the applications being evaluated with the specific hardware and system software that the organization would use to operate that application.

Resources Used: Technical information obtained when investigating the products, for example, information about the product, product literature and technical specifications, conversations with representatives from the vendor, and conversations with employeess from other organizations that are using the application.

Risk-Based Adjustments: A formal technical assessment of alternatives report isn't needed for low-risk systems.

Technical Assessment of Alternatives Report Outline	
Section	**Contents**
1. Cover page	■ Title. Include the type of solutions being evaluated. ■ Report date ■ Report author ■ Signature lines
2. Introduction	■ Identification of your company and, if relevant, the division conducting the selection ■ Identification of the type of system for which the alternative solutions are being evaluated ■ Identification of the individuals involved in the assessment ■ Overview of the evaluation processes

3. Summary of how well each solution meets technical requirements	■ Prepare a section for each solution that includes:
	  ☐ Identification of the sources of the information obtained about a solution (e.g., product literature, industry report, and discussion with representatives of the company)
	  ☐ A short description of the important technical aspects of the solution (e.g., type of platform and unique aspects of its architecture)
	  ☐ Overall rating of technical requirements

Section	Contents
	☐ Discussion of solution's strengths and weaknesses, especially regarding the most important technical requirements. Identification of any technical requirements with associated moderate or high risks that the solution doesn't meet. ■ Compare the solutions on their ability to meet technical requirements.
4. Conclusion	■ Conclusions regarding the ability of each solution to meet technical requirements ■ Identification of any solution that the selection committee has eliminated from further consideration and why
5. Appendices	■ Ratings of each solution on its ability to meet each technical requirement, as applicable

Preparation Tips: Discuss only significant differences in the report. Readers can consult the attachments for information on less important requirements.

Approvals and Signatures:
■ Report author
■ Members of the selection committee who participated in the assessment

| Deliverable 3.2 | User Assessment of Alternatives Report |

Purposes: The user assessment of alternatives report summarizes users' evaluations of how well competing applications meet user requirements, and how well competing vendors meet vendor requirements.

Resources Used: Information obtained about vendors during the initial screening, vendor demonstrations, demonstration CD evaluations, customer demonstrations, reference checking, conversations with vendor representatives, and other research.

Risk-Based Adjustments: A user assessment of alternatives report isn't needed for low-risk systems. The strengths and weaknesses of the application regarding the most important user and vendor requirements can be included in deliverable 3.5, the system selection report.

User Assessment of Alternatives Report Outline	
Section	**Contents**
1. Cover page	■ Title. Include the type of applications being evaluated ■ Report date ■ Report author ■ Signature lines
2. Introduction	■ Identification of your company and, if relevant, the division conducting the selection ■ Identification of the type of system for which the applications are being evaluated ■ Identification of the selection committee members ■ Overview of the application and vendor evaluation processes

3. Summary of how well each application meets user requirements	■ Prepare a section for each solution that includes:
	  □ Identification of the sources of information obtained on that application (e.g., vendor demonstrations, demo CD, product literature, industry report, customer references, or demonstrations)
	  □ A short description of the application (e.g., type of platform, unique aspects of its architecture, when it was released, its installed base, number of companies using it in your industry, and summary of third-party assessments)
	  □ Overall rating on user requirements
	  □ Discussion of strengths and weaknesses of the application, especially regarding the most important user requirements. Identification of

Section	Contents
	any user requirements with associated moderate or high risks that the application doesn't meet. ■ Compare the applications on their ability to meet user requirements.

4. Summary of how well each vendor meets the vendor organizational requirements	■ Prepare a section on each vendor that includes:
	  □ Identification of the information sources concerning the vendor who created the application (e.g., company Web site, company literature, industry report, company contacts, and industry journals)
	  □ A short description of the company and its history (e.g., when it was founded, ownership, size, financial performance and/or funding, other applications sold, product strategy, and importance of the application to the company)
	  □ Overall rating on the vendor requirements
	  □ Discussion of strengths and weaknesses of the vendor, especially regarding the most important vendor requirements
	
	■ Comparison of the vendors on their ability to meet the vendor requirements

5. Conclusion	■ Conclusions regarding the ability of each application to meet user requirements ■ Conclusions regarding each vendor's ability to meet vendor requirements ■ Identification of any application or vendor that the selection committee has eliminated and why
6. Appendices	■ Ratings of each application on its ability to meet each user requirement as applicable (e.g., from vendor and/or customer demonstrations) ■ Ratings of each company on its ability to meet each business requirement (as applicable)

Preparation Tips: Discuss only significant differences in the report. Readers can consult the attachments for information on less important requirements.

Approvals and Signatures:
■ Report author
■ Members of the selection committee who participated in the assessment

| Deliverable 3.3 | Vendor Audit Report |

Purpose: The vendor audit report summarizes the findings of the audit and identifies any nonconformances.

Resources Used: If a vendor audit checklist such as the one described in method 3.1 is used to conduct the audit and record the audit findings, the completed checklist can be used to prepare the report. If a checklist isn't used, information gathered during the audit as well as audit notes are used to prepare the report.

Risk-Based Adjustments: A vendor audit isn't recommended for low-risk systems. The audit report is the same for moderate- and high-risk systems.

Vendor Audit Report Outline	
Section	**Contents**
1. Cover page	■ Title. Include the name of the vendor audited. ■ Report date ■ Report author ■ Signature lines ■ Identification of your company and, if relevant, the division conducting the selection
2. Introduction	■ Vendor address, contact name, and phone number ■ The system for which the vendors is being qualified ■ Members of the audit team ■ The audit scope: facility(ies) audited, audited areas or departments within the facility, aspects of the quality system, and development process that were audited ■ Dates when the audit was conducted ■ Overview of the audit process ■ Identification of any reference documents and/or standards against which the audit was conducted and assessments made

3. Audit findings and conclusions	■ Organization of the audit findings by aspects of the development life cycle or by organizational unit
	■ For each subsection of audit findings (i.e., each aspect of the life cycle or quality system), report the following information:
	  □ Individuals interviewed
	  □ Materials reviewed

Section	Contents
	☐ Summary of the vendor's policies, procedures, and practices that meet expectations ☐ Nonconformances (i.e., expected aspects of the development life cycle or quality system that weren't present, weren't properly documented, or weren't properly practiced) ☐ Observations (i.e., items of concern that aren't nonconformances)
4. Summary of findings	■ A high-level summary of areas of compliance ■ List of nonconformances ■ An audit score, or the auditor's level of confidence that the vendor's products are likely to be at an appropriate quality level ■ If the likelihood of a system failure will be based on the vendor's software development process in phase 4's detailed risk analysis, the auditor can recommend a likelihood of failure rating to use (see appendix C).
5. Appendices	Completed checklists, as appropriate

Preparation Tips: Recommendations for improvement aren't included in the audit report. The report is prepared by the auditors. Once the report is finished, the auditors should meet with the quality manager and prepare feedback for the vendor, including any requests for corrective action.

The report is limited to audit findings. The outcome of the vendor qualification process (i.e., to qualify, conditionally qualify, or disqualify the vendor) is recorded on deliverable 3.4, the vendor qualification form.

Approvals and Signatures:
■ Report author
■ Other auditors

Deliverable 3.4 | Vendor Qualification Form

Purposes: The vendor qualification form records the qualification decision and its justification for a vendor. The report also reviews the qualification process used, summarizes the information obtained, and defines the requirements to be met if the qualification was conditional.

Resources Used: The vendor audit report and vendor survey provide much of the information needed to determine if an organization is an appropriate vendor. If the system has been used by the organization for a long period of time, any data on the system's performance is also important.

Risk-Based Adjustments: A vendor qualification form is completed for all vendors that are evaluated, regardless of their products' risk levels. The activities performed during the evaluation and information gathered will vary based on the type of product and associated risk.

Vendor Qualification Form Outline	
Section	**Contents**
1. Basic vendor information	■ Vendor name and location ■ Type of vendor (see table 5.3) ■ Vendor contact information ■ Report date ■ Report author ■ Product for which the evaluation was performed ■ Risk level of the vendor's products and services
2. Qualification activities required based on risk level	Check the evaluation activities that are required based on risk level (see table 5.3).
3. Summary of the qualification process	■ Summarize the qualification activities performed (the form could include a list that can be checked). ■ Include a list of the vendor's processes (including the documentation) that were reviewed.
4. Qualification decision	■ Indicate if the vendor is certified, conditionally certified, or disqualified. ■ If the qualification is conditional, indicate the requirements that must be met to change the status to qualified. ■ Provide a justification for the decision. ■ Effective date

Section	Contents
5. Signatures	See the "Approvals and Signatures" section below
6. Appendices	■ The original of the audit report, if an audit was conducted ■ The original of the vendor survey, if one was completed ■ Copies of any registration certifications (e.g., ISO 9001:2000), if provided ■ Copies of any procedures provided by the vendor and used in reaching the certification decision

Preparation Tips: Create a summary sheet of the activities performed. Rely on attached reports and material to provide backup information.

Approvals and Signatures:
■ The quality professional making the qualification decision
■ Other signatories might include someone from purchasing and/or information technology

| Deliverable 3.5 | System Selection Report |

Purpose: The system selection report summarizes the selection process. It documents the selection team's preference and reasons for the selection. The report is prepared to gain management approval to proceed with contract negotiations to purchase the preferred application.

Resources Used: Information for the system selection report comes from the selection activities and the following deliverables:
- Technical assessment of alternatives (see deliverable 3.1)
- User assessment of alternatives (see deliverable 3.2)
- Vendor qualification form (see deliverable 3 .4)

Risk-Based Adjustments: The system selection report for low-risk systems can be limited to descriptions of the differences between the applications for the most important requirements. These differences can be documented in a memo to file rather than a formal report.

System Selection Report Outline	
Section	**Contents**
1. **Cover page**	■ Title. Include the type of applications evaluated ■ Report date ■ Report author ■ Signature lines ■ Identification of your company and, if relevant, the division conducting the selection
2. **Introduction**	■ Identification of the system for which the applications are being evaluated ■ Discussion of the application's vision statement ■ Identification of the selection committee members ■ Overview of the selection process
3. **The selection committee's preference and reasoning**	■ Selection committee's conclusion as to which application ought to be purchased ■ Overall ratings of the applications and vendors reviewed for user, business, and technical requirements ■ A discussion about why the selected application is preferred, including the most important differences between the choices on user, business, and technical requirements, and other items of critical importance

Section	Contents
4. Comparison on costs	■ A cost comparison of the different applications ■ Identification of the time required of internal resources for implementing and validating the system. Estimates normally include members of the following departments: ☐ Users ☐ Information technology ☐ Quality assurance ☐ Validation
5. Vendor qualification	■ The status (i.e., qualified, conditionally qualified, disqualified) of each vendor ■ Any action items that must be addressed by the chosen vendor ■ The results of the evaluation of known defects, if applicable
6. Special contractual terms to negotiate	Identification of any special contractual terms that must be negotiated and the reasons why the terms are important
7. Appendices	■ Technical assessment of alternatives (see deliverable 3.1) ■ User assessment of alternatives (see deliverable 3.2) ■ Vendor qualification forms (see deliverable 3.4)

Preparation Tips: Draw heavily from the conclusion sections of deliverable 3.2, User Assessment of Alternatives, and deliverable 3.1, Technical Assessment of Alternatives.

Approvals and Signatures:
■ Report author
■ Members of the selection committee who participated in the assessment

Method 3.1	Assessment of Vendor Software Development

Purpose: The material provided below can be used to develop a survey for obtaining information from a software developer or for developing an audit checklist. Both items, with appropriate adaptation, would apply to developers of commercial or custom software.

Use of Vendor Questionnaire or Audit Form in the Life Cycle

Life cycle phase	Use	Notes
Phase 3: Select vendors and systems	One of the major activities in phase 3 is qualifying vendors. Two of the components of the vendor qualification process described in table 5.3 are the vendor survey and the on-site vendor audit.	This method brief identifies software development as well as verification and validation activities that can be included in a vendor survey or audit form.

Method; Prepare a vendor survey by formulating questions from the material below. Create an audit checklist by identifying the development activities that must be audited and the deliverables from those activities.

Assessment of Vendor Software Development

Development phase or activity	Practice to audit
Established quality system	
Formal quality system	■ Is a documented quality system in place? ■ Has that system been registered by a third party as complying with a quality system standard (e.g., ISO 9001:2000)?
Quality manual	■ Has a quality manual been prepared, approved, and implemented?
Responsibilities and authority	■ Has management defined the roles and responsibilities for quality and given the responsible functions independence and authority to act as necessary to ensure quality products?
Company resources	■ Are the needed resources (including people, tools, and infrastructure) in place to ensure a quality product?
Contract review	■ Are contracts reviewed to ensure that customer requirements are defined (including promises made to customers)? ■ Are contracts reviewed to ensure that the customer's requirements can be met and that promises made to the customer can be met?
Quality system internal audits	■ Are internal audits of the quality system performed by independent auditors?
Corrective action	■ Are quality issues tracked and resolved through a corrective-action system? Are corrective actions closed in a timely manner?
Training	■ Do training requirements exist for employees and/or job classes? Is training performed to the defined requirements? Are training records up to date? ■ Have employees been trained as required?
Software development life cycle	■ Has a software development life cycle been documented, implemented, and maintained?

Development phase or activity	Practice to audit
Management reviews	■ Are management reviews of the quality system conducted on a defined schedule?
Phase 1: Plan	
Management approval process	■ Is a process in place for management approval of development projects?
Project organization	■ How are resources for a development project organized? ■ Is there a project manager? Is a team assigned? ■ Does the team include someone from software verification and validation (or quality control or quality assurance)? ■ How many people are assigned to work on developing a new revision on the software you're evaluating? ■ How many are assigned to work on defect support (i.e., bug repair) of the software you're evaluating? ■ How many are assigned to provide call center support?
Design input sources	■ How are design inputs gathered? ■ What sources are used? ■ Are inputs obtained from current or potential users? ■ Will such input provide the critical information needed to ensure that the application would meet the needs of your industry?
Design input assessment	■ How are decisions made about what to include in a new release? ■ How are decisions made on which defects to repair in the next release? ■ How are the design inputs evaluated?
Design input deliverables	■ Are product objectives formulated? ■ What deliverables are created that define what will be in the new product? ■ Is a market requirements document prepared?
Feasibility	■ Are feasibility studies conducted or pilots used to test out new ideas or concepts?
Project planning	■ Are plans created for development projects? ■ Do the plans include management review of the project at key points of the project?
Risk management	■ Has a risk assessment been performed? ■ Has the system's risk level been established? ■ Has a risk management plan been developed if the system is of moderate to high risk?
Verification and validation plan	■ Is a high-level verification and validation plan prepared? Are verification and validation activities selected based on the system's risk level?
Phase 2: Define requirements	
Methods used to define requirements	■ Is a defined methodology or process used to create the software requirements? ■ How are the design inputs tied into the documented software requirements?
Functional and/or performance requirements	■ Are user or functional and performance requirements documented, reviewed, and approved before development starts? ■ Do the requirements include hardware, operator, user, and software interface requirements? ■ What sources are used to define these requirements? ■ What input is obtained from current or future users? ■ Were the results of a risk assessment used when the user, functional, and/or performance requirements were developed?
Technical requirements	■ Are technical requirements defined in advance (e.g., development platform, database platform, and operating system)?

(continues)

Method 3.1	Assessment of Vendor Software Development (continued)

Development phase or activity	Practice to audit
Functional specification	■ Is a functional specification developed to state how the application will meet each of the user requirements?
Criticality assessment	■ Has the criticality of requirements been assessed to identify key performance or critical areas of the software?
Requirements review	■ Has formal inspection of the requirements been conducted
Phase 3: Select vendors and systems	
Qualifications of internal developers	■ How is the development team selected? ■ What knowledge, education, and experience are required? ■ Are the criteria followed? ■ Are members of the development team adequately trained and experienced?
Qualifications of contractors and vendors	■ Are vendors (e.g., service contractors and others) that might affect the product's quality appropriately evaluated and approved? ■ Is there an approved vendor list?
Management of vendors and contractors	■ How are vendors managed? ■ How are development life cycle requirements communicated to contract developers? ■ Is there a quality agreement signed by contract developers that specifies the use of a defined life cycle or specific engineering practices? ■ What steps are taken to ensure that the work done by contractors is at an adequate level of quality? ■ Are contract developers required to follow the vendor's life cycle? ■ If so, are they trained on it? ■ How are software requirements communicated to contractors? ■ Is vendor performance periodically reviewed? ■ Is there a mechanism for providing feedback and getting vendors to make needed improvements? ■ How can vendors be decertified?
System test plan generation	■ Has a high-level test plan been developed for verifying, in the development environment, that the software will satisfy system objectives? ■ Have system test criteria been agreed upon?
Acceptance test plan generation	■ Has an acceptance test plan been created to determine if the software meets its requirements in an operational environment (e.g., at beta sites)? ■ Have acceptance requirements been agreed upon?
Phase 4: Design the system	
High-level system design	■ Has a high-level design been created? ■ Does it provide a description of the application's structure?

Detailed design	■ Review the detailed design for the system. Does it map out the structure of the application (e.g., units or modules, components, subsystems, and systems)?
	■ Does the detailed design include for each module, component, subsystem, and system:
	  ☐ Objectives
	  ☐ Needed inputs
	  ☐ Analyses and/or operations to be performed on the data
	  ☐ Outputs of analyses

Development phase or activity	Practice to audit
	■ Is there a traceability matrix that relates every software requirement to the detailed design? ■ Has the information flow been diagramed for the system? ■ Has the results of the risk assessment or management efforts been used in designing the system?
Database design	■ Has the database been designed? ■ Has a data dictionary been prepared?
Quality reviews	■ Has an informal group design review been conducted? ■ Has a formal design walk-through or inspection been conducted? ■ Have the results of the design reviews been appropriately recorded and tracked? ■ Have issues been resolved?
Module or component level test plan	■ Have test plans been developed at the module or component level to determine if each correctly meets its requirements? ■ Has a traceability matrix been created that traces requirements for modules or components specified in the detailed design to the module or component test plan and test cases?
Integration test plan	■ Is integration testing planned to determine if software modules, components, and subsystems work together to comply with increasingly larger sets of functional requirements? ■ Has a traceability matrix been created that traces requirements specified in the high-level design for subsystems to integration test plans and cases?
Phase 5: Build the system	

Defect prevention methods	■ What defect prevention methods are in use?
	■ Have coding standards or conventions been agreed to?
	  ☐ Are they in use?
	  ☐ How are they enforced?
	■ Is a library of highly reliable modules kept in a controlled library for reuse in new systems?
	■ Are tested and reliable code-generation tools used?
	■ Is data flow analyzed and diagramed?
	■ Are audits conducted of engineering practices against procedures, such as:
	  ☐ Verification that deliverables required by the development life cycle are being created, reviewed, and approved per the procedure
	  ☐ Verification that the deliverables required as the output of one phase are approved before the beginning of subsequent phase
	  ☐ Review of the deliverables against content requirements
	  ☐ Verification that documents created upstream are used as intended later in the process (e.g., coding is done per the design)
	  ☐ Verification that coding conventions are followed
	  ☐ Verification that the configuration management of software revisions is effective
	  ☐ Verification that bug reporting, tracking, and repair is performed following the defined process
	  ☐ Verification that software is released following the release process

Defect detection tools	■ What defect detection methods are in use:
	  ☐ Requirement reviews and/or walk-throughs?
	  ☐ Design checks by the author?

(continues)

Method 3.1	Assessment of Vendor Software Development (continued)

Development phase or activity	Practice to audit
	☐ Formal walk-throughs or reviews of the design? ☐ Code checks by the author? ☐ Formal code reviews or walk-throughs? ☐ Test walk-throughs? ☐ Test readiness review? ☐ Documentation review?
Code documentation	■ Is a header included in each program that provides information about the programmer, explains the objectives of the module or component, defines inputs and outputs, and annotates the changes made in various revisions? ■ Are sufficient comments provided in the programs to explain each program's logic and facilitate defect identification and troubleshooting?
Code traceability	■ Is each program traceable back to the detailed design and ultimately to the user and/or functional requirements? ■ Is there traceability from the detailed design to the source code?
Control of code	■ How is source code controlled? ■ Is a configuration management tool used to maintain version control of the software and system configurations?
Test development	■ Are formal tests and test procedures developed and documented for module or component testing, integration testing, system testing, and acceptance testing?
Test execution	■ Has testing been done for modules or components, integration testing, system testing, and acceptance testing?
Repair of defects found during development	■ Are defects discovered during testing logged? ■ What process is used to determine if the defect will be corrected? ■ How is the resolution of defects found during testing tracked? ■ What classifications are used to identify the severity of a defect? ■ What guidelines are used for fixing defects at the various severity levels? ■ Are the guidelines adhered to? ■ Will the defect-repair practices result in the quality of software your organization needs? ■ Is module or component testing performed on defect repairs? ■ Is integration testing performed on defect repairs? ■ Is regression testing performed on defect repairs?

Preparation of technical documentation	■ Is sufficient documentation included in programs to facilitate defect identification and troubleshooting?
	■ Are changes made to programs noted in the program?
	■ Does the system documentation contain the information needed to maintain the system, including:
	  ☐ Capabilities and known limitations
	  ☐ High-level and detailed designs
	  ☐ Lists of all components, including programs and their interrelationships
	  ☐ Data dictionary and database structure
	  ☐ Installation, operation, and maintenance instructions
	■ Is technical documentation up-to-date with the latest changes to the system? Is technical documentation complete and easy to use?
	■ Is technical documentation controlled under configuration management?
	■ Has technical documentation been tested and/or reviewed for accuracy and completeness?

Development phase or activity	Practice to audit
Preparation of user documentation	■ Has user documentation been written for the system? ■ Is user documentation up-to-date with the latest changes to the system? ■ Is user documentation complete and easy to use? ■ Is user documentation controlled under configuration management? ■ Has user documentation been tested and/or reviewed for accuracy and completeness?
Acceptance testing	■ What quality standards are applied to determine if the code can be released for alpha tests? ■ What quality standards are applied to determine if the code can be released for beta sites? ■ Has a procedure been developed for obtaining and managing feedback from alpha and beta sights? ■ How are identified defects at alpha and beta sites tracked and resolved? ■ Is performance monitoring used at alpha and/or beta sites to determine whether the system and software performance requirements are met?
Software release	■ Has a formal release process been documented? ■ What quality standards are applied to determine if the code can be released for commercial use? ■ What level of defect is permitted when code is released? ■ Is a physical audit conducted to ensure internal consistency of the software, its documentation, and its readiness for delivery?
Phase 6: Customer support	

Supportive services	■ What services are available to customers:
	  ☐ Installation?
	  ☐ Integration support?
	  ☐ Customization?
	  ☐ Training of application administrators?
	  ☐ Training of end-users?
	  ☐ Technical training?

Defect support	■ What defect support services are available for customers? ■ How are defects recorded? ■ How are they tracked once they're reported? ■ How is the severity of defects determined? ■ What criteria are used to determine if and when defects will be corrected? ■ What type of testing is done on a defect repair? Is integration and regression testing performed to determine the effect of a repair on other parts of the system? ■ Are records kept of defect processing, repair, and testing? ■ Are the defects of each level of severity repaired within the time frames specified in documented procedures?
Information on known defects	■ How are customers notified of known solutions? ■ Is a defect database, as well as known fixes, available online? ■ How are patches distributed to customers? ■ Are changes to the system downloaded without the customers' knowledge?
Software security	■ What security is in place to protect code that's under development as well as the masters for released software? ■ Is there a software security procedure in place? ■ Is the security procedure followed? ■ What physical security measures are taken to protect servers and network equipment? ■ What measures are taken to protect software from viruses and attack?

(continues)

| Method 3.1 | Assessment of Vendor Software Development (continued) |

Development phase or activity	Practice to audit
Backup and restore	■ Is a written backup and restore procedure in place? ■ Have the backup and restore processes been validated? ■ Are tests performed periodically to ensure the integrity and viability of the backups? ■ Are backups performed on a regular basis? ■ Are backup logs checked after each backup and missed files backed up manually to complete the record? ■ Are back copies kept in an off-site archive?

Deliverables: Completed vendor surveys are kept with the vendor's record. The conclusions reached from reviewing the vendor survey are recorded on deliverable 3.4, the vendor qualification form.

The results of an on-site audit are summarized in deliverable 3.3, the vendor audit report. The completed checklist will be stored with the audit as backup information.

References:
- Stein, R. Timothy. "Computer System Vendor Audit Checklist," Business Performance Associates, 2003. (See *www.bpaconsultants.com.*)
- ANSI/AAMI SW68:2001. Medical Device Software—Software Life Cycle Processes. Association for the Advancement of Medical Instrumentation, 2001.
- IEEE 1012-1998, IEEE Standard for Software Verification and Validation Plans. March 9, 1988.
- IEEE 12207.0-1996, IEEE/EIA Standard: Industry Implementation of International Standard ISO/IEC 12207:1995 Standard for Information Technology—Software Life Cycle Processes.
- ISO 9001:2000, Quality management systems—Requirements
- PDA Committee on Validation of Computer-Related Systems, Technical Report No. 18, "Validation of Computer-Related Systems, Supplement, Section 4.3. " *PDA Journal of Pharmaceutical Science and Technology*, Vol. 49, No. 1, January-February 1995.

| Deliverable 4.1 | Risk Assessment Report |

Purpose: A risk analysis and evaluation report records the manner in which the risk assessment was performed and documents the assessment results when it's created during phase 4. The revision of the risk assessment and evaluation report created in phase 5 also reports the overall residual risk and the risk and/or benefit analysis, if one is performed.

Resources Used: Any of the following tools can be used to perform a risk analysis:
■ Failure mode and effects analysis (FMEA)
■ Hazard analysis and critical control points
■ Fault-tree analysis

An example of a FMEA risk assessment table is presented in exhibit 6.1. Such tables can be summarized in the results section and the tables themselves attached as an appendix.

Stein, R. Timothy. "Risk Management Procedure." Business Performance Associates, 2003. (See *www.bpaconsultants.com.*)

Risk-Based Adjustments: The risk level of the system doesn't affect the risk analysis and evaluation report content.

| \multicolumn{2}{c}{**Risk Analysis and Evaluation Report Outline**} ||
Section	Contents
1. Cover page	■ Title. Include the item or system on which the analysis was performed. ■ Report date ■ Report author ■ Signature lines ■ Company information
2. Introduction	■ Purpose of the risk assessment ■ Date the risk assessment was performed ■ Description of what was included in the assessment ■ Participants
3. Procedure	■ Reference established procedures that were used to perform the risk analysis and evaluation, and describe modifications to the procedures or variances in their use. ■ Describe the process used if an established procedure wasn't followed. ■ Record the severity and likelihood classifications used, or reference established classifications. ■ Provide a table (or equivalent information) on how the security and likelihood levels were translated into a risk level.

(continues)

| Deliverable 4.1 | Risk Assessment Report (continued) |

Section	Contents
4. Results	■ Summary of risk ratings ■ Summary of the mitigations that must be performed ■ Thresholds of occurrence of a hazard during post-production that will trigger an immediate review of the risk management effort for the item
5. Overall residual risk	Record the overall residual risk level when it's determined in phase 5
6. Risk/benefit analysis	If the overall residual risk is high, a risk-benefit analysis is performed. Record: ■ How the risk-benefit analysis was conducted ■ The results of the analysis

7. Conclusion	■ Overall system risk level
	  □ The overall residual risk (added when the risk assessment and evaluation report is revised in phase 5)
	  □ The results of the risk-benefit analysis, if one is conducted (added when the report is revised in phase 5)
	
	■ Failure or hazards that need further risk reduction
	■ Planned risk mitigations

8. Appendices	Risk evaluation tables (as illustrated in exhibit 6.1). The risk evaluation tables are updated three times during the RiskVal process: ■ First, during phase 5, when the effect of the mitigations is added, the residual risk is evaluated, and a risk-benefit analysis is performed, if needed ■ Second, during phase 8, when the risk levels are revised to reflect the results of the validation testing, the residual risk is reassessed and a risk-benefit analysis is performed, if needed. ■ Third, if the post-implementation review of system performance causes a revision in the risk assessment or evaluation

Preparation Tips: Discuss only potential hazards of significance in the report. Attach completed risk analysis tables to the report.

Approvals and Signatures:
■ Report author
■ Participants in the risk assessment
■ Quality assurance

| Deliverable 4.2 | Validation Plan |

Purpose: The validation plan is created to define the validation approach, activities, responsibilities, process, and deliverables for validating a specific item (e.g., a piece of equipment, process, or computer system).

Resources Used: Information about the system documented in the computer system project proposal as well as information gathered during the selection process provides the background on the system needed for the validation plan. Information about what to include in the plan may be available in your company's procedures and is provided in this deliverable brief.

Stein, R. Timothy. "Validation Plan Template." Business Performance Associates, 2003. (See *www.bpaconsultants.com.*)

Risk-Based Adjustments: A validation plan isn't needed for simple and/or low-risk, commercial-off-the-shelf systems and simple and/or low-risk applications built with database packages such as Excel, SAS, and Access.

	Validation Plan Outline
Section	**Contents**
1. **Cover page**	■ Title, including the name of the item being validated ■ Report date ■ Report author ■ Signature lines ■ Identification of your company and, if relevant, the division that owns the system
2. **Table of contents**	
3. **Purpose and scope**	■ Name of the system ■ System's location ■ High-level description of the system ■ Scope of the validation ■ Any necessary justification for the scope of the system and/or the validation
4. **Background**	■ A statement of the vision for the system (i.e., why it's being implemented) ■ A high-level description of the system's functionality ■ Identification of the system owner ■ Identification of the major users and their intended uses

(continues)

Deliverable 4.2	Validation Plan (continued)

Section	Contents
5. References	The policy and procedures with which the validation plan must comply. (*Note:* Don't list reference materials for the system such as technical and users' manuals.)
6. Definitions	Definitions of terms that aren't commonly known by the reviewers or that must be interpreted in a special manner relative to the validation of the system
7. Responsibilities	A list of the major responsibilities for each functional area regarding the validation. Provide only a high-level summary. The responsibilities to approve documents that are part of the validation record are provided in appendix III.
8. Training requirements related to responsibilities	Description of any training that's required for those providing the functions described in the responsibilities section of the validation plan. Training records should be in place for these individuals. The diagrams of the system can be placed in appendices I and II of the validation plan.
9. System definition and description	■ A high-level description of the major elements of the system. The validation plan must identify the system and its major components so that the validation approach can be determined. ■ A context for the system as required by the EC Commission Directive for medicinal products, Annex 11, item 4: ☐ Principles and objectives of the system ☐ Security measures ☐ Scope of the system ☐ Main features of the way in which it will be used ☐ How it interacts with other systems and procedures
10. Implementation strategy	Description of the strategy for system rollout and implementation: ■ Will there be pilot groups? ■ Will the implementation involve partial functionality at first, followed at a later time by additional uses? ■ Will different groups of users, or different locations, begin to use the system at different times?

Section	Contents

11. Validation strategy	■ Overall approach
	■ Identification of the validation as prospective, concurrent, or retrospective. If not prospective, justify. Indicate if the approach is different for different parts of the system.
	■ The planned type of qualifications. Possibilities include:
	  □ Installation qualification (IQ)
	  □ IQ combined with an operational qualification (OQ)
	  □ OQ
	  □ OQ combined with a performance qualification (PQ)
	  □ PQ
	
	■ The validation of the system as a whole or as a group of subsystems
	■ The timing for the validation of different parts of the system (e.g., the entire system will be validated before the system is used, or the electronic approval of documents will be validated prior to the implementation of phase 2)
	■ General effect of risk level. State the rigor with which the validation activities must be conducted based on the risk level of the system (see tables 6.15 and 9.5).

12. Validation activities	■ Validation activities. Identify the life cycle activities that must be performed for the system. The appropriate activities depend on the risk level of the system. A list can be attached (as appendix III) that identifies the required activities, the required deliverables created during the activities, and the approval requirements. (See exhibit 12.1.) ■ Validation testing. Describe the validation testing that will be performed (e.g., IQ, OQ, and PQ). Include the prerequisites, what each will cover, and the acceptance criteria. ■ Variances. State that any variance in using a protocol or in actual results from expected results must be documented in a variance report. State what type of actions are allowed to resolve variances (see chapter 9).
13. System release	■ System release for use in production. Specify when the system will be ready for use in the production environment, and if the validation testing isn't complete (e.g., the PQ still must be performed), the conditions under which the items produced using the system can be released. ■ System acceptance criteria. Define the standards that must be met once the validation testing is complete in phase 8 for the system to be deemed suitable for use.

(continues)

Deliverable 4.2	Validation Plan (continued)

Section	Contents
	■ Final validation report. Indicate that the final validation report will follow the content requirements stated in your procedure. Describe and explain any differences.
14. System maintenance and support strategy	■ User and/or problem support. Reference the procedure that will be used for user support for first, second, and third levels of support. If an external organization will be providing support, identify the company and the nature of the support to be provided. (A copy of the purchase order or service agreement will be included in the validation record.) ■ Required calibration of any equipment used in the system. Reference calibration procedures or, if the calibration will be performed by an external organization, identify the organization.
15. Maintaining a validated state	■ Revalidation of the system after a change. State how revalidation will be handled (see chapter 6). ■ System revalidation. Specify the conditions under which a complete system revalidation must be performed (see chapter 6).
16. Appendices	I. High-level system hardware configuration diagrams II. High-level software components list or diagram (e.g., system software, tools, applications) III. Documents that form the validation record and approval requirements. List the life cycle deliverables that are considered part of the validation record and their approval requirements.

Preparation Tips: Prepare a template for use in creating validation plans. Place generic material in a procedure so that it doesn't have to be repeated in every plan, such as generic aspects of the following:
■ Responsibilities
■ System maintenance and support
■ Training requirements
■ Implications of risk level on validation
■ Contents of the final validation report
■ Revalidation
■ System revalidation

Approvals and Signatures:
- Report author
- Head of the department that owns the system
- Validation
- Information technology
- Quality assurance

Method 4.1	Failure Mode and Effects Analysis

Purpose: Failure mode and effect analysis (FMEA) is one of the methods that can be used to determine the risk associated with potential system failures and hazards.

Using FMEA in the Life Cycle

Life cycle phase	Use	Notes
Phase 1: Conceptualize	An initial risk assessment is conducted to: ■ Assess the system's risk level as high, moderate, or low ■ Guide the application of the RiskVal life cycle for the system. ■ Identify user requirements related to the control of risk. ■ Set priorities for the validation of existing systems.	The analysis is performed by evaluating the harm associated with the failure of the system to meet intended uses or user requirements. (This is discussed in chapter 3.)
Phase 4: Design solutions to issues	A detailed risk assessment is conducted using information concerning the features and functions of a purchased system or, in the case of custom software, of the system as designed. This analysis is used to: ■ Guide qualification testing ■ Identify needed risk mitigation ■ Determine if the system poses too great of a risk to be used	The detailed analysis is conducted by evaluating the likelihood of failures and the harm associated with the potential failures or hazards of each feature and function of the system.

Method: Potential failures of the system or hazards associated with the system are identified. The consequences of such failures, such as those related to product safety, company costs, and compliance with regulations are identified and rated on severity (see exhibit 6.2). The likelihood that the system will fail and cause the harm is estimated. The risk associated with each failure or hazard is determined by considering both severity and likelihood. (More details about the FMEA method are presented in chapter 6.)

Step	Actions
Prepare	■ Obtain information on user requirements and/or intended uses ■ Prepare a list of possible hazards and failures in the system's performance of its intended functions or its ability to meet user requirements. ■ Define severity and likelihood classifications to be used for categorizing risk.
Conduct FMEA session	■ Work with each failure or hazard one at a time. Discuss failure or hazard and record the harm that could come about as a result of it, the severity of the effect, and the likelihood of the failure or hazard. ■ Discuss and record existing mechanisms that mitigate the probability or severity of the effect of the failure or hazard. ■ Assess and record the risk.

Step	Actions
Meeting follow-up	■ A designated person researches or clarifies the probability and severity of failures. Revise the analysis, if needed, based on research.
Report preparation	■ A designated person drafts the risk analysis report (see deliverable 4.1).

Deliverables: Risk assessment report (see deliverable 4.1). Note that the risk assessment report also includes risk evaluation, which isn't included in this deliverable.

References
■ IEC 60812, Analysis techniques for system reliability—Procedures for failure mode and effect analysis (FMEA).
■ DeSain, C., and Sutton, C. V. *Risk Management Basics.* Cleveland, Ohio: Advanstar Communication, 2000.
■ Falla, Mike, ed. *Advances in Safety Critical Systems—Results and Achievements from the DTI/EPSRC R&D Programme in Safety Critical Systems.* Chapter 3, "Hazard Analysis," available at *www.comp.lancs.ac.uk/computing/resources/scs/.* Not dated.
■ Ippolito, L. M., and Wallace, D. R. *A Study on Hazard Analysis in High-Integrity Software Standards and Guidelines.* National Institute of Standards and Technology, 1995.
■ ISO 14971:2000, Medical devices—Application of risk management to medical devices. ISO, 2000.
■ Stein, R. Timothy. "Failure Mode and Effects Analysis." Business Performance Associates, 2003. (See *www.bpaconsultants.com.*)

Method 4.2	Fault-Tree Analysis

Purpose: Fault-tree analysis (FTA) is one of the methods used for risk analysis. Typical applications include assessing the risk associated with hardware products once designed or with automated systems that involve extensive detectors and other specialized hardware components.

Using FTA in the Life Cycle

Life cycle phase	Use	Notes
Phase 4: Design solutions to issues	A detailed risk assessment is conducted of a purchased system or, in the case of custom software, of the system as designed. This analysis is used to: ■ Guide validation testing ■ Identify needed risk mitigation ■ Determine if the system poses too great of a risk to be used	The detailed analysis is conducted by evaluating the likelihood of failures and the harm associated with potential failures or hazards of each component of the system.

Method: Fault-tree analysis takes a top-down perspective that involves assessing the likelihood of the occurrence of harm and the severity of the harm associated with a system failure. Each potential system failure or hazard is analyzed. The immediate causes of the failure, called "first-level causes," are identified. For example, the system might fail because of a subassembly failure. That failure might be caused by a failure in a component of the subassembly. The component failure is a second-level cause. The failure in the subassembly might be caused by a failure of a part, a third-level cause. The fault tree analysis is continued until it contains at its lowest level, components that can't be further analyzed. Causes of failures are identified at all levels.

The probabilities of the causes are mathematically combined to estimate the likelihood of the failure or hazard. The intent is to base, to the extent possible, the assessment of the probability of failure of mechanical and electric parts on known reliability data. The severity of the harm caused by each failure and hazard is evaluated, and a level of risk is identified for each combination of severity and likelihood.

Step	Actions
Prepare	■ Define severity, likelihood, and risk classifications to be used for assessing risk. ■ Obtain information on the system's components and subcomponents, including the functions and the reliability of each. ■ Prepare a list of the potential hazards or failures of each component part and/or subassembly, and first- and second-level causes of such failures.
Conduct the FTA session	■ Work with each failure or hazard one at a time. Discuss failure or hazard and record the harm that could come about as a result of the failure or hazard and the severity of the effect of the harm. ■ Calculate the probability of each failure or hazard based on an analysis of the causes of the failure or hazard.

Step	Actions
	☐ Start calculating the probability of the failure or hazard at the part level and work up to calculate the probability of a particular failure of the system ☐ If more than one cause must be present concurrently to cause the failure and/or cause, multiply the probabilities of the failure of each cause. For example, If there are three causes of a failure that must occur simultaneously, the probability of the failure is the product of the probabilities on each of the three failures. Probability of the failure = P(1) x P(2) x P(3) ☐ If each cause can create the failure or hazard independent of other causes, the probability of the failure or hazard is the sum of the probabilities of all possible causes with a correction for the times when the causes occur simultaneously. Probability of the failure = P(1) + P(2) + P(3) − [P(1) x P(2) + P(1) x P(3) + P(2) x P(3)] + [P(1) x P(2) x P(3)]. ■ Assess and record the risk.
Meeting follow-up	A designated person researches or clarifies and questions from the analysis. Revise the analysis, if needed, based on the research.
Report preparation	A designated person drafts the risk analysis report (see deliverable 4.1, Risk Assessment Report).

Deliverables: Risk assessment report (see deliverable 4.1). Note that the risk assessment report also includes risk evaluation which isn't included in this deliverable.

References
- IEC 61025, Fault tree analysis (FTA).
- DeSain, C., and Sutton, C. V. *Risk Management Basics.* Cleveland, Ohio: Advanstar Communication, 2000.
- Falla, Mike, ed. *Advances in Safety Critical Systems—Results and Achievements from the DTI/EPSRC R&D Programme in Safety Critical Systems.* Chapter 3, "Hazard Analysis." Available at *http:/www.comp.lancs.ac.uk/computing/resources/scs/*
- Ippolito, L. M., and Wallace, D. R. *A Study on Hazard Analysis in High-Integrity Software Standards and Guidelines.* National Institute of Standards and Technology, 1995.
- ISO 14971:2000, Medical devices—Application of risk management to medical devices, ISO, 2000.
- Stein, R. Timothy. "Fault-Tree Analysis." Business Performance Associates, 2003. Note that the risk assessment report also includes risk evaluation, which isn't included in this deliverable. (See *www.bpaconsultants.com.*)

Method 4.3	Hazard Analysis and Critical Control Points

Purpose: Hazard analysis and critical control points (HACCP) is one of the methods used for risk analysis. The most common application in conjunction with computer systems is the analysis of risk associated with an automated process, especially manufacturing.

<table>
<tr><th colspan="3">Using HACCP in the Life Cycle</th></tr>
<tr><th>Life cycle phase</th><th>Use</th><th>Notes</th></tr>
<tr>
<td>Phase 4: Design solutions to issues</td>
<td>A detailed risk assessment is conducted of a purchased system or, in the case of custom software, of the system as designed. This analysis is used to:
■ Guide validation testing
■ Identify needed risk mitigation
■ Determine if the system poses too great of a risk to be used</td>
<td>The detailed analysis is conducted by evaluating the harm associated with potential failures or hazards of each component of the system.</td>
</tr>
</table>

Method: Hazard analysis and critical control point assessment is a risk analysis method used to identify the risk associated with process control points. Risk is judged by determining if variability or failure at a step could affect process reliability or effectiveness. Consider the effect that variability, differences, or failures of automated or human actions, materials or components, equipment or utility systems, processing or testing environments, or storage conditions or holding times for materials or intermediates could have on process reliability and effectiveness.

If a process failure can be tied directly to a type of product failure, the harm associated with the process failure is the same as the harm associated with the related product failure. For this reason the HACCP analysis focuses on the steps of the process that affect critical and important product characteristics or functions.

The harm that can be caused by a process failure or variability at a step is identified. The severity of harm and the probability of harm are rated. A risk level is assessed based on the severity and probability. The output of a HACCP analysis is the identification of the need for additional controls, and the identification of steps in a process that must be modified, and/or monitored and controlled, and validated.

Step	Actions
Prepare	■ Prepare or obtain documentation that provides information about the process (e.g., the inputs and outputs of the process, process steps, and the intended uses of the outputs). ■ Identify critical product features or specifications by reviewing the product risk analysis, if available, and/or by identifying all product features and performance requirements listed in the final product specification and labeling.

Step	Actions
Conduct the HACCP session.	■ Identify the steps of the process or method. ■ For each step, identify potential hazards, conditions, or failures that could cause unreliable or ineffective processing. ■ Identify process control points (i.e., steps in processing where controlling biological, chemical, or physical factors does or would provide greater assurance that a process will perform reliably). ■ Identify critical control points (i.e., the process control points at which failure-of-control will affect the safety of the product). ■ Identify essential control points (i.e., the process control points that don't affect product safety but that are nevertheless essential for process reliability and effectiveness). ■ Evaluate the risk associated with hazards, conditions, or failure at the critical and essential control points: ☐ Identify the harm that could occur because of the hazard, condition, or failure. ☐ Rate the severity of the harm. ☐ Calculate the probability of the hazard, condition, or failure given the controls that are currently in place. ☐ Determine the risk level based on the severity and probability. ■ Determine validation needs. ☐ All processes that contain critical control points should be validated. ☐ All computer systems that control or monitor critical control points or essential control points should be validated.
Meeting follow-up	A designated person researches or clarifies questions from the analysis. Revise the analysis, if needed, based on the research.
Report preparation	A designated person prepares the risk analysis report (see deliverable 4.1, Risk Assessment Report).

Deliverables: Risk assessment report (see deliverable 4.1 in appendix A). Note that the risk assessment report also includes risk evaluation, which isn't included in this deliverable.

References

- IEC 61025, Fault tree analysis (FTA).
- ISO 14971:2000, Medical devices—Application of risk management to medical devices. ISO, 2000.
- DeSain, C., and Sutton, C. V. *Risk Management Basics.* Cleveland, Ohio: Advanstar Communication, 2000.
- Stein, R. Timothy. "Hazard Analysis and Critical Control Points Assessment." Business Performance Associates, 2003. (See *www.bpaconsultants.com.*)

Mitigation Report

Purpose: A mitigation report describes the effectiveness of a measure taken to mitigate risks or address weakness in meeting requirements or regulations. The risk mitigation report, which is prepared only if formal testing is done, documents the investigation, testing, and data collection. In addition, a conclusion is drawn as to the effectiveness of the mitigation.

Resources Used: The method used to evaluate the effectiveness of a risk-reduction activity depends on the approach taken in the mitigation. Information is provided in chapter 7.

Risk-Based Adjustments: Risk mitigation isn't needed for low-risk situations.

The length of the mitigation report will vary depending on the complexity and magnitude of the remedial action and the method used to evaluate its effectiveness. A more informal format (e.g., a memo) can be used for simple mitigations.

Mitigation Report Outline	
Section	**Contents**
1. Cover page	■ Title. Include the name of the system. ■ Report date ■ Report author ■ Signature lines ■ Identification of your company and, if relevant, the division implementing the system
2. Introduction	■ Identification of the system for which the mitigation is being performed ■ Context for the mitigation: 　☐ If the mitigation is for risk reduction, explain the risk and reference the risk assessment table. 　☐ If the purpose of the mitigation is to close a gap between the system and a user requirement, state the user requirement and explain the system's limitations in being able to meet the requirement. 　☐ If the mitigation is to address a noncompliance, describe the nature of the noncompliance. 　☐ Explanation of how the planned mitigation will address the situation

Section	Contents
3. Actions performed to implement the planned mitigation	Summary of the actions performed to implement the mitigation
4. Effectiveness of the mitigation	■ Explanation of how the effectiveness of the mitigation was evaluated ■ Summary of the data collected
5. Conclusion	■ Explanation of the effect of the remedial action, based on the evidence collected as to its effectiveness ■ A conclusion as to the effectiveness of the remedial action ■ A conclusion as to the need for further mitigation
6. Appendices	The data collected and/or the notes made of observations and/or interviews

Preparation Tips: A mitigation report isn't needed if the effectiveness of the remedial actions was derived through professional judgment. Instead of preparing a report, document the judgment in the revised detailed risk assessment report.

Approvals and Signatures:
■ Report author
■ Person responsible for implementing the remedial action
■ Person responsible for the assessment of the effect of the remedial actions
■ Project manager

| Deliverable 6.1 | System Specification |

Purpose: The purpose of the system specification is to define the system with enough detail to enable it to be replicated exactly (i.e., with the exact components from the same manufacturer), and with identical configurations. The system specification specifies all hardware, system software, database, and application software, and all configurations that are set in the installation process and by administrators to enable the system to function the way they want it to function in their business processes.

Resources Used: The system description written for the validation plan (see deliverable 4.2) can be incorporated into the system specification.

The technical requirements can be used as a basis for creating a system specification. Identify each piece of equipment or software product that meets each of the technical requirements. Each item should be listed only once in the specification, even if it meets several requirements. If the manufacturer combines several system components into a single product, list only the combined product in the specification. If the manufacturer offers options that are selected when the item is purchased, identify which options have been selected. Configurations that result from adding optional components, such as communication cards and RAM, are also documented.

Stein, R. Timothy. "Computer System Specification Template," Business Performance Associates, 2005. (See *www.bpaconsultants.com*.)

Risk-Based Adjustments: The information contained in the system specification must be documented somewhere and kept current so that the system configuration can be determined at any time; however, a separate system specification document isn't always necessary. The information can be contained in a detailed system description in the validation plan or in the installation qualification (IQ). For systems that won't change much with time, the current configuration of the system can be easily determined by starting with the system description in the validation plan or IQ, and tracing changes through the change control documentation. With systems that will undergo frequent or dramatic changes, a system specification might be a better way of tracking the current configuration. The system specification is kept current with changes; at any point in time, it would accurately portray the current state of the system.

For commodity items, generic specifications can be given without the manufacturer information. Such items include highly reliable hardware components, such as cabling and memory chips, that can be replaced with a low risk of failure. When you treat an item as a commodity item, you're implicitly asserting that an item from one manufacturer can easily be substituted with one from a different manufacturer without a change in the probability of a failure. If this assumption isn't true, don't treat the item as a commodity item and specify the manufacturer of the item to be used.

	System Specification Outline
Section	**Contents**
1. Cover page	■ Title. Include "System Specification for" followed by the system's name. ■ Date ■ Author's name and signature ■ Revision number ■ Identification of your company and, if relevant, the division implementing the system.
2. Introduction	Identification of the system for which the system specification applies

3. System specification	■ A system description (see the discussion of a system description relative to the validation plan in chapter 6 or deliverable 4.2).
	■ Identification of the specific hardware and software that are included in the system. Give the component name and describe the item. Give the manufacturer's name, part number, and the required revision number, if appropriate. State all required specifications or technical requirements for each item. Include this information for:
	  □ All components of the system that are not bundled together by the manufacturer
	  □ All configurable items (options) that are selected when the item is purchased
	
	■ For commodity items such as cabling, a generic specification is sufficient; manufacturer information isn't needed.
	■ Include the following items in the specification:
	  □ Software service packs or defect patches
	  □ Any free programs, tools, or applications downloaded from the Internet. (*Note:* It's highly recommended that free software isn't incorporated into validated systems due to a lack of knowledge about how the software has been developed and because such systems generally aren't supported by the developer.)
	
	■ Include all configurations of hardware, system software, and database software that are required by the manufacturer of the application (see the application's technical manual) as well as those determined by information technology (IT) to be appropriate.
	■ Also include all configurations of the application that are required for the application to meet user requirements, such as workflows, user groups,

(continues)

Deliverable 6.1	System Specification (continued)

Section	Contents
	roles and privileges, and object types. If the configurations are captured in a separate document, reference that document.

Preparation Tips: Start the system specification with an actual inventory of the system as used in the test environment. Change the specification for differences between the test environment and the operational environment. If the application will be run using an existing infrastructure that's been qualified, only include any incremental hardware and software in the system specification.

Approvals and Signatures:
- Report author
- Information technology
- Quality assurance

| Deliverable 6.2 | Change Control Process |

Purpose: The change control procedure defines the process to be used to maintain a system in a validated state after an intentional change. That is, the change is made in a purposeful manner that safeguards against the introduction of defects and other potential causes of system failure. As a result, confidence is retained that the system will meet requirements.

Resources Used: This deliverable and the discussion in chapter 8 can be used to prepare the procedure.

Stein, R. Timothy. "Change Control for Validated Systems." Business Performance Associates, 2002. (See *www.bpaconsultants.com*.)

Risk-Based Adjustments: The same procedure will be used for all systems, irrespective of risk level.

The degree of validation testing conducted after the change is made is dependent on the risk associated with failure of the change and the possible effect of the change on other aspects of the system. The effect of risk on validation testing is discussed in reference to the validation plan in chapter 6

Change Control Procedure Outline	
Section	**Contents**
1. Purpose	Defines the purpose of the procedure
2. Scope	Defines what the change control procedure covers: all components of validated computer systems that are under change control. These items are identified in the validation plan for the system or the system specification.
3. Reference documents	List documents that are referenced in the text of the procedure.
4. Definitions	Provide definitions of terms that the reader isn't expected to understand or that have a special meaning in regard to this change control procedure.
5. Responsibility	Summarize the responsibilities of those functions involved in the procedure: the requester, change control board, system owner, information technology (IT), and validation.
6. Method	■ The initiator completes the initiator portion of the change request form (see deliverable 6.3).

(continues)

Deliverable 6.2	Change Control Process (continued)

Section	Contents
	■ The change control board evaluates the request and makes a decision on whether to proceed: ☐ Evaluate the business merits of the change. ☐ Review possible risks associated with the change. ☐ Conduct a risk analysis and evaluation to determine if mitigations are needed as part of the change control package. ■ IT or designee installs the change in a test environment. ☐ Prepare a test environment. ☐ Install the change. ■ Perform validation testing of the change to verify that the change functions as expected and that there's no negative effect on other parts of the system. ☐ Develop validation test protocols if the tests haven't been defined and approved on the change request form. ☐ Execute the tests. ☐ Prepare a validation report if necessary. ■ The change control board reviews the results of the validation testing and determines if the change can be implemented in the production environment. If issues must be addressed, the change control board determines an appropriate course of action. ■ Implement the change in the production environment. ☐ Prepare users for the changed system. ☐ Update documentation as needed (e.g., system specification and/or configuration diagram, technical system documentation, user procedures, and training materials). ☐ IT installs the change in the production environment. ☐ Perform validation testing in the production environment as specified on the change request form. ☐ Monitor the system for problems for the duration identified in the change request.

Section	Contents
	■ Change control under emergency situations: ☐ Define emergency situations. ☐ Describe the process of approval under emergency situations, and conducting the validation testing after the change is installed. ■ Maintain records of the change. ■ Modifications that can be made independent of the change control procedure: ☐ Changes described in an approved application administrative procedure (e.g., the addition of users, changing user privileges, deactivation of users). These methods ought to be qualified in the operational qualification. ☐ System administration activities that have been qualified in the operational qualification, such as archiving data, setting network communications for input and output devices, and allocating storage space ☐ Replacement of highly reliable hardware components that have a low likelihood of failure and low risk associated with a potential failure, e.g., cabling and memory chips ☐ Changes to items that aren't under change control, such as workstations and associated components like keyboards and mice ■ Close the change request ■ General requirements for when a system must be revalidated

Preparation Tips: Prepare the procedure at the level of detail that parallels the level of consistency needed in the execution of the process.

Approvals and Signatures: Follow your document control procedures for determining appropriate approvals. Approvers, however, would ordinarily include:
■ Quality assurance
■ Validation
■ Information technology

Deliverable 6.3	Change Request Form

Purpose: The change request form is used to record the following information:
- A description and justification of the request
- A description of the required validation testing
- An approval to conduct the validation testing
- An approval to implement the change
- A record of the closing of the change request

Resources Used: Similar information concerning the contents of the change request form is presented in deliverable 6.2, Change Control Procedure.

Stein, R. Timothy. "Change Control of Validated Systems." Business Performance Associates, 2002. (See *www.bpaconsultants.com*.)

Risk-Based Adjustments: The same form will be used for all systems, independent of risk.
The content written on the form will vary with the level of risk associated with potential failure of the system parts modified or added during the change. The degree of validation testing that's required as part of the change is dependent on the risk associated with failure of the modifications made and the possible effect of the modification on other aspects of the system. The effect of risk on validation testing is discussed in tables 6.15 and 9.5.

Change Request Form Outline	
Section	**Contents**
1. Requested change	■ System and/or equipment identification ■ Requestor identification ■ Requestor signature and date ■ Nature of change: normal or emergency ■ Description of requested change ■ List of documentation that needs to be updated in conjunction with the change ■ Any new moderate, or high risks that the change introduces, and any planned mitigations of the new risks ■ Justification for requested change ■ Planned validation testing for the change ■ Planned implementation for the change ■ Planned monitoring of the installation after the change

Section	Contents
2. **Initial processing by the head of the change review board**	■ Type of change ■ Type of items affected by the change (e.g., application programs and/or code, integration code, documentation, procedures, and training). ■ Processor's name, signature, and date

3. **Assessments of the change**	■ Comments by the system owner
	■ Comments by information technology
	■ Comments by validation
	■ Risk analysis by the change review board
	   ☐ Potential harm associated with failures
	   ☐ Probability that the system will fail and cause the harm
	   ☐ Risk level of the potential failures
	   ☐ Needed mitigations

4. **Approval to proceed with needed validation testing**	Approval signatures by: ■ System owner ■ Information technology (IT) ■ Validation ■ Quality assurance (QA)

5. **Approval to implement**	■ List of executed protocols and reports for the validation testing
	■ Approval signatures by:
	   ☐ System owner
	   ☐ IT
	   ☐ Validation
	   ☐ QA

6. **Post change effect**	■ List any new system problems or failures that are traced to the change or for which the change might be a possible explanation. Reference any change requests that are opened to resolve such difficulties. ■ Close the monitoring period with a conclusion regarding the viability of the change.
7. **List of amendments to the change request**	Amendment summary information: ■ Amendment subject ■ Amendment author ■ Amendment date

(continues)

Deliverable 6.3	Change Request Form (continued)

Section	Contents
	Amendment approval by: ■ System owner ■ IT ■ Validation ■ QA
8. Request closed	■ Check boxes for change request cancelled and change completed ■ Signature of the person closing the change request and date
9. Appendices	Amendments to the change request form

Preparation Tips: The initiator can save time in the review process by discussing the proposed change, its justification, the planned validation, and the planned implementation in advance with the reviewers.

Develop and qualify procedures for making routine application administrative and system administrative changes. Examples are given in the above outline for the procedure's content. If procedures are developed, qualified, and approved, you don't need to use the change control process for changes made following the procedure. Separate forms should be developed if needed to record such changes and associated testing.

Approvals and Signatures: Record the approvals given at different points in the change control process in the appropriate sections of the form. See the information provided in the outline above.

Deliverable 7.1	Installation Qualification Protocol

Purpose: The installation qualification (IQ) protocol provides a structured method for verifying that all components of the system, both hardware and software, meet the technical specifications and have been properly installed. In addition, the executed protocol serves as a record of the qualification.

Resources Used: Any detailed list of system components can be used as the foundation of the IQ. The best source is the system specification because it identifies all system components and the technical requirements for each component. Other possibe sources include the system description in the validation plan and an inventory of the system..

   An IQ template from Business Performance Associates. (See *www.bpaconsultants.com.*)

Risk-Based Adjustments: The IQ is the most basic aspect of validation; it provides a foundation for subsequent validation testing. If any differentiation is made between low- and high-risk systems, consideration should be given to the amount of testing that's done to confirm the functioning of aspects of the system that are less relevant to its overall performance. For example, with a low-risk system, you might choose not to verify that a dedicated printer has printer drivers that are able to print your information accurately. Such aspects of the system can be verified informally after the system is put into use, or they can be included in the operational qualification (OQ).

Installation Qualification Protocol Outline	
Section	**Contents**
1. **Cover page**	■ Title ■ Protocol date ■ Protocol author ■ Signature lines ■ Identification of your company and, if relevant, the division that owns the system
2. **Purpose**	The purpose of the IQ, including the name of the system
3. **Scope**	The scope of the IQ (i.e., what's included in the system). State the system's name or give a brief descriptive statement. Include any key information that differentiates this system from similar systems in use at your organization, such as the functions or departments that will use the system and/or the intended uses for the system.

(continues)

Deliverable 7.1	Installation Qualification Protocol (continued)

Section	Contents
4. System description	■ System overview: Describe or list all of the major components of the system. ■ Detailed description. Include one of the following: ☐ A reference to a detailed system specification ☐ A reference to a detailed system description in the validation plan ☐ A detailed list of all system components that must be included in the IQ, presented either in the IQ text or an appendix
5. Responsibilities	List the responsibilities of all functional areas that will: ■ Participate in creating, approving, and executing the IQ ■ Write, review, or approve variances ■ Write, review, or approve the IQ report The functions normally included are information technology, quality assurance, and validation.
6. References	A list of all documents that must be used in executing this protocol or are referenced in it. Examples of required documents include: ■ Validation plan ■ System specification ■ Technical requirements ■ Validation procedures Procedures for the installation or setup of system components, including: ■ Application manuals ■ Database manuals ■ Manufacturer installation instructions
7. Equipment and/or materials needed	A list of all special equipment or materials that will be used during the installation qualification. Examples include: installation CDs for software and test equipment to ping devices over the network to test connectivity. Don't list the system components; they're listed in the system description.
8. Prerequisites	A list of the prerequisites that must be completed before executing the protocol (see chapter 9).

Section	Contents
9. Protocol acceptance criteria	A list of the criteria that must be met for the installation to be successfully completed. See the discussion of the IQ protocol acceptance criteria in chapter 9. If multiple test sections are prepared for this protocol, protocol acceptance criteria can be given for each test section instead of in this section.
10. General instructions for executing the protocol	Instructions to the individuals executing and reviewing the protocol (these instructions can be given in an approved procedure instead of each protocol). Cover the following areas: ■ Verification of prerequisites ■ Completion of the test sections ■ When a variance must be recorded; completing a variance form ■ When an amendment must be created; what must be included in an amendment ■ Instructions on how to review the completed protocol (for the reviewer)
11. Test sections	Instructions for verifying that the components of the system meet requirements, are installed, and are operable. Most systems involve many different types of items, such as a server, server operating system, application, and database. With IQs for such systems, the test section of the protocol is broken down into subsections (e.g., the IQ for the server). For each, prepare the following: ■ Objective statement ■ Materials and equipment required ■ Protocol acceptance criteria ■ Installation verification steps ☐ As discussed in chapter 9, write statements to confirm that an installed item meets the requirements and record the serial number of the item. You can also include in the IQ a simple performance test for each item to confirm operability. (See table 9.2 for examples of items to include and operability tests. See exhibit 9.1 for an example of an IQ protocol page.) ■ Conclusion regarding the meaning of the results If there's only one test section, the purpose, materials and equipment required, and protocol acceptance criteria don't need to be defined in the test section. The definition of these items in sections 2, 7, and 9, respectively, are sufficient.

(continues)

| Deliverable 7.1 | Installation Qualification Protocol (continued) |

Section	Contents
12. Appendix A: Test instrument calibration	A list of all test instruments that require calibration. Include the following for each: ■ Identify last calibration date ■ Identify calibration due date ■ Attach calibration certificates
13. Appendix B: Signature log	The printed names, written initials, and signatures of all personnel involved in executing or reviewing the protocol. (This appendix isn't needed if the signatures of all those involved are in a company log.)
14. Appendix C: Supporting documentation	A log of all supporting documentation collected during the protocol execution (e.g., screen printouts and computer-generated reports) collected during test execution, followed by the documentation
15. Appendix D: Variance procedure and form	The variance form and instructions for completing it. As the IQ is conducted, add the completed variances to this appendix. If your organization has an approved computer system validation variance form in a controlled document, use that. The appendix will then be used only as a place to attach the completed forms while the protocol is being executed.

Preparation Tips: The easiest way to prepare the IQ is to follow a detailed system specification that includes acceptable values and ranges item for item.

Some organizations will split the verification that the installed item meets the specifications from the tests to determine if the item is operable. They perform installation verification during the IQ and perform the tests of operability during an OQ.

Approvals and Signatures:
■ IQ author
■ Project manager or team leader
■ Quality assurance
■ Validation

Deliverable 7.2   Variance Report

Purpose: The variance form is used to record any occurrence during testing where:
- A required action couldn't be performed, or wasn't completed as specified.
- An actual result didn't match the expected result.

Resources Used: A variance form is available in the IQ, OQ, and PQ templates provided by Business Performance Associates. (See *www.bpaconsultants.com*.)

Risk-Based Adjustments: None.

\multicolumn{2}{c}{**Variance Report Outline**}	
Section	**Contents**
1. Contextual information	A properly identified variance report includes the following information: ■ Protocol name ■ Protocol number ■ Protocol revision ■ Variance report number for that protocol (e.g., two of four) ■ The protocol page number and test step number where the variance(s) occurred ■ A unique page number for each page of that variance report (e.g., one of two)
2. Observation	■ The person who was executing the protocol describes the error in the protocol, the problem encountered, or the difference between the expected and actual result. The person prints his or her name, then signs and dates the section.
3. Resolution	■ The information technology representative records the solution to the problem that he or she developed with input from the system owner or project manager. ■ Those involved with deciding how to resolve the issue print their names, sign, and date the resolution section.
4. Conclusion and/or effect	■ The system owner or project manager (as appropriate) records his or her conclusion concerning the effect of the variance resolution on the system's ability to reliably meet user requirements. ■ The system owner or project manager prints his or her name, then signs and dates the conclusion/effect section.

(continues)

| Deliverable 7.2 | Variance Report (continued) |

Section	Contents
	■ Any changes to be made to user requirements, or limits on system use, are clearly indicated.
5. Attachments	■ Any objective evidence of the system failure that might help document the error or aid in its resolution is attached (e.g., a printout of an error message or a printout of the screen showing an incorrect result). ■ Results of any tests performed demonstrates the effectiveness of the resolution.

Approvals and Signatures: The QA representative signs the report if he or she agrees with the resolution and the conclusion/effect statement.

Deliverable 7.3	Operational Qualification Protocol

Purpose: The operational qualification (OQ) protocol provides a structured method for gathering objective evidence when determining if the system operates as intended in a test environment. In addition, the executed protocol serves as a record of the qualification.

Resources Used:
- Information on sections of the OQ provided in chapter 9
- User requirements
- An OQ template, available from Business Performance Associates. (See *www.bpaconsultants.com*)
- ANSI/ASQC Z1.4-1993—Sampling Procedures and Table for Inspection by Attributes. American Society for Quality Control, 1993.
- ANSI/ASQC Z1.9-1993—Sampling Procedures and Table for Inspection by Variables for Percent Nonconforming. American Society for Quality Control, 1993.

Risk-Based Adjustments: See the discussion in chapter 9 on risk-based adjustments.

<table>
<tr><th colspan="2">Operational Qualification Protocol Outline</th></tr>
<tr><th>Section</th><th>Contents</th></tr>
<tr>
<td>1. Cover page</td>
<td>
<ul>
<li>Title, including name of the system being validated</li>
<li>Protocol date</li>
<li>Protocol author</li>
<li>Signature lines</li>
<li>Identification of your company and, if relevant, the division that owns the system</li>
</ul>
</td>
</tr>
<tr>
<td>2. Purpose</td>
<td>The purpose of the OQ, including the name of the system being validated</td>
</tr>
<tr>
<td>3. Scope</td>
<td>A high-level statement that summarizes the tests that are to be included in the OQ protocol</td>
</tr>
<tr>
<td>4. System description</td>
<td>A description or list of all of the major components of the system or a reference to another document that provides a description of the system, such as the validation plan, system specification, or the installation qualification</td>
</tr>
<tr>
<td>5. Responsibilities</td>
<td>The responsibilities of all functional areas that will:
<ul>
<li>Participate in creating, approving, and executing the OQ</li>
<li>Write, review, or approve variances</li>
<li>Write, review, or approve the OQ report</li>
</ul>
</td>
</tr>
</table>

(continues)

Deliverable 7.3	Operational Qualification Protocol (continued)

Section	Contents
	The functions normally included are: ■ The project manager or team leader ■ System owner ■ Information technology ■ Quality assurance ■ Validation
6. References	A list of all documents that must be used to execute this protocol or are referenced in it. Examples include: ■ Validation plan ■ User requirements ■ Sampling procedures ■ Validation procedures ■ Application manuals
7. Validation approach	A general statement about the validation approach taken in this protocol. An explanation of the conditions and/or setting of the tests and the logic used in the tests, if necessary, to explain how the tests meet the purpose of the protocol. Identify any tests that are performed to verify the effectiveness of risk mitigation activities.
8. Sampling plan	If appropriate, include information regarding the amount of data to be sampled, number of cases to be tested, etc. Explain the basis for the sampling plan if an explanation isn't given in the validation plan. Sample sizes and the criteria for pass/fail can be determined using sampling standards (see "Resources Used," above).
9. Equipment or materials needed	A list of special equipment or materials that will be used while executing this protocol. Don't list any hardware or software that's part of the system.
10. Prerequisites	A list of prerequisites that must be completed before executing the protocol (see chapter 9)
11. Protocol acceptance criteria	Criteria that must be met for the OQ to be successfully completed (see the discussion of the OQ protocol acceptance criteria in chapter 9). If multiple test sections are prepared, protocol acceptance criteria can be given for each section.

Section	Contents
12. General instructions for executing the protocol	Instructions to the persons executing and reviewing the protocol (these can be given in a procedure instead of each protocol). Cover the following areas: ■ Verifying prerequisites ■ Completing the test sections ■ Completing variance forms ■ Instructions on when an amendment is needed ■ Instructions on how to review the completed protocol
13. Test section	Most systems are used for several different types of processing and perform many different functions. As discussed in chapter 9, the OQ testing can be structured in multiple protocols and/or multiple sections within a protocol. If a protocol's test section is broken down into subsections, prepare the following for each subsection: ■ Objective statement ■ User requirements tested (for backward traceability). Provide a table that maps the tests to the user requirements that are tested. ■ Materials and equipment required ■ User setup and test data. Identify the users that must be set up in the system, including their user names, passwords, group memberships, assigned roles, and privileges (if not defined by group membership or role). Also identify the test data or conditions that must be set up to be able to perform the tests included in the protocol. ■ Test procedure ■ Protocol acceptance criteria ■ Conclusion regarding the meaning of the results If there's only one test section, the purpose, materials and equipment required, and protocol acceptance criteria don't need to be defined in the test section. The definition of these items in sections 2, 9, and 11, respectively, are sufficient.
14. Appendix A: Test instrument calibration	List all test instruments that require calibration, including the following for each: ■ Identify last calibration date ■ Identify calibration due date ■ Attach calibration certificates
15. Appendix B: Signature log	The printed names, written initials, and signatures of all personnel involved in executing or reviewing of the protocol. (This appendix isn't needed if the signatures of all those involved are in a company log.)

(continues)

Deliverable 7.3	Operational Qualification Protocol (continued)

Section	Contents
16. Appendix C: Supporting documentation	A log of all supporting documentation collected during the protocol execution (e.g., screen printouts and computer-generated reports) followed by the documentation
17. Appendix D: Variance procedure and form	The variance form and instructions for completing it. As the OQ is conducted, add the completed variances to this appendix. If your organization has an approved computer system validation variance form in a controlled document, use that. The appendix will then be used only as a place to attach the completed forms as the protocol is executed.

Preparation Tips: If the validation is being performed solely for meeting regulatory requirements, the OQ can be limited to functions that are used to perform work that's required by the regulations.

Approvals and Signatures:
■ Protocol author
■ Project manager or team leader
■ System owner
■ QA
■ Validation

Deliverable 7.4	Protocol Report

Purpose: A protocol report summarizes the results achieved during the execution of the protocol and states a conclusion as to whether the system meets the protocol acceptance criteria.

Resources Used: Each protocol report is written based on the results achieved while executing the protocol.

Risk-Based Adjustments: For low-risk systems, the report content can be limited to a high-level summary for each section. The completed protocol, including all attached materials and variances, is retained for future reference and/or auditing.

Protocol Report Outline	
Section	**Contents**
1. **Cover page**	■ Title. Include the type of qualification and the name of the system being validated. ■ Report author ■ Signature lines ■ Identification of your company and, if relevant, the division that owns the system
2. **Purpose**	A statement that asserts the purpose of the report is to summarize the results of an installation qualification (IQ) operational qualification (OQ), or performance qualification (PQ) and to determine if the results meet the acceptance criteria for the qualification
3. **Scope**	A statement that identifies the specific qualification (IQ, OQ, or PQ) that's the topic of the report and defines the scope of that qualification
4. **References**	A list of references that includes all documents that must be used to understand the nature of the findings or are referenced in the report. Include the protocol that's the subject of the report.
5. **Analysis of results**	■ A summary of the findings (i.e., how well the system met the acceptance criteria for the protocol) ■ List or summarize all the variances, state their criticality level, if appropriate, and give their current status. ■ Clearly identify all variances that are still open and discuss the affect of each on the ability of the system to function reliably to meet requirements.

(continues)

Deliverable 7.4	Protocol Report (continued)

Section	Contents
6. Conclusion	A conclusion as to whether the system meets the protocol acceptance criteria
7. Appendix	Attach or the reference the executed protocol, including all materials added to its appendices

Preparation Tips: Keep the report at a high level except for the discussion of open variances. Readers can consult the executed protocol and/or variances for more detailed information.

Approvals and Signatures: The individuals who approved the protocol also approve the report. This would normally be:
- Report author
- Information technology (at least for the IQ)
- System owner (for the OQ and PQ)
- Quality assurance (all reports)
- Validation (all reports)

Deliverable 8.1	Performance Qualification Protocol

Purposes: The performance qualification (PQ) protocol provides a structured method for gathering objective evidence that the system performs as intended in its normal operating environment. The executed protocol is part of the validation record.

Resources Used:
- Information on sections of the PQ provided in chapter 10
- User requirements
- A PQ template available from Business Performance Associates. (See *www.bpaconsultants.com.*)
- ANSI/ASQC Z1.4-1993—Sampling Procedures and Table for Inspection by Attributes. American Society for Quality Control, 1993.
- ANSI/ASQC Z1.9–1993—Sampling Procedures and Table for Inspection by Variables for Percent Nonconforming. American Society for Quality Control, 1993.

Risk-Based Adjustments: As stated in the FDA's guidelines regarding validation, "The level of validation effort should be commensurate with the risk posed by the automated operation." I recommend that this principle be implemented in the following manner; however, you must determine what's suitable for your circumstance. No performance qualification is needed for low-risk systems if sufficient evidence is obtained through the operational qualification that the system can function reliably. At most, the PQ should be limited either to system monitoring or confirming important transactions.

For moderate and high-risk systems, care must be taken at least to verify that the high- and moderate-risk requirements are being met in the operational/production environment.

Performance Qualification Protocol Outline	
Section	**Contents**
1. Cover page	<ul><li>Title</li><li>Protocol date</li><li>Protocol author</li><li>Signature lines</li><li>Identification of your company and, if relevant, the division that owns the system</li></ul>
2. Purpose	The purpose of the PQ, including the name of the system being validated
3. Scope	A high-level statement that summarizes the tests included in the PQ

(continues)

Deliverable 8.1	Performance Qualification Protocol (continued)

Section	Contents
4. System description	A description or list of all the major components of the system. Reference any other documents that provide further information on the system, such as the validation plan, the system specification, or the IQ.
5. Responsibilities	The responsibilities of all functional areas that will participate in creating, approving, and executing the PQ; writing, reviewing, and approving variances; and writing and reviewing the PQ report. The functions normally included are: the project manager or team leader, system owner, information technology, quality assurance, and validation.
6. References	References for any documents that must be used in the execution of this protocol, or are referenced in it. Examples include: ■ The validation plan ■ User requirements ■ Sampling procedures ■ Validation procedures ■ Application manuals
7. Validation approach	A general statement about the approach taken with the PQ and this protocol. An explanation of the conditions and/or setting of the tests and, if necessary, the logic used in the tests to explain how the tests meet the purpose of the protocol. A list of tests that are performed to verify the effectiveness of risk mitigation activities.
8. Sampling plan	Information regarding the amount of data to be sampled, the number of cases to be tested, etc. An explanation of the basis for the sampling plan, if an explanation isn't given in the validation plan. Sample sizes and criteria for pass/fail can be determined using sampling standards. (See "Resources Used.")
9. Equipment or materials needed	A list of any special equipment or materials that will be used during the execution of this protocol. Don't list any hardware or software that's part of the system.
10. Prerequisites	See the prerequisites listed in chapter 10.

Section	Contents
11. Protocol acceptance criteria	A statement of the criteria that must be met for the PQ to be successfully completed. (See the discussion of the PQ protocol acceptance criteria in chapter 10.) If multiple test sections are prepared, protocol acceptance criteria can be given for each section.
12. General instructions for executing the protocol	Instructions to the individuals executing and reviewing the protocol. (These can be given in a procedure instead of each protocol.) Cover the following areas: ■ Confirmation of prerequisites ■ Completion of the test sections ■ Completion of variance forms ■ When an amendment is needed ■ Instructions on how to review the completed protocol
13. Test section	Most systems are used for several different types of processing and have many different functions. The PQ testing can be structured in multiple protocols and/or multiple sections within a protocol. If a protocol's test section is broken down into subsections, prepare the following for each subsection: ■ Objective statement ■ User requirements tested (for backward traceability). Provide a table that maps the tests to the requirements that are tested. ■ Materials and equipment required ■ User setup and test data. Identify users that must be set up in the system, including their user names, passwords, group memberships, assigned roles, and privileges (if not defined by group membership or role). Also identify the test data or conditions that must be set up to perform the tests included in the protocol. ■ Test procedure If subsections aren't used in the test section, then the purpose, materials and equipment required, and protocol acceptance criteria defined for the entire protocol in sections 2, 9, and 11, respectively, are sufficient. All that must be given in the test section is the test procedure.
14. Appendix A: Test instrument calibration	List all test instruments, and for each: ■ Identify last calibration date ■ Identify calibration due date ■ Attach calibration certificates

(continues)

Deliverable 8.1	Performance Qualification Protocol (continued)

Section	Contents
15. Appendix B: Signature log	All personnel involved in the execution or review of the protocol print their name and sign and initial a row in the form. (This appendix isn't needed if the signatures of all those involved are in a company log.)
16. Appendix C: Supporting documentation	Log and attach all supporting documentation (e.g., screen printouts and computer-generated reports) collected during test execution.
17. Appendix D: Variance procedure and form	Provide the variance form and instructions for completing it.

Preparation Tips: The PQ can be limited to functions that are used to perform work that's required by the regulations.

Vary the form of the test sections to fit the approach used for the PQ. Checklists and tables can be used in place of the more common tables for recording data. (See the tables provided in exhibit 10.2 versus those given in exhibits 9.3 and 9.4.)

Prepare the tests so they can be done in parallel unless the results of one test are dependent on the outcome of the processing done in another test. Conducting tests simultaneously might shorten the duration required for the PQ.

Approvals and Signatures:
■ Protocol author
■ Project manager or team leader
■ System owner
■ Quality assurance
■ Validation

Deliverable 8.2 Risk Management Report

Purposes: The purposes of the risk management report are to:
- Summarize the risk management process.
- Identify aspects of the system that initially were moderate and high risks.
- Record the mitigations taken to:
  - ☐ Reduce the likelihood of a failure occurring.
  - ☐ Improve ability to detect a failure.
  - ☐ Reduce the harm that would occur from a failure.

- Document the effect of the mitigation actions on the risks.
- Record the residual risk. This is the risk that remains after the mitigations have had an effect. Make a judgment as to whether the residual risk is acceptable.
- Explain the results of any risk-to-benefit analysis.

Resources Used:
- Much of the risk management report consists of the risk assessment tables that have been developed and updated throughout the life cycle.
- ISO 14971:2000, Medical devices—Application of risk management to medical devices. International Organization for Standardization, 2000.
- Stein, R. Timothy. "System Risk Management Procedure." Business Performance Associates, 2002. (See *www.bpaconsultants.com*.)

Risk-Based Adjustments: If a system is judged to be low risk in phase 1 because a failure to meet requirements will have an inconsequential effect along all the important dimensions of harm, detailed risk assessment and risk management reports aren't needed as long as the results of the initial risk assessment are appropriately documented.

Risk Management Report Outline	
Section	**Contents**
1. Cover page	■ Title. Include the name of application that's being evaluated. ■ Report date ■ Report author ■ Signature lines ■ Identification of your company and, if relevant, the division that owns the system
2. Purpose	To summarize the risk management process and results and to draw a conclusion regarding the residual risk of the system at the time of its initial use in production

(continues)

| Deliverable 8.2 | Risk Management Report (continued)) |

Section	Contents
3. References	List the documents identified in the report.
4. Summary of the risk management process	A recap of the steps taken during the risk management process with references to the documents or reports that record the outcome of the activities
5. Risk assessment and evaluation	A summary of the risk assessment results, including decisions on which risks required mitigation, the mitigation actions taken, the success of those mitigations, and risk level that remains after the mitigations. This information can be presented in a single table. (See the example given in chapter 10.)
6. Residual risk	■ A statement of the residual risk level for the system ■ A conclusion as to whether the residual risk is acceptable based on the criteria established in the validation plan, the risk management plan, or a company policy or procedure on risk management. ■ A summary of the risk-to-benefits analysis, if one was conducted, and the conclusion of that analysis ■ If the system will be used in the presence of a substantial risk, a summary of a contingency processes for responding to system failures and maintaining business processes after a system failure. Reference such a process or include it in an appendix.
7. Summary and conclusion	A summary statement as to the residual risk level of the system. If the residual risk is substantial, summarize the result of the risk-to-benefit analysis, and include a reference to the processes that have been developed for responding to system failures and for maintaining business processes after a system failure.
8. Appendix A	Risk assessment report
9. Appendix B	Risk-benefit report (if a risk to benefit analysis is conducted)
10. Appendix C	Contingency process for response to system failures (if the system will be used in the presence of substantial risk)

Preparation Tips: The risk assessment report is first prepared as part of the detailed risk assessment in phase 4 and is revised at several points, including phase 8 after the effectiveness of the mitigations is determined. Develop the risk assessment report in such a manner that traceability can be seen for each hazard from risk analysis, to evaluation (i.e., whether risk mitigation is necessary), to mitigation, and the estimate of the residual risk. Such traceability is required in Section 8 of ISO 14971. An example of a tabular format for reporting this data is shown in exhibit 10.3. The risk assessment report can be incorporated directly into the risk management report.

Approvals and Signatures:
- System owner
- Information technology
- Quality assurance
- Validation

Deliverable 8.3	Validation Final Report

Purposes: The purposes of the validation final report are to:
- Summarize the validation process.
- Report on the results obtained during the validation process.
- Record the extent to which the validation as conducted met the requirements stated in the company's validation policy and procedures as well as the validation plan written for the system.
- Address any outstanding issues regarding how the validation was conducted or the results of the validation.
- Draw a definitive conclusion regarding the ability of the system to perform to requirements throughout its operating ranges and make a recommendation regarding the ongoing use of the system.

In preparing the report, the author must check the entire validation record to make sure that all required activities specified in the validation plan have been performed, and all required deliverables are complete, appropriately approved, and archived as part of the validation record.

The validation final report can also include an assessment of the business question of whether the system is successful and cost effective in meeting the company's automation needs.

Resources Used: The documents created during the life cycle are used in preparing the report.
- The validation plan defines what was to be done during the validation and why. It also identifies the documents that form the validation record, and states the system acceptance criteria that must be met.
- Protocol reports—e.g., for the installation qualification (IQ), operational qualification (OQ), and performance qualification (PQ)—provide information on whether the required prerequisites were completed and evaluate the results obtained in light of the protocol acceptance criteria.
- The risk management report summarizes the risk management process and its results. The residual risk is identified, and the results of the risk-benefit analysis, if conducted, are reported.
- A validation final report template available from Business Performance Associates. (See *www.bpaconsultants.com*.)

Risk-Based Adjustments: If the validation testing is performed through a single protocol, the protocol report can be written in such a manner that it also serves as the validation final report. This can be accomplished with simple or low-risk systems. However, for high-risk systems a review of the findings related to the high-risk aspects of the system should also be included.

Validation Final Report Outline	
Section	**Contents**
1. Cover page	<ul><li>Title. Include the system that was evaluated.</li><li>Report date</li><li>Report author</li><li>Signature lines</li><li>Identification of your company and, if relevant, the division that owns the system</li></ul>
2. Purpose	To summarize the validation process and results for a named system and to draw a conclusion as to whether it meets the system acceptance criteria. Include a brief description of the system.
3. References	References for all of the documents sited in the report
4. Summary of the validation approach	A summary of the validation approach as presented in the validation plan
5. Analysis of the validation process	An analysis of how well the validation process, activities, and deliverables required by the validation plan were performed. Identify any discrepancies. If a variance was prepared and approved for a deviation in the validation process or deliverables, discuss the variance. If a variance wasn't created, justify the discrepancy.
6. Analysis of the validation results	<ul><li>A list of the life cycle deliverables identified in the validation plan that will be included in the validation record. The current status of each of the deliverables (all should be complete and approved). An identification of any shortcomings.</li><li>A summary of the results of the protocols that were executed as part of the validation (e.g., IQ, OQ, and PQ) and the variances for each. A discussion of the effect of each open variance on the system's ability to meet requirements.</li><li>A discussion of the changes to the system made to resolve variances. A conclusion regarding whether all related documentation was appropriately updated. (See chapter 10.)</li></ul>

(continues)

Deliverable 8.3	Validation Final Report (continued)

Validation Final Report Outline	
Section	**Contents**
7. Risk mitigation and residual risk	■ A discussion, for functions that were assessed as high-risk without the influence of mitigations or the validation results, of the evidence that supports the proper functioning of each high-risk aspect of the system and functions that are intended to mitigate the high risk ■ A listing of all remaining moderate- and high-risk items and a discussion of why the risks associated with these aren't being further reduced ■ A discussion of the overall residual risk of the system ■ A summary of the risk-benefit justification for using the system if the residual risk is high
8. System acceptance criteria	A summary of the data that are related to each system acceptance criterion and a conclusion regarding the degree to which each is met
9. Conclusion	■ An overall conclusion, based on the acceptance criteria regarding the ability of the system to consistently meet requirements throughout its operating range ■ A statement regarding the use of the system in a production environment. The statement can be that the system is ready for unconditional use for its intended purposes, that part of the system can be used, or that the system can't be used.

Preparation Tips: The bulk of the material contained in the report should come from other documents and reports as outlined in "Resources Used."

When all of the testing is performed through a single protocol, one report can be prepared that combines the protocol report and the validation final report.

Approvals and Signatures:
■ System owner
■ Information technology
■ Quality assurance
■ Validation

Appendix B

Summary of RiskVal Risk-Management Activities

Appendix B highlights the risk management activities that are performed during the Computer System Risk Management and Validation (RiskVal) life cycle. This summary will enable readers to trace the risk management activities through the life cycle and identify the deliverables that have risk management content.

Table B.1 presents risk management-related activities for each RiskVal phase along with their associated deliverables. In the biotech industries, ISO14971:2000 has become the standard for risk management.[1] Although the standard is written for managing risks associated with medical devices, the steps defined in it are rapidly becoming the standard for risk management across regulated industries. Table B.1 also gives the corresponding ISO 14971:2000 steps for each risk-management activity defined in the RiskVal life cycle. Each of the ISO 14971:2000 steps has a corresponding activity in the RiskVal model. Following table B.1 the 13 risk management steps defined in ISO 13487 are summarized.

Note: Table B.1 identifies only risk-management activities (i.e., the identification, evaluation, and reduction of risk). RiskVal activities that aren't related to risk management haven't been included.

Table B.1		RiskVal Life Cycle Risk-Management Activities		

RiskVal phase	RiskVal risk-management activities	Risk-related purpose of the activity	RiskVal deliverable and/or method	ISO 14971 Step
1. Conceptualize	Create the computer system validation capability	Prepare a risk management policy, procedure, and instructions on methods to: ■ Establish when risk management is required. ■ Define the requirements for appropriate risk management. ■ Provide a process for the management of risk associated with computer systems. ■ Train employees. ■ Provide tools for risk assessment. (See phase 4.)	■ Risk management policy ■ Risk management procedure	0 (Section 4.1)
	Clarify and state the needs for the system as intended uses.	The intended uses set the context in which potential harm can be assessed.	Deliverable 1.5—Computer System Project Proposal	1
	Perform an initial risk analysis.	To make an initial assessment of the risk level of the system to: ■ Alert management to potential risks of the system being proposed. ■ Use the system level as a guide in applying the RiskVal life cycle. ■ Identify some of the user requirements. ■ Set the priority for the validation of existing systems.	Deliverable 1.5—Computer System Project Proposal	N/A
2. Define requirements.	N/A			
3. Select vendors and systems.	N/A			
4. Design solutions to issues.	Conduct a detailed risk assessment and evaluation.	■ To prepare the severity of harm and the likelihood of harm scales for use in the assessment, and develop a method for determining the risk level (if these aren't already specified in the risk management procedure). ■ To determine the risk level of potential failures of the system ■ To evaluate if measures must be taken to mitigate a risk	■ Deliverable 4.1 —Risk Assessment Report ■ Method 4.1—Failure Mode and Effect Analysis ■ Method 4.2—Fault-Tree Analysis ■ Method 4.3—Hazard Analysis and Critical Control Points	2, 3, 4
	Plan mitigations	■ To develop methods for reducing the risks associated with the system, as needed. Risk is lowered by:	Planned mitigations are recorded in deliverable 4.1—Risk Assessment Report.	5, 9

RiskVal phase	RiskVal risk-management activities	Risk-related purpose of the activity	RiskVal deliverable and/or method	ISO 14971 Step
		☐ Reducing the frequency with which the failure will occur ☐ Reducing the likelihood that the failure will result in the harm ☐ Diminishing the harm that results from the failure ☐ Improving the detectability of a hazard of failure before it can create harm ■ Methods for reducing the occurrence of the failure can include: ☐ Modifying the system ☐ Introducing preventive or protective measures into the process ☐ Providing training, instructions, and/or warnings to the user ■ Evaluate the possible mitigations to determine if they'll introduce additional risks	If the implementation of the mitigations is complex, or if numerous mitigations are necessary, a mitigation plan might be prepared.	
	Prepare a risk management plan	The validation plan includes a plan for managing risk associated with the system	Deliverable 4.2—Validation Plan	Section 3.5
5. Construct solutions to issues.	Implement the mitigation plan.	To put in place methods designed to reduce risk during phase 4	Documentation is updated for the mitigation actions, including requirements, user procedures, user instructions, user training, and warnings. Software changes are documented in the programs and system documentation. Hardware changes are documented in system configuration documentation and system specification.	6
	Test the effectiveness of the mitigations.	To formally or informally test the mitigations to determine if they're effective and adequate	Mitigation report (if formal testing is done)	6
	Evaluate residual risk for each potential failure.	To revise the risk assessment of individual failures based on the formal or informal assessment of the effectiveness of the mitigations	Revised Deliverable 4.1—Risk Assessment Report	6
	Determine and evaluate the overall residual risk	To determine the overall risk of the system based on the risks that remain for each potential failure	Revised deliverable 4.1—Risk Assessment Report	10, 7

(continues)

Table B.1		RiskVal Life Cycle Risk-Management Activities (continued)		
RiskVal phase	**RiskVal risk-management activities**	**Risk-related purpose of the activity**	**RiskVal deliverable and/or method**	**ISO 14971 Step**
	Risk-benefit analysis	To determine if the benefits outweigh the risks of using the system	Revised deliverable 4.1—Risk Assessment Report	8
6. Prepare for use.	N/A			
7. Qualify the system.	N/A			
8. Use in a production environment.	Update the risk assessment.	To revise the risk assessment based on: ■ Tests of the mitigations in the operational and/or performance qualifications ■ A change in the assumption of the likelihood of a software failure based on the validation results, if appropriate	Revised deliverable 4.1—Risk Assessment Report	10
	Evaluate the overall residual risk	■ To revise the estimate of the overall residual risk based on the revisions of the risk assessments for the individual failures ■ If the overall residual risk is higher than desired, determine if further reduction of risk is practical. If so, define and implement the mitigations.	If further mitigations are taken, they're recorded in the revised deliverable 4.1—Risk Assessment Report.	11
	Perform a risk-benefit analysis.	If the overall residual risk is higher than desired, and further reduction of the risk is impractical, determine if the benefits of using the system outweigh the risks.	Revised deliverable 4.1—Risk Assessment Report	11
	Write a risk management report.	To document the risk management aspects of the life cycle and to summarize the state of the system from a risk management perspective	Risk management report	12
	Prepare the validation final report.	To summarize the risk management aspects of the life cycle and the state of the system from a risk management perspective	Validation final report	12
	Post-implementation risk management	■ To review information on the frequency and nature of system failures to determine if the judgments made in the risk assessment and evaluation were correct ■ To conduct periodic reviews of moderate- and high-risk systems to determine if: ☐ Previously unrecognized hazards are present ☐ Judgments concerning likelihood of harm and the severity of harm were wrong ☐ Additional mitigations are needed ☐ System should be discontinued because of the level risk associated with specific failures or residual risk	Periodic system review summary	13

RISK MANAGEMENT STEPS FROM ISO 14971:2000

ISO 14971:2000, Medical devices—Application of risk management to medical devices, is written so that its risk-reduction steps are performed on one potential failure at a time. These steps include:

- Step 5—Option analysis
- Step 6—Implementation of risk control measures
- Step 7—Residual risk evaluation
- Step 8—Risk-benefit analysis

The RiskVal life cycle is written so that each of these steps is performed at approximately the same time for all potential failures.

Following are the risk management steps referenced above for ISO 14971:2000 and the key activities performed in each step.

Risk management plan (Section 3.5). The risk management plan is prepared before the first step. The plan includes:

- Scope of the plan
- A verification plan
- Allocation of responsibilities
- Requirements for review of risk management activities
- Criteria for risk acceptability

Step 1—Define the intended use and/or intended purpose and identify aspects of the system that could affect safety:

- Describe the intended use and/or intended purpose.
- Describe any reasonable foreseeable misuses.
- List the qualitative and quantitative characteristics that could affect the safety of the device.

Step 2—Identify known or foreseeable hazards.
Step 3—Estimate the risk(s) of each hazard.
Step 4—Risk evaluation
Step 5—Option analysis:

- Identification of alternative risk control measures

Step 6—Implement risk control measures:

- Implement the risk control measures.
- Verify the implementation of the risk control measures.
- Verify the effectiveness of the risk control measures and record.

Step 7—Evaluate residual risk:

- Evaluate the residual risk using the criteria defined in the risk management plan.
- Apply further control measures if the residual risk doesn't meet the criteria.
- If the residual risk is acceptable, all relevant information necessary to explain the residual risk shall be put in documents supplied by the manufacturer.

Step 8—Conduct risk-benefit analysis:

Step 9—Review risk control measures to see if other hazards were introduced.

- Assess new risks and mitigate the new risks as necessary.

Step 10—Completeness of risk evaluation:

- Verify that all identified hazards have been evaluated.

Step 11—Overall residual risk evaluation:

- Decide if the overall residual risk is acceptable.
- If the residual risk is unacceptable, perform a risk-benefit analysis to determine if the benefits justify the residual risk.

Step 12—Risk management report:

- Record the results of the risk management process.
- Provide traceability from each hazard to the risk analysis, risk evaluation, implementation of risk control measures, and the determination of whether the residual risk is acceptable.

Step 13—Post-production information:

- Establish and maintain a systematic procedure for the review of post-release information about the system that's relevant to the management of system risks.
- Feed back the results of the evaluation as input to the risk management process.
- Determine if the execution of the risk management steps need to be modified.
- If the acceptability of the residual risk has changed, evaluate the adequacy of previously implemented risk control measures (i.e., mitigations).

Appendix C

Advanced Computer System Risk Assessment

This appendix offers an alternative to the discussion of detailed risk assessment presented in chapter 6. The assumption is made there that the software is developed with few defined methods, and the likelihood of failure is set at probable. The discussion here presents the task of risk assessment in greater depth and provides guidance if you wish to develop your own scale for the severity of harm or the likelihood of a software failure. Appendix C:

- Describes and compares three common methods of risk analysis: failure mode and effects analysis (FMEA, see method 4.1 in appendix A), fault-tree analysis (FT, see method 4.2), and hazard analysis and critical control points (HACCP, see method 4.3)

- Provides guidance on the development of risk analysis scales for those who want to develop their own

- Presents an example of a likelihood of software failure scale based on software development methodologies.

- Presents a risk evaluation table for determining risk levels and deciding if further mitigation is needed

As a prelude to discussing risk analysis and mitigation, several terms should be clarified.[1] "Risk analysis" means identifying hazards and estimating the associated risk level. "Risk evaluation" involves evaluating the risk level to determine if it's acceptable. "Risk assessment" is the process of performing both a risk analysis and evaluation. "Risk mitigation" means using methods to reduce the risk associated with failure. (See the glossary for exact definitions.)

Risk analysis, assessment, mitigation, and management as discussed in this book are best performed within the context of a risk management policy and procedure such as the one discussed in chapter 3.[2, 3] Although the discussion is from the point of view of commercial-off-the-shelf (COTS) and configured systems, these concepts also apply to existing and custom systems.

A detailed risk analysis isn't necessary if the initial risk analysis (performed during phase 1) has documented that the system is low-risk.

RISK ANALYSIS METHODOLOGIES

Three primary methods are used for analyzing risk.[4, 5] These are described in the following table C.1, Comparison of Risk Analysis Methods. The table indicates the most common uses of each method in conjunction with computer systems, and what knowledge is required to use the method. FMEA, the most common method, can be used to assess the risks associated with any computer system.

Table C.1	Comparison of Risk Analysis Methods		
Name	**Approach to identifying failures and risks**	**Required knowledge**	**Most common uses**
Failure mode and effect analysis (method 4.1)[6]	Possible failures and hazards are identified for each function the system will perform.	■ Intended uses and user requirements ■ How the system works on a functional level	Software and systems where the structure of the system is unknown
Fault tree (method 4.2)[7]	Failures are identified for the system, and possible causes are identified within the structure of the system down to a level where further analysis isn't possible.	■ Understanding of the system's structure, how each component and subsystem works, and how they work together ■ Knowledge of how a failure of one component of the system will affect other components	Evaluation of hardware when the frequencies of failure data are available at the component and/or subsystem levels. FT is often used with automated systems that include embedded software. It's also used for hazard analysis of custom code based on the design.[8]
Hazard analysis and critical control points (method 4.3)[9]	Possible failures and hazards of the system are identified for steps of the process controlled by the system.	The flow of the business process to be automated	Automated manufacturing processes

The first preparatory task for all methods is to develop the rating scales to be used in the analysis.[10] If such scales aren't contained in your risk management procedure described in chapter 3, they must be created prior to starting the risk analysis.

SEVERITY OF HARM SCALE

To create a rating scale for severity, start by making a general list of the types of harm that could result from system failures. Not only will the list be useful in setting up the severity rating scale, but it also will help when you brainstorm the harm that could result from specific failures. Some examples of dimensions of harm are provided in exhibit 6.2 in chapter 6. Keep in mind that if you intend to use the risk analysis as a determinant of the rigor and intensity of your validation effort, you need to include in your analysis any consequences of a failure on the safety and efficacy of the product, and the accuracy and reliability of quality records.

Once the general list of the types of harm has been created, define qualitative or quantitative levels of severity along the dimensions of harm you've identified. Examples of severity levels are provided in chapter 6's exhibit 6.2, which gives a scale with four levels for seven types of harm. The Food and Drug Administration (FDA) has defined three levels of concern related to the safety for medical devices that can be used as severity levels. These are defined in chapter 6.

Four severity levels are used here that follow the IEEE Standard for Software Verification and Validation, annex B, and Military Standard 882C so as to differentiate two levels of high severity.[11, 12] When the business implications of a failure are taken into account in addition to potential harm, it's useful to use a four-level scale. The bottom two levels of the scale presented in this book are equivalent to the lower two levels of the FDA scale. In essence the FDA's highest level has been split into two. Death to one or more individuals is placed at the catastrophic level and serious injury at the critical level. These levels are depicted in exhibit 6.2 in chapter 6. Examples of how to apply the severity of impact scales are given in chapter 6.

As an example, consider the manufacture of a drug in a reactor. When the raw materials are added to the reactor, the reaction takes place. The reaction gives off heat, and a cooling jacket that surrounds the reactor keeps the reactor and its contents from getting too hot. Software controls the temperature of the coolant and its circulation through the jacket. If the temperature rises too high, the drug will decompose, which will result in a lower yield and more byproducts that could lead to serious injury. Quality control tests are performed to identify the level of byproducts in the final crystallized drug. If the level of byproducts is too high, the batch will have to be destroyed. The severity of the loss of the batch, which is valued at $100,000, is at the moderate level as defined in exhibit 6.2. The release of a batch with too high of a level of byproducts could cause serious injury and would be assigned a severity level of critical per the definitions of severity levels given in exhibit 6.2.

A second example involves a CD burner used to duplicate instructions for using an instrument to diagnose allergies, including allergies that could be fatal. Nurses in doctors' offices are potential users in addition to professional test labs. The CD burner does a sum check on 100 percent of the CDs after they're written. The worse consequence of the CD writer failing would be a misdiagnosis of a severe allergy because the operator didn't use the instrument properly. Because this could result in death, the severity level is catastrophic. A second consequence might be anticipated along the lines of customer satisfaction. The user who receives an instrument with a blank or corrupted CD can be expected to be dissatisfied, which would rate as moderate severity.

A SCALE FOR THE LIKELIHOOD THAT THE SYSTEM WILL FAIL

The second task is to develop a way to determine the likelihood that the system will fail.[13, 14] If you're evaluating the probability of a hardware failure, you can use the manufacturer's or industry's failure rate data for components in the fault-tree approach (see method 4.2) to calculate the probability of failure. With such an approach, the likelihood scale consists of ranges of probability values.[15]

Two Options for Assessing the Likelihood of a Software Failure

It's difficult to determine the likelihood (or probability) of a software failure. As ISO 14971 points out, software errors are systematic errors (i.e., they'll occur under a particular combination of input or contextual conditions). The problem is estimating the probability that software will have a defect that will cause a particular function to fail. It's especially difficult when you haven't had experience with the software. There are two options. The first is to take a conservative approach and assign a high probability of failure to all functions. This approach is taken in chapter 6, where the likelihood of a software failure is assigned at the probable level.

Note: Because a definitive scale can't be developed for rating the likelihood of a software failure, the FDA advises regulated companies to use this approach.

The second approach is to assign a likelihood of failure based on the methods used to develop the software. Information on the development methods is gathered during the vendor audit. A likelihood of failure level is then assigned using a scale that relates development practices to the likelihood of failure. Both ISO 14971 and Gamp 4 recognize that there's a relationship between the quality of the development process and the possibility of a systematic fault being introduced and/or remaining undetected.[16, 17]

It's difficult to develop a likelihood of software failure scale that's based on research rather than assumptions or intuition. The best way, given the limited research that has been conducted, is to develop a scale based on research results at a high rather than a detailed level.

Note: The following example presented in table C.3 represents such a scale and shouldn't be considered definitive. Exercise caution in using it. If you do use such an approach, adjust your likelihood ratings, if needed, after the system has been put into use. Be aware of the frequency with which the software is failing. If necessary, change your judgment of the likelihood of failure and recalculate the risk levels. Examine the revised risk ratings and determine if additional mitigations are needed.

The first option (i.e., assuming a high likelihood of failure) is the more conservative approach. The second option is advantageous if you're confident in evaluating the development practices of software vendors. Based on your audit, you might be able to make an initial assumption about the likelihood of failure that's more accurate than assuming it's at the probable level. When the likelihood of failure level is initially assessed at the occasional level or lower, the risk levels will be lower and less will have to be done to reduce them to an acceptable level.

Research Related to the Likelihood of Software Failure

In this section some of the research that relates software development practices to the level of software defects will be reviewed as a background for creating a likelihood of software failure scale.

For readers who aren't interested in the specifics of the research, here are my conclusions. These form the basis for the likelihood of software failure scale presented in table C.2:

- In general, the greater the number of defect-detection and -prevention methods used, the fewer defects that are inadvertently created during development and the higher the percentage of defects found before the software is shipped to customers.

■ Different combinations of defect-detection methods can lead to similar levels of defect detection.

■ It's difficult to develop a clear-cut scale that can be used to accurately predict the quality of the software. Consequently, such scales should be used conservatively in analyzing the risk level of a software package. Estimates of the likelihood of a system failure based on a scale like that presented in table C.3 should be revised, as needed, based on your experience with the system once it's in use.

Capers Jones reports on the effectiveness of various defect-removal methods and their effectiveness when used in combination. His results are presented in exhibit C.1. The findings show a dramatic difference between systems that are developed without any defect-detection methods or formal quality assurance (QA) system, and systems that include defect-detection methods extensively used within a formal quality system. Jones reports a model of the defect efficiency of sixteen scenarios in which four defect-detection techniques are used individually and in combination.[18] The four techniques are:

■ Design inspections
■ Code inspections
■ Formal quality assurance program
■ Formal testing

The scenarios are clustered into five groups of similar defect-detection results. The data, which are reproduced with permission, appear in exhibit C.1; a summary is provided in table C.2. To approximate the average defect removal of the scenarios clustered at a level, the median values reported by Jones and shown in exhibit C.1 have been averaged.

Table C.2	Defect Removal Efficiencies	
Cluster	**Description of defect removal methods**	**Defect removal efficiency value**
1	None of the four methods are used.	40%
2	One of the four methods is used by itself or a combination of two of any of the following three: code inspections, QA, and formal testing.	60%
3	Combination of formal design review with any one of the other three methods	80%
5	Combination of any three of the methods	92%
6	All four methods are used.	99%

Exhibit C.1 Efficiency of Defect-Removal Techniques Used Individually and in Combination

Cluster	Description	Defect-detection method				Defect-removal efficiency			
		Design inspection	Code inspection	QA	Formal testing	Lowest	Median	Highest	Average of median values
1	None of the four	X	X	X	X	30%	40%	50%	40%
2	Any one of the methods or any two except design inspections	X	X	Yes	X	32%	45%	55%	60%
		X	X	X	Yes	37%	53%	60%	
		X	Yes	X	X	43%	57%	65%	
		Yes	X	X	X	45%	60%	68%	
		X	X	Yes	Yes	50%	65%	75%	
		X	Yes	Yes	X	53%	68%	78%	
		X	Yes	X	Yes	55%	70%	80%	
3	Design inspections and any one of the other three	Yes	X	Yes	X	60%	75%	65%	80%
		Yes	X	X	Yes	65%	80%	87%	
		Yes	Yes	X	X	70%	85%	90%	
4	Any three of the methods	X	Yes	Yes	Yes	75%	87%	93%	92%
		Yes	X	Yes	Yes	77%	90%	95%	
		Yes	Yes	Yes	X	83%	95%	97%	
		Yes	Yes	X	Yes	85%	97%	99%	
5	All four	Yes	Yes	Yes	Yes	95%	99%	99%	

X = Method wasn't used
Yes = Method was used

These data are reprinted with permission from Capers Jones, "Software Quality in 2003: A Survey of the State of the Art," February 20, 2003. Software Productivity Research, *www.spr.com*. The median values of the system have been clustered and averaged here.

In other research, Jones shows that other combinations of activities can also lead to a high level of defect removal.[19] Jones also found that using the ten most effective defect-detection methods resulted in removing 99 percent of the defects before the system was put into use in more than half of the systems he studied. The top ten defect detection methods are:

- Personal checking of design or documents by the author
- Informal group design reviews
- Formal design inspections
- Modeling or prototyping during programming
- Personal checking of code by the author
- Formal code inspections
- Unit testing (single modules)
- Functional testing (related modules)
- Integrated testing (complete system)
- Field testing (live beta testing)

Jones concludes, based on empirical observations of nearly 7,000 software projects derived from close to 600 companies, that a combination of defect prevention and removal activities are necessary to ensure good to excellent quality software.[20] His list of minimum requirements is presented in exhibit C.2.

Likelihood of Software Failure Scale

Table C.3 defines a qualitative scale for the likelihood of a software failure or the failure of a specific software function based on life cycle practices. Adjustments can be made for the presence of other factors that influence the software's quality. The likelihood levels are derived based on the assumption that the application is of moderate size and complexity. It's difficult to create a definitive likelihood scale because more than forty defect-removal practices had been developed by 1986.[21] As Jones illustrates, different combinations of these methods will have different levels of effectiveness.[22] It's not practical to include all possible combinations of these methods in a scale. What's been developed is a yardstick with rough demarcations but with clear differences in the quantity of defect-prevention and -detection methods used. Readers can create their own likelihood scales based on other research with which they're familiar.

An explanation is needed for two statements made in table C.3. First, if a system is developed without any of the development practices recommended by industry

| Exhibit C.2 | Minimum Software Development Practices for Good to Excellent Quality |

In *Software Quality: Analysis and Guidelines for Success,* Capers Jones concludes that the following sequence of defect-prevention and -removal activities is necessary to ensure good to excellent quality.

Defect-Prevention Approaches
- Formal requirements analysis such as joint application design (JAD)
- Formal risk-analysis early in development
- Prototyping
- Structured or formal specifications methods
- Structured programming methods
- Certified reusable design and code components

Non-Test Defect-Removal Methods
- Requirements inspections
- Design inspections
- Code inspections
- Test plan reviews
- Test-case inspections
- User documentation editing or reviews

Testing Defect-Removal Methods
- Unit test by individual programmers
- New function testing
- Regression testing
- Performance testing
- Integration testing
- System testing
- Field test (external beta test)

Reprinted with permission from Jones, Capers. *Software Quality: Analysis and Guidelines for Success.* London: International Thomson Computer Press, 1997, p. 164.

standards, guidance documents, or activities listed in exhibit C.2 (i.e., no written requirements, design or technical documentation, coding standards, tools or inspections, formal testing, and QA), the likelihood of failure is assigned as frequent. Such vendors and their systems should be disqualified unless the system is low risk or there's no other reasonable choice. The quality of such systems depends entirely on the skills and abilities of the developer(s), and its reliability must be regarded as highly suspect.

If such a system is brought into an organization, extensive testing must be performed as part of the validation process. Extensive testing must also be performed after most changes because it's difficult to predict how a change in part of such a system will affect other parts. In fact, many organizations will freeze such applications (except when very simple programming is involved) and won't allow any changes under any circumstances. The future value of such applications is greatly limited because they can't be adapted to changes in how business is done.

The same thinking applies to systems developed internally. For example, many organizations have developed their own quality system software using a database application. If such a system has been developed as handcrafted software (i.e., with no written requirements, design or technical documentation, coding standards, and formal testing), the likelihood of failure should be evaluated as frequent and, as is the case with external developers, the developer should be disqualified. The software shouldn't be used unless it's a low-risk system or if no reasonable alternative is available, including discarding the system and starting over. As mentioned in chapter 5, internal developers must be qualified in the same manner as external developers.[23] Second, as discussed in chapter 1, differences in operating systems, such as different versions of UNIX used on different types of servers, can result in code that works properly in one environment but fails miserably in another. A customized and/or configured document-control system developed for a diagnostic company, for example, passed all tests performed in the development environment. However, when it was installed at the company and the same tests were performed, thirty-three defects, including some serious security problems, were identified.[24] Many software companies will certify their COTS applications for specific releases of certain operating systems. If a system isn't certified for the operating system software you're using, there's a danger of compatibility issues regardless of the how well the software is engineered.

This concern has been incorporated into the criteria given in table C.3 for determining the likelihood of software failures. For the likelihood to be assessed at the remote or improbable levels, the application must be certified for the operating system you're using. For systems that aren't certified in that manner, a likelihood of occasional or higher must be assigned. The likelihood of software failure presented in table C.3 is based on the research reviewed.

Note: As stated previously, the scale shouldn't be considered definitive. Exercise caution in using it. Be conservative. If you're unsure if a developer qualifies for a level, assign a lower likelihood level.

Table C.3		Likelihood Levels for Software Failures
Likelihood	**Definition**	**Software development life cycle activities**
Frequent (ad hoc develop-ment)	High probability of occurrence	■ No formal development methods ■ No coding tools used ■ No deliverables from the development process except for the programming ■ Limited informal testing by the developer Note: See the discussion above about disqualifying such software

Probable (un-documented methods)	Moderate probability of occurrence	■ Undocumented methods
		■ Unstructured development
		■ No coding tools used
		■ A few defect-prevention and -detection practices, such as a written require-ments statement, and one or more of the following:
		  ☐ Design inspections
		  ☐ Code inspections
		  ☐ Formal QA process
		  ☐ Formal testing
		
		■ Defects identified during the development process are tracked, and problems are fixed.

Occasional (defined process)	Will occur occasionally	■ Defined development process that includes defined requirements for life cycle activities ■ Extensive formal testing
Remote (formal life cycle)	Unlikely to occur	■ Structured methods/life cycle for requirements, design, development, verifica-tion, and support ■ Several defect prevention or detection methods beyond formal testing, includ-ing requirements review, design inspections, and code inspections ■ Software is certified by the developer for the system software and database versions that you'll use with the system.
Improbable (managed life cycle)	Probability of occurrence is so small that the event isn't expected to occur.	■ Structured methods or life cycle for requirements, design, development, verifi-cation, and support ■ Extensive defect detection methods are used, including but not limited to re-quirements review, design inspections, code inspections, and formal testing. ■ Activities are measured per quality and cost. ■ Formal programs are undertaken for the improvement of life cycle effective-ness and software quality. ■ Software is certified by the developer for the system software and database versions that you'll use with the system.

Once the system is validated, and the results indicate that it operates to requirements in your environment, you might be able to lower the likelihood of failure. If you perform only black-box testing on the system, your validation testing would be, at best, equivalent to the level of testing conducted on applications judged to be at the occasional likelihood of failure or higher. Based on black-box validation testing alone, you wouldn't be able to lower the probability beyond the occasional level. So why perform validation testing on systems with a likelihood of failure of occasional or lower? Because validation testing verifies that the system works effectively in your technical environment, and that it's effective in meeting your intended purposes in your automated process.

THE RISK EVALUATION

Use this likelihood scale, or a similar one you've developed, to determine the likelihood that a software failure will occur. Conduct a risk analysis and evaluation following the eight-step process described in chapter 6, or any other appropriate risk assessment method. For the pharmaceutical plant example in chapter 6, it's assumed that the likelihood of a software failure, before the validation is conducted, is occasional. Be careful in applying the steps to your situation if the likelihood of failure of your system is different. As described in the eight-step process, take into account the controls built into the system or the business process to control the risk when the risk level is determined. The need for mitigation is based on the risk level. Tables 6.6, 6.7, 6.8, 6.9, 6.10, and 6.11 in chapter 6 can be used for determining the risk level and evaluating if further mitigation is needed. Alternatively, the table given in exhibit C.3 can be used. The risk levels and recommendations are the same in the exhibit as they are in chapter 6. Record the results of your risk assessment as illustrated in exhibit 6.1, Risk Assessment Form, in chapter 6.

Exhibit C.3	Assessing Software Risks

Business Performance Associates (BPA) developed the following matrix for assessing software risks. The matrix estimates a likelihood of failure level based on development practices. Then, the matrix identifies a risk level for the combination of each likelihood level and each severity of impact level. Recommendations for mitigation are also provided. The recommendations are similar to those made in ISO 14971:2000.[25] See chapter 6 for a discussion of risk mitigation.

This table is built on the scales presented in appendix C. Note that these values for the likelihood of software failure are based on limited research and must used cautiously. A conservative approach is recommended when determining risk levels. Likelihood levels can be modified as you gain experience using the system. If your experience with the software indicates that the system fails more or less often that you expected, you should modify your risk assessments accordingly.

BPA Risk Assessment and Evaluation Matrix for Software					
Software development practices	**Likelihood of software failure**	**Software risk level and recommendations regarding mitigation based on the severity of harm caused by a failure**			
		Marginal	**Moderate**	**Critical**	**Catastrophic**
Ad hoc ■ No formal development methods ■ No coding tools used ■ No deliverables from the development process except for the programming ■ Limited informal testing by the developer Note: See text about disqualifying such software	**Frequent** High probability of occurrence	**Moderate risk** Mitigate if practicable	**High risk** Disqualify vendor; don't use software	**High risk** Disqualify vendor; don't use software	**High risk** Disqualify vendor; don't use software
Undocumented methods ■ Unstructured development ■ No coding tools used ■ A few defect-prevention or -detection practices: a written requirements statement and one or more of the following: ☐ Design inspections ☐ Code inspections ☐ Formal quality assurance process ☐ Formal testing ■ Defects identified during the development process are tracked and problems are fixed.	**Probable** Moderate probability of occurrence	**Low risk** Acceptable	**Moderate risk** Mitigation strongly advised	**High risk** Mitigate or justify use	**High risk** Mitigate or justify use

(continues)

| Exhibit C.3 | Assessing Software Risks (continued) | | | | |

Software development practices	Likelihood of software failure	Software risk level and recommendations regarding mitigation based on the severity of harm caused by a failure			
		Marginal	**Moderate**	**Critical**	**Catastrophic**
Defined process ■ Defined development process that includes defined requirements for life cycle activities ■ Extensive formal testing	**Occasional** Will occur occasionally	**Low** Acceptable	**Moderate risk** Mitigate if practicable	**Moderate risk** Mitigation strongly advised	**High risk** Mitigate or justify use
Formal life cycle ■ Structured methods for requirements, design, development, and verification and support ■ Several defect-prevention or -detection methods beyond formal testing, including requirements review, design inspections, and code inspections ■ Software is certified by the developer for the system software and database versions used with the system	**Remote** Unlikely to occur	**Low** Acceptable	**Low** Acceptable	**Moderate risk** Mitigate if practicable	**Moderate risk** Mitigation strongly advised
Managed life cycle ■ Structured methods or life cycle for requirements, design, development, verification, and support ■ Extensive defect-detection methods are used, including but not limited to: ☐ Requirements review ☐ Design inspections ☐ Code inspections ☐ Formal testing ■ Activities are measured re: quality and cost. ■ Formal programs are undertaken for improving life cycle effectiveness and software quality. ■ Software is certified by the developer for the system software and database versions that are used with the system.	**Improbable** Probability of occurrence so remote that it is not expected of occur	**Low** Acceptable	**Low** Acceptable	**Low** Acceptable	**Moderate risk** Mitigate if practicable

Appendix D

RiskVal Policies and Procedures

The following are the minimum set of validation policies and procedures recommended for organizations that meet the following criteria:

- You use a very small number of systems that require validation.
- You're not going to perform a detailed risk analysis and therefore won't treat separate functions differently during validation based on a detailed risk analysis.
- You're not required to meet the European Community Commission's directive for the manufacture of medicinal products.

This group of documents is available from Business Performance Associates as a starter kit (see *www.bpaconsultants.com*). The kit includes the following validation polices and procedures but doesn't include information technology (IT) procedures:

- Validation policy
- Validation of commercial off-the-shelf (COTS) computer systems. (This is a combined shorter version of the two computer-system validation procedures listed in table D.1.)
- Change control for validated systems
- Computer system project proposal
- Computer system vendor qualification and management
- Validation plan template
- Computer system technical requirements template
- Computer system specification template
- Installation qualification (IQ) template

- Operational qualification (OQ) template
- Performance qualification (PQ) template
- Validation final report template
- IT policy

Comprehensive List for Extensive Automation Companies

Table D.1 presents a more extensive list of documents that would be appropriate for an organization with extensive computer system validation needs. The policies and procedures that have been discussed in regard to the RiskVal life cycle are included in the table. If a deliverable brief describes the content of the policy or procedure, the deliverable is listed by name. The purpose and value of the procedure is also indicated. References are included only if any standard or regulatory document requires a documented policy or procedure. A reference isn't given if a standard or regulation only discusses an activity, such as qualifying a vendor, but doesn't explicitly call for a procedure.

The purpose of a procedure is to define a method to be used so that the work performed will meet requirements and be acceptable to your organization and, if relevant, regulatory bodies. A procedure is recommended if there's sufficient business or regulatory compliance reason for consistency in what and how something is done, or if those who will perform the procedure need instructions on what activities to perform or how to perform them. The procedures your organization needs depend upon the training of the individuals who will be performing the tasks, the business need for consistency, and the regulations with which you must comply. Many of the documents provided in table D.1 are available from Business Performance Associates. (See *www.bpaconsultants .com.*)

Table D.1	Software Validation Policies and Procedures Relevant to the RiskVal Life Cycle	

RiskVal policy or procedure and deliverable	Purpose or value	Requirement reference
Validation		
Deliverable 1.1, Validation policy	To define what must be validated and when, and to define requirements for different types of validations	None
Deliverable 1.2, Computer System Risk Management and Validation Life Cycle Procedure, two procedures were defined during phase 1 that together meet the needs of a validation procedure; this is the first.	To define the requirements and process for developing, selecting, validating, and using computer systems for the purposes of ensuring quality and complying with regulations	21 CFR 11, Section 11.10 a; ISO 13485, 7.5.2.1
Deliverable 1.4, Requirements for Computer System Validation Plans, Protocols, and Reports, two procedures were defined that together meet the needs of a validation procedure; this is the second.	To describe the content requirements for computer system validation plans, protocols, and reports, including the validation plan for a system, its IQ, OQ, and PQ validation protocols, protocol reports, and the final validation report	21 CFR 11, Section 11.10 a; ISO 13485, 7.5.2.1
Deliverable 6.2, Change Control Procedure; Deliverable 6.3, Change Control Request Form	To define a procedure for making alterations to a system. Change control includes validating, approving, and implementing a change. Change control ensures that a system remains in a validated state when changes are made.	ISO 13485, 7.5.2.1; EC Annex 11, No. 11; 21 CFR 11, Section 11.10 k 2
Deliverable 1.5, Computer System Project Proposal	To define informational needs and provide a form for recording the information about a proposed computer system, including an initial risk analysis. This document provides the information management needs to determine if the organization should proceed with the project.	None
Computer system vendor audit checklist	To provide guidance for auditing a software vendor and a form for recording findings	None
Computer system vendor qualification and management	To describe the requirements and process for qualifying and managing vendors that provide system software, application software, computer hardware, support services, or software development or integration services	21 CFR 820, Section 820.50 a; ISO 13485, Section 7.4.1 (Both documents require a procedure that covers all vendors)

(continues)

Table D.1	Software Validation Policies and Procedures Relevant to the RiskVal Life Cycle (continued)	
RiskVal policy or procedure and deliverable	**Purpose or value**	**Requirement reference**
Creating, validating, and using spreadsheets in conjunction with quality records	To provide a process for creating, validating, and using spreadsheets in conjunction with quality records	21 CFR 11, Section 11.10 a (A procedure is required if spreadsheets are validated by a different process than is used for other computer systems)
Guidance		
Risk-based guidance on computer system life cycle activities for types of systems	To provide guidance on the performance of life cycle activities based on the risk level of the system	None
Validation plan template	To provide a template for a validation plan for a system or piece of equipment	None
Computer system technical requirements template	To provide a template for preparing technical requirements for systems to be purchased. The template can include requirements for typical equipment and system software that can be edited	None
Computer system specification template	To provide a template for preparing system specifications for new and existing systems. The template can include specifications for typical equipment and system software that can be edited	None
IQ template	To provide a template for creating an IQ protocol for validating a system or piece of equipment. Such a template can include IQ items for typical pieces of equipment and system software.	None
OQ template	To provide a template for creating an OQ protocol for validating a system or piece of equipment	None
PQ template	To provide a template for creating a PQ protocol for validating a system or piece of equipment	None
Validation final report template	To provide a template for creating a validation report for a system or piece of equipment	None
21 CFR Part 11		
Assessing and achieving compliance with Part 11	To define the process for determining if Part 11 applies, assessing compliance with the regulation, and creating a remediation plan	None

RiskVal policy or procedure and deliverable	Purpose or value	Requirement reference
Creating and managing electronic records	■ To define the process for creating, managing, and retaining electronic quality records ■ To define acceptable standards for recording data and/or changing electronic quality records	ISO 13485:2003 Section 4.2.4 requires a procedure that defines the controls needed for the identification, storage, protection, retrieval, retention time, and disposition of quality records.
Risk management		
Risk management policy	A policy that defines when a formal process must be used to manage risks, the requirements for such a process, and identifies what are acceptable risks	ISO 14971:2000 Section 3.3
Risk management procedure	A procedure that defines the process for assessing and managing risk	ISO 14971:2000 Section 3.2
Failure mode and effects analysis (FMEA)	This procedure defines a process for conducting an FMEA analysis	None
Instrument and equipment management		
Instrument and equipment management	To describe the process for managing equipment, including receiving, establishing item history files, qualification, use logs, calibration, and preventive maintenance	None
Calibration and maintenance	■ To describe the process for calibrating equipment and maintaining calibration records. ■ To define the process for conducting preventive and corrective maintenance on equipment	21 CFR 211, Section 211.68 a; 21 CFR 820, Sections 820.70 g 1 and 820.72
Equipment qualification	To define the process for qualifying test and measurement equipment	None
Information technology		
Deliverable 1.3, Information Technology Policy	■ The establishment of written policies that hold individuals accountable and responsible for actions initiated under their electronic signatures to deter record and signature falsification. ■ To define the IT policy for procuring, managing, supporting, maintaining, and using computer systems and the infrastructure	21 CFR 11, Section 11.10 j
Backup, restore, and archive	To define a process for backing up computer systems and data, restoring lost or corrupted data, and moving data from active directories to an archive location	None

(continues)

Table D.1	Software Validation Policies and Procedures Relevant to the RiskVal Life Cycle (continued)	
RiskVal policy or procedure and deliverable	**Purpose or value**	**Requirement reference**
Network adds, changes, and deletes	To define the procedure for issuing, canceling, and altering authorization to enter and amend data, including changing personnel passwords	EC Annex 11, No. 8 21 CFR 11, Section 11.300 c
Disaster recovery and contingency plans	To define the procedure to be followed if systems fail or breaks down	EC Annex 11, No. 16
Logical and physical security	■ To establish procedures and controls for limiting system access to authorized individuals ■ To define controls over the distribution of, access to, and use of documentation for system operation and maintenance	21 CFR 11, Section 11.10 c and d EC Annex 11, No. 8
System support	To provide a procedure for recording and analyzing errors and to enable corrective action to be taken. The procedure includes issue tracking and resolution	EC Annex 11, No. 11 and 17
System maintenance	To establish the process for maintaining computing resources	21 CFR 211, Section 211.67; QSR, 820.70 g 1
Printer setup and driver verification	To establish a protocol for verifying that a printer is capable of printing accurate representations of electronic data, records, and reports	None
Desktop and laptop setup	To provide a procedure for setting up desktops and laptops so that all needed software is installed and configuration requirements of controlled software are met	None

Glossary

Acceptable quality level (AQL): The maximum amount of nonconformities (expressed in either a percentage or number per hundred units) that, for purposes of sampling inspection, can be considered satisfactory as a process average.[1, 2]

Acceptance criteria: The criteria a system or process must meet to satisfy a test or other requirements.[3]

Administrative change: Changes to documents that don't affect the product's form, fit, function, or how work is performed.

Application administrator: An individual trained to perform the administrative functions of an application, such as creating users, assigning users to groups, and assigning privileges to groups.

Applications created using database packages: Applications created by using a commercial package for storing, manipulating, and retrieving data. The package user typically creates an application using tools provided in the package for creating input screens, formulae, or macros for performing calculations and creating reports. Examples of such packages include Excel, Access, FileMaker Pro, and SAS.

Application software: A set of macros or computer program(s) designed to fulfill specific user needs. An application typically stores and/or processes data or information entered by input devices or users.

Archiving data: To remove data from an active database for storage in an archive.

Backward traceability: The ability to trace from a test conducted as part of a protocol back to a requirement for the item being tested.

Black-box testing: Testing conducted to evaluate the compliance of a system or component that ignores the internal structural mechanism of the system or component, focusing instead on the outputs generated in response to selected inputs and execution conditions.[4]

Boundary testing: A testing technique that uses input values at, just below, and just above the defined limits of an input domain, resulting in outputs that are at, just below, and just above the defined limits of the output domain.[5]

Boundary-value testing: See boundary testing.

Business harm: The effect a failure and/or hazard will have on equipment, processes, other company assets, or company efficiency or productivity.

Business Performance Associates (BPA): A consulting firm that specializes in software validation and the development of quality systems. See *www.bpaconsultants.com.*

Business sponsor: The manager responsible for the function or department that owns the system or item. This person usually has budget responsibilities as well.

Business systems: Computer systems that are used in conjunction with business processes for collecting and analyzing information.

Center for Devices and Radiological Health (CDRH): A division of the U.S. Food and Drug Administration.

CFR: Code of Federal Regulations

Change control: A formal system by which qualified representatives of appropriate disciplines review proposed or actual changes that might affect a validated status. To ensure that the system is maintained in a validated state, the actions taken are identified, tested, approved, and documented when completed.[6]

Clinical harm: The effect a failure and/or hazard will have on the quality of the product and, as a result, the safety of a patient.

Compliance harm: The effect of a failure and/or hazard on compliance with the company's policy, and/or external standards and regulations.

Computer system: Software components and associated hardware designed and assembled to perform a specific function or group of functions.[7]

Computer system validation: Confirmation by examination and providing objective evidence that a computer system's specifications conform to user needs and intended uses, and that the particular requirements implemented through the computer system can be consistently fulfilled.[8]

Computer system risk management and validation life cycle (RiskVal): A life-cycle process for a computer system that integrates achieving compliance (i.e., meeting requirements for performing regulated activities), ensuring software quality, managing the risks associated with system failures, and validation.

Computerized system specification: A document or set of documents that describes how a computerized system will satisfy the system requirements of the computer-related system.[9]

Concurrent validation: Documentation that a system meets acceptance criteria based on an approved validation protocol using information generated during actual process and/or system operation. The validation is conducted concurrently with the routine use of the system. Product manufactured with the system being validated must meet its predetermined specifications and quality characteristics before it's released for use.

Configured business applications: Applications that are tailored to the company's use by configuring predefined modules and/or developing new application functionality by means of embedded tools. At least three types of configuration are possible: selecting preferences, creating functionality using embedded tools, and customizing input screens and reports.

Configured business systems: Systems that use configured business applications.

Contingency plans: Alternative arrangements for operating processes when the automated system breaks down.

COTS (commercial off-the-shelf) application: A software product that's commercially available and hasn't been specifically designed to meet an individual purchaser's specifications or modified by creating custom program code. The product is used as developed with minimal or no configuration.

COTS (commercial off-the-shelf) system: A system that uses only software products that are commercially available and haven't been specifically designed to meet an individual purchaser's specifications. In addition, to be considered off the shelf, the system's software can't have been modified. The product is used as developed with minimal or no configuration. Commercial off-the-shelf doesn't include "freeware," "share ware," and other uncontrolled software that's available from the Internet and other sources.

Cosmetic defect: Any defect that's immaterial to the functioning of a system, data quality, or meeting any requirement.

Critical defect: Any defect that causes a down system, harm of any type at the catastrophic or critical levels, would result in the corruption of critical data, or the nonfulfillment of a critical requirement.

Critical requirements: Absolutely required for an intended use the first day of production. The system can't be used for an intended use if this function isn't present or doesn't work properly; such a defect must be fixed before the system can be used for the intended use. The system isn't worth purchasing and installing for the intended use if such a feature or function is missing, malfunctions, or can never be achieved.

Current good manufacturing practices (cGMP): Regulations set by the FDA for the manufacturing, processing, packing, or holding products for administration to humans or animals.

Custom software: Software that isn't available prepackaged "off the shelf" but is designed and developed specifically to an organization's specifications.

Custom system: A system that uses application software that isn't available for commercial-off-the-shelf purchase but is designed and developed specifically to an organization's specifications.

Database package system: A system that uses application software developed by means of a database package. The application is used for such things as storing, manipulating, and retrieving data. The application is created by using tools in the database package to prepare input screens and reports, and/or to define data processing. Examples of such database packages include Excel, Access, and SAS.

Database applications: Applications for storing, manipulating, and retrieving data that are created by using a database package.

Development environment: The hardware and operating system software that are used for developing application software. This environment is controlled and used by the system developers.

Device software: Software that is itself a medical device (e.g., blood establishment software), and software that's used as a component of or accessory for a medical device.

Electronic document management system (EDMS): A system used to control documents.

Emergency change: A change made to a system in a situation where immediate action is required to prevent product quality, safety, or integrity from being jeopardized, maintain personnel safety, restore proper operation to a system or a critical component of a system, or address an urgent GxP or business need.

Engineering change order (ECO): A form used to approve the creation, modification, or obsolescence of a controlled document such as a procedure or engineering drawing.

Enhancement: An improvement of the system, usually by adding functionality or upgrading equipment.

Enterprise resource planning systems (ERP II): Used to plan and manage materials and production.

Equipment: A piece of machinery used to perform a function.

Execution of a protocol: Occurs when actions stated in the protocol are performed and required data regarding the results of the actions are recorded.

Existing system: A system of any type that's currently in use.

Expected results: The acceptable values or allowable specification range for the results of a test. The expectation is that the test will be passed, and therefore the expected results are the same as the values that constitute a pass for the test.

Failure mode and effects analysis (FMEA): A qualitative technique by which the consequences of an individual component fault mode are systematically identified and evaluated.[10]

Food and Drug Administration (FDA): The agency of the U.S. government that's charged with protecting public health by ensuring the safety, efficacy, and security of human and veterinary drugs, biological products, medical devices, the food supply, cosmetics, and products that emit radiation.

Fix: A system change that repairs a problem with a system or equipment, such as a software defect, failing device, or piece of equipment.

Forward traceability: The ability to trace from a requirement to test(s) in a validation protocol where the ability of the system to meet that requirement is assessed.

Functional requirements: Statements that describe functions a computer-related system must be capable of performing. In the RiskVal life cycle, functional requirements are part of the user requirements.[11]

Functional specifications: Statements of how a computerized system will satisfy functional requirements for a computer-related system.[12]

Functional testing: A process for verifying that software, a system, or a system component performs its intended functions.[13]

Good clinical practice (GCP): Regulations for planning, performing, and recording research in a clinical setting on a product's efficacy.

Good lab practices (GLP): Regulations for conducting research on product safety and efficacy that uses animals.

GxP: A generic designation for all FDA regulations, including GLP, GCP, and cGMP, as applicable to an industry.

Harm: Physical injury to people's health, damage to property or the environment, or impairment to a company's ability to comply with appropriate regulations.[14]

Hazard: A potential source of physical harm as the result of an item failure, misuse, or breakdown.[15, 16]

High-risk system: A system for which the highest risk associated with a potential failure is determined through a formal process to be unacceptable.

Important requirement: Without this feature or function, the system is useable but loses significant value and effectiveness.

Infrastructure: The infrastructure includes what's referred to in this book as the infrastructure platform and infrastructure services. The infrastructure platform is the collection of hardware and software used to host business applications, to communicate within and outside of an organization, and to provide infrastructure services. The infrastructure services are functions performed by the infrastructure hardware and software to safeguard systems, preserve data integrity, and provide network communications.

Infrastructure platform: The collection of hardware and software used to host both infrastructure services and applications.

Infrastructure services: The functions performed by the infrastructure platform hardware and software to provide a safe and effective technical environment for the operation of business applications. Infrastructure services safeguard business systems, preserve data integrity, and provide network communications.

Installation qualification: Documented verification that all key aspects of hardware and software installation adhere to appropriate codes and the computerized system specification.[17]

Installation qualification protocol: A written method for gathering objective evidence that system components meet technical specifications and have been properly installed.

Instance: An independent working copy of an application or database.

Instrument: A measuring device that can be either stand-alone or bundled with a piece of equipment.

Integration testing: Testing of the transfer of data and control across a program's internal and external interfaces. External interfaces are those with other software (including operating system software), system hardware, and the users and can be described as communication links.[18]

In-vitro diagnostics: A medical diagnosis made outside of the body, such as analyzing a blood sample.

Intensity applied to a life cycle task: Refers to the scope of analysis across all normal and abnormal system operating conditions.

Thousand lines of code (KLOC): A metric used to measure the size of a piece of software or application.

Low-risk system: A system for which the highest risk associated with a potential failure is assessed through a formal process as being low.

Major defect: Any defect that results in an error with, or the inoperability of, an important function, causes harm at the moderate level, or results in an unfulfilled important requirement.

Major nonconformance: The absence or total breakdown of a quality system element to meet a requirement. Included are nonconformances that would result in the probable shipment of a nonconforming product or would render critical process controls ineffective.[19]

Medical device reporting (MDR): An FDA requirement stipulating that events involving serious injury to a user or death be reported.[20]

Metadata: Descriptive information that gives data meaning and context. For a document it might include title, document number, document revision, originator, status, effective date, etc.

Minor defect: Any defect that's immaterial to the functioning of a system, quality of data, or leads to the nonfulfillment of a "nice to have" requirement

Minor nonconformance: A nonconformance of the quality system that's unlikely to result in the failure of a quality system element, shipping nonconforming product, or causing critical processes to be ineffective. Such nonconformances might involve a limitation or weakness of a quality element that, despite the limitation, achieves the purpose intended by the regulation or standard.

Mitigation plan: A plan for implementing and evaluating mitigations.

Mitigation report: A report that describes the results of investigations into a mitigation's effectiveness.

Mixed system: A system that includes the combination of more than one type of system, such as commercial off-the-shelf, database package system, configured business system, or custom system.

Moderate-risk system: A system for which the highest risk associated with a potential failure is assessed through a formal process and is deemed to be as low as is reasonably practical.

Nice-to-have requirement: The absence or loss of this feature or function will have little effect on the system's effectiveness and value from the standpoint of the organization's intended uses.

NIST: National Institute of Standards and Technology

Network: The hardware and software used to transmit electronic information between devices and to protect the data integrity of the information during transmission.

Objective evidence: Information that can be proven true, based on facts obtained through observation, measurement, testing, or other means.[21]

Operational environment: The hardware and system software configuration in place to support a system when it's used for performing work. See also: production environment.

Operational qualification: Documented verification that a system operates according to written and preapproved specifications throughout all specified operating ranges.[22]

Operation qualification protocol: A written plan for gathering objective evidence that a system operates in a test environment to its intended uses and meets user requirements. The protocol includes test methods, expected results, and protocol acceptance criteria.

Operational use: Using a system to conduct business either in production or in an operating nonproduction processes. See also: production use.

Product data management (PDM) system: An electronic system that manages documents and data related to products and their components and/or ingredients. Similar to an EDMS, but a PDM system also provides information about parts and their relationships, such as the structure of parts in a bill of materials.

Performance qualification: Documented verification that the integrated computerized system performs as intended in its normal operating environment.[23]

Performance qualification protocol: A written plan for gathering objective evidence that a system operates to its intended uses and meets user requirements as it's used in performing work (i.e., in an operational environment). The protocol includes test methods, expected results, and acceptance criteria.

Phase review: A review conducted either during or at the end of a phase to evaluate the activities and deliverables of a phase for compliance with phase requirements and planned activities. The review is normally conducted with the project team and representatives of management such as the steering committee or business sponsor (i.e., author).

Predicate rule: A requirement specified in an FDA regulation.

Production environment: The hardware and system software used to run the application for performing work. See also: operational environment.

Production instance: The copy of the application software used by an organization for performing work.

Production use: Using the system to conduct business either in production or in operating nonproduction processes. See also: operational use.

Prospective validation: Documented evidence that a system meets acceptance criteria based on performance demonstrated during the execution of an approved validation plan and protocols. The validation is performed prior to the system's use in the production environment.

Protocol: See validation protocol.

Protocol acceptance criteria: The criteria a system or process must meet to satisfy the requirements stated in a qualification protocol. The protocol acceptance requirements are based on the specification and/or requirements tested by the protocol.

Qualification: The procedure of collecting appropriate data that, when documented properly, provides a high level of assurance that a computerized system will operate in accordance with the system specification.[24]

Quality record: A record required by a quality system regulation or standard as documented evidence that an event occurred, or that a measured value was obtained. Or, a similar record identified in the company's quality system as a quality record.

Records retention period: The period of time a record must be kept and accessible for review and/or use.

Regression testing: Rerunning test cases that a program has previously executed correctly to detect errors caused by changes or corrections made during software development and maintenance.

Requalification: See revalidation.

Residual risk: The risk that remains after protective measures have been taken.[25]

Retrospective validation: Validation of an item, process, or system that's already in use for performing regulated activities. The validation is based on data of the system's accumulated performance in production, testing and/or use.

Revalidation: Relative to software changes, revalidation means validating the change itself, assessing the nature of the change to determine potential ripple effects, and performing the necessary regression testing.[26]

Rigor: The formality of the methods used for life cycle activities and recording their results.[27]

Risk: The probability that harm will occur, combined with its projected severity.[28, 29]

Risk analysis: The systematic use of available information to identify and estimate the risk of failures or hazards.[30]

Risk assessment: A process comprised of a risk analysis and risk evaluation.[31]

Risk control: The process through which decisions are reached and protective measures are implemented for reducing risks to, or maintaining risks within, specified levels.[32]

Risk evaluation: Judgment, on the basis of risk analysis, of whether an acceptable risk has been achieved in a given context based on the current values of society.[33]

Risk management: Systematic application of management policies, procedures, and practices to the tasks of analyzing, evaluating, and controlling risk.[34]

Risk management file: A set of records and other documents, not necessarily contiguous, that are produced by a risk management process.[35]

Risk mitigation: Reduction in the severity of a hazard, the likelihood of its occurrence, or both.[36]

RiskVal: Computer system risk management and validation life cycle

RiskVal procedure: An organization's documented procedure for managing risk and validating computer systems.

Server farm: Servers that are interconnected so that the processing load can be distributed across the servers to maintain performance and maximize efficient use of the equipment.

Service pack: A collection of software programs issued by a software manufacturer to repair a number of software defects.

Severity: The measured extent of harm that can be created by a hazard.

Specification: Any requirement with which a product, process, service, or other item must conform.[37]

Supportive operations: Operations used by the system to perform the functions mandated in the user requirements. For example, if it's a user requirement to be able to approve a record with an electronic signature, some of the supportive operations the system must perform are determining if the signer has authority, recording the date and time that the signature was entered, and protecting the signature from change.

System acceptance criteria: Standards or requirements specified in a validation plan or protocol that must be met to demonstrate acceptability of a given system.

System administrator: An individual trained to perform the technical functions required to manage the system, including such things as monitoring the use of system resources, configuring the system's hardware and software as needed for the application, and resolving system problems.

System integration: The progressive linking and testing of system components into a complete system.[38]

System owner: The manager or designee of the department most affected by, or the primary user of, the system.

System revalidation: A validation of a previously validated system to determine if it's currently able to perform to predetermined specifications and/or requirements. When performed, a new validation plan is approved that specifies the revalidation activities.

System software: Software designed to facilitate the operation and maintenance of a computer system and its associated programs, such as operating systems, assemblers, utilities, and executive programs. System software is generally independent of the specific application.[39]

System specification: A complete listing of all the hardware and software components that need to be separately installed to create a specific system. The system specification includes the requirements for each item and the required configurations.

System tests: Tests that demonstrate that all specified functionality exists and that the software product is trustworthy.[40]

Technical requirements: Requirements related to a system's technical aspects. The technical requirements are used to select appropriate hardware and system software for the system.

Test environment: Hardware and software installation used for testing a system. The test environment is used prior to the start of the validation testing for phase 4 and 5 activities, including the creation of integrations. Once the system is put into operation, the test environment is used to test changes before they're installed in the operational environment.

Test instance: A copy of the application software used in the test environment.

Traceability matrix: A map showing how one concept or item from one document has been incorporated into another.

Unit testing: Testing of individual programs as independent units.

Use case: An analysis of how a system is used. The analysis is conducted to identify requirements for human interactions and system functions.

User requirements: Requirements of potential system users.

Validated state: A system's state after validation has been successfully completed. A system is maintained in a validated state by controlling and validating changes, and performing necessary maintenance according to validated maintenance procedures. Such change control and maintenance procedures provide sufficient objective evidence to sustain confidence that the system will reliably function to meet requirements.

Validation: A process that establishes documented evidence and provides a high degree of assurance that a specific system will consistently produce a product that meets predetermined specifications and quality attributes.[41] In the Quality System Regulation, the FDA presents a more general definition: "...confirmation by examination and provision of objective evidence that the particular requirements for a specific intended use can be consistently fulfilled."[42]

Validation environment: Hardware and software installation used for conducting the installation and operational qualifications.

Validation instance: A copy of the application software used in the validation environment.

Validation master plan: A high-level plan that identifies all the equipment, systems, and/or processes at a site that require validation and sets priorities and time frames for such validations.

Validation plan: A plan that defines the approach, activities, responsibilities, procedures, and requirements for validating a specific item, such as a piece of equipment, process, or computer system.

Validation protocol: A written plan stating how the validation, or an aspect of it, will be performed, including tests to be conducted and definitions of what constitutes acceptable test results.

Validation testing: Formal testing conducted to provide objective evidence that one or more system requirements are consistently fulfilled.

Variance: Any discrepancy that occurs during testing when a required action wasn't performed as specified. Or, when an actual result doesn't match the corresponding expected result.

Vendor organizational requirements: Requirements set for the business viability and expertise of providers of hardware, software, or services.

Verification: Confirmation by examination and providing objective evidence that specified requirements have been fulfilled.[43, 44]

White-box testing: Software tests that are based on the logical structure used in the software.

Workflow: A sequence of automated process activities and approvals. The sequence can be preset or determined by the system dynamically based on situational data.

Worst case: A set of conditions encompassing upper and lower processing limits and circumstances, including those within standard operating procedures, that pose the greatest chance of process or product failure when compared to ideal conditions. Such conditions don't necessarily induce product or process failure.

References

PREFACE

1. 21 CFR 820, Medical Devices—Current Good Manufacturing Practices (cGMP) Final Rule; Quality System Regulation. *Federal Register 52602*. October 7, 1996, 2003 Revision.
2. EC Commission Directive, *The Rules Governing Medicinal Products in the European Union*, Vol. 4. Good Manufacturing Practices, Annex 11, Computerised Systems, October 8, 2003.
3. ISO 13485, Medical devices—Quality management systems—Systems requirements for regulatory purposes. International Organization for Standardization, 2003.
4. IEEE/EIA 12207.0 Industry Implementation of International Standard ISO/IEC 12207:1995, Standard for Information Technology—Software Life Cycle Processes. Institute of Electrical and Electronics Engineers, March 1998.
5. PDA Committee on Validation of Computer-Related Systems. Technical Report No. 18, "Validation of Computer-Related Systems." *PDA Journal of Pharmaceutical Science and Technology*. Vol. 49, No. 1. January–February 1995 Supplement.
6. ANSI/AAMI SW68:2001, Medical Device Software—Software Life Cycle Processes. Association for the Advancement of Medical Instrumentation, 2001.
7. *General Principles of Software Validation. Final Guidance for Industry and FDA Staff.* Center for Devices and Radiological Health, Center for Biologics Evaluation and Research, Food and Drug Administration, January 11, 2002.
8. Ibid.
9. EC Commission Directive, *The Rules Governing Medicinal Products in the European Union.*
10. ISO 9001, Quality management systems—Requirements. International Organization for Standardization, 2000.
11. ISO 13485:2003.

12. ISO 14971:2000, Medical devices—Application of risk management to medical devices. International Organization for Standardization, 2000.

13. Stein, R. Timothy, "Avoiding Software Meltdown." *Quality Digest,* March 2005.

14. Stein, R. Timothy. "Life Cycle for Off-the-Shelf Software Validation." Presentation made at the 57th American Quality Congress, Sponsored by the American Society for Quality, Kansas City, May 19, 2003.

15. PDA Committee on Validation of Computer-Related Systems, Technical Report No. 18, "Validation of Computer-Related Systems."

16. ISO 14971:2000, Section 1.

17. EC Commission Directive, *The Rules Governing Medicinal Products in the European Union.*

18. ISO 9001:2000.

19. ISO 13485:2003.

20. ISO 14971:2000.

21. 21 CFR Part 11, Electronic Records—Electronic Signatures. Food and Drug Administration. *Federal Register*, Vol. 62, No. 54. March 20, 1997.

CHAPTER 1

Notes

1. Jones analyzes the effectiveness of various methods for preventing defects and for defect removal. (Jones, Capers. *Software Quality, Analysis and Guidelines for Success,* pp. 158–173. New York: International Thomson Computer Press, 1997.) The average percent of defects that were detected and repaired before software was sold was 85 percent for U.S. software developers at the time of Jones' studies. However, the best companies were able to remove 99.99 percent of the defects by using a combination of many of the methods.

2. (*General Principles of Software Validation. Final Guidance for Industry and FDA Staff,* Section 6.1. Center for Devices and Radiological Health, Center for Biologics Evaluation and Research, Food and Drug Administration, January 11, 2002.) The guidance goes on to discuss the practice of having high-risk and low-risk systems in the same environment: "Risk mitigation techniques such as memory partitioning or other approaches to resource protection may need to be considered when high-risk applications and low-risk applications are to be used in the same operating environment."

References

1. "After Shutdown, All Systems 'Go' on Station." *USA Today*. May 21, 2002.

2. "Microsoft Discloses More Flaws in OS." *San Jose Mercury News*. September 20, 2002.

3. IEEE 1012-1998, IEEE Standard for Software Verification and Validation. Software Engineering Standards Committee of the IEEE Computer Society, March 1998.

4. Jones, Capers. *Conflict and Litigation Between Software Clients and Developers*, Version 12. Software Productivity Research, April 26, 2004.

5. Humphrey, Watts S. *Managing the Software Process*. Boston: Addison-Wesley Publishing Co., 1989.

6. Jones, Capers. *Software Quality, Analysis and Guidelines for Success*, p. 164. New York: International Thomson Computer Press, 1997.

7. Ibid., p. 167.

8. Jones, Capers. *Software Quality: A Survey of the State of the Art*. Cambridge, MA: Software Productivity Research, 1988.

9. Jones, Capers. *Software Quality in 2003: A Survey of the State of the Art*. Cambridge, MA: Software Productivity Research, February 20, 2003.

10. Humphrey, Watts S. "What if Your Life Depended on Software?" Paper presented at the American Society for Quality's 56th Annual Quality Congress, May 20–22, 2002.

11. Ibid.

12. Stein, R. Timothy. Personal experience, 1997.

13. Jones, Capers. *Conflict and Litigation Between Software Clients and Developers*, Version 12. Cambridge, MA: Software Productivity Research, April 26, 2004.

14. Jones, Capers. *Software Quality in 2003*.

15. *General Principles of Software Validation. Final Guidance for Industry and FDA Staff*, Section 2.4. Center for Devices and Radiological Health, Center for Biologics Evaluation and Research, Food and Drug Administration, January 11, 2002.

16. ISO 14971:2000, Medical devices—Application of risk management to medical devices. International Organization for Standardization, 2000.

17. 21 CFR 820, Medical Devices—Current Good Manufacturing Practices (cGMP) Final Rule, Quality System Regulation, Section 820.70 i. *Federal Register 52602*. October 7, 1996, 2003 revision.

18. *General Principles of Software Validation*, Section 2.4.

19. Guidance for Industry Part 11, Electronic Records—Electronic Signatures—Scope and Application, Section III C 1. U.S. Department of Health and Human Services, Food and Drug Administration, August 2003.

20. 21 CFR 820, Section 30 g.

21. 21 CFR Part 11, Electronic Records—Electronic Signatures. Food and Drug Administration. *Federal Register*, Vol. 62, No. 54. March 20, 1997.

22. Ibid., Section 11.1 b.

23. Guidance for Industry Part 11, Electronic Records—Electronic Signatures—Scope and Application, Section III B 2.

24. EC Commission Directive, *The Rules Governing Medicinal Products in the European Union,* Vol. 4. Good Manufacturing Practices, Annex 11, Computerised Systems, October 8, 2003.

25. Ibid., Section 2.

26. ISO 13485, Quality systems—Medical devices—Particular requirements for the application of ISO 9001. International Organization for Standardization, 1996.

27. CAN/CSA-ISO 13485–98, Quality systems—Medical devices—Particular requirements for the application of ISO 9001, Section 4.9 f. National Standards of Canada, 1998.

28. ISO 13485, Medical devices—Quality management systems—System requirements for regulatory purposes, Section 7.5.2.1. International Organization for Standardization, 2003.

29. *General Principles of Software Validation*, Section 3.1.2.

30. IEEE/EIA 12207.0 Industry Implementation of International Standard ISO/IEC 12207:1995, Standard for Information Technology—Software Life Cycle Processes. March 1998.

31. McConnell, Steve. *Rapid Development: Taming Wild Software Schedules*, ch. 7. Microsoft Press, 1996.

32. ANSI/AAMI SW68:2001, Medical Device Software—Software Life Cycle Processes. Association for the Advancement of Medical Instrumentation, 2001.

33. *General Principles of Software Validation*.

34. EC Commission Directive, *The Rules Governing Medicinal Products in the European Union*.

35. *General Principles of Software Validation*, Section 4.3.

36. Guidance for Industry Part II, Electronic Records—Electronic Signatures—Scope and Application, Section III C1.

37. IEEE 1012-1998, IEEE Standard for Software Verification and Validation, p. iii.

38. Ibid.

CHAPTER 2

Notes

1. A distinction is drawn between qualification and validation. Qualification is "the process to demonstrate the ability to fulfill specified requirements." (GAMP Forum. Gamp 4, GAMP Guide for Validation of Automated System, Vol. 4. December 2001.) Qualification establishes the ability of an item or system to function according to the requirements for how that item ought to work. However, if a piece of automated equipment or a system works properly (i.e., is qualified), it doesn't necessarily imply that it will work the way that an organization wants to use it in an automated process. You still have to demonstrate that it's effective in how you want to use it. Effective here means both that the system works as it's intended, and if the system could affect the quality of the product, that products meet specifications. This can be seen from the generic definition of validation used by the FDA; validation is "establishing documented evidence which provides a high degree of assurance that a specific process will consistently produce a product meeting its predetermined specifications and quality attributes." (*Glossary of Computerized System and Software Development Terminology.* Food and Drug Administration, August 1995.)

   The difference between qualification and validation can be seen in the following example of an automated welding machine. An automated welding machine is used to weld parts of a medical device. The welder uses a laser beam to melt a small area of two pieces of metal that are placed together. When the two metals melt, they form a mixture that cools and hardens. This weld forms a bond between the pieces of metal. The welder can be qualified to establish that it can place a weld of a certain size in a predetermined location, that a laser beam with certain energy will be focused on the spot for a specified duration, etc. The welder is qualified by demonstrating that it operates properly. If it doesn't operate properly, it can't be used. Once qualified, its use in a manufacturing process to meet specific product requirements can then be validated. Once the welder has been shown to work correctly, the device manufacturer needs to validate those settings because laser duration and intensity will create welds of a certain strength between two pieces of metal that are part of its medical device.

   The distinction between qualification and validation has more practical value in the validation of facilities, utilities, and equipment than it does with computer system validation. With facilities, utilities, and equipment, you can make a clear distinction between qualification and validation. With computer systems, the way in which the system is to be used (to meet the user requirements) is often identical to the way the manufacturer has designed and built the system. Consequently, qualifying the system is similar to validating it (unless the system is used directly in production, as with the example of the welder).

In addition, all intended uses of the system need to be tested, if possible, at least for moderate- and high-risk systems in a test environment before they're used in production. This is to avoid harmful effects from system failure. The operational qualification (OQ) is used, in part, to determine in a test environment that the system will function to meet all (or most of) the user requirements. The clause "in part" is used because supportive operations (discussed in chapter 9) are also included in the OQ. The performance qualification (PQ) is used to establish that, in the production environment, the system is able to meet the user requirements as part of the process in which the system is used. If the technical environments of the OQ and PQ are similar, the PQ may involve more limited testing than is conducted in the OQ. (The PQ will be discussed in detail in chapter 10.)

References

1. PDA Committee on Validation of Computer-Related Systems, Technical Report No. 18, "Validation of Computer-Related Systems." *PDA Journal of Pharmaceutical Science and Technology*, Vol. 49, No. 1. January–February 1995 Supplement.
2. Ibid.
3. 21 CFR 211, Current Good Manufacturing Practice for Finished Pharmaceuticals. Food and Drug Administration. *Federal Register 6385*. June 20, 1963, March 31, 2003 revision.
4. 21 CFR 820, Medical Devices—Current Good Manufacturing Practices (cGMP) Final Rule, Quality System Regulation, *Federal Register 52602*. October 7, 1996, March 10, 2004 revision.
5. ISO 13485, Medical devices—Quality management systems—Systems requirements for regulatory purposes. International Organization for Standardization, 2003.
6. *General Principles of Software Validation; Final Guidance for Industry and FDA Staff*. Center for Devices and Radiological Health, Center for Biologics Evaluation and Research, Food and Drug Administration. January 11, 2002.
7. ISO 14971:2000, Medical devices—Application of risk management to medical devices. International Organization for Standardization, 2000.
8. *Guidance for Industry, FDA Reviewers and Compliance on Off-the-Shelf Software Use in Medical Devices*. Food and Drug Administration, Center for Devices and Radiological Health, Office of Device Evaluation, September 9, 1999.

9. GAMP Forum. Gamp 4, GAMP Guide for Validation of Automated Systems, Vol. 4. December 2001.

10. PDA Committee on Validation of Computer-Related Systems, Technical Report No. 18, "Validation of Computer-Related Systems," Section 4.2.

11. ISO 9001, Quality management systems—Requirements. International Organization for Standardization, 2000.

12. PDA Committee on Validation of Computer-Related Systems, Technical Report No. 18, "Validation of Computer-Related Systems," Section 4.3.

13. EC Commission Directive, *The Rules Governing Medicinal Products in the European Union,* Vol. 4. Good Manufacturing Practices, Annex 11, Item 18, Computerized Systems, October 8, 2003.

14. PDA Committee on Validation of Computer-Related Systems, Technical Report No. 18, "Validation of Computer-Related Systems," Section 4.4.

15. Ibid., Section 4.5.

16. Ibid., Section 4.6.

17. Ibid.

18. Louie, Michael S. "Case Study: Qualifying Computer and Network Infrastructures (CNIs) for GxP Compliance." CPT Third Annual IT Infrastructure Qualification Summit, February 24, 2004, and personal communications.

19. 21 CFR 820, Section 70 i.

20. *General Principles of Software Validation,* Section 6.2.

21. EC Commission Directive, *The Rules Governing Medicinal Products in the European Union,* Item 7.

22. ISO 13485:2003, Section 7.5.2.1.

23. PDA Committee on Validation of Computer-Related Systems, Technical Report No. 18, "Validation of Computer-Related System," Section 4.8.

24. *General Principles of Software Validation,* Section 6.2.

25. GAMP Forum. Gamp 4, GAMP Guide for Validation of Automated Systems, Vol. 4. December 2001.

CHAPTER 3

Notes

1. Technical Report (TR) 18's title for the first phase is "Plan Validation Activities." (PDA Committee on Validation of Computer-Related Systems. Technical Report No. 18, "Validation of Computer-Related Systems," Section 4.1. PDA *Journal of*

Pharmaceutical Science and Technology, Volume 49, No. 1. January–February 1995 Supplement.) The RiskVal conceptualize phase partially follows TR 18's first phase in that both include the development of validation policies and standard operating procedures. The procedures provide detailed instructions for executing specific tasks. TR 18's first phase also includes preparing a validation project plan. It notes that the plan can be written for a single system or for an entire facility; however, an important purpose of a validation project plan is to establish specific responsibilities and expectations for each validation task. The term "validation plan" is used in this book instead of "validation project plan" because the shorter version is more commonly used.

The initial phase is usually too early for writing the validation plan. Although readers can prepare their plans whenever they think enough information is available, it's placed in phase 4 of the RiskVal life cycle. At that time, the system will have been procured, the detailed risk assessment completed, and risk mitigations designed. Based on that work, a more specific validation plan can be written. The activities that must be performed in phases one through four, before the validation plan, should be specified in your organization's RiskVal procedure.

The second focal point of RiskVal's phase 1 is formulating a high-level concept of the needs a system must meet. This aspect isn't mentioned in TR 18's first phase. However, some members of the PDA committee who prepared TR 18 published an article on key validation practices for computer systems two years after TR 18's release. (Grigonis, George Jr., Edward J. Subak Jr., and Michael L. Wyrick. "Validation Key Practices for Computer Systems Used in Regulated Operations," p. 75. *Pharmaceutical Technology*, June 1997.) Their first phase is called "conceptualization period." The activities they describe for this period are a combination of the analyses described in RiskVal phases one and two (i.e., modeling business operations and processes, and identifying information needs). Their conceptualization phase ends with the approval of a conceptual proposal and a decision to proceed with the system, just as the RiskVal phase 1 ends with the approval of the computer system project proposal.

References

1. PDA Committee on Validation of Computer-Related Systems, Technical Report No. 18, "Validation of Computer-Related Systems," Sections 4.1.1 and 4.1.2. *PDA Journal of Pharmaceutical Science and Technology*. Vol. 49, No. 1. January–February 1995 Supplement.

2. Stein, R. Timothy. "Validation Policy." Business Performance Associates, 2002 a.

3. Stein, R. Timothy. "Computer System Risk Management and Validation Life Cycle." Business Performance Associates, 2002 b.

4. ANSI/AAMI SW68:2001. Medical Device Software—Software Life Cycle Processes. Association for the Advancement of Medical Instrumentation, 2001.

5. *General Principles of Software Validation; Final Guidance for Industry and FDA Staff.* Center for Devices and Radiological Health, Center for Biologics Evaluation and Research, Food and Drug Administration, January 11, 2002.

6. Stein, R. Timothy. "Information Technology Policy." Business Performance Associates, 2004.

7. 21 CFR Part 11, Electronic Records—Electronic Signatures. Food and Drug Administration. *Federal Register*, Vol. 62, No. 54. March 20, 1997.

8. Stein, R. Timothy. "Risk Management Policy." Business Performance Associates, 2003 a.

9. Stein, R. Timothy. "Risk Management Procedure." Business Performance Associates, 2003 b.

10. Stein, R. Timothy. "Requirements for Computer System Validation Plans, Protocols, and Reports." Business Performance Associates, 2002 c.

11. IEEE 1012-1998 Standard for Software Verification and Validation, p. iii. Software Engineering Standards Committee of the IEEE Computer Society, March 1999.

12. 21 CFR Part 11, Section 11, 11.1 b.

13. 21 CFR 820, Medical Devices—Current Good Manufacturing Practices (cGMP) Final Rule, Quality System Regulation, Section 40. *Federal Register 52602.* October 7, 1996, 2003 revision.

14. Stein, R. Timothy. "Computer System Project Proposal." Business Performance Associates, 2002 d.

15. Stein, R. Timothy. "Validation Master Plan Item Information Form." Business Performance Associates, 2003 c.

CHAPTER 4

Notes

1. Technical Report 18 uses the term "computer-related system requirements" to define the overall set of requirements. (PDA Committee on Validation of Computer-Related Systems. Technical Report No. 18, "Validation of Computer-Related Systems," Section 4.2. *PDA Journal of Pharmaceutical Science and Technology*, Vol.

49, No. 1. January–February 1995 Supplement.) Within the requirements, TR 18 talks about functional and design requirements. Functional requirements define what the system must do. Design requirements define the structure of the system and other physical attributes. A list of areas to include in system requirements is given in appendix 1 of TR 18. (PDA Committee on Validation of Computer-Related Systems. Technical Report No. 18, "Validation of Computer-Related Systems," Appendix 1. *PDA Journal of Pharmaceutical Science and Technology*, Vol. 49, No. 1. January–February 1995 Supplement.) Although most of these areas are covered in the user and technical requirements presented in this book, the TR 18 list will serve as a good checklist for the completeness of your requirements, especially if the system is being custom developed.

2. Technical Report 18 recommends distinguishing between features that must be satisfied and those that are desirable. (PDA Committee on Validation of Computer-Related Systems. Technical Report No. 18, "Validation of Computer-Related Systems," Section 4.2. PDA *Journal of Pharmaceutical Science and Technology*, Vol. 49, No. 1. January–February 1995 Supplement.) TR 18 further recommends that the desired features should be prioritized as to their relative importance. The "critical" requirement level presented in this book corresponds to Technical Report 18's features and functions "which must be satisfied." TR 18 also recommends that desired features be prioritized. RiskVal's categories of "important" and "nice to have" requirements are equivalent to classifying desired features and functions into priority levels. The FDA guidance document on software validation also emphasizes the importance of documenting user requirements. (*General Principles of Software Validation. Final Guidance for Industry and FDA Staff*, Section 6.2. Center for Devices and Radiological Health, Center for Biologics Evaluation and Research, Food and Drug Administration, January 11, 2002.)

3. Capers Jones notes that ISO 9001:2000 certification hasn't yet demonstrated any significant software quality improvements. He considers his research on the relationship of the SEI capability maturity model with software quality as preliminary because of the small sample sizes at the higher levels. If possible, select a vendor that has attained at least level three. His results show an average number of defects delivered to the first buyer of about 0.75 defects per function point for level-one projects. By contrast, with level-five projects, an average of about 0.1 defects are delivered per function point. (Jones, Capers. *Software Quality, Analysis and Guidelines for Success*, New York: International Thomson Computer Press, 1997, pp. 391–392. Jones, Capers. *Conflict and Litigation between Software Clients and Developers*, Version 12. Software Productivity Research, April 26, 2004.)

References

1. PDA Committee on Validation of Computer-Related Systems, Technical Report No. 18, "Validation of Computer-Related Systems," Section 4.2. *PDA Journal of Pharmaceutical Science and Technology*, Vol. 49, No. 1. January–February 1995 Supplement.

2. ANSI/AAMI SW68:2001, Medical Device Software—Software Life Cycle Processes, Section 5.1.2. Association for the Advancement of Medical Instrumentation, 2001.

3. PDA Committee on Validation of Computer-Related Systems, Technical Report No. 18, "Validation of Computer-Related Systems," Section 4.2.

4. EC Commission Directive, *The Rules Governing Medicinal Products in the European Union*. Vol. 4. Good Manufacturing Practices, Annex 11, Item 6, Computerised Systems, October 8, 2003.

5. 21 CFR Part 11, Electronic Records—Electronic Signatures. Food and Drug Administration. *Federal Register,* Vol. 62, No. 54. March 20, 1997.

6. PDA Committee on Validation of Computer-Related Systems, Technical Report No. 18, "Validation of Computer-Related Systems," Section 4.2.

7. Wiegers, Karl E. *Software Requirements*. Redmond, Washington: Microsoft Press, 1999.

8. Jones, Capers. *Conflict and Litigation Between Software Clients and Developers*, Version 12. Software Productivity Research, April 26, 2004.

9. *General Principles of Software Validation, Final Guidance for Industry and FDA Staff*, Section 5.2.2. Center for Devices and Radiological Health, Center for Biologics Evaluation and Research, Food and Drug Administration, January 11, 2002.

10. GAMP Forum. Gamp 4, GAMP Guide for Validation of Automated Systems, Vol. 4, Section 6.1. December, 2001.

CHAPTER 5

1. PDA Committee on Validation of Computer-Related Systems. Technical Report No. 18, "Validation of Computer-Related Systems," Section 4.3. *PDA Journal of Pharmaceutical Science and Technology*. Vol. 49, No. 1, January–February 1995 Supplement.

2. ISO 9001, Quality management systems—Requirements. International Organization for Standardization, 2000.

3. PDA Committee on Validation of Computer-Related Systems. Technical Report No. 18, "Validation of Computer-Related Systems," Section 4.3.

4. IEEE/EIA 12207.0 Industry Implementation of International Standard ISO/IEC

12207:1995, Standard for Information Technology—Software Life Cycle Processes, Section 5.1. Institute of Electrical and Electronics Engineers, March 1998.

5. IEEE 1062-1998, IEEE Recommended Practice for Software Acquisition. Institute of Electrical and Electronics Engineers, 1998.

6. Stein, R. Timothy. "Computer System Vendor Qualification and Management." Business Performance Associates, 2003 a.

7. PDA Committee on Validation of Computer-Related Systems. Technical Report No. 18, "Validation of Computer-Related Systems," Section 4.3.2.

8. EC Commission Directive, *The Rules Governing Medicinal Products in the European Union*, Vol. 4. Good Manufacturing Practices, Annex 11, Item 5, Computerised Systems. October 8, 2003.

9. *General Principles of Software Validation, Final Guidance for Industry and FDA Staff,* Section 4.2. Center for Devices and Radiological Health, Center for Biologics Evaluation and Research, Food and Drug Administration, January 11, 2002.

10. Jones, Capers. *Conflict and Litigation Between Software Clients and Developers*, Version 12. Software Productivity Research, April 26, 2004.

11. Jones, Capers. *Software Quality in 2003: A Survey of the State of the Art.* Cambridge, MA: Software Productivity Research, February 20, 2003.

12. Jones, Capers. *Programming Productivity*. McGraw-Hill, 1986, p.179.

13. Jones, Capers. *Software Quality: Analysis and Guidelines for Success*, p. 164. London: International Thomson Computer Press, 1997.

14. PDA Committee on Validation of Computer-Related Systems. Technical Report No. 18, "Validation of Computer-Related Systems," Section 4.3.1.

15. *General Principles of Software Validation,* Section 6.3.

16. Ibid.

17. IEEE 1012-1998. IEEE Standard for Software Verification and Validation, Table 2. Software Engineering Standards Committee of the IEEE Computer Society, March 1998.

18. Stein, R. Timothy. "Computer System Vendor Audit Checklist." Business Performance Associates, 2003 b.

19. PDA Committee on Validation of Computer-Related Systems. Technical Report No. 18, "Validation of Computer-Related Systems," Section 4.3.2.

20. ISO 9001:2000.

21. PDA Committee on Validation of Computer-Related Systems. Technical Report No. 18, "Validation of Computer-Related Systems," Section 4.3.2.

22. IEEE/EIA 12207.0. Industry Implementation of International Standard ISO/IEC 12207:1995, Standard for Information Technology—Software Life Cycle Processes.

Institute of Electrical and Electronics Engineers, March 1998.

23. IEEE 1012-1998.

24. Jones, Capers, *Programming Productivity*. McGraw-Hill, 1986, p. 179.

25. Jones, Capers, *Conflict and Litigation between Software Clients and Developers*, Version 12. Software Productivity Research, April 26, 2004.

26. EC Commission Directive, *The Rules Governing Medicinal Products in the European Union*, Item 18.

CHAPTER 6

Notes

1. Phase 4 of Technical Report 18 is called "Design Computerized System." (PDA Committee on Validation of Computer-Related Systems. Technical Report No. 18, "Validation of Computer-Related Systems," Section 4.4. *PDA Journal of Pharmaceutical Science and Technology*, Vol. 49, No. 1, January–February 1995 Supplement.) This section of the report discusses a computerized system specification that's defined as "a document or set of documents that describe how a computerized system will satisfy the system requirements of the computer-related system." (Technical Report 18, Appendix 4.) The computerized system specification clearly and completely describes how the computerized system will operate and how it satisfies computer-related system requirements. It answers all the important questions about the installation and operation of the system. The report indicates that the information might be in other documents, such as the process description, system requirements, equipment manuals, and internal procedures. The common practice today is to include parts of this type of information in three types of documents: requirements, functional specifications, and a system specification.

   With the RiskVal life cycle, requirements are defined during phase 2. The foundation for the system specification is laid during the development of technical requirements, which occurs in phase 2. The system specification is written and finalized during phase 6 because at that point the specific hardware items to be included in the system should be finalized. A functional specification is an important document for custom systems because it identifies how the software will work to meet user requirements. Purchasers of commercial software needn't create a separate functional specification because any requirements for how the system should function can be included in the requirements document. Suggested content for the computerized system specification is given in Technical Report 18's appendix 3. (Technical Report 18, appendix 3.)

Technical Report 18 includes bringing the system in and integrating it with other systems as part of that document's phase 6, "Integrate and Install Computerized System." (Technical Report 18, Section 4.6.)

2. A validation protocol is a written plan stating how the validation or an aspect of it will be performed, including tests to be conducted and what constitutes acceptable test results. The content of the IQ, OQ, and PQ protocols are described in chapters 9 and 10.

3. There's no agreed scale to use for the likelihood of failure in a risk analysis. ISO 14971:2000 Annex E mentions a six-point scale. MIL-STD 882C, 1993; DeSain and Sutton, in their book *Risk Management Basics* (Advanstar Communication, 2000); and the LabCompliance *Risk Management Master Plan* (*www.labcompliance.com*) use a five-level scale similar to the one used in this book. IEEE 1012–1998 uses a four-point scale.

4. For more information on development activities, see the following:

IEEE/EIA 12207.0 Industry Implementation of International Standard ISO/IEC 12207:1995, Standard for Information Technology—Software Life Cycle Processes. The Institute of Electrical and Electronics Engineers, March 1998.

IEEE 1012–1998 IEEE Standard for Software Verification and Validation. Software Engineering Standards Committee of the IEEE Computer Society, March 1998.

ANSI/AAMI SW68:2001, Medical Device Software—Software Life Cycle Processes. Association for the Advancement of Medical Instrumentation, 2001.

General Principles of Software Validation; Final Guidance for Industry and FDA Staff. Center for Devices and Radiological Health, Center for Biologics Evaluation and Research, Food and Drug Administration, January 11, 2002.

PDA Committee on Validation of Computer-Related Systems. Technical Report No. 18, "Validation of Computer-Related Systems," *PDA Journal of Pharmaceutical Science and Technology*, Vol. 49, No. 1, January–February 1995 Supplement.

References

1. EC Commission Directive, *The Rules Governing Medicinal Products in the European Union*, Vol. 4. Good Manufacturing Practices, Annex 11, Item 3, Computerised Systems. October 8, 2003.

2. 21 CFR Part 11, Electronic Records—Electronic Signatures. Food and Drug Administration. *Federal Register,* Vol. 62, No. 54. March 20, 1997.

3. 21 CFR Part 11, Section 11.10 e.

4. 21 CFR Part 11, Section 11.10 g.

5. 21 CFR Part 11, Section 11.10 f.

6. 21 CFR Part 11, Section 11.200 a 1.

7. 21 CFR Part 11, Section 11.10 c.

8. 21 CFR 820, Medical Devices—Current Good Manufacturing Practices (cGMP) Final Rule, Quality System Regulation, Section 820.80 b, e. *Federal Register 52602.* October 7, 1996, 2003 revision.

9. Guidance for Industry Part 11, Electronic Records—Electronic Signatures—Scope and Application, U.S. Department of Health and Human Services, Food and Drug Administration, August 2003.

10. Guidance for Industry Part 11, lines 242–245.

11. Guidance for Industry Part 11, lines 247–250.

12. Guidance for Industry Part 11.

13. 21 CFR 820, Section 820.80 b.

14. 21 CFR 820, Section 820.80 e.

15. GAMP Forum. *GAMP Good Practice Guide: A Risk-Based Approach to Compliant Electronic Records and Signatures,* 2005.

16. Ibid., p. 16.

17. Stein, R. Timothy. "Process for Software Risk Assessment." Business Performance Associates, 2004.

18. ISO 14971:2000, Medical devices—Application of risk management to medical devices, Sections 4.3, 4.4, and 5. International Organization for Standardization, 2000.

19. ISO 14971:2000, Annex F.

20. ISO 14971:2000, Section E.4.3.

21. Ibid.

22. GAMP Forum. Gamp 4, GAMP Guide for Validation of Automated Systems, appendix M3, 4.2.4. December 2001.

23. Guidance for Industry and FDA Staff, *Guidance for the Content of Premarket Submissions for Software Contained in Medical Devices.* Food and Drug Administration, Center for Devices and Radiological Health, Office of Device Evaluation, May 11, 2005, p. 17.

24. Jones, Capers. *Software Defect Removal: The State of the Art in 2002.* Software Productivity Research, 2002.

25. ISO 14971:2000, Annex D.

26. IEEE 1012-1998 IEEE Standard for Software Verification and Validation, Table B-2. Software Engineering Standards Committee of the IEEE Computer Society. March 1998.

27. MIL-STD 882C. Military Standard System Safety Program Requirements, Section 4.5.1. U.S. Department of Defense, January 19, 1993.

28. *Guidance for Industry, FDA Reviewers and Compliance on Off-the-Shelf Software Use in Medical Devices*, Section 1.3. Food and Drug Administration, Center for Devices and Radiological Health, Office of Device Evaluation, September 9, 1999.

29. ISO 14971:2000, Section 5. ISO 14971 uses the term "risk evaluation" for the judgment, based on risk analysis, of whether a risk is acceptable.

30. ISO 14971:2000, Section E.3.3.

31. Ibid.

32. Ibid.

33. ISO 14971:2000, Section 6.2.

34. Ibid.

35. Ibid.

36. GAMP Forum. *GAMP Good Practice Guide: A Risk-Based Approach to Compliant Electronic Records and Signatures*, Section 4. 2005.

37. Stein, R. Timothy. "Risk Management Procedure." Business Performance Associates, 2002 a.

38. EC Commission Directive, *The Rules Governing Medicinal Products in the European Union*, Item 2.

39. ISO 13485, Medical devices—Quality management systems—Systems requirements for regulatory purposes, Section 7.5.2.1. International Organization for Standardization, 2003.

40. Pharmaceutical Inspection Convention, Pharmaceutical Inspection Co-Operation Scheme. *PIC/S Guidance, Good Practices for Computerized Systems in Regulated "GXP" Environments*, Section 16. July 2004.

41. PDA Committee on Validation of Computer-Related Systems. Technical Report No. 18, "Validation of Computer-Related Systems," Section 4.7.1. *PDA Journal of Pharmaceutical Science and Technology*, Vol. 49, No. 1, January–February 1995 Supplement.

42. Stein, R. Timothy. "Validation Plan Template." Business Performance Associates, 2002 b.

43. EC Commission Directive, *The Rules Governing Medicinal Products in the European Union*, Item 4.

44. Ibid.

45. PDA Committee on Validation of Computer-Related Systems. Technical Report No. 18, "Validation of Computer-Related Systems," Section 4.7.1.

46. IEEE 1012-1998 IEEE Standard for Software Verification and Validation, p. iii. Software Engineering Standards Committee of the IEEE Computer Society, March 1998.

47. Gamp 4, Good Automated Manufacturing Practice, GAMP Guide for Validation of Automated System, December 2001, Appendix M3.

48. Jones, Capers. *Software Defect Removal: The State of the Art in 2002,* Software Productivity Research, 2002.

49. PDA Committee on Validation of Computer-Related Systems. Technical Report No. 18, "Validation of Computer-Related Systems," Section 4.5.

50. Jones, Capers. *Software Quality: Analysis and Guidelines for Success.* London: International Thomson Computer Press, 1997, p. 164.

51. Falla, Mike, ed. *Advances in Safety-Critical Systems—Results and Achievements from the DTI/EPSRC R&D Programme in Safety-Critical Systems,* ch. 3. Available at *www. comp.lancs.ac.uk/computing/resources/scs/.* Not dated.

CHAPTER 7

Notes

1. The fifth phase in the Technical Report (TR) 18 process is called "Construct Computerized System." (PDA Committee on Validation of Computer-Related Systems. Technical Report No. 18, "Validation of Computer-Related Systems," Section 4.5. *PDA Journal of Pharmaceutical Science and Technology*, Vol. 49, No. 1. January–February 1995 Supplement.) The TR focuses on types of software (4.5.1) and the development of software. Section 4.5.2 discusses the types of testing that should be done within the development process, and section 4.5.3 discusses quality assurance within the context of the development process. TR 18 discusses the on-site testing of custom software during phases 7 and 8. In my view, the parallel for COTS and configurable systems is implementing the solutions developed in the previous phase to resolve issues.

References

1. ISO 14971:2000, Medical devices—Application of risk management to medical devices. International Organization for Standardization, 2000.

2. *Guidance for Industry, FDA Reviewers and Compliance on Off-the-Shelf Software Use in Medical Devices.* U.S. Food and Drug Administration, Center for Devices and Radiological Health, Office of Device Evaluation, September 9, 1999.

3. ISO 14971:2000, Section 6.3.

4. Stein, R. Timothy. "System Risk Management Procedure." Business Performance Associates, 2002.

5. ISO 14971:2000.

6. Ibid., Section 7.

7. Stein, R. Timothy. "System Risk Management Procedure." Business Performance Associates, 2002.

8. PDA Committee on Validation of Computer-Related Systems. Technical Report No. 18, "Validation of Computer-Related Systems," Section 4.5.3. *PDA Journal of Pharmaceutical Science and Technology*, Vol. 49, No. 1, January–February 1995 Supplement.

9. Jones, Capers. *Software Quality: Analysis and Guidelines for Success,* p. 164. London: International Thomson Computer Press, 1997.

10. PDA Committee on Validation of Computer-Related Systems. Technical Report No. 18, "Validation of Computer-Related Systems," Section 4.5.

11. IEEE/EIA 12207.0 Industry Implementation of International Standard ISO/IEC 12207:1995, Standard for Information Technology—Software Life Cycle Processes. The Institute of Electrical and Electronics Engineers, March 1998.

12. IEEE 1012-1998 IEEE Standard for Software Verification and Validation. Software Engineering Standards Committee of the IEEE Computer Society, March 1998.

13. ANSI/AAMI SW68:2001. Medical Device Software—Software Life Cycle Processes. Association for the Advancement of Medical Instrumentation, 2001.

14. *General Principles of Software Validation, Final Guidance for Industry and FDA Staff.* Center for Devices and Radiological Health, Center for Biologics Evaluation and Research, Food and Drug Administration, January 11, 2002.

15. PDA Committee on Validation of Computer-Related Systems. Technical Report No. 18, "Validation of Computer-Related Systems."

16. Ibid., Section 4.6.

CHAPTER 8

Notes

1. The title of phase 6 in Technical Report 18 is "Integrate and Install Computerized Systems." (PDA Committee on Validation of Computer-Related Systems. Technical Report No. 18, "Validation of Computer-Related Systems," Section 4.6. *PDA Journal of Pharmaceutical Science and Technology*, Vol. 49, No. 1, January–February 1995 Supplement.) "Integration" in this case refers to the integration of system hardware and software components at the developer's location. For custom software, this activity is included in the RiskVal life cycle during phase 6. For COTS, configurable, and custom systems after they're brought to the user site, the organization prepares to use the system and perform qualification testing. The phase 6 activities discussed in chapter 8 are directed at this preparation.

References

1. PDA Committee on Validation of Computer-Related Systems. Technical Report No. 18, "Validation of Computer-Related Systems," Section 4.6. *PDA Journal of Pharmaceutical Science and Technology*, Vol. 49, No. 1, January–February 1995 Supplement.

2. EC Commission Directive, *The Rules Governing Medicinal Products in the European Union*, Vol. 4. Good Manufacturing Practices, Annex 11, Computerised System. October 8, 2003.

3. 21 CFR 820, Medical Devices—Current Good Manufacturing Practices (cGMP) Final Rule, Quality System Regulation, Section 820.40. *Federal Register 52602*. October 7, 1996, 2003 revision.

4. EC Commission Directive, *The Rules Governing Medicinal Products in the European Union*, Items 15 and 16.

5. 21 CFR Part 11, Electronic Records—Electronic Signatures, Section 11.10 d, i, j. Food and Drug Administration. *Federal Register*, Vol. 62, No. 54. March 20, 1997.

6. EC Commission Directive, *The Rules Governing Medicinal Products in the European Union*, Item 8.

7. Ibid., Item 18.

8. 21 CFR 820, Section 820.70 i.

9. ISO 13485, Medical devices—Quality management systems—Systems requirements for regulatory purposes, Section 7.5.2.1. International Organization for Standardization, 2003.

10. EC Commission Directive, *The Rules Governing Medicinal Products in the European Union,* Item 11.

11. Stein, R. Timothy. "Change Control for Validated Systems." Business Performance Associates, 2002.

12. Ibid.

CHAPTER 9

Notes

1. A distinction is drawn between qualification and validation. Qualification is "the process to demonstrate the ability to fulfill specified requirements" (GAMP Forum. Gamp 4, GAMP Guide for Validation of Automated Systems, Vol. 4, Section 12, December 2001). Qualification establishes the ability of an item or system to function according to the requirements for how that item should work. However, if a piece of automated equipment or a system works properly (i.e., it's qualified), that doesn't necessarily imply that it will work the way an organization wants to use it in an automated process. You still must demonstrate that it's effective in how it's used in the automated process. "Effective" here means both that the system works as it's intended, and if the system could affect the quality of the product, that the product manufactured meets specifications. This can be seen from the generic definition of validation used by the FDA; validation is "establishing documented evidence which provides a high degree of assurance that a specific process will consistently produce a product meeting its predetermined specifications and quality attributes." (*Glossary of Computerized System and Software Development Terminology.* Food and Drug Administration, August 1995.)

   The difference between qualification and validation can be seen in the following example of an automated welding machine used to weld parts of a medical device. The welder uses a laser beam to melt a small area of two pieces of metal that are placed together. When the two metals melt, they form a mixture that cools and hardens. This weld forms a bond between the pieces of metal. The welder can be qualified to establish that it can place a weld of a certain size in a predetermined location, and that a laser beam with certain energy will be focused on the spot for a specified duration. The welder is qualified by demonstrating that it operates properly. If it doesn't operate properly, it can't be used. Once qualified, its use in a manufacturing process to meet specific product requirements can then be validated. Once the welder has been shown to work correctly, the device manufacturer must validate those settings because laser duration and intensity will create welds of a certain strength between two pieces of metal that are part of the medical device.

The distinction between qualification and validation has more practical value in the validation of facilities, utilities, and equipment than it does with computer system validation. With the former you can make a clear distinction between qualification and validation. With computer systems, the way in which the system is to be used (i.e., to meet the user requirements) is often identical to the way the manufacturer has designed and built it. Consequently, qualifying the system is similar to validating it (unless the system is used directly in production as with the example of the welder). In addition, all intended uses of the system are tested, if possible, at least for moderate- and high-risk systems in the validation environment before they're used in production. This is to avoid harmful effects from system failure. The operational qualification (OQ), in part, determines in the validation environment that the system will function to meet all, or most of, the user requirements. The clause "in part" is used because supportive operations (discussed in chapter 9) are also included in the OQ. The performance qualification (PQ) is used to establish that, in the production environment, the system is able to meet the user requirements as part of the process in which the system is used. If the technical environments of the OQ and PQ are similar, the PQ might involve more limited testing than is conducted in the OQ. (The PQ is discussed in detail in chapter 10.)

2. Gamp 4 recommends that a function specification be used as the basis of the OQ. Gamp 4 identifies the functional specification as a deliverable from the development life cycle of software, which is prepared by the developer based on the user requirements. The guideline defines functional specification as "...a description of the system to be supplied in terms of the functions it will perform and facilities required to meet the user requirements defined in the URS (User Requirements Specification). The Functional Specification should be written in such a way that both supplier and user understand it. This document is the controlling specification, against which the system will be functionally tested." (GAMP Forum. Gamp 4, GAMP Guide for Validation of Automated Systems, Vol. 4, Section 8.1.3. December 2001). In GAMP's scheme, the OQ verifies that the system can perform the functions as stated in the functional specification.

For the validation of purchased systems, Gamp 4 is often interpreted as requiring that a functional specification be prepared, although this isn't explicitly stated in the document (GAMP Forum. Gamp 4, GAMP Guide for Validation of Automated Systems, Vol. 4, December 2001). When users create a functional specification for a purchased system, it's often with great difficulty. There's confusion as to whether a function belongs in the user requirements or the functional specification. This struggle isn't necessary. The specifications and/or requirements for supportive operations can be included in the user requirements; the user requirements are then used as the "controlling specification against which the system will be functionally tested." Often the user requirements written during phase 2 are at a high level because the project team isn't yet familiar with the operations that the system must perform for the requirements to be met. This level of detail can be added after the team is more familiar with how the system works. If the detail isn't added, and the user requirements remain at too high a level to direct the testing of the "facilities required to meet the user requirements," then the OQ can be written to include tests of the supportive operations that the system uses to meet user requirements. The requirements for the supportive operations are included in the expected results statements of the OQ tests. This is discussed further in chapter 9's introduction and in the section on OQ objectives.

3. "The extent of validation evidence needed for such [commercial applications] software depends on the device manufacturer's documented intended use of that software. For example, a device manufacturer that chooses not to use all the vendor-supplied capabilities of the software only needs to validate those functions that will be used and for which the device manufacturer is dependent upon the software results as part of production or the quality system" (*General Principles of Software Validation. Final Guidance for Industry and FDA Staff,* Section 6.1. Center for Devices and Radiological Health, Center for Biologics Evaluation and Research, Food and Drug Administration. January 11, 2002).

4. With boundary testing, input values are used just below and just above the defined limits for data being input to the system. Boundary testing of output involves inputting values that cause the outputs to be at just below and just above the defined limits of an output. (*Glossary of Computerized System and Software Development Terminology.* Food and Drug Administration, August 1995.)

5. I'm most grateful for the assistance of Michael Louie in preparing the infrastructure qualification section.

References

1. Louie, Michael S. "Case Study: Qualifying Computer and Network Infrastructures (CNIs) for GxP Compliance." CPT Third Annual IT Infrastructure Qualification Summit, February 24, 2004, and personal communications.

2. Phase 7 of the PDA process consists of installation and operational qualifications. PDA Committee on Validation of Computer-Related Systems, Technical Report No.

18, "Validation of Computer-Related Systems," Section 4.7.3. *PDA Journal of Pharmaceutical Science and Technology*, Vol. 49, No. 1, January–February 1995 Supplement.

3. PDA Committee on Validation of Computer-Related Systems, Technical Report No. 18, "Validation of Computer-Related Systems," Section 4.7.3. *PDA Journal of Pharmaceutical Science and Technology*, Vol. 49, No. 1, January–February 1995 Supplement.

4. 21 CFR 820, Quality System Regulation, Section 820.70 i. Food and Drug Administration, 2003.

5. PDA Committee on Validation of Computer-Related Systems, Technical Report No. 18, "Validation of Computer-Related Systems," Sections 4.7 and 4.8.1. *PDA Journal of Pharmaceutical Science and Technology*, Vol. 49, No. 1, January–February 1995 Supplement.

6. Ibid., Section 4.7.2.

7. Ibid., Section 4.7.3.

8. The content for the installation verification (procedure) and test is taken from "Installation Qualification Template," by R. Timothy Stein. Business Performance Associates, 2003 a.

9. Michael Louie and David Tsao, Gilead Sciences Inc., personal communications, 2004.

10. 21 CFR Part 11, Electronic Records—Electronic Signatures, Section 11.10 k. Food and Drug Administration. *Federal Register,* Vol. 62, No. 54. March 20, 1997. Part 11 requires that system documentation be controlled, including distribution, access, and use of the documentation.

11. PDA Committee on Validation of Computer-Related Systems, Technical Report No. 18, "Validation of Computer-Related Systems," Section 4.7.2. *PDA Journal of Pharmaceutical Science and Technology*, Vol. 49, No. 1, January–February 1995 Supplement.

12. Stein, R. Timothy. "Completion of Quality Records." Business Performance Associates, 2004 a.

13. Stein, R. Timothy. "Installation Qualification Template." Business Performance Associates, 2003 b.

14. PDA Committee on Validation of Computer-Related Systems, Technical Report No. 18, "Validation of Computer-Related Systems," Section 4.7.3.

15. Ibid., Section 4.7.2.

16. Stein, R. Timothy. "Protocol Report Template." Business Performance Associates, 2003 c.

17. PDA Committee on Validation of Computer-Related Systems, Technical Report No. 18, "Validation of Computer-Related Systems," Section 4.7.3.

18. Louie, Michael, and David Tsao. Gilead Sciences, Inc., personal communications, 2004.

19. EC Commission Directive, *The Rules Governing Medicinal Products in the European Union*, Vol. 4. Good Manufacturing Practices, Annex 11, Items 6, 7, and 9, Computerised Systems. October 8, 2003.

20. 21 CFR Part 11, Electronic Records—Electronic Signatures. Food and Drug Administration. *Federal Register,* Vol. 62, No. 54. March 20, 1997.

21. EC Commission Directive, *The Rules Governing Medicinal Products in the European Union.*

22. 21 CFR Part 11, Section 11.10 d.

23. Ibid., Sections 11.10 e and 11.30.

24. EC Commission Directive, *The Rules Governing Medicinal Products in the European Union*, Item 10.

25. 21 CFR Part 11, Section 11.10 g.

26. EC Commission Directive, *The Rules Governing Medicinal Products in the European Union*, Items 8 and 10.

27. Ibid., Item 19.

28. 21 CFR Part 11, Sections 11.10 and 11.30.

29. EC Commission Directive, *The Rules Governing Medicinal Products in the European Union*, Item 13.

30. Ibid., Item 12.

31. *General Principles of Software Validation; Final Guidance for Industry and FDA Staff*, Section 6.3.

32. EC Commission Directive, *The Rules Governing Medicinal Products in the European Union*, Items 15 and 16.

33. EC Commission Directive, *The Rules Governing Medicinal Products in the European Union.*

34. 21 CFR Part 11, Sections 11.10 and 11.30.

35. *General Principles of Software Validation; Final Guidance for Industry and FDA Staff*, Section 6.2.

36. Perry, William. *Effective Methods for Software Testing* (John Wiley and Sons, 1995). Perry identifies dimensions of computer systems for testing (see pp. 61, 63, and 64), and a variety of test methodologies and test methods (see pp. 384–391). In chapter 22 of the book's second edition, he changes his framework and includes a chapter on "Testing Off-the-Shelf Software." See Perry, William. *Effective Methods for Software Testing*. Second edition, John Wiley and Sons, 2000.

37. Stein, R. Timothy. "Guidance—Items to Evaluate in an IQ, OQ, or PQ for a Computer System," Business Performance Associates. 2003 d.

38. *General Principles of Software Validation; Final Guidance for Industry and FDA Staff*, Section 6.3.

39. Ibid., Section 5.2.5.

40. PDA Committee on Validation of Computer-Related Systems, Technical Report No. 18, "Validation of Computer-Related Systems," Section 4.7.3.

41. *General Principles of Software Validation; Final Guidance for Industry and FDA Staff*, Section 5.2.5.

42. Ibid.

43. *General Principles of Software Validation; Final Guidance for Industry and FDA Staff*, Section 6.1.

44. Stein, R. Timothy. "Operation Qualification Template." Business Performance Associates, 2003 e.

45. PDA Committee on Validation of Computer-Related Systems, Technical Report No. 18, "Validation of Computer-Related Systems," Section 4.7.2.

46. *General Principles of Software Validation; Final Guidance for Industry and FDA Staff*, Section 6.1.

47. Stein, R. Timothy. "Operation Qualification Template." Business Performance Associates, 2003 f.

48. The Institute of Validation Technology Network Infrastructure Qualification Committee, IVT Network Infrastructure Qualification Proposed Standard. *Journal of Validation Technology*, Vol. 10, No. 2, p. 164.

49. 21 CFR 211, Section 68 b.

50. EC Commission Directive, *The Rules Governing Medicinal Products in the European Union*, Item 14.

51. 21 CFR 820, Section 180.

52. Louie, Michael. "Developing a Practical IT Infrastructure Qualification Program Using a GXP-Risk Based Approach," 2003.

53. Ibid.

54. 21 CFR 820, Medical Devices—Current Good Manufacturing Practices (CGMP) Final Rule, section 820.70 i. Quality System Regulation, *Federal Register 52602*. October 7, 1996, 2005 revision.

55. *General Principles of Software Validation; Final Guidance for Industry and FDA Staff*, Section 6.2.

56. EC Commission Directive, *The Rules Governing Medicinal Products in the European Union*, Item 7.

57. ISO 13485, Medical devices—Quality management systems—System requirements for regulatory purposes, Section 7.5.2.1. 2003.

CHAPTER 10

Notes

1. The PDA Technical Report 18 title for phase 8, "Evaluate Computer-Related Systems," has been changed in this book to "Use in a Production Environment." (PDA Committee on Validation of Computer-Related Systems. Technical Report No. 18, "Validation of Computer-Related Systems," Section 4.8. *PDA Journal of Pharmaceutical Science and Technology*, Vol. 49, No. 1, January–February 1995 Supplement.)

References

1. PDA Committee on Validation of Computer-Related Systems. Technical Report No. 18, "Validation of Computer-Related Systems," Section 4.8.1. *PDA Journal of Pharmaceutical Science and Technology*, Vol. 49, No. 1, January–February 1995 Supplement.
2. 21 CFR 820, Medical Devices—Current Good Manufacturing Practices (cGMP) Final Rule, Quality System Regulation, Section 70 i. *Federal Register* 52602. October 7, 1996, 2003 revision.
3. *Glossary of Computerized System and Software Development Terminology.* Food and Drug Administration, August 1995.
4. EC Commission Directive, *The Rules Governing Medicinal Products in the European Union,* Vol. 4, Good Manufacturing Practices, Annex 11, Item 7, Computerised Systems. October 8, 2003.
5. Stein, R. Timothy. "Guidance—Items to Evaluate in an IQ, OQ, and PQ for a Computer System." Business Performance Associates, 2003 a.
6. Stein, R. Timothy. "Performance Qualification Template." Business Performance Associates, 2003 b.
7. Ibid., 2003 c.
8. ISO 14971:2000, Medical devices—Application of risk management to medical devices, Section 6.4. International Organization for Standardization, 2000.
9. Stein, R. Timothy. "System Risk Management Procedure." Business Performance Associates, 2002.
10. ISO 14971:2000, Section 6.5.

11. ISO 14971:2000, Section 8.

12. Stein, R. Timothy. "Validation Final Report." Business Performance Associates, 2004.

13. EC Commission Directive, *The Rules Governing Medicinal Products in the European Union,* Item 14.

14. ISO 9001, Quality management systems—Requirements, Section 7.6. International Organization for Standardization, 2000.

15. ISO 13485, Medical devices—Quality management systems—System requirements for regulatory purposes, Section 7.6. International Organization for Standardization, 2003.

16. 21 CFR 211, Current Good Manufacturing Practice for Finished Pharmaceuticals, Section 68 a. Food and Drug Administration, 2005.

17. 21 CFR 820, Section 72.

18. ISO 13485:2003, Section 6.3.

19. 21 CFR 211, Section 67.

20. 21 CFR 820, Section 70 g 1.

21. EC Commission Directive, *The Rules Governing Medicinal Products in the European Union,* Item 17.

22. Stein, R. Timothy. "Problem Tracking and Resolution." Business Performance Associates, 2004.

23. ISO 14971:2000, Section 9.

24. Ibid.

25. 21 CFR 820, Section 70 i.

26. *General Principles of Software Validation; Final Guidance for Industry and FDA Staff,* Section 6.2. Center for Devices and Radiological Health, Center for Biologics Evaluation and Research, Food and Drug Administration, January 11, 2002.

27. EC Commission Directive, *The Rules Governing Medicinal Products in the European Union,* Item 7.

28. ISO 13485:2003, Section 7.5.2.1.

CHAPTER 11

Notes

1. The PDA Technical Report 18 doesn't include a retirement phase. (PDA Committee on Validation of Computer-Related Systems. Technical Report No. 18, "Validation of Computer-Related Systems," Section 4.8. *PDA Journal of Pharmaceutical Science and Technology,* Vol. 49, No. 1, January–February 1995 Supplement.)

References

1. 21 CFR 820, Medical Devices—Current Good Manufacturing Practices (cGMP) Final Rule, Quality System Regulation, Section 820.180 b. *Federal Register 52602*. October 7, 1996, 2003 revision.

2. 21 CFR Part 11, Electronic Records—Electronic Signatures, Section 11.10 c. Food and Drug Administration. *Federal Register,* Vol. 62, No. 54. March 20, 1997.

3. 21 CFR 820, Section 820.180 b.

4. 21 CFR Part 11, Section 11.10 c.

5. Guidance for Industry Part 11, Electronic Records—Electronic Signatures—Scope and Application, Section III C 5. U.S. Department of Health and Human Services, Food and Drug Administration, August 2003.

CHAPTER 12

1. *General Principles of Software Validation; Final Guidance for Industry and FDA Staff,* Section 3.1.2. Center for Devices and Radiological Health, Center for Biologics Evaluation and Research, Food and Drug Administration, January 11, 2002.

2. *General Principles of Software Validation.*

3. 21 CFR Part 11, Electronic Records—Electronic Signatures. Food and Drug Administration. *Federal Register,* Vol. 62, No. 54. March 20, 1997.

4. EC Commission Directive, *The Rules Governing Medicinal Products in the European Union,* Vol. 4. Good Manufacturing Practices, Annex 11, Computerised Systems, October 8, 2003.

5. GAMP Forum. Gamp 4, GAMP Guide for Validation of Automated Systems, Vol. 4. December 2001.

6. *General Principles of Software Validation,* Section 6.1.

7. Guidance for Industry Part 11, Electronic Records—Electronic Signatures—Scope and Application, Section III, C, 1. U.S. Department of Health and Human Services, Food and Drug Administration, August 2003.

8. 21 CFR 820, Medical Devices—Current Good Manufacturing Practices (cGMP) Final Rule, Quality System Regulation, Section 25 b. *Federal Register 52602*. October 7, 1996, 2003 revision.

9. Ibid., Section 70 i.

10. 21 CFR 211, Current Good Manufacturing Practice for Finished Pharmaceuticals, Section 68 a. Food and Drug Administration. *Federal Register 6385*. June 20, 1963, March 31, 2003 revision.

11. 21 CFR 820, Section 72.

12. 21 CFR 211, Section 68 b.

13. 21 CFR 820, Section 180.

14. 21 CFR 211, Section 67.

15. 21 CFR 820, Section 70 g 1.

16. Ibid., Section 25 b.

17. 21 CFR 211, Section 25.

18. 21 CFR Part 11, Section 11.10 i.

19. 21 CFR 820, Section 22.

20. Ibid., Section 70 i.

21. 21 CFR Part 11, Section 11.10 a.

22. Ibid., Section 11.10 j.

23. Ibid., Section 11.10 i.

24. Ibid., Section 11.10 k 2.

25. *General Principles of Software Validation*, Section 6.2.

26. EC Commission Directive, *The Rules Governing Medicinal Products in the European Union*, Item 2.

27. Ibid., Item 1.

28. Ibid., Item 4.

29. Ibid., Item 5.

30. Ibid., Item 7.

31. Ibid., Item 8.

32. Ibid., Item 11.

33. Ibid., Item 13.

34. Ibid., Item 13.

35. Ibid., Item 14.

36. Ibid., Item 16.

37. Ibid., Item 17.

38. Ibid., Item 18.

39. *General Principles of Software Validation*, Section 3.1.2.

40. Ibid., Section 6.1.

41. Ibid.

42. Ibid., Section 6.2.

43. Ibid., Section 6.3.

44. Ibid., Section 6.1.

45. Ibid.

46. *Guidance for Industry, FDA Reviewers and Compliance on Off-the-Shelf Software Use in Medical Devices.* Food and Drug Administration, Center for Devices and Radiological Health, Office of Device Evaluation, September 9, 1999.

APPENDIX B

1. ISO 14971:2000, Medical devices—Application of risk management to medical devices. International Organization for Standardization, 2000.

APPENDIX C

1. ISO 14971:2000, Medical devices—Application of risk management to medical devices, Section 2. International Organization for Standardization, 2000.

2. Stein, R. Timothy. "Risk Management Policy." Business Performance Associates, 2003 a.

3. Stein, R. Timothy. "Risk Management Procedure." Business Performance Associates, 2003 b.

4. ISO 14971:2000, Annex F.

5. DeSain, C., and C. V. Sutton. *Risk Management Basics.* Cleveland, Ohio: Advanstar Communication, 2000.

6. Stein, R. Timothy. "Failure Mode and Effects Analysis." Business Performance Associates, 2003 c.

7. Stein, R. Timothy. "Fault-Tree Analysis." Business Performance Associates, 2003 d.

8. Falla, Mike, ed. *Advances in Safety-Critical Systems—Results and Achievements from the DTI/EPSRC R&D Programme in Safety-Critical Systems,* ch. 3, "Hazard Analysis." Available at *www.comp.lancs.ac.uk/computing/resources/scs/.* Not dated.

9. Stein, R. Timothy. "Hazard Analysis and Critical Control Points Assessment." Business Performance Associates, 2003 e.

10. ISO 14971:2000.

11. IEEE 1012–1998 IEEE Standard for Software Verification and Validation, Table B-2. Software Engineering Standards Committee of the IEEE Computer Society, March 1998.

12. MIL-STD 882C, Military Standard System Safety Program Requirements, Section 4.5.1. U.S. Department of Defense, January 19, 1993.

13. IEEE 1012-1998.

14. DeSain, C., and Sutton, C. V. *Risk Management Basics*. Cleveland, Ohio: Advanstar Communication, 2000.

15. Ibid., p. 10.

16. ISO 14971:2000, Section E 4.3.

17. GAMP Forum. Gamp 4, GAMP Guide for Validation of Automated Systems, Vol. 4. December 2001.

18. Jones, Capers. *Conflict and Litigation Between Software Clients and Developers*. Software Productivity Research, Version 12., April 26, 2004.

19. Jones, Capers. *Programming Productivity*, p. 179. McGraw-Hill, 1986.

20. Jones, Capers. *Software Quality, Analysis and Guidelines for Success*, p. 164. New York: International Thomson Computer Press, 1997.

21. Jones, Capers. *Programming Productivity*, pp. 172 and 173. McGraw-Hill, 1986.

22. Jones, Capers. *Software Quality, Analysis and Guidelines for Success*, pp. 170 and 171. New York: International Thomson Computer Press, 1997.

23. PDA Committee on Validation of Computer-Related Systems. Technical Report No. 18, "Validation of Computer-Related Systems," Section 4.3. *PDA Journal of Pharmaceutical Science and Technology*, Vol. 49, No. 1, January–February 1995 Supplement.

24. Stein, R. Timothy. Personal experience, 1998.

25. ISO 14971:2000, Annex E.

GLOSSARY

1. ANSI/ASQC Z1.4-1993—Sampling Procedures and Table for Inspection by Attributes. American Society for Quality Control, 1993, p. 2.

2. ANSI/ASQC Z1.9-1993—Sampling Procedures and Table for Inspection by Variables for Percent Nonconforming. American Society for Quality Control, 1993, p. 2.

3. PDA Committee on Validation of Computer-Related Systems. Technical Report No. 18, "Validation of Computer-Related Systems," Appendix 4. *PDA Journal of Pharmaceutical Science and Technology*, Vol. 49, No. 1. January–February 1995 Supplement.

4. The New IEEE Standard Dictionary of Electrical and Electronics Terms, IEEE Standard, 100-1992.

5. *Glossary of Computerized System and Software Development Terminology*. Food and Drug Administration, August 1995.

6. PDA Committee on Validation of Computer-Related Systems, Technical Report No. 18, "Validation of Computer-Related Systems."

7. Ibid.

8. *General Principles of Software Validation. Final Guidance for Industry and FDA Staff,* Section 3.1.2. Center for Devices and Radiological Health, Center for Biologics Evaluation and Research, Food and Drug Administration, January 11, 2002.

9. PDA Committee on Validation of Computer-Related Systems. Technical Report No. 18, "Validation of Computer-Related Systems," Appendix 4.

10. ISO 14971:2000, Medical devices—Application of risk management to medical devices, Appendix F. International Organization for Standardization, 2000.

11. PDA Committee on Validation of Computer-Related Systems. Technical Report No. 18, "Validation of Computer-Related Systems," Appendix 4.

12. Ibid.

13. PDA Committee on Validation of Computer-Related Systems. Technical Report No. 18, "Validation of Computer-Related Systems."

14. ISO 14971:2000, Section 2.

15. Ibid.

16. ANSI/AAMI SW68: 2001, Medical Device Software—Software Life Cycle Processes, Section 3. Association for the Advancement of Medical Instrumentation, 2001.

17. PDA Committee on Validation of Computer-Related Systems. Technical Report No. 18, "Validation of Computer-Related Systems."

18. *General Principles of Software Validation.*

19. *Glossary of Computerized System and Software Development Terminology.* Food and Drug Administration, August 1995.

20. 21 CFR 803, Medical Device Reporting, Food and Drug Administration, July 1996, April 2005 revision.

21. ISO 14971:2000, Section 2.

22. GAMP Forum. Gamp 4, GAMP Guide for Validation of Automated Systems, Vol. 4, Section 12. December, 2001.

23. PDA Committee on Validation of Computer-Related Systems. Technical Report No. 18, "Validation of Computer-Related Systems."

24. Ibid., Section 4.7.

25. ISO 14971:2000, Section 2.

26. *Glossary of Computerized System and Software Development Terminology.* Food and Drug Administration, August 1995.

27. IEEE 1012-1998 IEEE Standard for Software Verification and Validation, p. iii. Software Engineering Standards Committee of the IEEE Computer Society, March 1998.

28. ISO 14971:2000, Section 2.

29. ANSI/AAMI SW68: 2001, Section 3.

30. ISO 14971:2000, Section 2.

31. Ibid.

32. Ibid.

33. Ibid.

34. Ibid.

35. Ibid.

36. ANSI/AAMI SW68: 2001, Section 3.14.

37. 21 CFR 820, Medical Devices—Current Good Manufacturing Practices (cGMP) Final Rule, Quality System Regulation, Section 820.3 y. *Federal Register 52602.* October 7, 1996, 2003 revision.

38. *Glossary of Computerized System and Software Development Terminology.* Food and Drug Administration, August 1995.

39. PDA Committee on Validation of Computer-Related Systems. Technical Report No. 18, "Validation of Computer-Related Systems," Appendix 4.

40. *General Principles of Software Validation*, p. 25.

41. *Glossary of Computerized System and Software Development Terminology.* Food and Drug Administration, August 1995.

42. 21 CFR 820, Section 1, z.

43. ISO 14971:2000, Section 2.

44. ANSI/AAMI SW68: 2001, Section 3.

Index

About the Author

R. Timothy Stein, Ph.D., founded the consulting firm Business Performance Associates Inc. in Cupertino, California, in 1994 (*www .bpaconsultants.com*). Focusing on quality systems and software validation, he and his firm have consulted with more than eighty companies from eighteen industry segments; a majority of his clients have been from the medical device, pharmaceutical, biologics, and diagnostic industries.

Stein began his work with software quality in the late eighties by helping software developers improve the quality of their products. In addition to conduction validations, Stein trains companies and provides the tools  they need to efficiently conduct their own validations. He's also helped many companies develop FDA, ISO 9001:2000, and/or ISO 13485-compliant quality systems. As a fellow of the American Society for Quality, he's been an active contributor through leadership positions, program development, and frequent public speaking.

Stein holds a bachelor's degree in chemistry and a doctorate in organizational psychology. He can be contacted at (408) 366-0848, or by e-mail at *tstein@bpaconsultants.com*.